PULSE AND DIGITAL CIRCUITS

McGraw-Hill Electrical and Electronic Engineering Series

FREDERICK EMMONS TERMAN, *Consulting Editor*

W. W. HARMAN and J. G. TRUXAL, *Associate Consulting Editors*

Bailey and Gault · ALTERNATING-CURRENT MACHINERY
Beranek · ACOUSTICS
Bruns and Saunders · ANALYSIS OF FEEDBACK CONTROL SYSTEMS
Cage · THEORY AND APPLICATION OF INDUSTRIAL ELECTRONICS
Cauer · SYNTHESIS OF LINEAR COMMUNICATION NETWORKS, VOLS. I AND II
Cuccia · HARMONICS, SIDEBANDS, AND TRANSIENTS IN COMMUNICATION
    ENGINEERING
Cunningham · INTRODUCTION TO NONLINEAR ANALYSIS
Eastman · FUNDAMENTALS OF VACUUM TUBES
Evans · CONTROL-SYSTEM DYNAMICS
Feinstein · FOUNDATIONS OF INFORMATION THEORY
Fitzgerald and Higginbotham · BASIC ELECTRICAL ENGINEERING
Fitzgerald and Kingsley · ELECTRIC MACHINERY
Geppert · BASIC ELECTRON TUBES
Glasford · FUNDAMENTALS OF TELEVISION ENGINEERING
Happell and Hesselberth · ENGINEERING ELECTRONICS
Harman · FUNDAMENTALS OF ELECTRONIC MOTION
Harrington · INTRODUCTION TO ELECTROMAGNETIC ENGINEERING
Hayt · ENGINEERING ELECTROMAGNETICS
Hessler and Carey · FUNDAMENTALS OF ELECTRICAL ENGINEERING
Hill · ELECTRONICS IN ENGINEERING
Johnson · TRANSMISSION LINES AND NETWORKS
Kraus · ANTENNAS
Kraus · ELECTROMAGNETICS
LePage · ANALYSIS OF ALTERNATING-CURRENT CIRCUITS
LePage and Seely · GENERAL NETWORK ANALYSIS
Millman and Seely · ELECTRONICS
Millman and Taub · PULSE AND DIGITAL CIRCUITS
Rodgers · INTRODUCTION TO ELECTRIC FIELDS
Rüdenberg · TRANSIENT PERFORMANCE OF ELECTRIC POWER SYSTEMS
Ryder · ENGINEERING ELECTRONICS
Seely · ELECTRON-TUBE CIRCUITS
Seely · ELECTRONIC ENGINEERING
Seely · INTRODUCTION TO ELECTROMAGNETIC FIELDS
Seely · RADIO ELECTRONICS
Siskind · DIRECT-CURRENT MACHINERY
Skilling · ELECTRIC TRANSMISSION LINES
Skilling · TRANSIENT ELECTRIC CURRENTS
Spangenberg · FUNDAMENTALS OF ELECTRON DEVICES
Spangenberg · VACUUM TUBES
Stevenson · ELEMENTS OF POWER SYSTEM ANALYSIS
Storer · PASSIVE NETWORK SYNTHESIS
Terman · ELECTRONIC AND RADIO ENGINEERING
Terman and Pettit · ELECTRONIC MEASUREMENTS
Thaler · ELEMENTS OF SERVOMECHANISM THEORY
Thaler and Brown · SERVOMECHANISM ANALYSIS
Thompson · ALTERNATING-CURRENT AND TRANSIENT CIRCUIT ANALYSIS
Truxal · AUTOMATIC FEEDBACK CONTROL SYSTEM SYNTHESIS

Pulse and Digital Circuits

JACOB MILLMAN, Ph.D.

Professor of Electrical Engineering
Columbia University

HERBERT TAUB, Ph.D.

Associate Professor of Electrical Engineering
The City College of New York

McGRAW-HILL BOOK COMPANY, INC.

New York   Toronto   London

1956

PULSE AND DIGITAL CIRCUITS

Library of Congress Catalog Card Number 55-11930

VII

THE MAPLE PRESS COMPANY, YORK, PA.

To our wives

SALLY

and

ESTHER

PREFACE

The original motivation for the introduction of courses in *electronics* into many electrical-engineering curriculums was to provide the student with a background for the understanding of radio communication. However, particularly within the past 10 years, many other equally important fields have been developed which require a knowledge of electronic circuits which are often quite different from those found in radio systems. These newer fields include *radar, television, analogue* and *digital computers, control systems, data-processing systems, nucleonics, pulse communications, telemetering,* and *instrumentation* (physical, biological, medical, mechanical, psychological, etc.).

In radio engineering the waveforms encountered are essentially sinusoidal in nature. In the newer fields there occur a wider variety of waveforms which include narrow (microsecond or millimicrosecond) pulses, wide (millisecond or second) pulses, square waves, and time-base current and voltage waveforms. In radio engineering the prime signal source is a sinusoidal signal generator. In the newer electrical systems the signal sources also include such circuits as multivibrators, time-base generators, and blocking oscillators. In radio engineering, circuits are required to perform the operations of amplification, modulation, and detection. In the newer fields, circuits are required to perform many additional operations. Among these are circuits which change the shape of a wave (clipping), change the d-c level of a waveform (clamping), determine the occurrence of equality in voltage between two waveforms (amplitude comparison), mark the time of occurrence of some distinctive point on a waveform (time comparison), etc. All these latter circuits depend for their operation on the use of nonlinear circuit elements. Hence, the nonlinear characteristics of diodes, vacuum tubes, and transistors are a matter of more serious concern in the newer fields than in radio engineering. The bandwidths required of the linear passive and active (amplifier) transmission networks in a radio system rarely exceed several hundred kilocycles. In the newer fields, linear pulse (or video) amplifiers and wideband transmission networks of both the lumped- and distributed-parameter type are required with bandwidths extending from zero to tens of megacycles. Finally, we may note that in the newer fields

vii

an important technique has been developed which has no counterpart in radio engineering. This so-called *digital* technique is based on the use of tubes, transistors, and magnetic cores as switches which in operation are either turned *on* or *off* and never left in an intermediate state.

It is the purpose of this text to provide a description and an analysis of the circuits and techniques which are common to many of the newer fields of electrical engineering. It is to be emphasized that this text is not intended as a book on a specific terminal subject such as digital computers, television, radar, etc. Rather the circuits and techniques described here are basic to an understanding of many diversified specialized fields. (It is hoped that the title selected for this text gives some suggestion of its scope. Other authors have used such titles as "unconventional circuits," "waveforms," "advanced electronic circuits," "recurrent electrical transients," "pulse techniques," "timing circuits," etc.)

It is the feeling of the authors that a modern curriculum in electrical engineering should include at least three (and preferably four) courses in electronics. This sequence should begin with physical electronics, continue with what might now be called classical (radio) circuits, and should conclude with pulse and digital circuitry. This book is intended to serve as a text in pulse and digital circuitry for such an undergraduate sequence.

The subject of pulse and digital techniques has already assumed such importance that a two-term graduate sequence in this subject is certainly justified. This text contains adequate material for such a graduate course.

The authors have used almost all the material in this book (in note form and with constant revision) in their classes over the past eight years. The organization of the material has received careful attention and is as follows. First, an analysis is made of the response of linear networks, both active and passive, to the types of waveforms commonly encountered in pulse circuits. Then the basic nonlinearities of tubes and semiconductor devices are described and the effects of these nonlinearities on waveform transmission are studied. Waveform generating circuits and other fundamental building blocks are next analyzed in detail. Finally, the basic circuits, with which the reader is now familiar, are assembled into pulse and digital systems. The motivation behind the organization of each chapter has been to assemble, correlate, and analyze circuits and techniques required to perform a basic operation.

The philosophy of presentation which the authors have adopted has been to analyze a circuit on a physical basis so as to provide a clear understanding and intuitive feeling for its behavior. Mathematics (through differential equations) is used wherever required but only after the physical motivation behind the mathematics has been discussed. Since this text is intended for a course in electronics and not one in differential equations, the authors feel justified in omitting some of the mathematical details of solution. In most cases the roots of the characteristic equation (the poles of the transfer function) are examined carefully, since these provide a great deal of insight into the nature of the response. Then the analytical solution is written down, the response is plotted, and its physical significance is studied. It is assumed that the reader is familiar with the solution (either by the classical or the Laplace transform method) of linear differential equations with constant coefficients.

The principal emphasis in this text is upon a deep theoretical understanding of pulse and digital circuits and techniques. At the same time the authors have included enough practical details so as to make its usefulness felt immediately in the laboratory.

A number of illustrative examples are worked out in detail in the body of the text. A large number of homework problems (over four hundred) are included at the end of the text. Some of these are theoretical in nature, a few give the student practice in the solution of the differential equations set up in the text, and many others illustrate practical circuits and systems. In every case the order of magnitudes of the parameters have been chosen realistically so that the reader will learn what to expect as a practicing engineer. The tube characteristics needed in the solution of some of the problems are included in the Appendix.

It is expected that transistors will play an increasingly important role in pulse and digital circuits as the years go by. The purpose of Chap. 18 is to give a pedagogically sound presentation of the transistor as a basic circuit element. Enough semiconductor physics has been included so as to give the reader an appreciation of the properties of transistors and also of their limitations. It is therefore not necessary for the student to consult other references before reading Chap. 18. The emphasis in the chapter is on the use of the transistor as a switch in pulse and digital applications.

It is a pleasure to acknowledge the assistance received from many sources in the preparation of this book. The following companies supplied information in the form of component characteristics, instrument instruction manuals, etc.: Bell Telephone Laboratories, Berkeley Division of Beckman Instruments, Inc., A. B. Du Mont Laboratories, Inc., General Electric Company, Hewlett-Packard Company, Potter Instrument Company, Sylvania Electric Corporation, Tektronix, and Tel-Instrument Company. We are grateful for the many technical discussions with our friends and colleagues at Columbia University, The City College of New York, the Electronics Research Laboratories of Columbia University, and the Tel-Instrument Company. The Massachusetts Institute of Technology Radiation Laboratory Series of volumes on radar were also a source of a great deal of useful information.

We are pleased to acknowledge our indebtedness to the following persons for their assistance: Professors E. Brenner and G. J. Clemens and L. B. Lambert, R. Laupheimer, and D. L. Schacher read a great deal of the manuscript and made many valuable suggestions. Dr. S. Amarel supplied much valuable information in connection with comparators, Dr. J. W. Easley and Dr. J. L. Moll in connection with transistors, G. F. Bland in connection with the NORC computer, L. Packer in connection with some digital circuits, and R. P. Vogel in connection with transmission gates. H. J. Bickel, A. V. Mitchell, and R. P. Vogel suggested some of the problems. G. E. Kaufer assisted with some of the drafting. Miss J. Psygoda made many of the numerical calculations. We wish particularly to express our gratitude to Miss S. Silverstein, secretary of the Electrical Engineering Department at The City College, for her invaluable assistance in the preparation of the manuscript.

We are grateful to the following for assistance in proofreading: Professor E. Brenner and J. H. Bose, E. Cohen, and F. C. Schwarz.

J. MILLMAN
H. TAUB

CONTENTS

REVIEW OF AMPLIFIER CIRCUITS

Voltage- and current-feedback circuits, which find extensive application in many branches of electronics, are also used frequently in pulse systems. Among such circuits, which will appear throughout this text, are the cathode-follower, phase-inverter circuits, difference amplifiers, and operational amplifiers. Therefore we shall review briefly the principles of negative feedback and derive equivalent circuits which will give an intimate physical understanding of such circuits. Finally, these powerful methods of analysis will be applied to the circuits most commonly used in pulse applications.

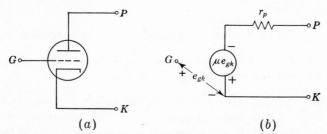

(a) (b)

FIG. 1-1. The equivalent circuit of a triode operating linearly.

1-1. Equivalent Circuit of a Vacuum Tube.[1]   Over the range of linear operation, the vacuum tube of Fig. 1-1a may be replaced by the equivalent circuit of Fig. 1-1b.   The symbol e_{gk} stands for the *voltage drop* from grid to cathode, and r_p is the plate resistance of the vacuum tube.   A circuit which involves vacuum tubes may be analyzed by replacing each tube by its equivalent circuit and by disregarding all those circuit features, such as supply and bias voltages, which have an influence only on the quiescent state.*   This replacement of the vacuum tube by its equivalent leaves a network which may be dealt with by linear circuit analysis.

EXAMPLE.   The triode of Fig. 1-2a has a plate resistance r_p and an amplification factor μ.   The externally applied voltage is e_e, as shown, and the output voltage is e_o. Find an equivalent circuit with respect to the output terminals selected.

* The symbols for voltage and current used throughout this chapter (with the exception of Sec. 1-7) represent variations from the quiescent value.

1

Solution.   The vacuum tube has been replaced by its equivalent circuit in Fig. 1-2b. The current i must satisfy the equation

$$\mu e_{gk} = i(r_p + R_L + R_k)$$

The voltage drop from G to K is

$$e_{gk} = e_e - iR_k$$

Eliminating e_{gk}, and solving for $e_o = iR_k$, we have

$$e_o = \frac{\mu}{\mu + 1} e_e \frac{R_k}{R_k + R_1}$$

where $R_1 = (R_L + r_p)/(\mu + 1)$.

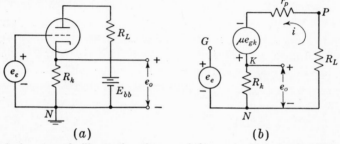

Fig. 1-2. An example illustrating the use of the equivalent circuit of Fig. 1-1b.

It appears from inspection of this last equation that the output voltage may then be computed from the equivalent circuit of Fig. 1-3a.

Thévenin's theorem states that *any two-terminal linear network may be replaced by a generator equal to the open-circuit voltage between the terminals in series with the equivalent output impedance.*   The *output imped-ance* is that impedance which appears between the output terminals when all energy sources are replaced by their internal impedances.   For exam-ple, in Fig. 1-3a the output impedance R is given by the parallel combina-tion of R_1 and R_k and the Thévenin generator voltage is given by

$$e_T = \frac{\mu e_e}{\mu + 1} \frac{R_k}{R_k + R_1}$$

This Thévenin equivalent circuit of Fig. 1-3a is shown in Fig. 1-3b.   We have also indicated in Fig. 1-3b that an external load may be added across the output terminals and that it will then draw a load current i_L [which will equal $e_T/(R + R')$].   Thus, the output impedance specifies the manner in which the output voltage $e_o = i_L R'$ is affected by an external load.   The output voltage is also given by $e_o = e_T - i_L R$.

The Thévenin equivalent of an amplifier circuit is indicated in Fig. 1-4a.   The input terminals are marked 1 and 2 and the input voltage is e.

The output terminals are marked 3 and 4. The external load is R' and the output impedance is R. Since the open-circuit voltage (no external load placed across the amplifier) is the amplifier gain A times the external voltage, the Thévenin generator is Ae, as indicated.

In Fig. 1-4a we have assumed that the circuit contains only resistive elements. If reactive elements are present, the circuit may be generalized as indicated in Fig. 1-4b. Capital letters are now used to define sinor

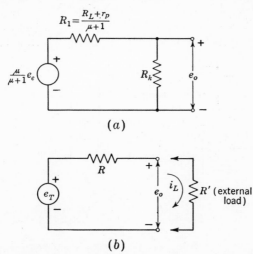

(a)

(b)

Fig. 1-3. Networks equivalent to the circuit of Fig. 1-2. The Thévenin generator e_T and the output impedance R are defined in the text.

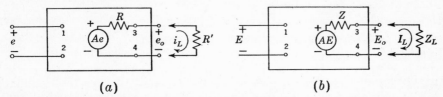

(a)

(b)

Fig. 1-4. Thévenin equivalent circuits for an amplifier (a) with resistive elements and (b) with reactive elements.

(phasor) quantities and resistances R are replaced by complex impedances Z. The output voltage is given by

$$E_o = AE - I_L Z \qquad (1\text{-}1)$$

where Z is the output impedance, A is the (unloaded) amplifier gain, and Z_L is the load impedance. This equation may be used to define A and Z for a particular circuit. For example, if we find that the output voltage of an amplifier varies linearly with load current as indicated in Eq. (1-1), then the factor multiplying the applied voltage E is the gain and the factor multiplying the load current I_L is the output impedance.

1-2. Voltage Feedback in Amplifiers.   A feedback amplifier may be defined tentatively as one in which the amplifier input signal is in part derived from an external source and in part from the amplifier output. Any amplifier, whether it involves feedback or not, may be analyzed by the method outlined in Sec. 1-1.   Where feedback is involved, however, it is more fruitful to try to deal separately with the amplifier proper and with the feedback network in order to be able to appreciate the influence of the feedback on the amplifier characteristics.   Since, with respect to its output terminals, the amplifier is specified by the gain and output impedance we shall inquire into the manner in which these two features

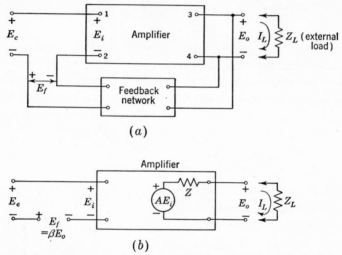

(a)

(b)

FIG. 1-5. (a) A block diagram of a voltage-feedback amplifier.   The feedback factor β is defined by $\beta \equiv E_f/E_o$, where $E_f = E_i - E_e$. (b) The equivalent circuit.

of the amplifier are modified by certain particular feedback arrangements.

Consider the feedback arrangement of Fig. 1-5a.   The signal at the input terminals to the amplifier is the sum of the externally impressed voltage E_e and a feedback voltage $E_f = \beta E_o$.   The feedback voltage is related to the output voltage by a factor β, which is determined by the feedback network.   The feedback network may be active or passive and in general β may be a complex quantity.   The convention with respect to the polarity of all signals is indicated, and this convention will be adhered to consistently in what follows.

Let A be the *forward gain without feedback* (the *open-loop gain*) between the input and output terminals of the amplifier with the load Z_L removed. We may define A by the following operational procedure.   Remove E_e, and apply a voltage E_i directly to the terminals 1 and 2.   The gain A is given by $A \equiv E_o/E_i$.

The *output impedance without feedback* Z of the amplifier is defined as follows. Remove E_e, and short-circuit terminals 1 and 2. Under these conditions Z is the impedance seen looking back into the output terminals 3 and 4. Note that the definitions of A and Z take into account the loading effect of the impedance of the feedback network.

The Thévenin equivalent circuit corresponding to Fig. 1-5a is indicated in Fig. 1-5b. *The distinguishing feature of voltage feedback is that the feedback voltage E_f is related to the output voltage E_o by $E_f = \beta E_o$, in which β is fixed independently of the external load Z_L.* We may write

$$E_o = AE_i - I_L Z \qquad \text{and} \qquad E_i = E_e + \beta E_o$$

Eliminating E_i from these equations, we find

$$E_o = \frac{A}{1 - A\beta} E_e - \frac{Z}{1 - A\beta} I_L \tag{1-2}$$

This equation is in the form of Eq. (1-1) and hence we conclude that the gain and output impedance with feedback are given by A_f (the *closed-loop gain*) and Z_f, respectively, where

$$A_f = \frac{A}{1 - \beta A} \tag{1-3}$$

and

$$Z_f = \frac{Z}{1 - \beta A} \tag{1-4}$$

The Thévenin equivalent circuit is indicated in Fig. 1-6. The effect of the feedback is, therefore, to modify both gain and impedance by the same factor. If $|A_f| < |A|$, the feedback is termed *negative* or *degenerative*. If $|A_f| > |A|$, the feedback is termed *positive* or *regenerative*. In the case of negative feedback,

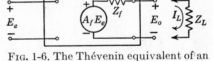

FIG. 1-6. The Thévenin equivalent of an amplifier taking voltage feedback into account.

which is of principal interest to us, the magnitude of both gain and impedance is divided by the factor $|1 - \beta A|$.

1-3. Current Feedback in Amplifiers. A *current-feedback* amplifier is shown in Fig. 1-7. The amplifier without feedback has a gain A and output impedance Z. The distinguishing feature of the present circuit is that *the feedback voltage is proportional to the current which flows through the external load Z_L and the factor of proportionality between E_f and I_L is independent of the output voltage E_o.* The feedback voltage is developed across the impedance Z_s, which is in series with the load.

We have

$$E_o = AE_i - (Z + Z_s)I_L \qquad \text{and} \qquad E_i = E_e + Z_s I_L$$

from which

$$E_o = AE_e - [Z + Z_s(1 - A)]I_L$$

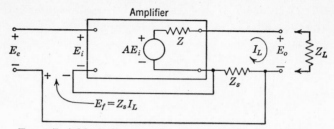

FIG. 1-7. A block diagram of a current-feedback amplifier.

Comparing with Eq. (1-1), we see that the gain and impedance in the presence of current feedback are therefore

$$A_f = A \qquad Z_f = Z + Z_s(1 - A) \qquad (1-5)$$

The gain has not been altered. If the amplifier were unaltered except that the feedback voltage were not returned to the input, the output impedance would be $Z + Z_s$. The effect of the current feedback is therefore to add to the output impedance the additional impedance $-AZ_s$. If, for example, A is a real negative number and Z_s is resistive, the output impedance with feedback will be greater than the impedance without feedback.

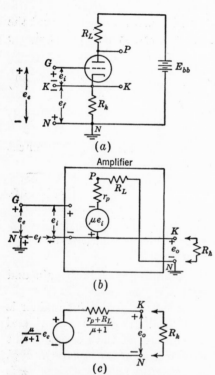

1-4. Illustrations of Current and Voltage Feedback. We shall now consider some examples of special one-tube amplifiers. The examples are selected because they illustrate the matters described above in connection with feedback and also because the circuits themselves are of much practical importance.

Suppose that in the circuit of Fig. 1-8a we *define* the output terminals to be K and N so that $e_o = e_{kn}$ and the input terminals to be G and K so that $e_i = e_{gk}$. The external signal generator is connected to G and N so that $e_e = e_{gn}$. The circuit may now be redrawn as in Fig. 1-8b,

FIG. 1-8. (a) Amplifier with plate and cathode resistors. (b) Circuit redrawn as a voltage-feedback amplifier. (c) Equivalent circuit with respect to output terminals between cathode and ground.

which corresponds to Fig. 1-5b. Independently of whether the resistor R_k is considered a part of the amplifier or an external load we have a case of voltage feedback in which $\beta = -1$ since $e_f = -e_o$. Let us consider that R_k is an external load and not a part of the amplifier. Then

$$A = \frac{e_o}{e_i} = \frac{e_{kn}}{e_{gk}} = \mu$$

and $1 - \beta A = 1 + \mu$. The impedance without feedback seen looking to the left between terminals K and N is $r_p + R_L$. The gain and impedance with feedback are found from Eqs. (1-3) and (1-4) to be

$$A_f = \frac{\mu}{\mu + 1} \qquad \text{and} \qquad R_f = \frac{r_p + R_L}{\mu + 1} \qquad (1\text{-}6)$$

The equivalent circuit is as indicated in Fig. 1-8c. This is the same circuit as in Fig. 1-3a, which was derived without the aid of feedback formulas.

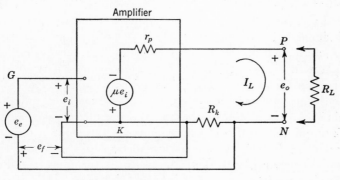

(a)

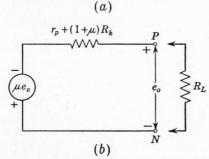

(b)

Fig. 1-9. (a) Amplifier with plate and cathode resistors drawn as a current-feedback amplifier. (b) Equivalent circuit with respect to output terminals between plate and ground.

Next, referring again to Fig. 1-8a, let us consider that again $e_i = e_{gk}$ and $e_e = e_{gn}$ but that now $e_o = e_{pn}$. The circuit is redrawn in Fig. 1-9a which corresponds exactly to the circumstances of current feedback in Fig. 1-7. Observe that here we have no choice but to require that R_L be considered an external load. The gain, with or without feedback, is $A = A_f = e_{pn}/e_{gk} = -\mu$. The output impedance neglecting feedback is $r_p + R_k$, so that altogether we have

$$A_f = -\mu \qquad \text{and} \qquad R_f = r_p + (1 + \mu)R_k \qquad (1\text{-}7)$$

The equivalent circuit is shown in Fig. 1-9b.

The above results are extremely important and should be emphasized. *If we look into the cathode of an amplifier, we see an equivalent circuit* (Fig. 1-8c) *consisting of a generator of value* $\mu/(\mu + 1)$ *times the external-source voltage and an impedance* $(r_p + R_L)/(\mu + 1)$. The latter may be small if μ is large. On the other hand, *if we look into the plate of an amplifier, we see an equivalent circuit* (Fig. 1-9b) *consisting of a generator of value* $-\mu$ *times the external-source voltage and an impedance* $r_p + (\mu + 1)R_k$. The latter may be large if μ is large.

It should be clear at this point that any discussion of feedback must necessarily take as its starting point a careful *definition* of what are to be considered as the input and output terminals of the amplifier, where the external signal is to be applied, what is to be considered a part of the amplifier, and what is external to the amplifier. For example, if in connection with Fig. 1-9, the resistor R_L were to be considered part of the amplifier, then the resultant circuit would correspond neither to voltage nor to current feedback as we have defined them. It might still be profitable in this latter case to consider the amplifier as some new type of feedback amplifier. But the point to note is that a circuit must conform in every detail to the circumstances specified in Figs. 1-5a and 1-7 before we can confidently apply to them the feedback formulas stated above.

1-5. Some Characteristics of Feedback Amplifiers. The three properties of feedback amplifiers which are most important for pulse circuit applications are the influence of negative feedback on the *stability* of amplifier gain, on the *frequency distortion*, and on *nonlinear distortion*. We shall consider first a voltage-feedback amplifier.

Stability. The variation due to aging, temperature, and replacement, etc., of the circuit components and tube characteristics of an amplifier is reflected in a corresponding lack of stability of the amplifier gain. The fractional change in gain with feedback is related to the fractional change without feedback by

$$\left| \frac{dA_f}{A_f} \right| = \frac{1}{|1 - \beta A|} \left| \frac{dA}{A} \right|$$

This equation is obtained by differentiating Eq. (1-3). If the feedback is negative, so that $|1 - \beta A| > 1$, the feedback will have served to improve the gain stability of the amplifier.

In particular, if $|\beta A| \gg 1$, then

$$A_f = \frac{A}{1 - \beta A} \cong -\frac{A}{\beta A} = -\frac{1}{\beta}$$

and the gain may be made to depend entirely on the feedback network. The worst offenders with respect to stability are usually the vacuum tubes involved. If the feedback network should then contain only passive elements, the improvement in stability may indeed be pronounced.

Feedback is used to improve stability in the following way. Suppose an amplifier of gain A_1 is required. We start by building an amplifier of gain, $A_2 = kA_1$, in which k is a large number. Feedback is now introduced to divide the gain by the factor k. The stability will be improved by the same factor, k, since both gain and stability are divided by the factor $k = |1 - \beta A_2|$. If now the instability of the amplifier of gain, A_2, is not appreciably poorer than the instability of the amplifier of gain without feedback equal to A_1, this procedure will have been useful. It often happens as a matter of practice that an amplifier gain may be increased appreciably without a corresponding loss of stability. Consider, for example, the case of a one-tube pentode amplifier. The gain is $g_m R_L$, g_m being the tube transconductance and R_L the plate-circuit resistor. The principal source of instability is in g_m. Hence the fractional change in gain is the same for a given fractional change in g_m independently of the size of R_L.

Frequency Distortion. It follows from the equation $A_f \cong -1/\beta$ that if the feedback network does not contain reactive elements then the overall gain is not a function of frequency. Under these circumstances a substantial reduction in frequency and phase distortion is obtained. It is to be noted, however, that negative feedback improves frequency response only at the expense of gain.

Nonlinear Distortion. Suppose that a large amplitude signal is applied to a stage of an amplifier so that the operation of the tube extends slightly beyond its range of linear operation and as a consequence the output signal is slightly distorted. Negative feedback is now introduced and the input signal is increased by the same amount by which the gain is reduced so that the output signal amplitude remains the same. For simplicity, let us consider that the input signal is sinusoidal and that the distortion consists of simply a second-harmonic signal generated within the tube. We shall also assume that the second-harmonic amplitude, in the absence of feedback, is equal to B_2. Because of the effects of feedback, a component B_{2f} actually appears in the output. To find the relationship that exists between B_{2f} and B_2, it is noted that the output will contain the term $A\beta B_{2f}$, which arises from the component βB_{2f} that is fed back to the input. Thus the output contains two terms: B_2, generated in the tube, and $A\beta B_{2f}$, which represents the effect of the feedback. Hence,

$$A\beta B_{2f} + B_2 = B_{2f}$$

or
$$B_{2f} = \frac{B_2}{1 - A\beta} \qquad (1\text{-}8)$$

Since A and β are generally functions of the frequency, they must be evaluated at the second-harmonic frequency.

The input voltage E_e to the feedback amplifier may be the actual signal externally available, or it may be the output of an amplifier preceding the feedback stage or stages under consideration. In order to multiply the input to the feedback amplifier by the factor $|1 - A\beta|$, it is necessary either to increase the nominal gain of the preamplifying stages or to add a new stage. If the full benefit of the feedback amplifier in reducing nonlinear distortion is to be obtained, these preamplifying stages must not introduce additional distortion because of the increased output demanded of them. Since, however, appreciable harmonics are introduced only when the output swing is large, most of the distortion arises in the last stage. The preamplifying stages are of smaller importance in considerations of harmonic generation.

It has been assumed in the derivation of Eq. (1-8) that the harmonic distortion generated within the tube depends only upon the grid swing of the fundamental signal voltage. The small amount of additional distortion that might arise from the second-harmonic component fed back from the output to the input has been neglected. Ordinarily, this will lead to little error. Further, it must be noted, the result given by Eq. (1-8) applies only in the case of small distortion. The principle of superposition has been used in the derivation and for this reason it is required that the tube must be considered to operate with at least approximate linearity.

Consider now a current-feedback amplifier. The three properties given above for the *output voltage* of a voltage-feedback amplifier are equally valid for the *output current* of a current-feedback amplifier. This statement may be confirmed as follows: From Fig. 1-7 and Eq. (1-5) the load current in a current-feedback amplifier is given by

$$I_L = \frac{AE_e}{Z + Z_s(1 - A) + Z_L} \cong \frac{-E_e}{Z_s} \tag{1-9}$$

provided that $|Z_s A| \gg |Z + Z_s + Z_L|$. Under these circumstances we note that the current depends only upon Z_s and not upon the other amplifier features. Hence, if the feedback impedance Z_s is a stable element, the load current is stable with respect to aging, temperature, and replacement of circuit components and tube characteristics. If Z_s is a resistor, then I_L is independent of frequency and the distortion in frequency and phase is greatly reduced. Note that this conclusion is valid even if the load impedance is a function of frequency. If Z_s is a linear element, then virtually no nonlinear distortion of load current results.

We may summarize the above discussion by stating that the load *current in a current-feedback amplifier is approximately independent of load impedance.* In other words, *the circuit behaves as a current device,* the magnitude of the load current being obtained by dividing the externally applied voltage by the feedback impedance Z_s.

1-6. The Cathode Follower. An example of a circuit which may profitably be viewed as a feedback amplifier is the *cathode follower* of Fig. 1-10a. This circuit is also referred to as a *grounded-plate amplifier.* The equivalent circuit of Fig. 1-10b may be drawn directly by setting $R_L = 0$ in Fig. 1-8c. The gain is always less than unity and is given by

$$A = \frac{\mu R_k}{r_p + (\mu + 1) R_k} \quad (1\text{-}10)$$

If $(\mu + 1) R_k \gg r_p$, then the gain is $\mu/(\mu + 1)$ or approximately unity. A gain of 0.95 or larger is not difficult to achieve. The polarity of the voltage at the cathode, the output signal, is the same as at the grid. The cathode voltage therefore *follows* very closely the grid voltage and this feature accounts for the name given to the circuit.

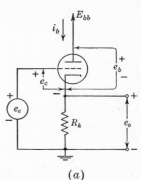

(a)

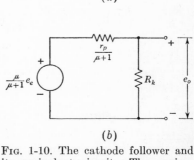

(b)

Fig. 1-10. The cathode follower and its equivalent circuit. The equivalent circuit is as shown in Fig. 1-8c except that $R_L = 0$.

If numerator and denominator of Eq. (1-10) are divided by r_p and if we recognize that usually $\mu + 1 \cong \mu$, we may rewrite Eq. (1-10) in the form

$$A = \frac{g_m R_k}{1 + g_m R_k} \quad (1\text{-}11)$$

in which $g_m = \mu/r_p$ is the transconductance of the tube.

The output impedance of the cathode follower is determined by the parallel combination of R_k and $r_p/(\mu + 1)$. Since $r_p/(\mu + 1) \cong 1/g_m$, the output impedance may be written, with small error, as

$$R = \frac{R_k}{1 + g_m R_k} \quad (1\text{-}12)$$

For $g_m R_k \gg 1$, $R = 1/g_m$. Since g_m, for a large variety of receiving-type tubes lies in the range 1 to 10 millimhos, R includes the range 100 to 1,000 ohms. A low output impedance is often an asset in an amplifier since it reduces the influence of the load on the amplifier output voltage.

The output impedance of a cathode follower is frequently appreciably smaller than the output impedance encountered in a conventional amplifier where the output signal is developed across an impedance in the plate circuit.

The conventional amplifier, however, provides gain.   To make a fair comparison between the two amplifier types, let us compare, for the two cases, a figure of merit F, which is defined as *the ratio of gain to output impedance*.   If, in the conventional amplifier, the resistor R_L is small in comparison with the tube plate resistance (as it would be even if the tube were a triode, but the interest was in securing a low output impedance), then $A = g_m R_L$ and $R = R_L$ approximately.   Therefore

$$F \text{ (conventional amplifier) } = \frac{g_m R_L}{R_L} = g_m$$

For a cathode follower,

$$F \text{ (cathode follower) } = \frac{g_m R_k}{1 + g_m R_k} \frac{1 + g_m R_k}{R_k} = g_m$$

It appears that if the gain of a conventional amplifier is made equal to that of a cathode follower, then the output impedance of the two circuits is the same.

Nevertheless where an amplifier of low output impedance is required, the cathode follower might still be the circuit of choice since it offers an advantage with respect to *stability* of gain not shared by the conventional amplifier.   In the light of the discussion in Sec. 1-5 this feature might well have been anticipated.   Consider, for example, that the g_m of the tube changes by, say, 10 per cent.   The gain of the conventional amplifier also changes by 10 per cent.   On the other hand, if a cathode follower were adjusted for approximately unity gain ($g_m R_k \gg 1$), the change in gain would be appreciably reduced.   We have

$$\frac{dA}{A} = \frac{1}{1 + g_m R_k} \frac{dg_m}{g_m}$$

so that, if, say, $g_m R_k = 10$ and $dg_m/g_m = 0.1$, then $dA/A = 0.1/11 \cong 0.01$. Thus, a 10 per cent change in g_m has now resulted in only a 1 per cent change in gain.   This is an improvement by a factor of 10 over the conventional amplifier.

A second advantage of the cathode follower lies in the linearity with which the output signal follows the input signal.   The advantage is most pronounced when a cathode follower of maximum possible gain, nominally unity, is compared with a conventional amplifier of comparable gain and consequently comparable output impedance.   Consider first a cathode follower in which R_k is made very large.

If an output signal swing Δe_o is required, the tube current must change by $\Delta e_o/R_k$, which is small since R_k is large. Since the nonlinearity introduced by a vacuum tube is largely determined by the range over which its current must vary, we may anticipate that the operation will be quite linear. The comparable conventional amplifier will require a plate-circuit resistor R_L nominally equal to $1/g_m$, which is only of the order of several hundred ohms. The tube current must then change by $\Delta e_o/R_L$, which is very much larger than $\Delta e_o/R_k$, and the linearity will suffer. With a cathode follower for which $g_m R_k \gg 1$ it is not difficult to achieve a linear output voltage whose peak-to-peak value is comparable to the total supply voltage. With a unity-gain amplifier the maximum output swing is the grid base (defined as the voltage swing from zero bias to cutoff). This swing is approximately $1/\mu$ times the supply voltage. Hence the swing obtainable from a unity-gain conventional amplifier is much smaller than that from a cathode follower.

1-7. Graphical Analysis of the Cathode Follower. We consider now how to use the characteristic curves of a vacuum tube to determine such matters as range of output voltage swing, proper bias voltage, and operating point for any arbitrary input voltage to a cathode follower. In Fig. 1-10a, e_c, e_b, and i_b are, respectively, the *total* instantaneous grid-to-cathode voltage, plate-to-cathode voltage, and plate current. We have

$$E_{bb} = e_b + i_b R_k \tag{1-13}$$

and
$$e_e = e_c + i_b R_k \tag{1-14}$$

Equation (1-13) is the equation of the load line corresponding to the plate voltage E_{bb} and the load resistor R_k. The procedure for constructing the dynamic characteristic (plate current vs. external input voltage) of a cathode follower is then the following:

1. On the plate characteristics draw the load line corresponding to the given value of E_{bb} and R_k.
2. Note the current value corresponding to each point of intersection of the load line with the characteristic curves. In each case relabel the individual plate characteristics with an input voltage e_e equal to $e_c + i_b R_k$, in accordance with Eq. (1-14). The procedure is illustrated in Fig. 1-11.
3. The required curve is now a plot of the current values vs. the input voltage. For example, i_{b2} and e_{e2} are corresponding values on the graph.
4. The output voltage corresponding to the current i_{b2} is $e_{k2} = i_{b2} R_k$, as is indicated in Fig. 1-11.

When cutoff occurs, there is, of course, no drop across the cathode resistor. Consequently, the externally applied voltage required to attain cutoff is independent of the size of the cathode resistor. When the input voltage swings positively, the cathode follows it and maintains itself positive with respect to the grid. The maximum input voltage is usually limited by grid current which takes place approximately at the place where the grid-cathode voltage is zero.

EXAMPLE. Consider a 6SN7 vacuum tube with $E_{bb} = 300$ volts and $R_k = 20$ K. Find the maximum positive and negative input voltages. (Refer to Fig. A-2.*)

Solution. From the plate characteristics and the load line it is found that the current corresponding to $e_c = 0$ is $i_b = 10$ ma. Hence, the maximum output voltage is $i_b R_k = 200$ volts, and since $e_c = 0$, the maximum input voltage is also 200 volts. The cutoff voltage for the 6SN7 corresponding to 300 volts is found to be -18 volts. Hence, the cathode follower may swing from $+200$ volts to -18 volts without drawing grid current or driving the tube beyond cutoff. The corresponding input range for an amplifier using the same tube and the same supply voltage is only 0 to -18 volts.

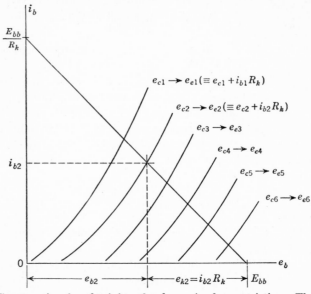

FIG. 1-11. Construction for obtaining the dynamic characteristics. The symbolism $e_{c1} \rightarrow e_{e1}$ means that e_{c1} is replaced by $e_{e1} = e_{c1} + i_{b1}R_k$.

From Eq. (1-14) it is clear that the instantaneous output voltage $i_b R_k$ is larger than the instantaneous input voltage e_e since e_c is a negative number. This result does not contradict the fact that the gain of a cathode follower must be less than unity. It must be remembered that it is only necessary that the change in output be less than the corresponding change in input voltage. For example, in the above illustration, the maximum input peak-to-peak swing is 218 volts but the maximum output swing is 200 volts.

It is often desirable to find the current corresponding to a specified input voltage without drawing the entire dynamic characteristic as outlined above. A very simple procedure is as follows:

* Figures A-1 to A-12 are to be found in the Appendix.

1. On the plate characteristics draw the load line corresponding to the given value of E_{bb} and R_k.

2. Corresponding to each value of e_c for which there is a plotted plate characteristic calculate the current for the specified value of input voltage E. In accordance with Eq. (1-14) this current is given by

$$i_b = \frac{E - e_c}{R_k}$$

The corresponding values of i_b and e_c are plotted on the plate characteristics as indicated by the dots in Fig. 1-12. These points are connected by a curve.

3. The intersection of this curve and the load line gives the plate current I_b corresponding to the given input voltage E.

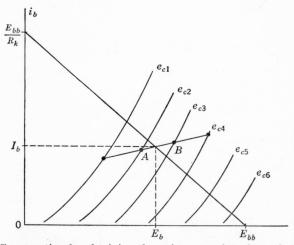

Fig. 1-12. Construction for obtaining the quiescent point of a cathode follower.

The procedure outlined above is very easy to carry out. It is not really necessary to use all values of e_c, but only two adjacent values which give currents above and below the load line, as indicated by points A and B in Fig. 1-12. The intersection of the straight line connecting A and B with the load line gives the desired current. In particular, it should be noted that if E is large compared with the range of values of e_c, then i_b will be almost constant and hence the curve connecting the dots in Fig. 1-12 will be approximately a horizontal straight line.

The analysis of the operation of an amplifier which has both a cathode resistor and a plate resistor, as in Fig. 1-8a, follows a procedure identical to the one described for the cathode follower with the single exception that the load line is drawn corresponding to a resistor equal to $R_L + R_k$ rather than to R_k.

1-8. Practical Cathode-follower Circuits. In the illustration given in Sec. 1-7 the input could swing 200 volts in the positive direction before drawing grid current but could only go 18 volts in the negative direction before driving the tube to cutoff. If a more symmetrical operation is desired, the tube must be properly biased. Figure 1-13 shows four biasing arrangements. In (a) the grid is maintained positive with respect to ground by the use of a voltage divider across the plate supply. In (b) the bottom of R_k is made negative with respect to ground, the voltage being obtained from a separate negative supply. In (c) self-bias is used, the self-biasing voltage appearing across R_1. That is, with no

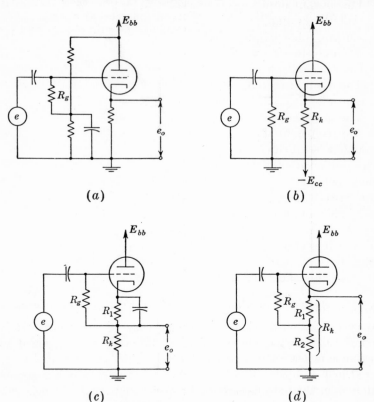

(a)   (b)

(c)   (d)

FIG. 1-13. Four biasing arrangements for a cathode follower.

input signal the grid-cathode voltage is the drop across R_1. This resistor is chosen so that the quiescent voltage across R_k is approximately half the peak-to-peak output swing. In the example of Sec. 1-7, where the total output swing was 200 volts, the quiescent value is chosen as 100 volts across the 20-K resistor. This corresponds to a quiescent plate current of 5 ma. From the plate characteristics of the 6J5 and the 20-K load line, the grid-cathode voltage corresponding to 5 ma is -7 volts. Hence, R_1 must be chosen equal to $\frac{7}{5}$ K = 1.4 K. Finally, in (d) the bypass capacitor across R_1 is removed, the output appears across the combination

R_1 and R_2, and the bias voltage is again equal to the d-c voltage drop across R_1. In the above example, $R_1 = 1.4$ K and

$$R_2 = R_k - R_1 = 20 - 1.4 = 18.6 \text{ K}$$

1-9. Characteristics and Applications of the Cathode Follower. The principal characteristics of the cathode follower may be summarized as:

1. High input impedance (low input capacitance).
2. Low output impedance.
3. Stability of amplification with tube changing, voltage variation, etc.
4. Output is linearly related to the input.
5. No inversion of the signal.
6. Gain is less than one but can be made almost equal to unity.
7. The input swing may be very large, approaching the supply voltage in magnitude.
8. The quiescent output voltage may be adjusted easily.
9. Any ripple in the supply voltages appears at the output greatly attenuated (see Prob. 1-6d).

The first characteristic is discussed in Chap. 3, where the high-frequency behavior of the cathode follower is considered. The other characteristics mentioned above have been studied in the preceding sections. The nonlinear properties of the cathode follower are discussed in Chap. 4.

Only a few applications will be listed, although many are suggested by the above properties. A cathode follower is usually employed when a high input impedance or a low output impedance or both are required. The input stage to almost all good-quality cathode-ray oscilloscopes is a cathode follower. Whenever it is required to transmit a signal over a relatively long distance, the capacitive loading of the long wires (or shielded cable) is minimized by taking advantage of the low output impedance of the cathode follower. One such application is the use of the cathode follower to couple the early stages of the amplifier of an oscilloscope, located near the front-panel input terminals, to the output stages, which are located near the back of the chassis at the base of the cathode-ray tube. Another such application is the use of the cathode follower to feed video signals, by means of a coaxial cable, from a receiver to a number of indicators many feet away.

If the output from one circuit acts as the input to another circuit, and the second circuit reacts back onto the first, then a cathode follower may be used as a buffer stage to eliminate this reaction.

Many electronic instruments take advantage of the great stability and linearity of cathode followers.

1-10. Cathode-follower-type Circuits.[2] There are a number of circuits which partake of some of the properties of cathode followers principally because they involve the use of a resistor in the cathode circuit.

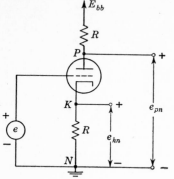

FIG. 1-14. The phase inverter.

Some of these which are commonly employed in pulse applications are described in this section.

The Phase Inverter. The *phase inverter* appears in Fig. 1-14. A single input signal provides two output signals: e_{kn}, which is of the same polarity as the input, and e_{pn}, which is of opposite polarity. Further, if the plate and cathode resistors are identical, the magnitudes of the two signals must be the same, since the currents in the plate and cathode resistors are equal. The gain $|A| \equiv |e_{kn}/e| = |e_{pn}/e|$ may be written directly by comparison with either of the equivalent circuits of Fig. 1-8c or 1-9b with the result that

$$|A| = \frac{\mu R}{r_p + (\mu + 2)R} \cong \frac{g_m R}{1 + g_m R} \tag{1-15}$$

The exact result differs from that given for the cathode follower, Eq. (1-10), only in the appearance of a factor $\mu + 2$ in place of the factor $\mu + 1$. The gain may be made to approach 1 if $g_m R \gg 1$. The ratio of the plate-to-cathode signal to the input signal may then approach 2. The output impedances at the plate and at the cathode are different, the plate impedance being higher than the cathode impedance.

One of the important uses for the phase inverter (and also the paraphase amplifier described below) is to convert a single-ended sweep voltage into a symmetrical deflection signal for an oscilloscope.

The Paraphase Amplifier. The *paraphase amplifier* of Fig. 1-15a serves the same purpose as the phase inverter but additionally provides some gain and equal output impedances. The two signals e_{o1} and e_{o2} are of opposite polarity and are nominally of equal amplitude. The equivalent circuit of Fig. 1-8c may again be used to advantage to analyze the operation of the paraphase amplifier. We replace each tube by its equivalent circuit as seen from the cathode. The resulting circuit is shown in Fig. 1-15b. The *signal* currents flowing, respectively, out of the cathode of T_1 and into the cathode of T_2 are i_1 and i_2. The output signals are $e_{o1} = -i_1 R_L$ and $e_{o2} = i_2 R_L$. By applying Kirchhoff's voltage law to the outside loop of Fig. 1-15b we find for the plate-to-plate gain

$$A \equiv \frac{e_{o2} - e_{o1}}{e} = \frac{(i_1 + i_2) R_L}{e}$$

$$= \frac{\mu R_L}{r_p + R_L} \tag{1-16}$$

which is the same gain that would be provided by a single-tube conventional amplifier with plate resistor R_L.

The output signals will be of equal magnitude if $i_1 = i_2$. This requirement will be satisfied nominally if $R_k \gg (r_p + R_L)/(\mu + 1)$. Typically

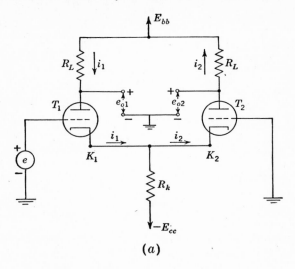

(a)

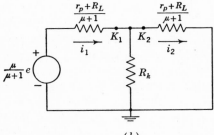

(b)

Fig. 1-15. Paraphase amplifier and its equivalent circuit.

if, say, $r_p = R_L = 10$ K and $\mu + 1 = 20$ as for a 12AU7 tube,

$$\frac{r_p + R_L}{\mu + 1} = 1 \text{ K}$$

and R_k should be selected to be about 10 K if an unbalance of no more than about 10 per cent is desired (see Prob. 1-14). If each tube carries a quiescent current of, say, 5 ma, the quiescent drop across R_k is 100 volts. We may require for convenience that the quiescent grid voltages be ground potential. In the linear range of operation the grid-to-cathode voltage of a tube is usually only of the order of several volts. The voltage at the cathodes is therefore also required to be in the neighborhood of ground potential. These requirements with respect to quiescent operating voltages may be satisfied by returning the cathode resistor, as in Fig. 1-15a, to an appropriately large negative voltage (in this example, $E_{cc} = 100$ volts).

The Difference Amplifier. Suppose that we have two signals e_1 and e_2, each measured with respect to ground. It is desired to generate a third signal, also to be referred to ground, which signal is to be proportional to the voltage difference $e_1 - e_2$. One such application would occur if it were required to convert the symmetrical signal, which appears at the plates of a paraphase amplifier, back to an unsymmetrical signal. A possible arrangement for this purpose would involve connecting a transformer primary from plate to plate in Fig. 1-15a. The required signal

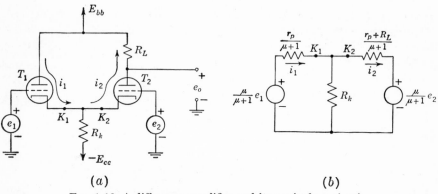

(a)   (b)

FIG. 1-16. A difference amplifier and its equivalent circuit.

is taken from the transformer secondary, one side of which is grounded. The impedance of the transformer must be high enough not to load down the circuit appreciably and its frequency response must be adequate for the application at hand. A much more generally applicable method is indicated in the difference amplifier of Fig. 1-16a. In this circuit one of the signals, e_2, is applied directly to the grid of the tube T_2 and the second signal, e_1, is applied to the cathode through the cathode follower T_1. The output of T_2 is proportional to its cathode-to-grid voltage and hence approximately proportional to the difference $e_1 - e_2$.

The equivalent circuit is given in Fig. 1-16b, where again each tube has been replaced by its equivalent seen looking back into the cathode. The output voltage is $i_2 R_L$. If we assume that $(\mu + 1)R_k \gg r_p$ and consequently neglect entirely the presence of R_k, then $i_1 = i_2$ and the output is exactly proportional to the difference $e_1 - e_2$, being given by

$$e_o = \frac{\mu R_L (e_1 - e_2)}{2r_p + R_L} \tag{1-17}$$

Ideally, in a difference amplifier, if the input signals were identical, $e_1 = e_2 = e_c$, the output signal would be zero. An identical signal on both grids is known as a *common-mode* signal. The gain for the common-mode signal would indeed be zero if R_k were infinite. However, if $(\mu + 1)R_k \gg r_p$ and $\mu \gg 1$, we find that

$$e_o = \frac{-R_L r_p}{R_k(2r_p + R_L)} e_c \qquad (1\text{-}18)$$

The matter may be summarized in the following manner. Any two arbitrary signals e_1 and e_2 may be expressed in terms of a *difference* signal $e_d \equiv e_1 - e_2$ and a common-mode signal $e_c \equiv (e_1 + e_2)/2$, as

$$e_1 = \frac{e_d}{2} + e_c \qquad e_2 = -\frac{e_d}{2} + e_c \qquad (1\text{-}19)$$

If the input signals are of equal amplitude and opposite polarity, $e_c = 0$. The voltage e_c is the mean value of the input signal. If the signals are of equal amplitude and the same polarity, $e_d = 0$. The output may then be written as

$$e_o = A_d e_d + A_c e_c \qquad (1\text{-}20)$$

in which A_d is the gain for the difference signal and A_c is the gain for the common-mode signal. These gains are given approximately, for $(\mu + 1)R_k \gg r_p$ and $\mu \gg 1$, by

$$A_d = \frac{\mu R_L}{2r_p + R_L} \quad \text{and} \quad A_c = -\frac{R_L r_p}{R_k(2r_p + R_L)} \qquad (1\text{-}21)$$

A quantity called the *common-mode rejection ratio* which serves as a figure of merit for a difference amplifier is $A_d/A_c = -\mu R_k/r_p = -g_m R_k$. If, for example, the common-mode rejection ratio is 1,000, this means that a 1 mv difference of voltage at the two grids gives the same output as 1 volt applied with the same polarity to both grids. Since μ and r_p vary with signal voltage, this ratio is *not* a constant independent of common-mode signal amplitude.

The discussion above neglects the possibility that the amplification factors of the two tubes may be slightly different. Neglecting the influence of a finite R_k, the ratio A_d/A_c is given by

$$\frac{A_d}{A_c} = \frac{\mu_1\mu_2 + (\mu_1 + \mu_2)/2}{\mu_1 - \mu_2} \simeq \frac{\mu^2}{\Delta\mu} \qquad (1\text{-}22)$$

in which $\Delta\mu = \mu_1 - \mu_2$ and μ is the nominal amplification factor of either tube. High μ tubes are therefore of advantage in difference amplifiers.

Current-feedback Amplifier as a Constant-current Source. The cathode follower, paraphase amplifier, and difference amplifier all operate with improved performance as the cathode resistor becomes larger. A large cathode resistor, however, results in a large d-c voltage drop due to the quiescent tube current. In Sec. 1-3 we showed that current feedback serves to increase the output impedance of an amplifier. If the output impedance is much greater than the load impedance, a current-feedback amplifier may be considered as a constant-current device and used to

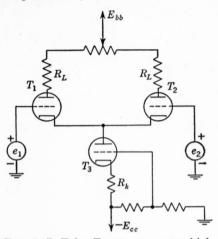

advantage in the cathode circuit to replace a large ordinary resistor. An arrangement of this type is shown in Fig. 1-17. Referring to Fig. 1-9b, it appears that the impedance seen looking into the plate of the tube T_3 in the cathode circuit is $r_p + (1 + \mu)R_k \cong \mu R_k$, if R_k is large. Under typical circumstances $-E_{cc}$ might be -300 volts, $R_k = 500$ K, and the cathode tube a 12AX7 with $\mu = 100$ and $r_p = 100$ K. The effective cathode impedance of the difference amplifier would then be about 50 Meg. In the circuit of Fig. 1-17, high μ, low-current tubes would be appropriate. Suppose, then, that the individual tubes carried only 0.1 ma of current.

FIG. 1-17. Tube T_3 acts as a very high dynamic resistor of value $r_p + (\mu + 1)R_k$, and hence the current in this tube remains essentially constant as e_1 and e_2 are varied.

The total cathode current is 0.2 ma and if an ordinary 50-Meg resistor were used, a negative supply voltage of 10,000 volts would be required. This voltage is, of course, impractically high, which demonstrates the advantage of tube T_3 over an ordinary 50-Meg resistor in this application. This circuit is used as a voltage comparator in Sec. 15-13.

1-11. The Operational Amplifier.[3] The feedback amplifier of Fig. 1-18 in which the gain A is real and negative is known as an *operational amplifier*. It is a type of voltage-feedback amplifier which does not, however, fall into a one-to-one correspondence with the voltage-feedback arrangement of Fig. 1-5. It is to be observed, for example, that in Fig. 1-18, if the gain of the amplifier proper were reduced to zero, an output signal would still appear, following the path from input to output through the path of the impedances Z_1 and Z'. In Fig. 1-5 such an alternative path is not present. This coupling between input and output around the amplifier would vanish if the output impedance of the amplifier were zero. For simplicity, let us neglect the output impedance in order that we may apply to the operational amplifier the feedback formulas derived above. The operational amplifier has the advantage over the feedback circuit of Fig. 1-5 in that the former ensures that one terminal of the external signal source is common with an amplifier output terminal.

We shall assume that negligible current flows into the input terminals of the amplifier proper. Such would be the case if the ungrounded input terminal of the amplifier were the grid of a vacuum tube whose grid-leak resistance was very large. Under these circumstances the current through Z_1 and Z' would be the same current I indicated in Fig. 1-18a.

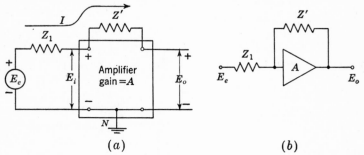

(a)   (b)

FIG. 1-18. Two representations of an operational amplifier.

From the principle of superposition we have

$$E_i = \frac{Z'}{Z' + Z_1} E_e + \frac{Z_1}{Z' + Z_1} E_o \tag{1-23}$$

Thus, the input consists of a linear combination of E_o and E_e in a manner which is independent of any external load, as is required for voltage feedback. On the basis of Eq. (1-23) the circuit of Fig. 1-18 may be replaced by an equivalent circuit as shown in Fig. 1-19. Figure 1-19 is now

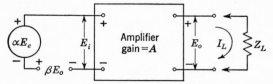

FIG. 1-19. Equivalent circuit of an operational amplifier. $\alpha = Z'/(Z' + Z_1)$; $\beta = Z_1/(Z' + Z_1)$.

identical to Fig. 1-5a except that we have taken into account that the external signal E_e is attenuated by the ratio $\alpha \equiv Z'/(Z' + Z_1)$ before application to the amplifier. The feedback factor $\beta \equiv Z_1/(Z' + Z_1)$ so that the gain with feedback is

$$A_f = \frac{\alpha A}{1 - \beta A} = \frac{Z'}{Z_1 + Z'} \frac{A}{1 - \dfrac{A Z_1}{Z_1 + Z'}}$$

$$= -\frac{Z'}{Z_1} \frac{1}{1 - \dfrac{1}{A}\left(1 + \dfrac{Z'}{Z_1}\right)} \tag{1-24}$$

Most importantly, we may now apply to the operational amplifier all our previous considerations with respect to stability of gain and linearity of operation. As A becomes very large,

$$A_f = -\frac{Z'}{Z_1} \tag{1-25}$$

which is independent of the amplifier gain.

The effect, on amplifier response, of the finite output impedance of the base amplifier is given in Prob. 1-25.

1-12. The Principle of the Virtual Ground in Operational Amplifiers. There is an alternative approach to the operational amplifier which gives a useful insight to the circuit which may not be immediately apparent from the feedback formulas employed above.

Let us calculate the impedance which is presented by the amplifier at its input terminals, E_i in Fig. 1-18. The voltage across Z' is

$$E_i - E_o = E_i - AE_i = E_i(1 - A)$$

and the impedance seen looking into the input terminals is

$$\frac{E_i}{I} = \frac{E_i}{E_i(1 - A)/Z'} = \frac{Z'}{1 - A} \tag{1-26}$$

An equivalent circuit which gives the same input current I from the source E_e, the same amplifier input voltage E_i, and consequently the

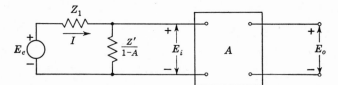

Fig. 1-20. Another equivalent circuit of the operational amplifier.

same output voltage is shown in Fig. 1-20. Consider now that A is infinite; then the impedance across the terminals E_i is zero and the generator E_e supplies a current $I = E_e/Z_1$. Referring now to Fig. 1-18, since E_i is zero, the output is

$$E_o = -IZ' = -\frac{Z'}{Z_1} E_e \tag{1-27}$$

and the over-all gain is $A_f = -Z'/Z_1$, which agrees with Eq. (1-25).

The operation of the circuit may now be described in the following terms. At the input to the amplifier proper there exists a *virtual short circuit* or *virtual ground*. The term *virtual* is used to imply that while the feedback serves to keep the voltage E_i at zero, no current actually flows through this short. The situation is depicted in Fig. 1-21, where the virtual ground is represented by the arrow. The current furnished by the generator E_e continues past this virtual short through the impedance Z'.

1-13. Basic Uses of Operational Amplifiers.[4] The operational amplifier derives its name from the fact that it may be used to accomplish a number of mathematical operations.

Sign and Scale Changes. If $Z_1 = Z'$, then $A_f = -1$, and the sign of the input signal has been changed. If the ratio $Z'/Z_1 = k$, a real

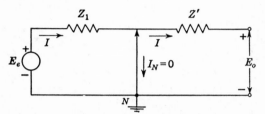

Fig. 1-21. Virtual ground in the operational amplifier.

constant, then $A_f = -k$ and the scale has been changed by a factor $-k$. Usually, in such a case of multiplication by a constant, -1 or $-k$, Z_1 and Z' are selected as resistors.

An interesting analogy may be drawn here between the amplifier and a lever. The virtual ground is represented by the fulcrum of the lever. If the ratio of the lengths of the lever arms is k, then a displacement of the end of one arm causes a displacement of the end of the other arm in the

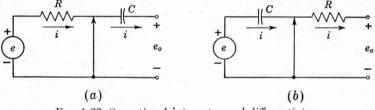

(a)   (b)

Fig. 1-22. Operational integrator and differentiator.

opposite direction which is k times as large. In Fig. 1-21, the voltages E_e and E_o represent the lever displacements.

Phase Shifter. Assume Z_1 and Z' are equal in magnitude but differ in angle. Then the operational amplifier shifts the phase of a sinusoidal input voltage, while at the same time preserving its amplitude. Any phase shift from 0 to 360° (or $\pm 180°$) may be obtained.

Integrator. If $Z_1 = R$ and a capacitor C is used for Z', then, as in Fig. 1-22a, $i = e/R$ and

$$e_o = -\frac{1}{C} \int i \, dt = -\frac{1}{RC} \int e \, dt \qquad (1\text{-}28)$$

The amplifier, therefore, provides an output signal which is proportional to the *integral* of the input voltage.

Differentiator. If Z_1 is a capacitor and $Z' = R$, as in Fig. 1-22b, $i = C(de/dt)$ and

$$e_o = -Ri = -RC \frac{de}{dt} \tag{1-29}$$

so that the output is proportional to the time derivative of the input.

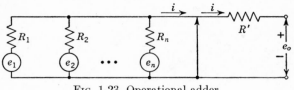

FIG. 1-23. Operational adder.

Adder. The arrangement of Fig. 1-23 may be used to obtain an output which is a linear combination of a number of input signals. Here

$$i = \frac{e_1}{R_1} + \frac{e_2}{R_2} + \cdots + \frac{e_n}{R_n}$$

and

$$e_o = -R'i = -\left(\frac{R'}{R_1} e_1 + \frac{R'}{R_2} e_2 + \cdots + \frac{R'}{R_n} e_n \right) \tag{1-30}$$

If $R_1 = R_2 = \cdots = R_n$, then

$$e_o = - \frac{R'}{R_1} (e_1 + e_2 + \cdots + e_n) \tag{1-31}$$

and the output is proportional to the sum of the inputs. In the more general case of Eq. (1-30) the scale of each input signal may be adjusted before adding.

There are, of course, many other methods which may be used to combine signals. The present method has the advantage that it may be extended to a very large number of inputs requiring only one additional resistor for each additional input. The result depends, in the limiting case of large amplifier gain, only on the resistors involved, and because of the virtual ground there is a minimum of interaction between input sources.

REFERENCES

1. Millman, J., and S. Seely: "Electronics," 2d ed., chaps. 16 and 17, McGraw-Hill Book Company, Inc., New York, 1951.
2. Valley, G. E., Jr., and H. Wallman: "Vacuum Tube Amplifiers," Massachusetts Institute of Technology Radiation Laboratory Series, vol. 18, chap. 11, McGraw-Hill Book Company, Inc., New York, 1948.

3. Ragazzini, J. R., R. H. Randall, and F. A. Russell: Analysis of Problems in Dynamics by Electronic Circuits, *Proc. IRE*, vol. 35, pp. 444–452, May, 1947.

4. Chance, B., et al.: "Waveforms," Massachusetts Institute of Technology Radiation Laboratory Series, vol. 19, chap. 2, McGraw-Hill Book Company, Inc., New York, 1949.

Korn, G. A., and T. M. Korn: "Electronic Analog Computers," McGraw-Hill Book Company, Inc., New York, 1952.

CHAPTER 2

LINEAR WAVE SHAPING: *RC*, *RL*, AND *RLC* CIRCUITS

If a sinusoidal signal is applied to a transmission network composed of linear elements, then, in the steady state, the output signal will have a waveshape which is a precise reproduction of the input waveshape. The influence of the circuit on the signal may then be completely specified by the ratio of output to input amplitude and by the phase angle between output and input. With respect to this feature of preserving waveshape in all linear networks, the sinusoidal signal is unique. No other periodic waveshape preserves its form precisely, and, in the general case, the input and output signal may bear very little resemblance to one another. The process whereby the form of a nonsinusoidal signal is altered by transmission through a linear network is called "linear wave shaping."

In pulse circuitry there are a number of nonsinusoidal waveforms which appear very regularly. The most important of these are the step, pulse, square wave, ramp, and exponential waveforms. The response to these signals of certain simple *RC*, *RL*, and *RLC* circuits will be described in this chapter.

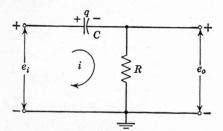

Fig. 2-1. The high-pass *RC* circuit. (If the input is sinusoidal, the lowercase letters should be replaced by capitals to represent sinor quantities. For example, e_i is replaced by E_i.)

2-1. The High-pass *RC* Circuit. The circuit of Fig. 2-1 is a rudimentary high-pass filter. For a sinusoidal input E_i, the output signal E_o increases in amplitude with increasing frequency.

Even in a case of a transmission network where no amplification is involved and in which the output is always smaller than the input, it is not uncommon to refer to the ratio E_o/E_i, for a sinusoidal signal, as the "gain" A of the circuit. For the circuit of Fig. 2-1, the magnitude of the gain $|A|$ and the angle θ by which the output leads the input are given by

$$|A| = \frac{1}{\left[1 + \left(\dfrac{f_1}{f}\right)^2\right]^{1/2}} \qquad \text{and} \qquad \theta = \arctan\frac{f_1}{f} \qquad (2\text{-}1)$$

28

where $f_1 = 1/2\pi RC$. At this frequency, f_1, the magnitude of the capacitive reactance is equal to the resistance and the gain is 0.707. This drop in signal level corresponds to a signal reduction of 3 decibels (db) and accordingly f_1 is referred to as the *lower 3-db frequency*. The maximum possible value of the gain (unity) is approached asymptotically at high frequencies. Equations (2-1) describe the response of the network to a sinusoidal signal. We shall now consider the response to the special waveforms listed above.

Step-voltage Input. A step voltage is one which maintains the value zero for all times $t < 0$ and maintains the value E for all times $t > 0$. The transition between the two voltage levels takes place at $t = 0$ and is accomplished in an arbitrarily short time interval. Thus in Fig. 2-2,

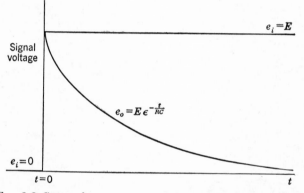

FIG. 2-2. Step voltage response of the high-pass RC circuit.

$e_i = 0$ immediately before $t = 0$ (to be referred to as time $t = 0-$), and $e_i = E$ immediately after $t = 0$ (to be referred to as time $t = 0+$).

From elementary considerations, the response of the network is exponential with a time constant RC and is of the form $B_1 + B_2\epsilon^{-t/RC}$. The constants B_1 and B_2 are determined from the initial and final values of the output. Assume that the capacitor is initially uncharged. Since the voltage across a capacitor cannot change instantaneously, then, if the input changes abruptly by E, the output must change discontinuously by the same amount. At $t = \infty$, the output must be zero because a capacitor cannot pass direct current. These facts lead to the results $B_1 = 0$ and $B_2 = E$, and the output is given by

$$e_o = E\epsilon^{-t/RC} \qquad (2\text{-}2)$$

Input and output are shown in Fig. 2-2.

Pulse Input. An ideal pulse has the waveform shown in Fig. 2-3a. The pulse *amplitude* is E and the pulse *duration* is t_p. It appears from Fig. 2-3a, b, and c that the pulse may be considered to be the sum of a step voltage $+E$ whose discontinuity occurs at $t = 0$ and a step voltage $-E$ whose discontinuity occurs at $t = t_p$.

If the pulse of Fig. 2-3a is applied to the circuit of Fig. 2-1, the response for times less than t_p is the same as that for the step-voltage input.

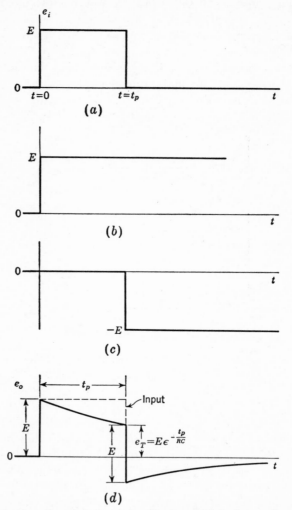

FIG. 2-3. (a) A pulse; (b and c) the step voltages which make up the pulse; (d) the pulse after transmission through the high-pass RC circuit.

Hence, the output at $t = t_p-$ is given by $e_o = E \exp (-t_p/RC) \equiv e_T$. At the end of the pulse, the input falls abruptly by the amount E, and, since the capacitor voltage cannot change instantaneously, the output must also drop by E. Hence, at $t = t_p+$, $e_o = e_T - E$. Since e_T is less than E, the voltage becomes negative and then decays exponentially to zero, as indicated in Fig. 2-3d. For $t > t_p$, e_o is given by

$$e_o = E(\epsilon^{-t_p/RC} - 1)\epsilon^{-(t-t_p)/RC} \tag{2-3}$$

Note the distortion which has resulted from passing a pulse through an RC coupling network. There is a tilt to the top of the pulse and an undershoot at the end of the pulse. If these distortions are to be minimized, then the time constant RC must be very large compared with the width t_p. However, for all values of the ratio RC/t_p there must always be an undershoot and *the area below the axis will always equal the area above*. The equality of areas results from the fact that the input and output are separated by a capacitor. As a consequence, independently of the d-c level of the input signal, the d-c or average level of the output signal must be zero.

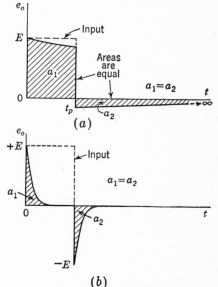

If the time constant is very large ($RC/t_p \gg 1$), there is only a slight tilt to the output pulse and the undershoot is very small. However, the negative portion decreases very slowly (as indicated in Fig. 2-4a), since its area must equal that of the positive portion. If the time constant is very small ($RC/t_p \ll 1$), the output consists of a positive *spike* or *pip* of amplitude E at the beginning of the pulse and a negative spike of

Fig. 2-4. (a) Pulse response if $RC/t_p \gg 1$; (b) pulse response if $RC/t_p \ll 1$.

the same size at the end of the pulse, as indicated in Fig. 2-4b. This process of converting pulses into pips by means of a circuit of short time constant is called *peaking*.

Square-wave Input. A waveform which maintains itself at one constant level for a time T_1 and at another constant level for a time T_2 and which is repetitive with a period $T_1 + T_2$, as indicated in Fig. 2-5a, is called a *square wave*.* We are interested in the *steady-state* output waveform which results if this square wave is impressed on the circuit of Fig. 2-1.

With respect to the circuit of Fig. 2-1 we have already established the following three points. First, the average level of the output signal is always zero independently of the average level of the input. The output must consequently extend in both the positive and negative direc-

* If $T_1 \neq T_2$, the waveform is sometimes referred to as a *rectangular wave*.

tion with respect to the zero-voltage axis. And the area of the part
of the waveform above the zero axis must equal the area which is below
the zero axis. Second, when the input changes discontinuously by
amount E, the output changes discontinuously by an equal amount and
in the same direction. Third, during any finite time interval when the

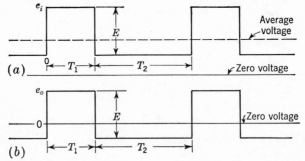

FIG. 2-5. (a) Square-wave input; (b) output voltage if the time constant is very large.
The d-c component of the output is always zero.

input maintains a constant level, the output decays exponentially toward
zero voltage. In the limiting case where RC/T_1 and RC/T_2 are both
arbitrarily large in comparison with unity, the output waveform will be
identical to the input except that the d-c component will be lacking.
Hence, the square wave of Fig. 2-5a, whose d-c level is different from zero,
will appear after transmission with an average value zero as in Fig. 2-5b.

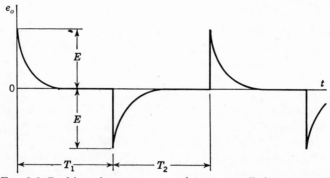

FIG. 2-6. Peaking of a square wave due to a small time constant.

At the other extreme, if T_1/RC and T_2/RC are both very large in comparison with unity, the output will consist of alternate positive and negative peaks as in Fig. 2-6. Observe in this case that the peak-to-peak
amplitude of the output is twice the peak-to-peak amplitude of the input.

More generally, the response to a square wave must have the appearance shown in Fig. 2-7. The equations from which to determine the

four quantities E_1, E_1', E_2, and E_2', indicated in Fig. 2-7, are

$$E_1' = E_1 \epsilon^{-T_1/RC} \qquad E_1' - E_2 = E$$
$$E_2' = E_2 \epsilon^{-T_2/RC} \qquad E_1 - E_2' = E \qquad (2\text{-}4)$$

A symmetrical square wave is one for which $T_1 = T_2 = T$. Because of the symmetry, $E_1 = -E_2$, and the two equations in the first line of

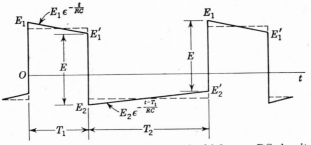

FIG. 2-7. The square wave response of a high-pass RC circuit.

Eq. (2-4) suffice to determine the output. When $T/RC \ll 1$, we have $\exp(-T/RC) \cong 1 - T/RC$ and in this case

$$E_1 \cong \frac{E}{2}\left(1 + \frac{T}{2RC}\right) \qquad E_1' \cong \frac{E}{2}\left(1 - \frac{T}{2RC}\right) \qquad (2\text{-}5)$$

The exponential portions of the output are now approximately linear as shown in Fig. 2-8. The effect of the coupling network has been to introduce a tilt on the waveform. The percentage tilt P is defined by

$$P \equiv \frac{E_1 - E_1'}{E/2} \times 100 \cong \frac{100T}{RC} \quad (2\text{-}6)$$

Since the low-frequency 3-db point is given by $f_1 = 1/2\pi RC$, we have the relationship

$$P = 100\pi \frac{f_1}{f} \qquad (2\text{-}7)$$

in which $f = 1/2T$ is the frequency of the applied square wave.

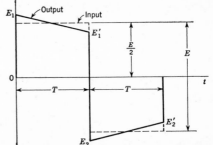

FIG. 2-8. Linear tilt of a square wave when $RC/T \gg 1$.

Exponential Input. From the preceding discussion on peaking (see Fig. 2-6) we are led to conclude that, if the time constant of the circuit is decreased, the peaks obtained will be narrower, but the amplitude of the peak will remain equal to the discontinuity E of the input square wave. This is true provided that the input has vertical sides, an impossibility in a practical waveform. If RC is made extremely small, the finite rise time of the input waveform must be taken into consideration.

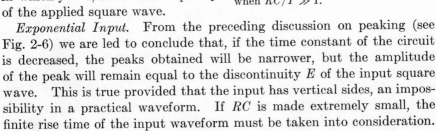

Consider a case in which the capacitor is initially uncharged and the input waveform rises rapidly but not discontinuously from zero to a

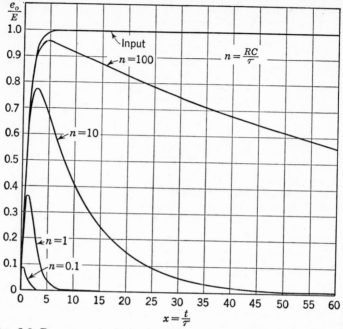

FIG. 2-9. Response of a high-pass RC circuit to an exponential input.

level E, as shown in Fig. 2-9.   The circuit of Fig. 2-1 is governed by the equation

$$e_i = \frac{q}{C} + iR = \frac{q}{C} + e_o \qquad (2\text{-}8)$$

in which q is the capacitor charge.   Differentiating Eq. (2-8) gives

$$\frac{de_i}{dt} = \frac{e_o}{RC} + \frac{de_o}{dt} \qquad (2\text{-}9)$$

Since $e_o = 0$ at $t = 0$, we have the result that

$$\left(\frac{de_i}{dt}\right)_{\text{initial}} = \left(\frac{de_o}{dt}\right)_{\text{initial}} \qquad (2\text{-}10)$$

And since the initial rate of change of input and output are identical and both start from zero, we may anticipate that in the neighborhood of $t = 0$ the output will follow the input quite closely.   Furthermore, unless the time constant RC is very large in comparison to the time required for e_i to attain its final value, the capacitor will have acquired appreciable charge in this time.   Also it is apparent from Eq. (2-8) that e_o will fall short of attaining the voltage E. Eventually, of course, the output must decay exponentially to zero.

An input waveform of the type described above which will be of special interest is the waveform given by

$$e_i = E(1 - \epsilon^{-t/\tau}) \tag{2-11}$$

Equation (2-9) then becomes

$$\frac{E}{\tau} \epsilon^{-t/\tau} = \frac{e_o}{RC} + \frac{de_o}{dt} \tag{2-12}$$

Defining x and n by

$$x \equiv \frac{t}{\tau} \quad \text{and} \quad n \equiv \frac{RC}{\tau} \tag{2-13}$$

the solution of Eq. (2-12), subject to the condition that initially the capacitor voltage is zero, is given by

$$e_o = \frac{En}{n-1} (\epsilon^{-x/n} - \epsilon^{-x}) \tag{2-14}$$

if $n \neq 1$ and

$$e_o = Ex\epsilon^{-x} \tag{2-15}$$

if $n = 1$. These equations are plotted in Fig. 2-9 and it is seen that they have the shape predicted above. Note that if RC is much greater than τ ($n \gg 1$), the second term of Eq. (2-14) is negligible compared with the first except for very small values of time. Then

$$e_o \cong \frac{En}{n-1} \epsilon^{-x/n} \cong E\epsilon^{-t/RC} \tag{2-16}$$

This equation agrees with the way the circuit should behave for an ideal step voltage. Near the origin of time the output follows the input. Also, *the smaller the circuit time constant, the smaller will be the output peak.* For example, if RC just equals the time constant of the input wave ($n = 1$), the peak output will only be 37 per cent of the peak input, but a very narrow pulse will result as shown in Fig. 2-9. The larger RC is relative to τ, the larger will be the peak output but also the wider will be the pulse. A value of RC is chosen to give the best compromise between these two conflicting characteristics for the particular application at hand. The choice is seldom critical.

Ramp Input. A waveform which is zero for $t < 0$ and which increases linearly with time for $t > 0$, $e = \alpha t$, is called a "ramp" or "sweep" voltage. Such a waveform is indicated as the "input" in Fig. 2-10a. If this waveform is applied to the circuit of Fig. 2-1, the output is governed by Eq. (2-9) which becomes

$$\alpha = \frac{e_o}{RC} + \frac{de_o}{dt}$$

This equation has the solution

$$e_o = \alpha RC(1 - \epsilon^{-t/RC}) \qquad (2\text{-}17)$$

For times t which are very small in comparison with RC, we may replace the exponential in Eq. (2-17) by a series with the result

$$e_o = \alpha t \left(1 - \frac{t}{2RC} + \cdots\right)$$

The output signal falls away slightly from the input, as shown in Fig. 2-10a. As a measure of the departure from linearity, let us define the transmission error ϵ_t as the difference between input and output divided by the input. The error at a time $t = T$ is then

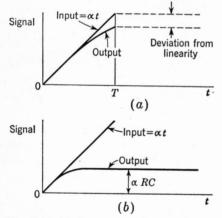

$$\epsilon_t \equiv \frac{e_i - e_o}{e_i} \cong \frac{T}{2RC} = \pi f_1 T \qquad (2\text{-}18)$$

where $f_1 = 1/2\pi RC$ is again the low-frequency 3-db point. For example, if we desire to pass a 2-msec sweep with less than 0.1 per cent deviation from linearity, the above equation yields

Fig. 2-10. (a) Response of a high-pass RC circuit to a ramp voltage for $RC/T \gg 1$; (b) response to a ramp voltage for $RC/T \ll 1$.

$$f_1 < 0.16 \text{ cps} \qquad \text{or} \qquad RC > 1 \text{ sec}$$

For large values of t in comparison with RC, the output approaches the constant value αRC, as indicated in Fig. 2-10b and Eq. (2-17).

2-2. The High-pass RC Circuit as a Differentiator. If, in Fig. 2-1, the time constant is very small in comparison with the time required for the input signal to make an appreciable change, the circuit is called a "differentiator." This name arises from the fact that under these circumstances the voltage drop across R will be very small in comparison with the drop across C and we may consider that the current is determined entirely by the capacitance. Then the current is $C\, de_i/dt$, and the output signal across R is

$$e_o = RC \frac{de_i}{dt}$$

Hence the output is proportional to the derivative of the input.

The derivative of a square wave is a waveform which is uniformly zero except at the points of discontinuity. At these points, precise differentiation would yield impulses of infinite amplitude, zero width, and alternating polarity. Referring to Fig. 2-6, we see that the RC differentiator provides, in the limit of a very small time constant, a waveform which is correct except for the fact that the amplitude of the peaks never exceeds E. We may expect such an error since at the time of the discontinuity the voltage across R is not negligible compared with that across C.

For the ramp $e_i = \alpha t$, the value of $RC\, de_i/dt$ is αRC. This result is verified in Fig. 2-10b except near the origin. The output approaches the proper derivative value only after a time has passed corresponding to several time constants. The error near $t = 0$ is again due to the fact that in this region the voltage across R is not negligible compared with that across C.

If we assume that the leading edge of a pulse can be approximated by a ramp, then we can measure the rate of rise of the pulse by using a differentiator. The peak output is measured on an oscilloscope, and from Fig. 2-10b we see that this voltage divided by the product RC gives the slope α. If R and C are not given to the desired accuracy, then the system must be calibrated by using a pulse of known rate of rise.

It is interesting to obtain a criterion for good differentiation in terms of steady-state sinusoidal analysis. If a sine wave is applied to the circuit of Fig. 2-1, the output will be a sine wave shifted by a leading angle θ such that

$$\tan \theta = \frac{X_c}{R} = \frac{1}{\omega RC} \qquad (2\text{-}19)$$

and the output will be proportional to $\sin (\omega t + \theta)$. In order to have true differentiation we must obtain $\cos \omega t$. In other words, θ must equal 90°. This result can be obtained only if $R = 0$ or $C = 0$. However, if $\omega RC = 0.01$, then $1/\omega CR = 100$ and $\theta = 89.4°$, which is sufficiently close to 90° for most purposes. If $\omega RC = 0.1$, then $\theta = 84.3°$, and for some applications this may be close enough to 90°.

If we use the criterion $\omega RC = 2\pi RC/T \leq 0.01$, where T is the period of the sine wave, then for

$$RC \leq \frac{0.01}{2\pi}\, T = 0.0016T$$

the differentiation will be satisfactory.

If the peak value of the input is E_m, the output is

$$\frac{E_m R}{\sqrt{R^2 + 1/\omega^2 C^2}}\, \sin (\omega t + \theta)$$

and if $\omega RC \ll 1$, then the output is approximately $E_m \omega RC \cos \omega t$. This result agrees with the expected value, $RC\, de/dt$. If $\omega RC = 0.01$, then the output is attenuated by 0.01.

These considerations with respect to the conditions required for differentiation of sinusoidal waveforms suggest an alternative point of view in connection with the differentiation of an arbitrary waveform. Suppose we resolve an arbitrary signal into its Fourier components. If each of the components is shifted in phase by 90° and if the amplitude of each component is multiplied by a factor proportional to the frequency, then the Fourier series will have been effectively differentiated term by term. From this point of view the requirement for good differentiation is that the time constant RC shall be small in comparison with the period of the highest frequency term of appreciable amplitude of the input signal.

Since it has been demonstrated that the output will be a small fraction of the input if the differentiation is satisfactory, then the output will frequently have to be followed by a high-gain amplifier. Any drift in amplifier gain will affect the level of the signal, and amplifier nonlinearity may affect the accuracy of differentiation. These difficulties are avoided by using the operational differentiator discussed in Sec. 1-13. This feedback amplifier does not suffer from the drifts just mentioned, the stability depending principally upon the constancy of R and C.

The operational amplifier equivalent circuit for a differentiator is a capacitor C in series with a resistor $R/(1 - A)$, where A is the gain. The phase shift angle θ between output and input for a frequency ω is given by

$$\tan \theta = \frac{1 - A}{\omega RC} \qquad (2\text{-}20)$$

Comparing Eq. (2-20) with Eq. (2-19), we see that for the same values of R and C the frequency range of proper differentiation for the operational amplifier is $(1 - A)$ times that of the simple RC circuit and the output voltage has essentially the same magnitude for both circuits.

If the RC product for the operational amplifier is $(1 - A)$ times that of the simple circuit, then the output from the former will be A times that of the latter, whereas the quality of the differentiation is the same for both. The same result can be obtained by following the simple RC circuit by an amplifier of gain A, but as already emphasized, this arrangement will not have the stability and linearity of the operational system.

These results are based on the assumption that the amplifier will be able to handle the input signal without waveform distortion. Any practical amplifier, particularly a high-gain amplifier of many stages, will usually produce some distortion due to the inability of the amplifier to pass all frequency components of the input signal. In any particular case it is necessary to look into the matter of the extent to which wave-form distortion may undo some of the anticipated advantages of the operational differentiator.

Again, in a practical operational amplifier it is possible, because of the feedback, that the amplifier will oscillate. Then it is necessary to find, if possible, some means of suppressing the oscillations without interfering too seriously with the normal operation of the amplifier. Also, a differentiator will accentuate any high-frequency noise present in the circuit.

2-3. Double Differentiation. Figure 2-11 shows two RC coupling net-works in cascade separated by an amplifier. It is assumed that the

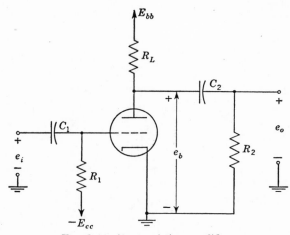

FIG. 2-11. A rate-of-rise amplifier.

amplifier operates linearly and that its output impedance is small rela-tive to the impedance of R_2 and C_2 so that this combination does not load the amplifier. If the time constants R_1C_1 and R_2C_2 are small rela-tive to the period of the input wave, then this circuit performs approxi-mately a second-order differentiation.

If the input is a ramp ($e_i = \alpha t$) of long duration, the output of the amplifier (the plate voltage) is as pictured in Fig. 2-10b and is given by [see Eq. (2-17)],

$$e_b = -A\alpha\tau_1(1 - \epsilon^{-t/\tau_1}) \qquad (2\text{-}21)$$

where A is the magnitude of the amplifier gain and $\tau_1 \equiv R_1C_1$. This exponential input to the R_2C_2 network leads in turn to an output which is, as given in Eq. (2-14),

$$e_o = -(A\alpha\tau_1)\left(\frac{n}{n-1}\right)(\epsilon^{-x/n} - \epsilon^{-x}) \qquad (2\text{-}22)$$

if $n \neq 1$, where $n \equiv \tau_2/\tau_1$, $\tau_2 \equiv R_2C_2$, and $x \equiv t/\tau_1$. Values of $-e_o/A\alpha\tau_1$ are plotted in Fig. 2-9 for values of n equal to 0.1, 1.0, 10, and 100. For $n = 1$, the output is given by

$$e_o = -A\alpha\tau x\epsilon^{-x} \tag{2-23}$$

This special case is plotted in Fig. 2-12. It should be noted that a ramp voltage has been converted into a pulse. *The initial slope of the output wave is the initial slope of the input multiplied by the gain of the amplifier.* For this reason the stage in Fig. 2-11 is called a "rate-of-rise amplifier." For a single RC circuit, we demonstrated in Sec. 2-1 that the initial rate of change of output equals the initial rate of change of input independently of the time constant. Obviously, the same conclusion can be

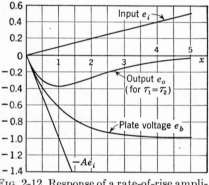

Fig. 2-12. Response of a rate-of-rise amplifier to a ramp input. $A = 10$, $\alpha\tau = 0.1$.

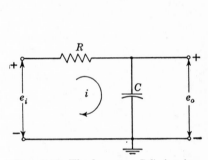

Fig. 2-13. The low-pass RC circuit.

drawn for multiple differentiation. A direct check can be made from Eq. (2-22), where we find that at $t = 0$, $de_o/dt = -A\alpha$.

2-4. The Low-pass RC Circuit. The circuit of Fig. 2-13 passes low frequencies readily, but attenuates high frequencies because the reactance of the capacitor C decreases with increasing frequency. If the input voltage e_i is sinusoidal, the magnitude of the steady-state gain A and the angle θ by which the output leads the input are given by

$$|A| = \frac{1}{\left[1 + \left(\dfrac{f}{f_2}\right)^2\right]^{1/2}} \quad \text{and} \quad \theta = -\arctan\frac{f}{f_2} \tag{2-24}$$

where $f_2 \equiv 1/2\pi RC$. The gain falls to 0.707 of its low-frequency value at the frequency f_2. Hence, f_2 is called the upper 3-db frequency.

Step-voltage Input. The response of the circuit of Fig. 2-13 to a step input is exponential with a time constant RC. Since the capacitor voltage cannot change instantaneously, the output starts from zero and rises toward the steady-state value E, as shown in Fig. 2-14. The output is given by

$$e_o = E(1 - \epsilon^{-t/RC}) \tag{2-25}$$

The time required for e_o to reach one-tenth its final value is readily found to be $0.1RC$ and the time to reach nine-tenths its final value is

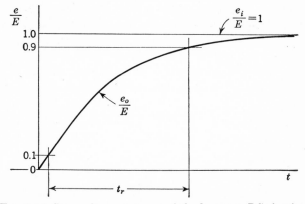

FIG. 2-14. Step voltage response of the low-pass RC circuit.

$2.3RC$. The difference between these two values, called "the rise time" t_r of the circuit, is an indication of how fast the circuit can respond to a discontinuity in voltage. We have

$$t_r = 2.2RC = \frac{2.2}{2\pi f_2} = \frac{0.35}{f_2} \tag{2-26}$$

Thus, the rise time is proportional to the time constant and inversely proportional to the upper 3-db frequency.

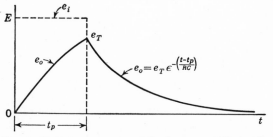

FIG. 2-15. Pulse response of the low-pass RC circuit.

Pulse Input. The response to a pulse, for times less than the pulse width t_p, is the same as that for a step input and is given by Eq. (2-25). At the end of the pulse the voltage is e_T and the output must decrease to zero from this value with a time constant RC, as indicated in Fig. 2-15. Note the distortion which has resulted from passing a pulse through a low-pass RC circuit. In particular, it should be observed that the output will always extend beyond the pulse width t_p, because whatever charge has accumulated on the capacitor C during the pulse cannot leak off instantaneously.

If it is desired to minimize the distortion, then the rise time must be small compared with the pulse width. If f_2 is chosen equal to $1/t_p$, then $t_r = 0.35t_p$. The output is as pictured in Fig. 2-16, which for many applications is a reasonable reproduction of the input. We often use the rule of thumb that *a pulse shape will be preserved if the 3-db frequency is approximately equal to the reciprocal of the pulse width.* Thus,

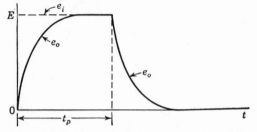

FIG. 2-16. Pulse response for the case $f_2 = 1/t_p$.

to pass a 0.5-μsec pulse reasonably well requires a circuit with an upper 3-db frequency of the order of 2 Mc.

Square-wave Input. Consider a square wave with an average value which is zero, as indicated in Fig. 2-17a. As we have already observed above, a reasonable reproduction of the input is obtained if the time constant is small compared with the pulse width. The steady-state response, in this case, is indicated in Fig. 2-17b.

If the rise time of the RC circuit is comparable with the period of the testing square wave, the output will have the appearance in Fig. 2-17c. The equation of the rising portion is determined by the fact that it must be an exponential of time constant RC and that the voltage would rise to the steady-state value E' if the input remained at E'. If E_1 is the initial value of the output voltage, then

$$e_{o1} = E' - (E' - E_1)\epsilon^{-t/RC} \qquad (2\text{-}27)$$

Note that this equation agrees with the conditions that at $t = 0$, $e_{o1} = E_1$, and at $t = \infty$, $e_{o1} = E'$. By a similar argument we can derive the equation for the falling portion. Thus

$$e_{o2} = E'' - (E'' - E_2)\epsilon^{-(t-T_1)/RC} \qquad (2\text{-}28)$$

If we set $e_{o1} = E_2$ at $t = T_1$ and $e_{o2} = E_1$ at $t = T_1 + T_2$, the two resulting equations can be solved for the two unknowns E_1 and E_2. If a symmetrical square wave is used so that $T_1 = T_2$ and $E' = -E'' = E/2$, these equations indicate that $E_1 = -E_2$. We can easily understand this result if we remember that the area per cycle in Fig. 2-17c must be zero, since we assumed an input with zero average value.

If the time constant is very large compared with the period of the input square wave, the output consists of exponential sections which are essentially linear, as indicated in Fig. 2-17d. *If the input square wave*

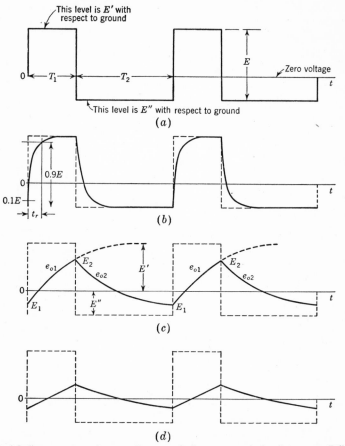

FIG. 2-17. (a) Square-wave input; (b, c, and d) output of the low-pass RC circuit. The time constant is smallest for (b) and largest for (d).

has an average value different from zero, then this d-c voltage must be added to all the curves of Fig. 2-17.

A square-wave signal is frequently used in conjunction with a cathode-ray oscilloscope to determine the rise-time response of an arbitrary circuit. In an experimental arrangement to measure rise time we must take into account the finite rise time of the input square wave and of the amplifiers of the oscilloscope. The order of magnitude of the errors which may otherwise be involved are indicated by the following. Consider, say, that the square-wave rise time is negligible and that the rise time t_r of the circuit under test is at least three times the rise time t_r' of the amplifier. In this case the error will be less than 10 per cent. On the other hand if $t_r' = t_r$, then the error is 53 per cent. These results will now be justified.

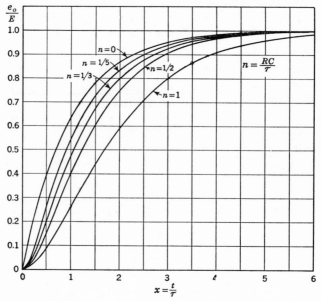

FIG. 2-18. Response of two cascaded low-pass RC networks.

Exponential Input. For an input of the form given in Eq. (2-11),

$$e_i = E(1 - \epsilon^{-t/\tau})$$

the voltage across the resistor is given by Eq. (2-14) for $n \neq 1$. Hence, the voltage output across the capacitor is the difference between Eq. (2-11) and Eq. (2-14). Performing this subtraction, we obtain, if $n \neq 1$,

$$\frac{e_o}{E} = 1 + \frac{1}{n-1} \epsilon^{-x} - \frac{n}{n-1} \epsilon^{-x/n} \tag{2-29}$$

and if $n = 1$

$$\frac{e_o}{E} = 1 - (1 + x)\epsilon^{-x} \tag{2-30}$$

The parameters x and n are defined by Eq. (2-13), namely, $x = t/\tau$ and $n = RC/\tau$. The outputs for $n = 0$, $\frac{1}{5}$, $\frac{1}{3}$, $\frac{1}{2}$, and 1 are plotted in Fig. 2-18. The larger the relative time constant n, the greater is the "delay" in output. The delay is defined as the time required for the waveform to reach 50 per cent of its final value.

Suppose that τ is the time constant of a circuit under test and that RC is the time constant of the oscilloscope amplifier. Then Fig. 2-18 shows the response of the two circuits in cascade. (It is assumed here that the oscilloscope can be represented by an equivalent single RC network.) The ratio of the rise time for the cascaded arrangement to the rise time of a single stage ($n = 0$ or $1/n = \infty$) is plotted in Fig. 2-19. The graph shows that if the oscilloscope time constant is less than one-third that of the circuit, the rise time is increased by less than 10 per cent.

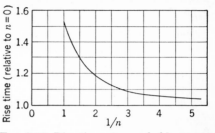

FIG. 2-19. Rise time of cascaded low-pass RC networks.

Ramp Input. For an input of the form $e_i = \alpha t$, the voltage e_R across the resistor is given by Eq. (2-17). The voltage across the capacitor is $e_i - e_R$ or

$$e_o = \alpha(t - RC) + \alpha RC \epsilon^{-t/RC} \qquad (2\text{-}31)$$

If it is desired to transmit the ramp with little distortion, then a small time constant must be used relative to the total ramp time T. The output is given in Fig. 2-20a where it is seen that the output follows the

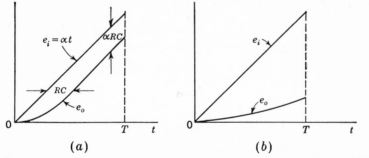

(a)   (b)

FIG. 2-20. Response of a low-pass RC circuit to a ramp voltage. (a) $RC/T \ll 1$; (b) $RC/T \gg 1$.

input but is delayed by one time constant RC from the input (except near the origin where there is distortion). The transmission error ϵ_t is defined as the difference between input and output divided by the input. For $RC/T \ll 1$, we find

$$\epsilon_t \cong \frac{RC}{T} = \frac{1}{2\pi f_2 T} \qquad (2\text{-}32)$$

where f_2 is the upper 3-db frequency. For example, if we desire to pass a 2-msec sweep with less than 0.1 per cent error, the above equation yields

$$f_2 > 80 \text{ kc} \qquad \text{and} \qquad RC < 2 \text{ } \mu\text{sec}$$

If the time constant is large compared with the sweep duration, $RC/T \gg 1$, the output is very distorted, as it appears in Fig. 2-20b. By expanding the exponential in Eq. (2-31) in a power series in t/RC, we find

$$e_o \cong \frac{\alpha t^2}{2RC} \tag{2-33}$$

A quadratic response is obtained for a linear input and hence the circuit acts as an integrator.

2-5. The Low-pass RC Circuit as an Integrator. If, in Fig. 2-13, the time constant is very large in comparison with the time required for the input signal to make an appreciable change, the circuit is called an "integrator." This name arises from the fact that under these circumstances the voltage drop across C will be very small in comparison to the drop across R and we may consider that the current is determined entirely by the resistor. Then the current is e_i/R and the output signal across C is

$$e_o = \frac{1}{RC} \int e_i \, dt$$

Hence the output is proportional to the integral of the input.

If $e_i = \alpha t$, the result is $\alpha t^2/2RC$, as given by Eq. (2-33). As time increases, the drop across C will not remain negligible compared with that across R and the output will not remain the integral of the input. As a matter of fact, Fig. 2-20a shows that the output will change from a quadratic to a linear function of time.

The integral of a constant is a linear function, and this agrees with the curves of Fig. 2-17d which correspond to $RC/T \gg 1$. As the value of RC/T decreases, the departure from true integration increases as indicated in Fig. 2-17c and b.

These examples show that the integrator must be used cautiously. We can obtain a criterion for good integration in terms of steady-state analysis by proceeding as in Sec. 2-2. If we define satisfactory integration as meaning that an input sinusoid has been shifted at least 89.4° (instead of the true value of 90°), then

$$RC > 15T$$

where T is the period of the sine wave.

Since the output is a small fraction of the input (because of the factor $1/RC$), amplification may be necessary. For the reasons given in Sec. 2-2, an operational amplifier may possibly be used to advantage. If the input to the operational amplifier is a square wave, the output is very linear, as shown in Fig. 2-17d. This output is called a "gated sweep" and is discussed in detail in Sec. 7-3.

Integrators are almost invariably preferred over differentiators in ana-
logue-computer applications for the following reasons. Since the gain
of an integrator decreases with frequency whereas the gain of a differentiator increases nominally linearly with frequency, it is easier to stabilize the former than the latter with respect to spurious oscillations. As a
result of its limited bandwidth an integrator is less sensitive to noise
voltages than a differentiator. Further, if the input waveform changes
very rapidly, the amplifier of a differentiator may overload. Finally,
as a matter of practice, it is more convenient to introduce initial conditions in an integrator.

2-6. *RL* Circuits. Suppose the capacitor C and resistor R of the preceding sections in this chapter are replaced by a resistor R' and an

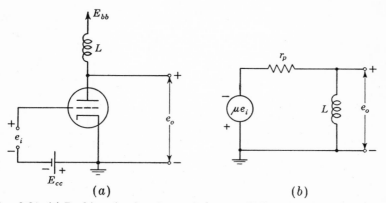

FIG. 2-21. (*a*) Peaking circuit using an inductor; (*b*) linear equivalent circuit.

inductor L, respectively. Then if the time constant L/R' equals the
time constant RC, all the preceding results remain unchanged.

The inductor is seldom used if a large time constant is called for because
a large value of inductance can be obtained only with an iron core
inductor which is physically large, heavy, and expensive relative to the
cost of a capacitor for a similar application. Such an inductor will be
shunted with a large amount of stray distributed capacitance. Furthermore, the nonlinear properties of the iron causes distortion which may be
undesirable. If it is desirable to pass a very low frequency through a
circuit in which L is a shunt element, then the inductor may become
prohibitively large. For example, with a lower 3-db frequency of 10 cp°
and for $R' = 100$ K the inductance required is 1,600 henrys! Of course,
in circuits where a small value of R' is tolerable, then a more reasonable
value of inductance may be used.

The small, inexpensive air-core inductor is used in low time-constant
applications. Figure 2-21*a* shows how a square wave may be converted
into pulses by means of the peaking coil L. It is assumed that the bias

voltage and the size of the input are such that the tube operates linearly. The equivalent circuit is as indicated in Fig. 2-21b. The peak of the output pulse (measured with respect to the quiescent plate voltage E_{bb}) is the amplification factor of the tube times the jump in voltage of the input square wave, as indicated in Fig. 2-22. The physical reason for this fact is that since the current through an inductor cannot change instantaneously it acts as an open circuit at the time of the discontinuity.

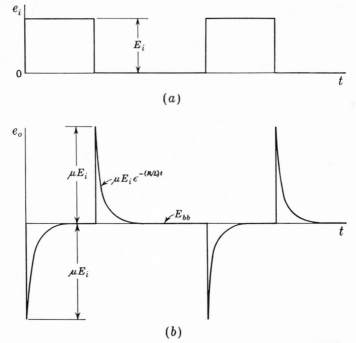

(a)

(b)

Fig. 2-22. Input e_i and output e_o for the circuit of Fig. 2-21, with $R = r_p$.

Under this condition the plate-voltage change is μ times the grid-voltage change.

The rate-of-rise amplifier of Fig. 2-11 often uses a peaking inductor in the plate circuit instead of the R_2C_2 differentiating combination shown.

The situation where the square wave is large enough to cut the tube off, so that the circuit acts in a nonlinear manner, is considered in Sec. 4-7, where it will be found that the negative peaks are of smaller magnitude than the positive ones.

2-7. RLC Circuits. In Fig. 2-21 there should be indicated a capacitor C across the output to include the effect of coil-winding capacitance, plate-cathode capacitance, and wiring capacitance from plate to ground. This capacitance will modify the results of Sec. 2-6, as we shall now show.

Figure 2-23 shows a signal e_i applied through a resistor R to a parallel LC circuit. From the differential equations for this network, and assuming a solution in the form ϵ^{pt}, we find for the roots p of the characteristic equation[1] (or for the poles of the transfer function)

$$p = -\frac{1}{2RC} \pm \left[\left(\frac{1}{2RC}\right)^2 - \frac{1}{LC}\right]^{\frac{1}{2}} \qquad (2\text{-}34)$$

Let us introduce the *damping constant* k and the *resonant* or *undamped period* T_o defined by

$$k \equiv \frac{1}{2R}\sqrt{\frac{L}{C}} \qquad \text{and} \qquad T_o = 2\pi\sqrt{LC} \qquad (2\text{-}35)$$

in which case Eq. (2-34) can be put in the form

$$p = -\frac{2\pi k}{T_o} \pm j\frac{2\pi}{T_o}(1 - k^2)^{\frac{1}{2}} \qquad (2\text{-}36)$$

If $k = 0$, we see that the roots are purely imaginary, $\pm j2\pi/T_o$, and hence that the response is an undamped sinusoid of period T_o. If $k = 1$, the two roots are equal, corresponding to the *critically damped* case. If $k > 1$, there are no oscillations in the output, and the response is said to be *overdamped*. If $k < 1$, the output will be a sinusoid whose amplitude decays with time, and the response is said to be *underdamped*.

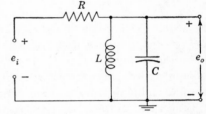

FIG. 2-23. A signal e_i is applied through a resistor R to a parallel LC circuit.

The damping factor is inversely proportional to the Q of the circuit consisting of a parallel combination of R, L, and C. Thus

$$Q \equiv \omega_o RC = \frac{2\pi RC}{T_o} = \frac{RC}{\sqrt{LC}} = R\sqrt{\frac{C}{L}} = \frac{1}{2k}$$

If the input to Fig. 2-23 is a step voltage E and *if the initial current through the inductor is zero and the initial voltage across the capacitor is zero*, the response is given by the following equations in which $x \equiv t/T_o$:

Critical Damping, $k = 1$. For the case of critical damping, we have

$$\frac{e_o}{E} = 4\pi x\epsilon^{-2\pi x} \qquad (2\text{-}37)$$

If use is made of Eqs. (2-35), with $k = 1$, Eq. (2-37) can be put in the equivalent form

$$\frac{e_o}{E} = \frac{4Rt}{L}\epsilon^{-2Rt/L} \qquad (2\text{-}38)$$

Overdamped, $k > 1$. In the overdamped case, it is convenient to rewrite Eq. (2-36) as

$$p = -\frac{2\pi k}{T_o} \pm \frac{2\pi k}{T_o} \sqrt{1 - \frac{1}{k^2}}$$

If we apply the binomial expansion to the radical and assume that *k is large enough so that $4k^2 \gg 1$*, we find for p the approximate values $-\pi/T_o k$ and $-4\pi k/T_o$. Subject to this restriction on the size of k, the response is

$$\frac{e_o}{E} \cong \epsilon^{-\pi x/k} - \epsilon^{-4\pi kx} \tag{2-39}$$

The first term is less than 1 everywhere except at $x = 0$. The second term is equal to the first term raised to the power $4k^2$. Hence, the second term is negligible compared with the first except near the origin. Thus, Eq. (2-39) can be approximated by

$$\frac{e_o}{E} \cong \epsilon^{-\pi x/k} = \epsilon^{-\pi t/kT_o} = \epsilon^{-Rt/L} \tag{2-40}$$

in which we have made use of Eqs. (2-35). This result shows that the response approaches that for the zero capacitance case (Fig. 2-21) as k becomes much greater than unity. Physically, this is just what we should expect, because Eq. (2-35) shows that a large value of k means a small value of C for a given value of R and L.

Since the voltage on the capacitor cannot change instantaneously, then Eq. (2-40) is in error at $t = 0$ and the more correct equation (2-39) must be used near the origin. The outputs for $k = 3$ and $k = 1$ are compared with that for $k = \infty$ $(C = 0)$ in Fig. 2-24.

If L and C are held fixed and k is varied by adjusting R, the response is as given in Fig. 2-25. For $k = \infty$, $R = 0$, and the output equals the input as indicated. We note from Fig. 2-23 that the smaller the value of R, the larger must be the source current.

Underdamped, $k < 1$. In the underdamped case, we have

$$\frac{e_o}{E} = \frac{2k}{\sqrt{1 - k^2}} \epsilon^{-2\pi kx} \sin 2\pi \sqrt{1 - k^2}\, x \tag{2-41}$$

where, as above, $x = t/T_o$. The damped period is seen to be $T_o/(1 - k^2)^{1/2}$ and hence is larger than the free period T_o. The response for several values of k is given in Fig. 2-26.

An amplifier with a coil in the plate circuit, and in which the parameters L, C, and r_p are adjusted to make the damping factor k slightly less than unity, makes an excellent peaking circuit. This conclusion is confirmed in Fig. 2-26.

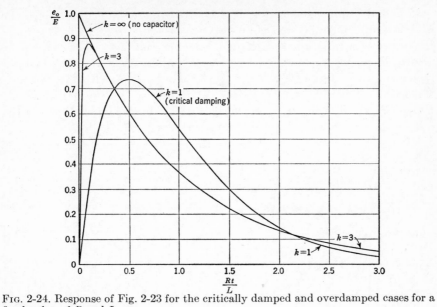

FIG. 2-24. Response of Fig. 2-23 for the critically damped and overdamped cases for a fixed value of R and L.

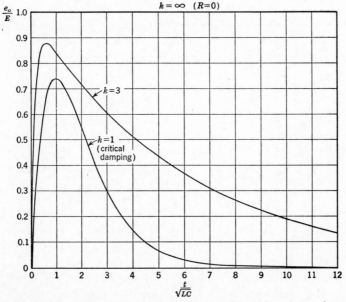

FIG. 2-25. Response of Fig. 2-23 for the critically damped and overdamped cases for a fixed value of L and C.

If L and C are fixed and it is desired to increase the damping, the resistance R must be decreased. If this resistor represents the plate resistance of a tube, then to change its value we must either change the operating point or change the tube. A more satisfactory method for increasing the damping is to shunt the LC combination with an additional resistor, as indicated in Fig. 2-27a. If the circuit to the left of points P and N in this figure is replaced by its Thévenin equivalent, the

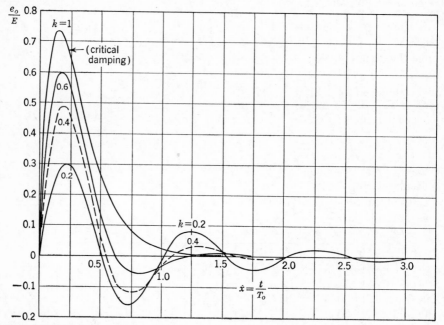

Fig. 2-26. Response of Fig. 2-23 for the critically damped and underdamped cases.

result is as in Fig. 2-27b. The resistor R represents R_1 and R_2 in parallel, and a is the attenuation factor. Specifically,

$$R \equiv \frac{R_1 R_2}{R_1 + R_2} \quad \text{and} \quad a \equiv \frac{R_2}{R_1 + R_2} \tag{2-42}$$

Comparing Fig. 2-27b with Fig. 2-23, we see that the results obtained for the latter circuit are also valid for the former, provided that we multiply the output by the factor a.

2-8. Ringing Circuit. In Sec. 2-7 the emphasis was on obtaining a pulse from a step voltage (peaking). We showed that the circuit should operate in the neighborhood of the critically damped condition. In this section we are interested in having as nearly undamped oscillations as possible. Such a circuit is called a *ringing circuit*. If k is small, the circuit will ring for many cycles. It is often of interest to know the required value of the Q of a circuit which will ring for a given number N of cycles before the amplitude decreases to $1/\epsilon$ of its initial value. From Eq. (2-41) we see that this decrement results when $2\pi kx = 1$. Since $x = t/T_o = NT_o/T_o = N$ and $k = 1/2Q$, we have

$$Q = \pi N \qquad (2\text{-}43)$$

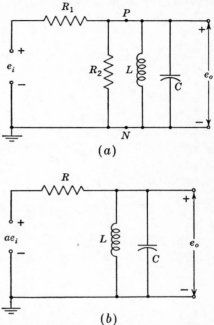

(a)

To keep the damping small, the resistors R_1 and R_2 of Fig. 2-27a must be made large. If the parallel LC combination is in either the plate or cathode circuit of a tube and *if the tube is cut off by a step voltage*, then R_1 is effectively infinite. The equivalent circuit is given in Fig. 2-28. For maximum ringing, no shunting resistor is added and R represents an effective resistor to account for the losses in the coil. The current I is the quiescent tube current before the step is applied. The direction of I in Fig. 2-28 is for the case where the resonant elements are in the plate circuit so that P_1 represents

(b)

Fig. 2-27. (a) The circuit of Fig. 2-23 modified by the inclusion of a damping resistor R_2; (b) the equivalent circuit.

the plate terminal and P_2 the E_{bb} supply terminal. If the LC combination is in the cathode circuit, then P_1 represents the cathode terminal, P_2 is ground, and the direction of I must be reversed.

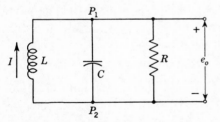

Fig. 2-28. Ringing circuit with capacitor initially uncharged.

Outwardly, the circuits of Fig. 2-23 and Fig. 2-28 appear quite different. When, however, the input to Fig. 2-23 is taken to be a step of amplitude E, the output of the two circuits can be shown to be identical, provided only that the initial inductor current I of Fig. 2-28 is taken to be E/R. The two circuits have the same characteristic roots given in Eq. (2-34). And, under the circumstance that $E = IR$, the conditions that apply in both cases to the output voltage are that at $t = 0$, $e_o = 0$ and $de_o/dt = I/C$ and that at $t = \infty$, $e_o = 0$. Hence, provided we make the replacement of E by IR, all the equations from (2-37) to (2-41) apply equally well to the circuit of Fig. 2-28.

If we neglect the damping and assume $k = 0$ because R approaches infinity, Eq. (2-41) becomes

$$e_o = I \sqrt{\frac{L}{C}} \sin \frac{2\pi t}{T_o} \tag{2-44}$$

To obtain this result, we must remember that kE is independent of R because

$$Ek = IR \frac{1}{2R} \sqrt{\frac{L}{C}} = \frac{I}{2} \sqrt{\frac{L}{C}}$$

We can easily verify that the amplitude of oscillation given in Eq. (2-44) is correct by remembering that the initial magnetic energy stored in the inductor is converted into electric energy in the capacitor at the end of one-quarter cycle. Thus

$$\frac{1}{2} L I^2 = \frac{1}{2} C E_{max}^2 \qquad \text{or} \qquad E_{max} = I \sqrt{\frac{L}{C}} \tag{2-45}$$

A ringing circuit may be used to generate a sequence of pulses regularly spaced in time. These pulses are obtained from the train of sine waves.

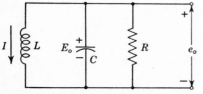

The sequence starts when the tube delivering the current I is cut off. These pulses find application in many timing operations, as will be described later.

FIG. 2-29. Ringing circuit with initial current I in inductor and initial voltage E_o across capacitor.

Consider now the ringing circuit of Fig. 2-29 in which there is an initial voltage E_o across the capacitor C as well as an initial inductor current I.

It is now convenient to introduce a parameter Δ, defined as *the ratio of coil current to resistor current at $t = 0$*:

$$\Delta \equiv \frac{I}{E_o/R} = \frac{IR}{E_o} \tag{2-46}$$

The output e_o/E_o can be expressed as a function of time ($x = t/T_o$) with Δ and k as parameters. The definitions of k and T_o, Eqs. (2-35), are repeated here for convenience:

$$k = \frac{1}{2R} \sqrt{\frac{L}{C}} \qquad \text{and} \qquad T_o = 2\pi \sqrt{LC}$$

Critical Damping, $k = 1$

$$\frac{e_o}{E_o} = [1 - (1 + 2\Delta)(2\pi x)]\epsilon^{-2\pi x} \tag{2-47}$$

Overdamped, with $4k^2 \gg 1$

$$\frac{e_o}{E_o} = -\left(\frac{1}{4k^2} + \Delta\right)\epsilon^{-\pi x/k} + (1 + \Delta)\epsilon^{-4\pi kx} \qquad (2\text{-}48)$$

Underdamped, $k < 1$

$$\frac{e_o}{E_o} = \left[-(1 + 2\Delta)\left(\frac{k}{\sqrt{1 - k^2}}\right) \sin 2\pi \sqrt{1 - k^2}\, x \right.$$
$$\left. + \cos 2\pi \sqrt{1 - k^2}\, x\right]\epsilon^{-2\pi kx} \quad (2\text{-}49)$$

These responses are plotted in Figs. 2-30 to 2-32. We note that even for the critically damped case there may be an *undershoot;* i.e., the output which starts at a positive value drops to a negative value before

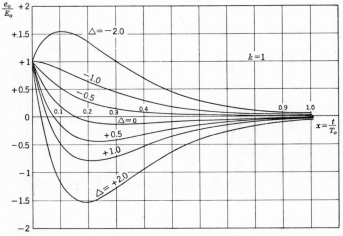

Fig. 2-30. Plot of Eq. (2-47).

returning asymptotically to zero. If E_o and I have the relative polarities indicated in Fig. 2-29, then Δ is positive. If the relative polarity differs from that indicated, then Δ is negative. For a negative Δ, the output may rise first (see the curve for $\Delta = -2.0$) before falling to zero. The physical reason for this initial increase in output is that the inductor current (with the polarity opposite to that in Fig. 2-29) may charge the capacitor to a more positive voltage before C discharges through the resistor. We see that the waveform depends upon the inductor and resistor currents (the sign and magnitude of Δ) and upon the amount of damping (the value of k).

The areas under each curve of Figs. 2-30 to 2-32 is $-k\Delta/\pi$. This can be verified by direct integration or much more easily by proceeding

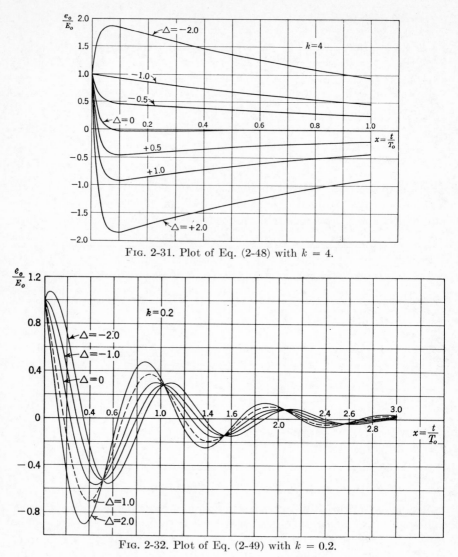

FIG. 2-31. Plot of Eq. (2-48) with $k = 4$.

FIG. 2-32. Plot of Eq. (2-49) with $k = 0.2$.

as follows.   Since

$$e_o = L \frac{di}{dt} \quad \text{or} \quad \frac{e_o}{E_o} = \frac{L}{E_o T_o} \frac{di}{dx}$$

then   Area $\equiv \int_0^\infty \frac{e_o}{E_o} dx = \frac{L}{E_o T_o} \int_0^\infty di = -\frac{LI}{E_o T_o} = -\frac{L\Delta}{R T_o}$

$$= -\frac{L\Delta}{(1/2k) \sqrt{L/C}} \frac{1}{2\pi \sqrt{LC}} = -k\Delta/\pi \qquad (2\text{-}50)$$

When a pulse is passed through a transformer, the response at the end of the pulse is given by one of the equations (2-47), (2-48), or (2-49), but Δ is always positive. The pulse transformer is discussed in Chap. 9.

Other combinations of the basic three linear elements R, L, and C are important in pulse circuits and are discussed in the sections where the appropriate physical background which leads to the circuit configuration is introduced.

REFERENCE

1. Salvadori, M. G., and R. J. Schwarz: "Differential Equations in Engineering Problems," Prentice-Hall, Inc., New York, 1954.

CHAPTER 3

LINEAR PULSE AMPLIFIERS

Frequently the need arises in pulse systems for amplifying a signal with a minimum of distortion. Under these circumstances the vacuum tubes involved must operate linearly. In the analysis of such circuits the first step is the replacement of the actual circuit by its linear equivalent. Thereafter it becomes a matter of circuit analysis to determine the distortion produced by the transmission characteristics of the linear network. In this sense the present discussion is an extension of the material of Chap. 2 with the following important differences. Previously we were satisfied with simply observing the distortion introduced, by

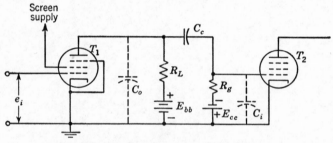

Fig. 3-1. A stage of amplification.

various simple transmission networks, for several representative waveforms. Now we shall be concerned with the problem of how the distortion may be minimized and how the signal may be amplified.

The frequency range of the amplifiers discussed in this chapter extends from a few cycles (or possibly from direct current) up to about 10 Mc. The original impetus for the study of such wideband amplifiers was supplied because they were needed to amplify the pulses occurring in a television signal. Therefore, such amplifiers are often referred to as *video amplifiers*.

3-1. The *RC* Coupled Amplifier Stage.[1] The circuit of Fig. 3-1 is representative of a complete stage of amplification in that it includes the elements of a single amplifier (T_1) and the elements required to couple this stage to the next (T_2). The plate-circuit resistor is R_L, C_c is a blocking capacitor used to keep the d-c component of voltage which appears at the plate of T_1 from reaching the grid of T_2, and R_g is a grid-leak resistor. The capacitances C_o and C_i represent, respectively, capacitances which are referred to as the *output* and *input capacitances* of the tube. These capacitors have been indicated by dotted lines because they have not been included deliberately but are rather unavoidable attributes of the vacuum tubes employed. In any practical mechanical arrangement of the amplifier components there are also capacitances associated with the tube sockets and the proximity to the chassis of components and signal leads. It is necessary to include these additional *stray capacitances* in any computation of practical interest. In referring to the gain of the amplifier, we shall mean the gain from the grid of one tube to the grid of the succeeding tube. We shall assume throughout this chapter that the signal amplitude is small enough so that the tube operates linearly, unless specifically stated otherwise.

3-2. Steady-state Analysis of an Amplifier. A criterion which may be used to compare one amplifier with another with respect to fidelity of reproduction of the input signal is suggested by the following considerations. Any arbitrary waveform of engineering importance may be resolved into a Fourier spectrum. If the waveform is periodic, the Fourier spectrum will consist of a series of sines and cosines whose frequencies are all integral multiples of a fundamental frequency. The fundamental frequency is the reciprocal of the time which must elapse before the waveform repeats itself. If the waveform is not periodic, the fundamental period extends in a sense from a time $-\infty$ to a time $+\infty$. The fundamental frequency is then infinitesimally small, the frequencies of successive terms in the Fourier series differ by an infinitesimal amount rather than by a finite amount, and the Fourier series becomes instead a Fourier integral. In either case the spectrum includes terms whose frequencies extend, in the general case, from zero frequency to infinity.

If the *gain* and *time delay* of an amplifier are independent of the frequency, then the amplifier must necessarily reproduce precisely the form of the input waveshape. For, under these circumstances, the relative amplitudes of the Fourier components are identical for input and output as are also the relative position on a time scale of input and output components.

We shall now show that the *time delay* D of a sinusoidal signal is equal to the phase shift produced by a transmission network divided by the angular frequency ω. Consider that a sinusoidal signal is represented by $A\epsilon^{j(\omega t+\phi)}$, in which A is the amplitude and ϕ is an arbitrary phase angle. Suppose that this signal suffers a phase lag of amount θ so that the signal becomes $A\epsilon^{j(\omega t+\phi-\theta)} = A\epsilon^{j\omega[t+(\phi/\omega)-(\theta/\omega)]}$. The new signal is identical to the original signal with the exception that it has been translated along the time axis in the positive direction by an amount $D = \theta/\omega$, which is the magnitude of the delay in seconds. If the time delay is to be independent of frequency, it is required that the transmission network introduce a phase shift θ which is proportional to frequency.

This discussion suggests that the extent to which an amplifier's amplitude response is not uniform and the extent to which its time delay is not constant with frequency may serve as a measure of the lack of fidelity to be anticipated in an amplifier. In principle, it is really not necessary to specify both amplitude and delay response since, for most practical circuits, the two are related and, one having been specified, the other is uniquely determined. However, in particular cases, it may well be that either the time-delay response or amplitude response is the more sensitive indicator of distortion.

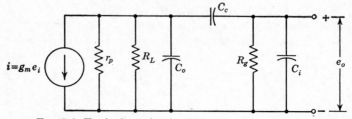

FIG. 3-2. Equivalent circuit of a stage of amplification.

3-3. Amplitude and Time-delay Response of an RC Coupled Amplifier Stage. If an amplifier stage of the type shown in Fig. 3-1 were intended for use with pulse-type waveforms, typical values for the components would be $R_L \cong 1$ K, $C_o \cong C_i \cong 10$ $\mu\mu f$, $C_c \cong 0.2$ μf, and $R_g \cong 1$ Meg. It is reasonably apparent, then, that the frequency characteristics of the amplifier may be divided into three ranges. First, there is the range where the frequency is so low that the shunt capacitances have no appreciable effect but the influence of C_c is marked. Second, there is a range where the frequency is high enough to permit us to neglect C_c, but in which the influence of the shunt capacitances must be taken into account. Finally, there is a range, which falls between the low- and high-frequency regions, in which, to a good approximation, we may neglect all the capacitances.

In the circuit of Fig. 3-2 the pentode of Fig. 3-1 has been replaced by a current source $g_m e_i$ in parallel with r_p. The circuits of Fig. 3-3a, b, and c are, respectively, the equivalent circuits which apply in the midband and in the high- and low-frequency bands. In drawing these equivalent circuits, we have replaced the current generator and shunt resistors R_L and r_p by a Thévenin equivalent and have further taken into account that $R_g \gg R_L$ and $r_p \gg R_L$.   The capacitance C of Fig. 3-3b is the sum of C_o and C_i and all the stray shunt capacitances of the circuit.

From Fig. 3-3a we see that the midband gain A_o is given by

$$A_o = -g_m R_L$$

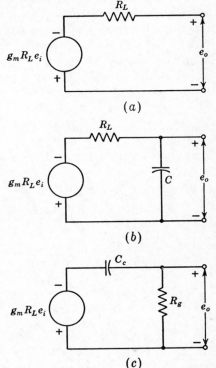

The low-frequency equivalent circuit is identical to the high-pass RC circuit of Fig. 2-1, while the high-frequency equivalent circuit is identical to the low-pass RC circuit of Fig. 2-13.   We have, then, that the ratio of the gain at low frequency A_1 to the midband gain A_o is [see Eq. (2-1)]

$$\left| \frac{A_1}{A_o} \right| = \frac{1}{\sqrt{1 + (f_1/f)^2}} \quad (3\text{-}1)$$

where $f_1 = 1/2\pi R_g C_c$ is the lower 3-db frequency.   The ratio of the gain at high frequency A_2 to the midband gain is [see Eq. (2-24)]

$$\left| \frac{A_2}{A_o} \right| = \frac{1}{\sqrt{1 + (f/f_2)^2}} \quad (3\text{-}2)$$

where $f_2 = 1/2\pi R_L C$ is the upper 3-db frequency.   The normalized time delays, D_1 and D_2, for the low- and high-frequency ranges, respectively, are given by

FIG. 3-3. Equivalent circuits of an amplifier. (a) Midband equivalent; (b) high-frequency equivalent; (c) low-frequency equivalent.

$$f_1 D_1 = \frac{f_1 \theta_1}{\omega} = -\frac{1}{2\pi} \frac{f_1}{f} \arctan \frac{f_1}{f} \qquad (3\text{-}3)$$

and

$$f_2 D_2 = \frac{f_2 \theta_2}{\omega} = \frac{1}{2\pi} \frac{f_2}{f} \arctan \frac{f}{f_2} \qquad (3\text{-}4)$$

In the above expressions θ_1 and θ_2 represent the angle by which the output lags the input, neglecting the initial 180° phase shift through the amplifier.   The frequency dependence of the gains in the high- and low-frequency range is to be seen in Fig. 3-4.

The frequency range from f_1 to f_2 is called the *bandwidth* of the amplifier stage.   We may anticipate in a general way that a signal, all of whose Fourier components of appreciable amplitude lie well within the range

f_1 to f_2, will pass through the stage without excessive distortion. This criterion must be applied, however, with extreme caution, as will be indicated in the following discussion.

Suppose we apply to an amplifier a symmetrical square wave whose repetition frequency is $f = 30f_1$. Let us assume that the upper-frequency-3-db point is arbitrarily high. Under these circumstances we might be inclined to feel that the frequency components, all of which are of frequency f or higher, lie sufficiently well within the passband

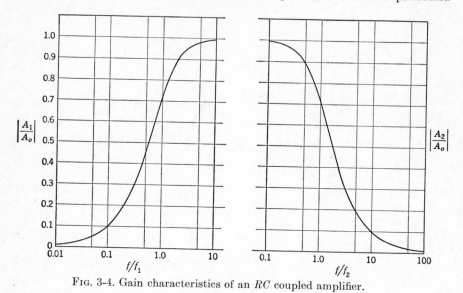

Fig. 3-4. Gain characteristics of an RC coupled amplifier.

so that the signal distortion will be small. However, from Eq. (2-7), we see that the square wave would have a percentage tilt

$$P = \frac{100\pi f_1}{f} = \frac{100\pi}{30} = 10.5\%$$

and so large a tilt is hardly to be considered as a small distortion. We shall now demonstrate that the reason for this apparently anomalous situation is to be found in the extreme sensitivity of the shape of the output to a shift in phase of the fundamental frequency component.

A symmetrical square wave of unity amplitude and of fundamental frequency f has a Fourier series,

$$e = \frac{4}{\pi}\left(\sin \alpha + \frac{1}{3}\sin 3\alpha + \frac{1}{5}\sin 5\alpha + \cdots\right) \qquad (3\text{-}5)$$

in which $\alpha = 2\pi ft$. Consider first only the influence on the square wave of the phase shift of the fundamental. The phase shift is

$$\theta_1 = \arctan\frac{f_1}{f} \cong \frac{f_1}{f}$$

for small angles. The output is obtained by replacing α in Eq. (3-5) by $\alpha + \theta_1$. The waveform is then modified by

$$\Delta e = \frac{4}{\pi}\left[\sin\left(\alpha + \frac{f_1}{f}\right) - \sin\alpha\right]$$

Since, for small angles, $\cos(f_1/f) \cong 1$ and $\sin(f_1/f) \cong f_1/f$, this equation reduces to

$$\Delta e \cong \frac{4}{\pi}\frac{f_1}{f}\cos\alpha = \delta\cos\alpha \qquad (3\text{-}6)$$

where $\delta \equiv 4f_1/\pi f$. The waveform, modified by the addition of Δe, is shown in Fig. 3-5. The percentage tilt is

$$P = 2\delta \times 100 = \frac{8}{\pi}\frac{f_1}{f} \times 100$$

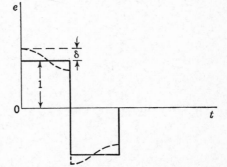

For $f_1/f = \frac{1}{30}$, $P = 8.5$ per cent. To take into account the effect of the phase shift of the remaining harmonics (which will, incidentally, change the cosine tilt into a linear tilt), we need but to note that the

FIG. 3-5. Modification of a square wave due to the phase shift of the fundamental.

nth harmonic is of relative amplitude $1/n$ and is shifted in phase $1/n$th as much as the fundamental. Hence the above result may be corrected by writing

$$P = 8.5\left(1 + \frac{1}{3^2} + \frac{1}{5^2} + \frac{1}{7^2} + \cdots\right) = 8.5 \times 1.20 = 10.2\%$$

This result agrees very well with the value $P = 10.5$ per cent given above.

From Eq. (3-1) we find that the relative gain at the fundamental frequency, $f/f_1 = 30$, is approximately 0.9995. This is close enough to 1 to justify our having neglected the amplitude characteristics in the above calculation of the distortion of the square wave.

3-4. Unit Step Response of an Amplifier. An alternative criterion of amplifier fidelity is the response of the amplifier to a particular input waveform. Of all possible available waveforms, the most generally useful is the step voltage. In terms of a circuit's response to a unit step, the response to an arbitrary waveform may be written very easily in the form of the familiar superposition integral. Another feature which recommends the unit step is the fact that the waveform is one which permits small distortions to stand out clearly. Additionally, from an experimental point of view, the unit step (or, better, the repeated unit step which forms a square wave) is not a particularly difficult waveform to generate.

We have already noted the correlation between amplifier frequency response and the response to a unit step. The finite rise time t_r and percentage tilt P introduced by the amplifier are related to the high and low 3-db frequencies, respectively, by Eqs. (2-26) and (2-7).

$$f_2 t_r = 0.35 \tag{3-7}$$

and
$$P = 100\pi \frac{f_1}{f} \tag{3-8}$$

where f is the frequency of the testing square waves.

Quite generally, even for more complicated amplifier circuits than the one indicated in Fig. 3-1, there continues to be an intimate relationship between the distortion of the leading edge of a unit step and the high-frequency response. Similarly, there is a close relationship between the low-frequency response and the distortion of the flat portion of the unit step. We should, of course, expect such a relationship since the high-frequency response measures essentially the ability of the amplifier to respond faithfully to rapid variations in signal, while the low-frequency response measures the fidelity of the amplifier for slowly varying signals. An important feature of a unit step is that it is a combination of the most abrupt voltage change possible and of the slowest possible voltage variation.

In spite of the fact that the frequency response and unit step response both provide the same information, we shall generally find that the unit step response is much more useful. The principal reason for this circumstance is that we shall often find that the waveforms which are of interest to us consist essentially of a superposition of unit steps. For voltages of this type (pulses or square waves), the unit step response will yield immediately useful information which may be secured from the frequency response only through laborious calculation.

An important experimental procedure (called *square-wave testing*) for the adjustment of an amplifier for optimum performance involves the examination of an oscillograph of the response of an amplifier to an applied square wave. It is possible to improve the fidelity of an amplifier stage by using a coupling network between tubes which is more complicated than the network indicated in Fig. 3-1. It is a great convenience to be able to adjust circuit parameters and to be able to observe simultaneously, by the method of square-wave testing, the effect of the adjustment on the amplifier response. The alternative is to take data, after each successive adjustment, from which to plot the amplitude and phase responses. Aside from the extra time consumed in this latter procedure we have the problem that it is usually not obvious which of the attainable amplitude and phase responses corresponds to optimum fidelity.

It is possible, by judicious selection of the square-wave testing frequency, to examine individually the high-frequency and low-frequency distortion. For example, consider an amplifier which has a high-frequency time constant of 1 μsec and a low-frequency time constant of 0.1 sec. A square wave of half period equal to several microseconds, on an appropriately fast oscilloscope sweep, will display the rounding of the leading edge of the waveform and will not display the tilt. At the other extreme, a square wave of half period approximately 0.01 sec on an appropriately slow sweep will display the tilt and not the distortion of the leading edge.

It should *not* be inferred from the above comparison between steady-state and transient response that the phase and amplitude responses are of no importance at all in the study of amplifiers. The frequency characteristics are useful for the following reasons. In the first place, much more is known generally about the analysis and synthesis of circuits in the frequency domain than in the time domain, and for this reason the design of coupling networks is often done on a frequency-response basis. Second, it is often possible to arrive at least at a qualitative understanding of the properties of a circuit from a study of the steady-state response in circumstances where transient calculations are extremely cumbersome. Finally, it happens occasionally that an amplifier is required whose characteristics are specified on a frequency basis, the principal emphasis being to amplify a sine wave.

3-5. Transient Response of an RC Coupled Amplifier Stage. As we have already noted, the high- and low-frequency equivalent circuits of the RC amplifier are identical, respectively, with the RC integrating and differentiating circuits of Figs. 2-13 and 2-1. The unit step response of these circuits is described in Chap. 2. It remains only to make some general observations about the amplifier.

The rise time of the amplifier may be improved by reducing the product $R_L C$. Every attempt should be made to reduce C by careful mechanical arrangement to reduce the shunt capacitance. The rise time may also be decreased by reducing R_L, but this reduces simultaneously the nominal amplifier gain. A figure of merit which is very useful in comparing tube types is obtained by computing the ratio of the nominal gain to the rise time in the limiting case where stray capacitance is considered to have been reduced to zero. We have

$$\frac{|A_o|}{t_r} = g_m R_L \frac{1}{2.2 R_L (C_o + C_i)} = \frac{g_m}{2.2 (C_o + C_i)}$$

in which $C_o + C_i$ is the sum of the input and output capacitances of the tube. The ratio $g_m/(C_o + C_i)$ is listed in Table 3-1 for several receiving-type tubes of high figure of merit.

TABLE 3-1. CAPACITANCES AND FIGURE OF MERIT OF SEVERAL
RECEIVING-TYPE TUBES

Tube type	Input cap., C_i, $\mu\mu$f	Output cap., C_o, $\mu\mu$f	Total cap., $C_i + C_o$, $\mu\mu$f	$g_m \times 10^6$	$[g_m/(C_i + C_o)] \times 10^{-6}$
6AC7	11.0	5.0	16.0	9,000	560
6AG7	13.0	7.5	20.5	11,000	540
6AH6	10.0	2.0	12.0	9,000	750
6AK5	4.0	2.8	6.8	5,100	750
6CL6	11.0	5.5	16.5	11,000	670
6AG5	6.5	1.8	8.3	5,000	600
6AU6	5.5	5.0	10.5	5,200	500

We can obtain a rough estimate of the upper-frequency limit of a conventional amplifier by considering that, to increase the bandwidth, we have reduced the gain of a stage to, say, 2. If the gain were much smaller, the amplifier would hardly be worthwhile. Using a 6AK5 vacuum tube, the rise time is

$$t_r = \frac{2.2(C_o + C_i)|A_o|}{g_m} = \frac{2.2 \times 6.8 \times 10^{-12} \times 2}{5,100 \times 10^{-6}} \cong 6 \times 10^{-9} \text{ sec}$$

and the upper 3-db frequency is

$$f_2 = \frac{0.35}{t_r} = \frac{0.35}{6} \times 10^9 \cong 60 \text{ Mc}$$

In a practical circuit, the inevitable extra stray capacitance might easily reduce the bandwidth by a factor of 2. Hence we may probably take a bandwidth of 30 Mc as a reasonable estimate of a practical upper limit for an uncompensated amplifier using lumped parameters. If the desired gain is 10 instead of 2, the maximum 3-db frequency is about 6 Mc. If more bandwidth is needed, then distributed amplifiers are used (see Sec. 10-7).

The extension of the bandwidth in the downward direction depends on the time constant $C_c R_g$. Except in very special cases, the upper limit for R_g is about 1 Meg. Larger grid-leak resistors usually result in instability because of positive ion current due to residual tube gas. A limit to the value of C_c is set by the increased shunt capacitance associated with the physical bulk of the coupling capacitor. Coupling capacitors rarely exceed 1 μf in value. The response may be extended to zero frequency by dispensing entirely with the coupling capacitor in favor of a coupling arrangement which provides a d-c path.

3-6. Shunt Compensation to Improve Rise-time Response.[2–4] One of the simplest methods which is available for improving the rise-time response (or high-frequency response) of an amplifier without loss of gain is shown in Fig. 3-6a. The method involves simply including an inductor L in series with the plate-circuit resistor. This arrangement puts the inductor in parallel with the capacitor C and hence the circuit is called a "shunt-compensated" or "shunt-peaked" amplifier. The high-frequency equivalent circuit is given in Fig. 3-6b.

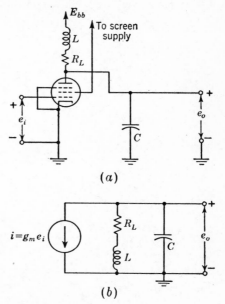

(a)

(b)

Fig. 3-6. (a) A shunt-compensated stage; (b) equivalent circuit if $r_p \gg R_L$.

Let us consider the response of the network to an applied unit step of negative polarity as a consequence of which the current generator provides a current step of magnitude i_o. Writing down the differential equation for the network, and assuming a solution of the form e^{pt}, we find for the roots of the characteristic equation

$$p = -\frac{R_L}{2L} \pm \sqrt{\left(\frac{R_L}{2L}\right)^2 - \frac{1}{LC}} \tag{3-9}$$

It is convenient here to introduce the parameters K and f_2 defined by

$$K \equiv R_L \sqrt{\frac{C}{L}} \qquad f_2 \equiv \frac{1}{2\pi R_L C} \tag{3-10}$$

in which case

$$p = -\pi f_2 K^2 \pm j\pi f_2 K^2 \sqrt{\frac{4}{K^2} - 1} \tag{3-11}$$

The parameter f_2 is, of course, the upper 3-db frequency of the uncompensated amplifier ($L = 0$), while $K = 1/Q_o$. Here Q_o is the Q at the resonant frequency ($\omega_o = 1/\sqrt{LC}$) of the series combination of R_L, L, and C so that $Q_o = \omega_o L/R_L$.

The required solutions for the output e_o must satisfy the conditions that $e_o = 0$ and $de_o/dt = i_o/C$ at $t = 0$ and $e_o = R_L i_o$ at $t = \infty$. Depending on whether K is equal to or smaller than or larger than 2, the response will be critically damped, underdamped (oscillatory), or overdamped. Letting $x \equiv t/(2\pi R_L C) = f_2 t$, the results for the various cases are:

Critical Damping, K = 2

$$\frac{e_o}{R_L i_o} = 1 - \epsilon^{-4\pi x} - 2\pi x \epsilon^{-4\pi x} \qquad (3\text{-}12)$$

Underdamped, K < 2

$$\frac{e_o}{R_L i_o} = 1 + \epsilon^{-\pi K^2 x} \left(\frac{2 - K^2}{K\sqrt{4 - K^2}} \sin \pi K \sqrt{4 - K^2} x \right.$$
$$\left. - \cos \pi K \sqrt{4 - K^2} x \right) \qquad (3\text{-}13)$$

Overdamped, K ≫ 2. In this case of large K, the roots p are given approximately by $p = -2\pi f_2 K^2$ and $p = -2\pi f_2$. The term in the solu-

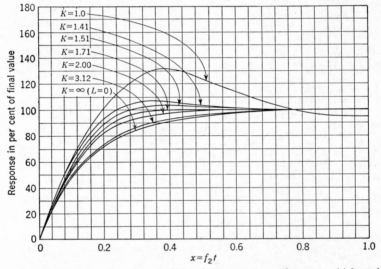

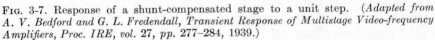

Fɪɢ. 3-7. Response of a shunt-compensated stage to a unit step. (*Adapted from A. V. Bedford and G. L. Fredendall, Transient Response of Multistage Video-frequency Amplifiers, Proc. IRE, vol. 27, pp. 277–284, 1939.*)

tion associated with the first of these roots will decay very rapidly and we may therefore neglect it and write

$$\frac{e_o}{R_L i_o} \cong 1 - \epsilon^{-2\pi f_2 t} = 1 - \epsilon^{-t/RC} \qquad (3\text{-}14)$$

as is to have been expected.

From Eq. (3-10) the inductance L is given by

$$L = m R_L^2 C \qquad (3\text{-}15)$$

where $m \equiv 1/K^2$.

The unit step response for several values of K is shown in Fig. 3-7. As the peaking inductor is increased in value, there is a progressive improvement in rise time without accompanying overshoot up to the point of critical damping. Beyond this point the amplifier response exhibits a progressively larger overshoot. The factor by which the rise time is improved (divided) by compensation is $\rho \equiv t_r/t_r'$, in which t_r and t_r' are, respectively, the rise time of the amplifier before and after compensation. The parameter ρ and the percentage overshoot, γ, are plotted in Fig. 3-8. For the case of critical damping, the rise time is improved by the factor 1.43.

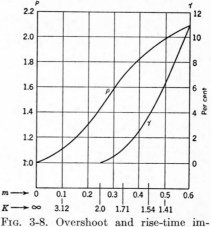

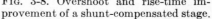

FIG. 3-8. Overshoot and rise-time improvement of a shunt-compensated stage.

It is of interest to consider the steady-state response of the compensated amplifier. It is easy to compute that the normalized gain as a function of the frequency is given by

$$\left|\frac{A_2}{A_o}\right| = \sqrt{\frac{1 + \dfrac{1}{K^4}\left(\dfrac{f}{f_2}\right)^2}{\left[1 - \dfrac{1}{K^2}\left(\dfrac{f}{f_2}\right)^2\right]^2 + \left(\dfrac{f}{f_2}\right)^2}} \tag{3-16}$$

and the normalized time delay is given by

$$f_2 D = f_2 \frac{\theta_2}{\omega} = \frac{f_2}{2\pi f} \arctan\left\{\frac{f}{f_2}\left[1 - \frac{1}{K^2} + \left(\frac{1}{K^2}\frac{f}{f_2}\right)^2\right]\right\} \tag{3-17}$$

The steady-state amplitude and time-delay characteristics of the amplifier are given, respectively, in Figs. 3-9 and 3-10.

The curve having the most uniform amplitude response (maximum flatness) corresponds to $K \cong 1.54$. The curve having the most constant

TABLE 3-2. OVERSHOOT AND RISE-TIME IMPROVEMENT

K	$m \equiv 1/K^2$	γ, %	ρ	Characteristic
2	0.25	0	1.43	Critical damping
1.71	0.34	1.0	1.70	Most constant delay
1.54	0.41	3.8	1.90	Maximum flatness
1.41	0.50	6.5	2.00	$\lvert A_2/A_o \rvert = 1$ at $f/f_2 = 1$

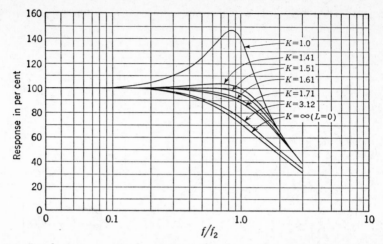

FIG. 3-9. Steady-state amplitude response of a shunt-compensated stage. (*Adapted from A. V. Bedford and G. L. Fredendall, Transient Response of Multistage Video-frequency Amplifiers, Proc. IRE, vol. 27, pp. 277–284, 1939.*)

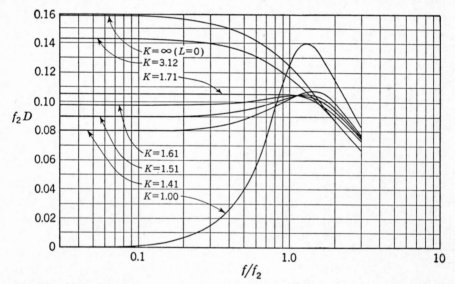

FIG. 3-10. Time-delay response of a shunt-compensated stage. (*Adapted from A. V. Bedford and G. L. Fredendall, Transient Response of Multistage Video-frequency Amplifiers, Proc. IRE, vol. 27, pp. 277–284, 1939.*)

time delay is given by $K \cong 1.71$. The curve for which $|A_2/A_o| = 1$ at $f/f_2 = 1$ is given by $K = 1.41$. The overshoot γ and rise-time improvement ρ for these special cases are summarized in Table 3-2.

The amount of overshoot which is tolerable is very largely a function of the application of the amplifier. For example, for an amplifier to be used in oscillography, any visible overshoot would be objectionable. On the other hand, in television amplifiers, overshoots as large as 5 per cent not only may be acceptable but may actually improve the quality of the resultant picture. If the number of stages used is large, then the overshoot should be kept below about 2 per cent (see Sec. 3-9).

In the case of no compensation it will be recalled [see Eq. (2-26)] that the product $t_r f_2 = 0.35$. It is of interest to note that the same rule also applies quite well in the present case of shunt compensation. For example, we may calculate that for critical damping the amplitude response falls by 3 db at $f/f_2 = \sqrt{2}$. Since we estimated above that in this case the rise time was divided by the factor 1.43, we have that $t_r' f_2' = (0.35 \times \sqrt{2})/1.43 \cong 0.35$, where t_r' and f_2' are the rise time and bandwidth for critical damping.

An initial estimate of the peaking inductance required may be made by estimating the total shunt capacitance. The required inductance is usually in the range 1 to 100 μh. Adjustable coils are available for this application and the final adjustment is made experimentally by the method of square-wave testing. The inductance is changed by varying the depth of insertion into the coil form of a powdered iron slug. The square-wave frequency is set so that the half period of the square wave is several times the rise time and the inductance is adjusted to give the type of response most suitable for the application for which the amplifier stage is intended.

Even when a square-wave generator and oscillograph are already immediately available, having been used to adjust the peaking coil, it is not uncommon to follow this adjustment by a measurement of f_2, using a sinusoidal oscillator. This 3-db frequency is then either used directly as a measure of the fidelity of the amplifier or else the rise time is estimated from the 3-db frequency. Of course, in either case the percentage overshoot must also be stated. The reason for following this procedure rather than stating the rise time directly is that to make a precise rise-time measurement it is necessary to have a precisely calibrated timing signal. Additionally the finite rise time of the square wave and oscilloscope must often be taken into account. Moreover, it is not always convenient to operate with so fast a sweep voltage that the 10 per cent and 90 per cent points may be determined accurately.

Before leaving the subject of shunt peaking we may note that some small improvement in performance is possible by shunting the peaking coil with a capacitor C_1, as in Fig. 3-11. The most generally useful case results when $L = 0.35 R_L^2 C$ and $C_1 = 0.22C$. Under these circumstances the rise-time improvement over the completely uncompensated case is 1.77 and the overshoot is only 1 per cent. This result is to be compared with the straight shunt compensation case mentioned above where

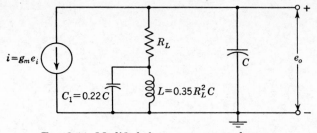

FIG. 3-11. Modified shunt-compensated stage.

$m = 0.34$ gives an overshoot of 1 per cent and rise-time improvement of 1.70. The difference is slight, but sometimes it is possible to arrange the mechanical layout of components so that C_1 consists of stray capacitance across the coil and no additional capacitance need be added. The circuit of Fig. 3-11 gives a particularly uniform delay response.

3-7. Additional Methods of Rise-time Compensation.[5,6] Some improvement over the shunt-compensated amplifier may be achieved by the use of a four-terminal coupling network which separates the output capacitance of a tube from the input capacitance of the succeeding tube. The detailed analysis of these circuits is quite complicated because of the large number of reactive elements involved. Since the improvement which results through their use is not very great, we shall content ourselves with simply indicating representative component values for some of these circuits to get an idea of the order of magnitude of the improvement possible.

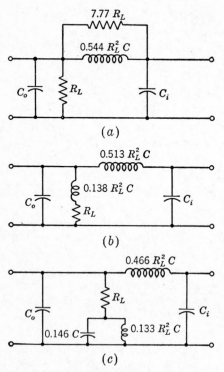

FIG. 3-12. Four-terminal compensating networks. The capacitance $C = C_o + C_i$ and the circuit parameters are given for the case $C_o/C_i = \frac{1}{2}$. (a) Series peaking; (b) shunt-series peaking; (c) Dietzold network.

Three of these circuits are shown in Fig. 3-12. These are the circuits referred to as *series peaking, shunt-series peaking,* and *shunt m-derived peaking.* This latter arrangement is also known as the Dietzold network.

work. These circuits and the shunt peaking circuit and the tuned shunt peaking circuits are compared in Table 3-3. Optimum performance of

TABLE 3-3. COMPARISON OF HIGH-FREQUENCY COMPENSATING CIRCUITS

Circuit	Rise-time improvement ρ	Overshoot γ, %	Ratio of overshoot duration to t_r'	Bandwidth improvement f_2'/f_2	Rise time–bandwidth product $f_2't_r'$
Shunt peaking (Fig. 3-6) with $L = 0.42R_L{}^2C$	1.85	3.0	2.7	1.72	0.33
Tuned shunt peaking (Fig. 3-11) with $L = 0.43R_L{}^2C$ $C_1 = 0.21C$	1.89	3.0	1.8	1.83	0.34
Series peaking (Fig. 3-12a).........	1.90	3.0*	0.59	2.07	0.38
Shunt-series peaking (Fig. 3-12b).........	2.21	3.0	2.2	2.28	0.36
Dietzold (Fig. 3-12c)...	2.47	0.3†	1.3	2.48	0.35

* Ringing.
† Smear.

the four-terminal networks results when the output capacitance of the amplifier tube C_o is related to the input capacitance C_i of the succeeding tube by a factor of 2. Each of the circuits, therefore, is adjusted so that $C_o/C_i = \frac{1}{2}$. In the cases of series and shunt-series peaking a worthwhile improvement in rise time results if a small amount of overshoot is permitted. For ease of comparison all the circuits except the Dietzold network are given for the case of 3.0 per cent overshoot. In the case of the series-peaking circuit the resistor across the series coil is not essential to the circuit but is useful for the purpose of damping the oscillations in the response.

The rise-time improvement in Table 3-3 is given as the ratio $\rho = t_r/t_r'$. The response of the series peaking circuit has not only an overshoot but also a ringing. It is possible to eliminate the ringing in favor of a single overshoot but only at the expense of increasing the rise time. The Dietzold network response displays a feature which is referred to as *smear*. This term refers to the fact that, after the response has approached very close to the steady-state value, an abnormally long time is required for the response to cover the small remaining separation from the steady state voltage. The overshoot duration stated is normalized with respect to the rise time for the *compensated* circuit and serves as a measure of the duration of the overshoot, or, where ringing takes place, measures the duration of the first overshoot.

In each of the cases listed the steady-state amplitude response shows an increase in the upper 3-db frequency with an essentially monotonic reduction in gain at high frequencies. That is, there is no increase in gain before the gain finally starts to fall, as is the case in Fig. 3-9 for, say, $K = 1.41$. The improvement in bandwidth, as well as the product $f_2' t_r'$, is given in Table 3-3. Again we see that the approximate rule

$$f_2 t_r \cong f_2' t_r' \cong 0.35$$

holds quite well.

The method of square-wave testing must be used for a final adjustment of the parameters in the four-terminal networks. The process of adjusting for optimum response is usually quite complicated because the various parameters interact with one another. Because of the difficulties of adjustment, the larger number of adjustable circuit components required and the fact that it is not easy to achieve a response entirely free of overshoot, ringing, or smear and still be left with a rise-time improvement, four-terminal networks are not as popular as simple shunt peaking. On the other hand, the use of a four-terminal network may sometimes make possible the elimination of a stage of amplification in a multistage amplifier and thus effect a worthwhile economy of parts.

3-8. Rise-time Response of Cascaded RC Coupled Amplifiers.[7] The unit step response of n identical cascaded (uncompensated) RC coupled amplifiers is given by

$$\frac{e_o}{(-g_m R_L)^n} = 1 - \left[1 + x + \frac{x^2}{2!} + \frac{x^3}{3!} + \cdots + \frac{x^{n-1}}{(n-1)!} \right] \epsilon^{-x} \quad (3\text{-}18)$$

in which $x = t/RC$. The response for the cases $n = 1$ to $n = 10$ is shown in Fig. 3-13. We observe that as n increases not only does the rise time increase but there is also introduced in the response a progressively longer delay.

Suppose that we have an amplifier which consists of n stages in cascade, each amplifier being free of overshoot. Let the rise times of the individual amplifiers be $t_{r1}, t_{r2}, \ldots, t_{rn}$, and let us apply to this amplifier a step signal which is similarly free of overshoot and has a rise time t_{ro}. In such a case in the limit of a very large number of stages it is possible to prove that the output signal will have no overshoot and will have a rise time

$$t_r = \sqrt{t_{ro}^2 + t_{r1}^2 + t_{r2}^2 + \cdots + t_{rn}^2} \quad (3\text{-}19)$$

Unfortunately this rule does not work very well when only a few stages are involved. It is still useful as a rough estimate. On this basis, if we have an amplifier of n identical stages of rise time t_r, we may expect the over-all rise time $t_r^{(n)}$ to be

$$t_r^{(n)} = \sqrt{n}\, t_r \tag{3-20}$$

Values of $t_r^{(n)}/t_r$ computed directly from Eq. (3-18) have been tabulated

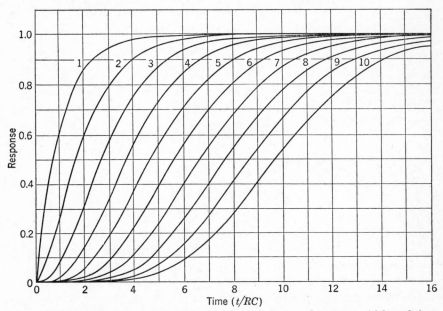

FIG. 3-13. Response of cascaded identical uncompensated stages. (*Adapted from G. E. Valley, Jr., and H. Wallman, "Vacuum Tube Amplifiers," Massachusetts Institute of Technology Radiation Laboratory Series, vol. 18, chap. 1, fig. 1·25, McGraw-Hill Book Company, Inc., New York,* 1948.)

in Table 3-4 and for comparison the corresponding values of $\sqrt{n}$ are listed also. We observe that while the agreement is far from perfect the correspondence is close enough so that Eq. (3-20) will serve as a useful approximate rule.

TABLE 3-4. COMPARISON OF RISE-TIME RATIOS WITH RATIOS GIVEN BY SQUARE-ROOT RULE AND BANDWIDTH RULE

n	1	2	3	4	5	6	7	8	9	10
$\dfrac{t_r^{(n)}}{t_r}$ [Eq. (3-18)]	1.0	1.5	1.9	2.2	2.5	2.8	3.0	3.3	3.45	3.6
$\sqrt{n}$ [Eq. (3-20)]	1.0	1.4	1.7	2.0	2.2	2.45	2.65	2.8	3.0	3.2
$(2^{1/n} - 1)^{-\frac{1}{2}}$ [Eq. (3-23)]	1.0	1.55	2.0	2.3	2.6	2.85	3.1	3.3	3.5	3.7

From Table 3-4 we see that if we wish to have an over-all bandpass of 1 Mc with a two-stage amplifier then the upper 3-db frequency of each must be 1.5 Mc. If 1 Mc is desired with a three-stage amplifier, then each (identical) stage must be 1.9 Mc wide, etc.

We noted earlier that even for a circuit which is more complicated than a single RC combination the rise-time bandwidth product remained approximately constant at 0.35. This result suggests that we try to calculate the rise time from the bandwidth. The upper 3-db frequency for n cascaded amplifiers is $f_2^{(n)}$ and may be computed from

$$\left[\frac{1}{\sqrt{1 + \left(\frac{f_2^{(n)}}{f_2}\right)^2}}\right]^n = \frac{1}{\sqrt{2}} \tag{3-21}$$

so that

$$\frac{f_2}{f_2^{(n)}} = \frac{1}{\sqrt{2^{1/n} - 1}} \tag{3-22}$$

Therefore, if we assume that $t_r^{(n)}f_2^{(n)} = t_r f_2$, we have

$$\frac{t_r^{(n)}}{t_r} = \frac{1}{\sqrt{2^{1/n} - 1}} \tag{3-23}$$

Values of $(2^{1/n} - 1)^{-\frac{1}{2}}$ are also listed in Table 3-4. It is to be noted that the agreement with the correct values of rise-time ratios is very much better in the present instance than for those given by Eq. (3-20). In the limit of large n both methods will give the same result.

The delay associated with the curves of Fig. 3-13 may be specified by the time required for the response to go from zero to 0.5. We see that each stage beyond the first introduces the same amount of delay. For n amplifiers, the delay is given approximately by $(n - 0.3)RC$. This delay is not ordinarily considered as a distortion.

3-9. Rise-time Response of Cascaded Amplifiers with Overshoot.[2] When identical stages, which individually have overshoot, are cascaded, it is still possible to make some general rules concerning the over-all response. These rules apply only very roughly but are nevertheless of some value.

When the individual stages have very small overshoot, of the order of 1 or 2 per cent, the overshoot increases very slowly with the number of stages or may even fail entirely to increase. In this case the response approaches a fixed waveform except for a progressive stretching in the direction of the time axis. These features are displayed by the response of a multistage shunt-compensated amplifier for $K = 1.61$ in Fig. 3-14. The overshoot for a single stage is about 1 per cent, at 16 stages has grown to only about 4 per cent and is still about the same at 64 stages. The rules $t_r^{(n)} = \sqrt{n}\, t_r$ and $f_2^{(n)}t_r^{(n)} = f_2 t_r$ also hold reasonably well in this case.

Circumstances are different when the overshoot is in the range 5 to 10 per cent. In this case the rise time increases appreciably more slowly than as $\sqrt{n}$, while the overshoot instead grows approximately as $\sqrt{n}$. These features may again be verified from Fig. 3-14. If, then, an amplifier is to have a fairly large number of stages, it is clear that the individual stages must be adjusted for very slight or no overshoot.

3-10. Attenuators. Intimately associated with the problem of amplifier design is the problem of providing for signal attenuation. In an oscilloscope, for example, we would like to be able to adjust the amplifier gain so that the display on the screen is of convenient size.

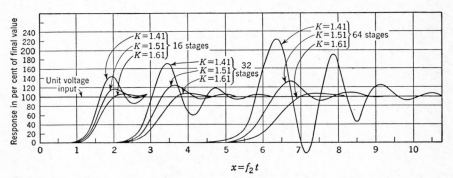

FIG. 3-14. Response of cascaded overcompensated amplifiers. (*Adapted from A. V. Bedford and G. L. Fredendall, Transient Response of Mutistage Video-frequency Amplifiers, Proc. IRE, vol. 27, pp. 277–284, 1939.*)

The simple resistor combination of Fig. 3-15 would attenuate the input signal by the ratio $a = R_2/(R_1 + R_2)$ independently of the frequency, were it not for the inevitable stray capacitance C_2 which shunts R_2. The capacitance C_2 may be, for example, the input capacitance of a stage of amplification. Using Thévenin's theorem, the circuit in Fig. 3-15a may be replaced by its equivalent in Fig. 3-15b, in which R is equal to the parallel combination of R_1 and R_2. We ordinarily want both R_1 and R_2 to be large so that the nominal input impedance of the attenuator may be large enough to prevent loading down the input signal. If, say,

$$R_1 = R_2 = 1 \text{ Meg} \quad \text{and} \quad C_2 = 15 \ \mu\mu\text{f}$$

then the rise time in Fig. 3-15b is $2.20(0.5)15 \ \mu\text{sec} = 16.5 \ \mu\text{sec}$. So large a rise time is ordinarily entirely unacceptable.

The attenuator may be *compensated*, so that its attenuation is once again independent of the frequency, by shunting R_1 by a capacitance C_1, as indicated in Fig. 3-15c. The circuit has been redrawn in Fig. 3-15d to suggest that the two resistors and capacitors may be viewed as the four arms of a bridge. If $R_1 C_1 = R_2 C_2$, the bridge will be balanced, and no current will flow in the branch connecting the point X to the point Y. For the purpose of computing the output, the branch X-Y may be omitted and the output is again equal to ae_i independently of the frequency. In practice, C_1 will ordinarily have to be made adjustable, and the final adjustment for compensation is made experimentally by the method of square-wave testing. This procedure is necessary because the compensation is critically dependent on the condition $R_1C_1 = R_2C_2$ being satisfied precisely.

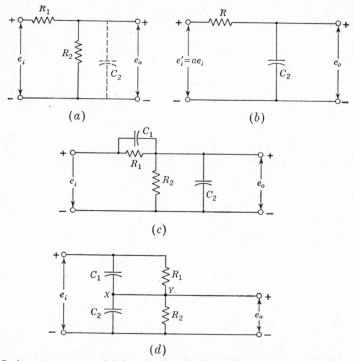

FIG. 3-15. An attenuator. (a) Actual circuit; (b) equivalent circuit; (c) compensated attenuator; (d) compensated attenuator redrawn as a bridge.

It is of interest to consider what the appearance of the output signal will be for a step-voltage input if the compensation is slightly incorrect, Assume, say, that the capacitance across R_1 is slightly larger than is required and is equal to $C_1 + \Delta C$. Let the input step have an amplitude E. Initially the voltage division will be determined by the capacitors so that the output is $[(C_1 + \Delta C)/(C_1 + \Delta C + C_2)]E$. Eventually the output must become $aE = [C_1/(C_1 + C_2)]E$. If $C \equiv C_1 + C_2$ and if $\Delta C/C \ll 1$, then the difference between these two levels is

$$\Delta e_o = \frac{C_2 \, \Delta C}{C^2} E$$

The resultant waveform is shown in Fig. 3-16a. It is also not difficult to see that the decay from the initial to the final level takes place with a time constant $\tau = RC$, where R is the equivalent of the parallel combination of R_1 and R_2. If C_1 is smaller by ΔC than the value of capacitance required for exact compensation, the output appears as in Fig. 3-16b.

The compensated attenuator will reproduce faithfully the signal which appears at its input terminals. However, if the output impedance of the

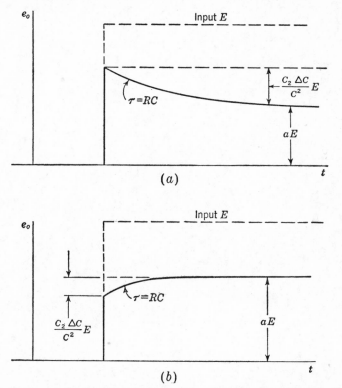

Fig. 3-16. Response of misadjusted attenuator. (a) Overcompensated; (b) undercompensated.

generator driving the attenuator is not zero, the signal may be distorted right at the input to the attenuator. This situation is illustrated in Fig. 3-17a in which a generator of a step voltage E and of output impedance R_o is connected to the attenuator. Since, as was noted earlier, the lead which joins point X to point Y may be open-circuited, the circuit in Fig. 3-17a may be redrawn as in Fig. 3-17b. If $R_o \ll R_1 + R_2$, as is usually the case, the input to the attenuator will be an exponential of time constant R_oC' in which C' is the capacitance of the series combination of C_1 and C_2. It is this exponential waveform rather than the d-c step which the attenuator will transmit faithfully.

If the generator terminals were connected to the terminals to which the attenuator output is connected, the generator would see a capacitance C_2. In this case the waveform at these terminals would be an exponential with time constant R_oC_2. When the attenuator is used, the time constant is R_oC'. Since $C' < C_2$, an improvement in waveform results. For example, if the attenuation a is equal to $\frac{1}{10}$, then $C_1 = C_2/9$ and $C' = 0.1C_2$ so that the rise time of the waveform will have been improved

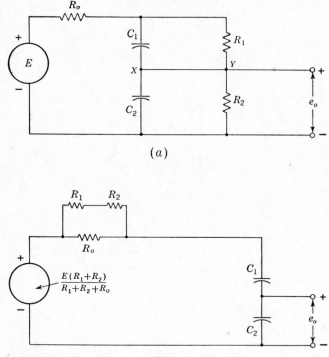

(a)

(b)

Fig. 3-17. (a) Compensated attenuator including impedance of source; (b) equivalent circuit.

by a factor of 10. If we are able to afford a loss of signal level, this reduction of input capacitance may be used to advantage.

As an example of such an application, consider the problem associated with connecting the input terminals of an oscilloscope to a signal point in a circuit. If the point at which the signal is available is some distance from the oscilloscope terminals, and particularly if the signal appears at a high impedance level, we shall want to use shielded cable to connect the signal to the oscilloscope. The shielding is necessary in this case to shield the input lead from stray fields such as the ever-present 60-cycle field. The capacitance seen looking into several feet of cable may be as high as 100 to 150 $\mu\mu$f. This combination of high input capacitance together with the high output impedance (say resistive) of the signal source will make it impossible to observe faithfully fast waveforms. A "probe" assembly which permits the use of shielded cable and still keeps the capacitance low is indicated in Fig. 3-18. Typically, the attenuation introduced through use of the probe assembly is 10 or 20 and the input capacitance to the probe assembly is about 15 or 8 $\mu\mu$f, respectively. There are also units commercially available at present which consist of a probe assembly with an attenuation of 100 followed by an amplifier of gain 100. The over-all gain is 1, but the probe input capacitance may be as little as 2 or 3 $\mu\mu$f.

The problem of providing continuously adjustable attenuation is not so easily solved. In this case the resistors R_1 and R_2 must be replaced

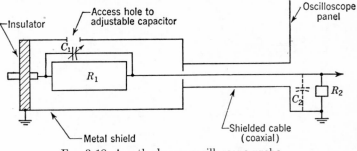

FIG. 3-18. A cathode-ray oscilloscope probe.

by a potentiometer, and since the required compensating capacitor depends on the setting of the attenuator, the only practicable thing to do is to leave the attenuator uncompensated. The bandpass is then a minimum when the potentiometer is set at its mid-point and is given by

$$(f_2)_{\min} = \frac{2}{\pi RC} \tag{3-24}$$

in which R is the total potentiometer resistance and C the total shunt capacitance between the potentiometer arm and ground. If, say, $C = 20$ $\mu\mu$f and $(f_2)_{\min}$ is to be 10 Mc, $R = 3$ K. The conflict of the necessary high potentiometer resistance to avoid loading down the signal source and at the same time the necessity for low potentiometer resistance to maintain the bandpass suggests using a cathode follower with the potentiometer in the cathode circuit.

3-11. Rise-time Compensation in the Cathode Circuit.[7] In Fig. 3-19 is shown a pentode stage of amplification in which a resistor R_k and capacitor C_k have been included in the cathode circuit. The capacitance C represents as usual the total capacitance shunting the output signal lead to ground. The rise time of the amplifier would be $t_r = 2.2R_LC$ if R_k and C_k were not present. It will be shown below that if we adjust

$R_k C_k = R_L C$, the bandwidth will be multiplied by the factor $1 + g_m R_k$. However, at the same time the nominal gain will be divided by the same factor so that unlike the compensation methods described above (shunt peaking, etc.) the gain-bandwidth product will remain unaltered. If the circuit served no other purpose than to extend the bandwidth at the expense of gain, it would be of little interest, since the same end may be achieved by the much simpler expedient of reducing the plate-circuit resistor R_L. However, comparing the present circuit with that of Fig. 1-9 we see that we have here a case of current feedback. We may then expect to find that this circuit has better stability of gain and more linearity of operation.

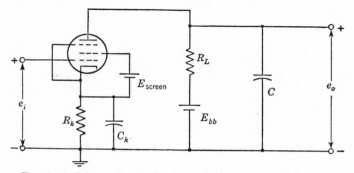

FIG. 3-19. Schematic circuit of a cathode-compensated stage.

To calculate the effect of the cathode impedance on gain and bandwidth, we replace the circuit by its equivalent, as shown in Fig. 3-20a. Here we have used the result stated in Sec. 1-4 that the impedance seen looking toward the tube between plate and ground is equal to $r_p + (1 + \mu)Z_k$, in which r_p is the plate resistance and Z_k the impedance in the cathode circuit. If we adjust $R_k C_k = R_L C$, the four elements between points A and B constitute a compensated attenuator. The circuit is the same as that shown in Fig. 3-17a and may therefore be redrawn as in Fig. 3-20b, in which

$$e_i' = \frac{\mu e_i[(\mu + 1)R_k + R_L]}{r_p + (\mu + 1)R_k + R_L} \tag{3-25}$$

$$R' = \frac{r_p[(\mu + 1)R_k + R_L]}{r_p + (\mu + 1)R_k + R_L} \tag{3-26}$$

and the total capacitance is

$$C' = \frac{C\dfrac{C_k}{\mu + 1}}{C + \dfrac{C_k}{\mu + 1}} = \frac{R_L C}{(\mu + 1)R_k + R_L} \tag{3-27}$$

if $R_k C_k = R_L C$.

The time constant of the circuit is

$$\tau_c = R'C' = \frac{R_L C}{1 + g_m R_k + \dfrac{R_k + R_L}{r_p}} \cong \frac{R_L C}{1 + g_m R_k} \tag{3-28}$$

if $R_k + R_L \ll r_p$. Thus the time constant has been divided by and the bandwidth has been multiplied by the factor $1 + g_m R_k$.

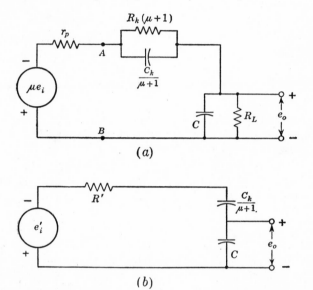

(a)

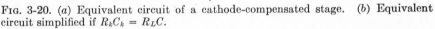

(b)

FIG. 3-20. (a) Equivalent circuit of a cathode-compensated stage. (b) Equivalent circuit simplified if $R_k C_k = R_L C$.

The nominal gain of the amplifier (i.e., at a frequency where the capacitors may be neglected) is easily computed to be

$$A = -\frac{g_m R_L}{1 + g_m R_k}$$

If the input e_i consists of a negative step of amplitude E, the corresponding output is

$$e_o = \frac{g_m R_L E}{1 + g_m R_k} (1 - e^{-t/\tau_c})$$

If the cathode were connected directly to ground, the output would be

$$e_o = g_m R_L E (1 - e^{-t/\tau_o})$$

in which $\tau_o = R_L C$. In either case the ratio of gain to rise time is the same and equals $g_m/2.2C$.

In order to see some of the useful features of cathode compensation, let us compare two amplifiers, one with and one without cathode compensation. The first amplifier, without compensation, has a plate resistor R_L. The second amplifier has a plate resistor αR_L and a cathode resistor selected to make

$$1 + g_m R_k = \alpha$$

The quiescent tube current and voltage are to remain as before, which means that the plate resistor αR_L must be returned to a higher supply voltage. It may happen that the cathode resistor selected will furnish the bias required for optimum linearity of tube operation. More generally, however, some additional external bias will be required. The capacitance C shunting the plate to ground is to be the same in both cases. These two amplifiers now have the *same gain* and the *same bandwidth*.

One advantage of the compensated amplifier that is readily apparent is its greater stability of nominal gain with respect to variation of tube parameters. In the case where the nominal gain is given by $-g_m \alpha R_L / (1 + g_m R_k)$ the gain will be a less sensitive function of g_m than in the case where the gain is given by $-g_m R_L$. In the limiting case in which $g_m R_k \gg 1$ the gain for the compensated case is simply $-\alpha R_L / R_k$, independently of g_m.

A second advantage of the compensated amplifier is an improvement in linearity of operation. The nonlinearity of a pentode amplifier results from the variation of transconductance g_m with tube current. The effective transconductance of the compensated stage is $g_m / (1 + g_m R_k)$. For large values of $g_m R_k$ the effective transconductance becomes quite insensitive to variations in the g_m of the tube. Additionally, since the load resistor is α times as large in the compensated as in the uncompensated stage, the current swing in the compensated amplifier will be $1/\alpha$ times the current swing in the uncompensated amplifier for the same output signal. Hence for the same input signal to the two amplifiers the output of the compensated amplifier will be more linear. For comparable linearity in the two cases the compensated stage can handle a somewhat larger input signal and provide a larger output signal.

If the capacitor C_k were not present, then because of cathode-follower action the amplifier would handle a peak-to-peak input signal larger than the grid base of the tube. However, it must be emphasized that because of the presence of C_k the input signal must be restricted in amplitude to the grid base. Otherwise the operation of the circuit will be highly nonlinear, as explained in Sec. 4-9.

We have considered only the special case $R_k C_k = R_L C$. An improvement in rise time is possible if some overshoot is tolerable. The general solution for arbitrary values of $\rho \equiv R_k C_k / R_L C$ and $\alpha \equiv 1 + g_m R_k$ is given in Prob. 3-19. We find that if $\alpha = 2$, then for $\rho = 1.15$ the over-shoot is 2 per cent but the rise time improves by only 10 per cent and is hardly worthwhile. Thus, there is usually little advantage in using a value of ρ other than unity. The optimum value is determined, as with compensation in the plate circuit, by the method of square-wave testing.

3-12. The Cathode Follower at High Frequencies. Our previous discussion of cathode followers (Sec. 1-6) neglected the influence of the tube capacitances. These capacitances will now be taken into account.

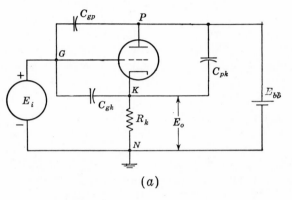

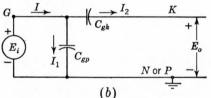

Fig. 3-21. (a) Cathode follower including all capacitances; (b) equivalent circuit for computing input impedance. Note that P is at ground potential for a-c signals.

An important advantage of the cathode follower over a conventional triode amplifier is that the capacitive impedance seen looking into the grid of the cathode follower is appreciably larger than the capacitive impedance looking into the amplifier. In Fig. 3-21a is shown a cathode follower in which all capacitances are included. A circuit which is equivalent for the purpose of computing the current I which must be delivered by the generator E_i is given in Fig. 3-21b. The current $I_1 = E_i(j\omega C_{gp})$ and $I_2 = E_i(1 - A)(j\omega C_{gk})$, where $A \equiv E_o/E_i$ is the amplifier gain. Hence, the input admittance

$$Y_i \equiv \frac{I}{E_i} = \frac{I_1 + I_2}{E_i}$$

is given by

$$Y_i = j\omega C_{gp} + j\omega C_{gk}(1 - A) \tag{3-29}$$

In general, Y_i contains a resistive as well as a capacitive component. If the frequency is low enough so that A may be considered a real number, then the input impedance consists of a capacitance C_i, and hence $Y_i = j\omega C_i$. From Eq. (3-29) the input capacitance is given by

$$C_i \text{ (cathode follower)} = C_{gp} + C_{gk}(1 - A) \tag{3-30}$$

In a similar manner the input capacitance of a conventional amplifier is found to be

$$C_i \text{ (amplifier)} = C_{gk} + C_{gp}(1 - A) \tag{3-31}$$

A numerical comparison is interesting. Consider a half section of a 12AU7, first as a cathode follower of nominal gain, say, equal to 0.8, and then as an amplifier of nominal gain, say, equal to -10. The capacitances are $C_{gp} = 1.5 \ \mu\mu\text{f}$, $C_{gk} = 1.6 \ \mu\mu\text{f}$. At a frequency at which the capacitances do not yet have a marked effect on the gain, we have

$$C_i \text{ (cathode follower)} = 1.5 + 0.2 \times 1.6 = 1.8 \ \mu\mu\text{f}$$
and
$$C_i \text{ (amplifier)} = 1.6 + 11 \times 1.5 = 18 \ \mu\mu\text{f}$$

This exaggeration of the effect of the grid-plate capacitance in an amplifier is called the Miller effect. The large input capacitance to a triode amplifier shunts the load resistor of the preceding stage and is the most important reason for not using triodes ordinarily as pulse amplifiers.

A fairer comparison may be made by comparing the cathode follower to a conventional amplifier of equivalent gain. In this case

$$C_i \text{ (amplifier)} = 1.6 + 1.8 \times 1.5 = 4.3 \ \mu\mu\text{f}$$

which is still more than twice that for the cathode follower.

The output impedance or, more conveniently, the output admittance Y_o of a cathode follower, taking interelectrode capacitances into account, is easily computed by a direct method. A signal E_a is applied to the output terminals and the current I_a which flows through E_a with the grid grounded is computed. The output admittance is $Y_o = I_a/E_a$. The cathode follower showing capacitances is indicated in Fig. 3-21a. For $E_i = 0$, the equivalent circuit (neglecting R_k) is shown in Fig. 3-22a, where we note that G and P are at ground potential (for a-c signals). The capacitance from cathode to ground is C_{kn} and includes the capacitance from cathode to heater if, as usual, the heater is grounded. In Fig. 3-22b we have set $E_{gk} = -E_a$ and defined $C_T \equiv C_{pk} + C_{gk} + C_{kn}$. We have

$$I_a = E_a Y_T + \frac{E_a + \mu E_a}{r_p}$$

or
$$Y_o = \frac{I_a}{E_a} = Y_T + Y_P + g_m \tag{3-32}$$

where $Y_T = j\omega C_T$ and $Y_P = 1/r_p$. Since $g_m = \mu Y_p$ and assuming $\mu \gg 1$, we may neglect Y_p compared with g_m and consider that the output admittance is unaffected by the capacitance until Y_T becomes large enough to be comparable to g_m.

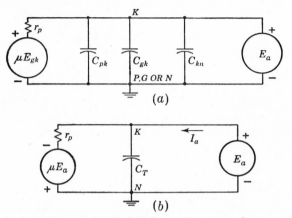

FIG. 3-22. Equivalent circuits of cathode follower for computing output admittance.

The gain of the cathode follower may be calculated, with the result

$$A = \frac{(g_m + j\omega C_{gk})R_k}{1 + \left(\dfrac{\mu + 1}{r_p} + j\omega C_T\right)R_k} \tag{3-33}$$

Assuming $\mu + 1 \cong \mu$ and $g_m R_k \gg 1$,

$$A \cong \frac{g_m + j\omega C_{gk}}{g_m + j\omega C_T} \tag{3-34}$$

The term $j\omega C_{gk}$ in the numerator represents the effect of the coupling from input to output through C_{gk}. If the cathode follower is driving a capacitive load C_L, the expression for A need but be modified by adding C_L to C_T. The 3-db frequency is approximately the frequency at which $\omega(C_T + C_L) = g_m$. Typically, if the total capacitance is say 50 $\mu\mu$f and $g_m = 3$ millimhos as for a half section of a 12AU7, then $f_2 \cong 9.5$ Mc.

The high input impedance of a cathode follower makes it ideal for applications where the loading on a signal source must be kept at a minimum. The low output impedance permits it to support a heavy capacitive load. These features, together with its stability and linearity, account for the many applications which are found for cathode followers. For example, the cathode follower is almost universally used as the input tube in oscilloscope amplifiers. It is also used where a signal must be transmitted through a short section of coaxial cable or shielded wire with its attendant high shunt capacity.

A special problem arises when a signal must be transmitted over a very long coaxial cable. Such a circumstance may arise in a television studio or a radar station where signals may have to be transmitted over distances which range from several feet to several thousand feet. The capacitance per foot of cable such as RG-59/U is 21.0 $\mu\mu$f and the net capacitance is too large to be handled by either a cathode follower or a conventional amplifier. The procedure here is to terminate the cable in its characteristic impedance so that the impedance seen looking into the sending end of the cable is equal to the nominally resistive characteristic impedance of the cable. The characteristic impedance of RG-59/U cable is about 75 ohms. In terminating the cable, we have eliminated the problem of capacitive loading, but since the characteristic impedance is low, a high-current tube will be required to develop a substantial voltage.

The situation here is one which requires a driver for a low impedance load. We might have imagined that a cathode follower would be most suitable, but actually the advantage may lie in placing the load in the plate circuit. Consider that a 6AV5 tube ($g_m = 5$ millimhos) is to be used to drive the load. If the load is in the plate circuit, the gain is

$$g_m R_L = 5 \times 10^{-3} \times 75 = 0.375$$

In the cathode circuit the gain is

$$\frac{g_m R_k}{1 + g_m R_k} = \frac{0.375}{1.375} = 0.273$$

Placing the load in the plate circuit, therefore, gives a worthwhile increase in gain. The usual advantage of the cathode follower with regard to linearity and gain stability do not apply very well in the present case since it is no longer true that $g_m R_k \gg 1$.

Often it is desirable to terminate the cable at the sending end as well to absorb reflections which would result if there should happen to be a slight mismatch at the receiving end or if there should happen to be any small discontinuities in the cable itself. One such arrangement in which the cable appears in the plate circuit is shown in Fig. 3-23. The blocking capacitor is used to isolate the cable and the 75-ohm resistors from the high plate voltage. The 2-K plate resistor serves to increase the time constant of the coupling circuit. If a 125-μf coupling capacitance is used, then this time constant is $2037.5 \times 125 \times 10^{-6} \cong 0.25$ sec. Note that the impedance at the sending end remains essentially constant even if the tube is driven from cutoff to clamp. Such operation would be perfectly acceptable if the signal to be transmitted consisted of a flat-topped pulse and would actually be required to make the tube yield maximum output. Since the effective plate load is only 37.5 ohms, a current of 119 ma is required for a 4-volt signal, which is the standard signal level at which many of the television signals are transmitted in a television studio.

If the cable load is to be placed in the cathode, we may take advantage of the fact that the output impedance of the tube itself is only 200 ohms. Hence the termination on the input end of the cable may be increased to 120 ohms, since the parallel combination of 200 ohms and 120 ohms gives the required 75 ohms. The load on the cathode follower is now $(120 \times 75)/195 = 46$ ohms. The gains in the two cases now turn out to be nearly the same at about 0.19. The fact that the output impedance of the cathode follower is low enough to be comparable to the characteristic impedance helps the gain somewhat but is actually an inconvenience·

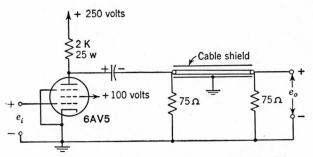

FIG. 3-23. Output amplifier to feed a terminated cable.

The output impedance of the cathode follower is $1/g_m$ and g_m is unfortunately not constant. If, for example, the tube should be driven to cutoff, the termination on the input end becomes 120 ohms instead of the required 75 ohms. On the other hand, the d-c level at the cathode may easily be adjusted to be zero, in which case the coupling capacitor may be removed.

3-13. Low-frequency Compensation.[8] Low-frequency compensation may be attained by using a high resistance in series with the plate load R_L and bypassing this resistor to ground with a large capacitance, as shown in Fig. 3-24a. The proper values of R_d and C_d are obtained from the following analysis. We shall make the simplifying assumptions that:

1. The pentode is a perfect current source.

2. The resistor R_d is infinite. In this case the circuit of Fig. 3-24a may be replaced by the circuit of Fig. 3-24b. We consider that a negative step voltage is applied to the grid of the pentode and I_0 is the constant current delivered by the tube.

The reason for starting the analysis with the above simplifying assumptions is that Fig. 3-24b represents a bridge circuit and that we can conclude that if the bridge is balanced the output will exactly reproduce the input. This fact is made clear by redrawing Fig. 3-24b as indicated in

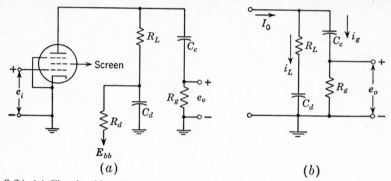

FIG. 3-24. (a) Circuit of low-frequency compensation; (b) equivalent circuit neglecting R_d.

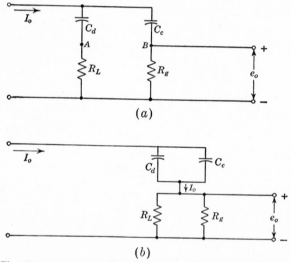

FIG. 3-25. Circuits which are equivalent to that of Fig. 3-24b if $R_L C_d = R_g C_c$.

Fig. 3-25a. If the bridge is balanced, that is, if

$$R_L C_d = R_g C_c$$

then points A and B of Fig. 3-25a are at the same potential and may be connected together as shown in Fig. 3-25b. Then

$$e_o = I_0 \frac{R_g R_L}{R_L + R_g} \cong I_0 R_L$$

since $R_g \gg R_L$. This equation shows that the output exactly reproduces the input and hence that perfect compensation has been attained.

If the bridge is not exactly balanced, what is the form of the output for a step input? This query is answered by solving the network of Fig. 3-24b. Thus,

$$I_0 = i_L + i_g \qquad (3\text{-}35)$$

$$R_L i_L + \frac{q_d}{C_d} = R_g i_g + \frac{q_c}{C_c} \qquad (3\text{-}36)$$

in which q_d and q_c are, respectively, the charges on C_d and C_c. Differentiating Eq. (3-36), we have

$$R_L \frac{di_L}{dt} + \frac{i_L}{C_d} = R_g \frac{di_g}{dt} + \frac{i_g}{C_c} \qquad (3\text{-}37)$$

Solving Eq. (3-37) for i_g, using Eq. (3-35), and using the initial condition $i_g = R_L I_0/(R_L + R_g)$ at $t = 0$, we have

$$y = \frac{1}{\rho}[(\rho - 1)\epsilon^{-x} + 1] \qquad (3\text{-}38)$$

where $\qquad y \equiv \dfrac{e_o}{I_0 R_L} \qquad \rho \equiv \dfrac{C_d R_L}{C_c R_g} \qquad$ and $\qquad x \equiv \dfrac{t}{R_g C_c} \qquad (3\text{-}39)$

In deriving Eq. (3-38), it is assumed that $R_g \gg \rho R_L$. Usually R_L and the maximum size of C_c are determined from high-frequency considerations and R_g is determined by the grid-current characteristics of the tube in the succeeding stage. Let us, then, inquire about the output waveform as a function of C_d. The results are shown in Fig. 3-26.

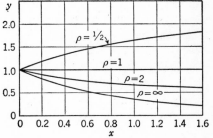

For $\rho \gg 1$,

$$y \cong \epsilon^{-x} \qquad (3\text{-}40)$$

This case corresponds to no compensation at all (C_d is very large). For

FIG. 3-26. Response of a compensated stage for various degrees of compensation. $\rho = C_d R_L / C_c R_g$.

times small compared with the time constant $R_g C_c$ so that $x \ll 1$, we have approximately

$$y \cong 1 - x \qquad (3\text{-}41)$$

For $\rho = 1$,

$$C_d = \frac{C_c R_g}{R_L} \qquad \text{and} \qquad y = 1 \qquad (3\text{-}42)$$

This case corresponds to perfect compensation.

For $\rho = 2$,

$$y = \tfrac{1}{2}(1 + \epsilon^{-x}) \qquad (3\text{-}43)$$

This case corresponds to using a value of C_d which is twice that required for perfect compensation.

For $\rho = 2$ and $x \ll 1$,

$$y \cong 1 - \frac{x}{2} \tag{3-44}$$

In this case the percentage tilt is one-half the tilt of the uncompensated case as may be seen by comparing Eq. (3-44) and Eq. (3-41).

For $\rho = \frac{1}{2}$,

$$y = 2 - \epsilon^{-x} \tag{3-45}$$

For $\rho = \frac{1}{2}$ and $x \ll 1$,

$$y \cong 1 + x \tag{3-46}$$

In this case the positive tilt is equal to the negative tilt of the uncompensated amplifier. Note that if "overcompensation" (an upward tilt) is observed in square-wave testing of an amplifier, it is to be corrected by *increasing* the size of C_d.

The curves of Fig. 3-26 are unrealistic because of the assumption that I_0 is constant and R_d is assumed infinite. For large values of t, the capacitors C_c and C_d act as open circuits and hence eventually all the current must flow through R_d and not R_g. Thus, all curves of Fig. 3-26 must eventually drop to zero. For example, the curve marked $\rho = \frac{1}{2}$ would then have a rounded top. It is to be noted that, if a square wave were to be applied to the amplifier for testing purposes, we would normally select the half period of the square wave to be $T \cong 0.1 R_g C_c$. In this case the initially flat tops of the input square wave would, after transmission through the amplifier, have the appearance of one of the curves of Fig. 3-26 for the range $x = 0$ to $x = 0.1$.

The effect of the finite value of R_d is now to be investigated. If it is desired that the slope di_g/dt be zero at $t = 0$, then it is found from an exact analysis that $C_c R_g = C_d R_L$. This is the condition for perfect compensation with $R_d \rightarrow \infty$ and it is now seen that this is still a good criterion if R_d is finite. The output voltage is found to be

$$y = \frac{1}{n - 1} (n \epsilon^{-x/n} - \epsilon^{-x}) \qquad \text{if } n \neq 1 \tag{3-47}$$

where $n \equiv R_d/R_L$ and where it has been assumed that $R_g \gg R_L + R_d$. If $R_d = R_L$ or $n = 1$, the result is

$$y = (1 + x)\epsilon^{-x} \tag{3-48}$$

For $x \ll 1$, Eq. (3-48) reduces to

$$y \cong (1 + x)(1 - x + \frac{x^2}{2}) \cong 1 - \frac{x^2}{2} \tag{3-49}$$

It is now seen that the tilt is parabolic and not linear. The amount of tilt to be expected is given by the following example. If the uncompensated tilt is, say, 10 per cent so that $x = 0.1$, then Eq. (3-49) gives a compensated tilt of only $(0.1)^2/2 \times 100$ per cent = 0.5 per cent; and this is for R_d only equal to R_L.

If $n \neq 1$ for small x, Eq. (3-47) reduces to

$$y = 1 - \frac{x^2}{2n} \tag{3-50}$$

From this result it is seen that the per cent tilt is multiplied by

$$\frac{1}{n} = \frac{R_L}{R_d}$$

Thus, if $R_d = 10R_L$, the tilt is $\frac{1}{10}$ of the above value, or 0.05 per cent. Note that if $x^2/2n$ is not much less than 1, the tilt must be calculated from Eq. (3-47) instead of Eq. (3-50).

The above theory indicates that the proper procedure for low-frequency compensation is to choose R_d as large as possible and then to choose $R_L C_d = R_g C_c$. The upper limit on R_d is determined by the fact that the quiescent tube current passes through R_d and that the power supply must be able to furnish this voltage drop.

It may not be convenient to satisfy $R_L C_d = R_g C_c$ because the required value of C_d may be too large. For example, if $C_c = 0.1$ μf and $R_g = 1$ Meg and $R_L = 1$ K, then $C_d = 100$ μf. Even if the size of C_d turns out not to be a problem, the variation of capacitance with age may cause difficulty. Occasionally one will find a compensated stage in which R_g is made adjustable to allow for a drift in C_d. More usually no such correction is made since the low-frequency compensation reduces tilt considerably even if the condition $R_L C_d = R_g C_L$ is not exactly satisfied. Also, as noted earlier, where good low-frequency response is of prime importance, it is usually most practicable to use direct coupling instead of capacitive coupling.

We have not considered the effect of the finite plate resistance of the tube, since ordinarily the finite size of R_d has a larger effect on the tilt than does r_p.

3-14. Effect of a Cathode Bypass Capacitor on Low-frequency Response. If a cathode resistor R_k is used for self-bias in an amplifier and if it is desired to avoid the degeneration and hence the loss of gain due to R_k, then we might attempt to bypass this resistor with a very large capacitor C_k. The circuit is indicated in Fig. 3-27. It will be shown that if the input is a square wave, the output is a square wave with a tilt similiar to that due to the coupling capacitor between stages.

Consider that the applied voltage is a d-c step of amplitude E. At $t = 0$, the capacitor acts as a short circuit and there is no degeneration.

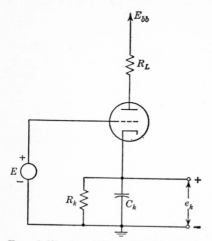

Hence, the plate current is $i = g_m E$ and this current also passes through the capacitor C_k. If we assume that to a first approximation the current remains constant, then the voltage across C_k (which is the cathode voltage e_k) increases linearly with time. Thus $e_k = it/C_k = g_m Et/C_k$. The grid-to-cathode voltage is $e_{gk} = E - g_m Et/C_k$ and the next approximation to the plate current is $i = g_m e_{gk}$, or the output $e_o = -iR_L$ is

$$e_o = -g_m R_L E \left(1 - \frac{g_m t}{C_k}\right) \quad (3\text{-}51)$$

Fig. 3-27. Amplifier with bypassed cathode resistor.

This is an interesting result, showing that the tilt depends only upon g_m and C_k and is independent of R_k and R_L, provided that the tilt is small so that the above approximations are valid.

If we wish to reproduce a 50-cps square wave with a tilt of less than 10 per cent, then

$$\frac{g_m T}{C_k} < 0.1 \qquad \text{or} \qquad C_k > 10 g_m T$$

and if $g_m = 5$ millimhos and $T = 0.01$ sec is the time for a half cycle, then

$$C_k > 10(5 \times 10^{-3})10^{-2} \text{ farad} = 500 \ \mu\text{f}$$

For a 1 per cent droop, C_k would have to be at least 5,000 μf. Such large values of capacitance are impractical and it must be concluded that if accurate reproduction of the flat top of a square wave of low frequency is desired the cathode bias resistor must be unbypassed. The flatness will then be obtained at the sacrifice of gain because the output magnitude will be constant at the value $g_m R_L/(1 + g_m R_k)$. If the loss in gain cannot be tolerated, external bias must be used. On the other hand, if a cathode bias resistor is used, the stage may be cathode-compensated with a small capacitor (see Sec. 3-11) so that we make up in rise time what is lost in gain.

The above discussion gives only the low-frequency response. The output of course has a finite rise time which depends upon the total capacitance C shunting the load R_L.

3-15. Effect of Screen Bypass on Low-frequency Response. The screen grid circuit consists of a voltage-dropping resistor R_s and a capacitor C_s from screen to ground, as in Fig. 3-28a. If a positive step voltage is applied to the grid, the plate current increases and hence so does the screen current. At $t = 0$, the screen voltage E_s is at its quiescent voltage. As time passes, the capacitor must discharge to a steady-state voltage equal to the plate-supply voltage minus the new value of screen current

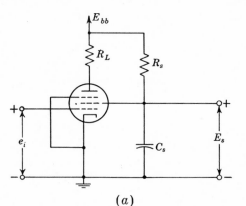

(a)

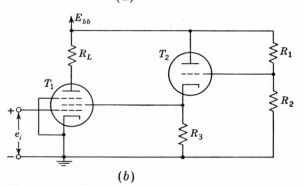

(b)

Fig. 3-28. (a) Use of screen-dropping resistor and bypass capacitor to supply screen voltage. (b) Use of cathode follower to supply screen voltage.

times R_s. Hence, there is a droop in screen voltage with time and a corresponding tilt in output plate voltage. The wave shape is similar to that encountered with an inadequately bypassed cathode resistor.

The method of calculating the size of the screen capacitor to keep the tilt below a certain value is best illustrated by a numerical case. Consider a 6AG7 with a quiescent current of 20 ma and $E_s = 150$ volts. Because of a step input to the grid, the plate current increases to 30 ma. What is the minimum value of C_s if the tilt is to be less than 10 percent for a 50-cps square wave?

The screen current for a 6AG7 is approximately one-fourth the plate current. Hence, the screen quiescent current is 5 ma and the screen current under signal conditions is 7.5 ma. The difference, or 2.5 ma, must come from the screen capacitor, and this current will discharge the capacitor. If we assume that the plate current is approximately proportional to the screen voltage, then we can allow only 10 per cent drop in E_s, or 15 volts. Thus

$$\Delta E_s = \frac{(\Delta I_s)T}{C} \tag{3-52}$$

where T is the time for half a cycle = 0.01 sec. Thus

$$C = \frac{(\Delta I_s)T}{\Delta E_s} = \frac{2.5 \times 10^{-3}}{15} \times 10^{-2} = 1.7 \ \mu\text{f}$$

This is a reasonable value and hence screen grids are usually bypassed.

When it is desired to decrease even the small tilt which might be introduced by the screen circuit and when an appropriate low impedance screen power supply is not available, the arrangement of Fig. 3-28b is often used. Here the cathode follower T_2 acts as a simple voltage regulator and supplies screen voltage at an impedance level of the order of a few hundred ohms. If the screen current changes by 2.5 ma as in the above illustration and if the cathode follower impedance is, say, 400 ohms, then the change in screen voltage is $2.5 \times 10^{-3} \times 400 = 1$ volt only. The screen voltage is approximately equal to the voltage of the junction point of the resistor R_1 and R_2.

3-16. Flat-top Response of Cascaded Stages.[9] If, upon application of a d-c step, a single resistance-capacitance coupling circuit produces a tilt of P_1 per cent and if a second circuit produces a tilt of P_2 per cent, the effect of cascading these circuits is to produce a tilt of $P_1 + P_2$ per cent. This result applies only if the individual tilts and combined tilt are small enough so that in each case the voltage falls approximately linearly with time.

For a d-c step input of amplitude E, the output of the first circuit is $E\epsilon^{-t/\tau_1} \cong E(1 - t/\tau_1)$, in which τ_1 is the time constant. If this signal is applied to the second circuit of time constant $\tau_2 = R_2C_2$, then, neglecting the possible gain of the tube, the result may be computed from the equation

$$R_2 i + \frac{q}{C_2} = E\left(1 - \frac{t}{\tau_1}\right)$$

Differentiating this equation with respect to t, remembering that $e_o = R_2 i$, yields

$$\frac{de_o}{dt} + \frac{e_o}{\tau_2} = -\frac{E}{\tau_1}$$

The solution for the output voltage e_o subject to $e_o = E$ at $t = 0$ is

$$e_o = -E \frac{\tau_2}{\tau_1} + E \left(1 + \frac{\tau_2}{\tau_1} \right) \epsilon^{-t/\tau_2}$$

$$\cong E \left(1 - \frac{t}{\tau_1} - \frac{t}{\tau_2} \right) \tag{3-53}$$

Since t/τ_1 is the tilt due to the first network and t/τ_2 is the tilt due to the second network, Eq. (3-53) verifies the rule stated above: the resultant tilt caused by two RC circuits in cascade is the sum of the tilts due to each network. Since the output again has a linear tilt, we may extend the result to an arbitrary number of stages, provided only that the net tilt remains small enough to be represented by a linear fall.

It was noted earlier that, within a single amplifier stage, tilt may be introduced by the coupling circuit, the screen circuit, and the cathode circuit. Since each of these produces its tilt by a mechanism which is independent of the others, the net tilt produced by an individual stage may be computed again by simply adding the individual tilts. And the over-all tilt of an amplifier consisting of a number of stages is the sum of the tilts of each stage.

For an amplifier consisting of n identical stages in which the low-frequency response is limited only by the finite time constant of the d-c blocking capacitor C_c and grid-leak resistor R_g, the normalized response is given by

$$\frac{e_o}{EA} = \frac{1}{(n-1)!} \frac{d^{n-1}}{dx^{n-1}} (x^{n-1} \epsilon^{-x}) \tag{3-54}$$

in which E is the input step amplitude, A is the nominal over-all amplifier gain, and $x = t/R_g C_c$.

For small values of x, we may write $\epsilon^{-x} = 1 - x$ in Eq. (3-54), which then reduces to

$$\frac{e_o}{EA} = 1 - nx = 1 - \frac{nt}{R_g C_c} \tag{3-55}$$

This equation again verifies the fact that the tilt of n identical stages is n times the tilt of a single stage.

A pulse of width t_p may be considered to be the result of the superposition of a positive step which occurs at $t = 0$ and a negative step at $t = t_p$. Suppose that a pulse of width t_p is applied to a cascade of a number of amplifiers with identical coupling-circuit time constants. The response at the end of the pulse (for $t \gtrless t_p$) may be obtained from Eq. (3-54) by forming the difference $e_d \equiv e_o(t) - e_o(t - t_p)$. For very small values of t_p (more specifically if $t_p \ll R_g C_c$), we may write approximately

$$e_d = t_p \frac{de_o}{dt} = \frac{t_p}{R_g C_c} \frac{de_o}{dx} = x_p \frac{de_o}{dx}$$

where $x_p \equiv t_p/R_g C_c$.

Using Eq. (3-54), we have

$$y \equiv \frac{e_d}{EA} = \frac{x_p}{(n-1)!} \frac{d^n}{dx^n} (x^{n-1}\epsilon^{-x}) \tag{3-56}$$

The response at the end of the pulse is shown in Fig. 3-29 where the quantity y/x_p has been plotted as a function of x for the cases $n = 1, 3,$

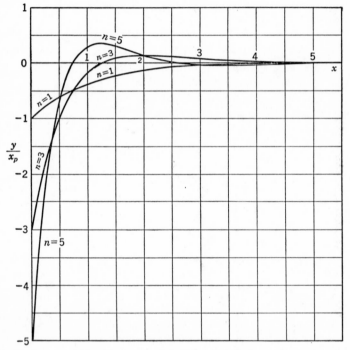

FIG. 3-29. Response of identical cascaded RC coupled stages to an input pulse for $t \geq t_p$.

and 5. Theoretically there should be $n - 1$ crossings of the zero axis, but because the attenuation is so great not all of these are clearly visible in Fig. 3-29. The pulse itself is not indicated in Fig. 3-29, since it would be very tall and narrow if drawn to scale. For example, if the tilt of a single stage is 10 per cent, then $x_p = t_p/R_g C_c = 0.1$. The quantity y, during the time of the pulse, is nominally 1; hence $y/x_p = 10$. Thus on the scale of Fig. 3-29 the pulse has an amplitude of 10 units and a width from $x = -0.1$ to $x = 0$, independently of the value of n. The practical importance of these results is that the response to the pulse persists for a very long time relative to the pulse duration itself.

3-17. The Totem-pole Amplifier.[10] A description of amplifier stages suitable for driving terminated lengths of coaxial cables is given in Sec. 3-12. We noted there that the effective load into which the vacuum tube must work is quite low. As a consequence, it will normally be necessary to operate the tube over a large current swing in order to develop a reasonable voltage across the cable. Under these circumstances the linearity of operation of the amplifier stage must necessarily suffer. One method of reducing distortion is to replace the single tube in the amplifier by two tubes operating in push-pull. It will be recalled

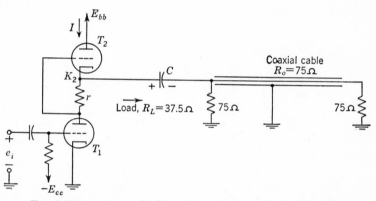

FIG. 3-30. A totem-pole driver for a terminated coaxial cable.

that in push-pull operation the even-harmonic distortion currents produced by the two tubes are in opposite directions. An exact cancellation of these even-harmonic components requires that the two tubes have identical characteristics and be driven with signals which are identical except for opposite polarity.

In push-pull operation, the output signal will be available as a symmetrical signal which appears between two terminals, neither one of which is grounded. These terminals might be the two plates of the amplifier tubes. The coaxial cable clearly requires a single-ended signal, that is, a signal which appears between terminals, one of which is ground. It is possible to change a symmetrical signal to a single-ended signal through the use of a transformer but the ability of a transformer to transmit a signal without frequency distortion is quite limited.

An amplifier that approximates push-pull operation and provides a single-ended signal without a transformer is shown in Fig. 3-30. The amplifier is indicated driving a 75-ohm coaxial cable terminated at both ends. The circuit enjoys a wide popularity in color television systems where linearity of operation is extremely important. It has acquired the name *totem-pole amplifier*. Qualitatively, the operation of the circuit is as follows. In the absence of an input signal e_i, the current I through both tubes is the same and the load current is zero. Suppose now that the input signal makes a positive excursion. Then the current in the tube T_1 will increase by an amount ΔI. A voltage drop $-r\,\Delta I$ will develop between the grid and cathode of tube T_2 and hence the current in the upper tube will decrease by an amount $(\Delta I)'$. The difference current $\Delta I + (\Delta I)'$ will flow through the load. If r is selected correctly, we may make $(\Delta I)' = \Delta I$, and under these circumstances the maximum advantage, with respect to freedom from distortion, will be obtained. It should be noted, however, that the signals applied to the tubes are not truly push-pull, because the voltage across r contains the harmonics generated in tube T_1.

A straightforward analysis of the totem-pole amplifier may be made by replacing the tubes in Fig. 3-30 by their linear equivalent representations of Sec. 1-1. The result is a two-mesh circuit which may be solved for the signal currents in the two tubes by applying Kirchhoff's laws to each mesh. The cathode resistor r across which the bias for tube T_2 is developed appears as a parameter in this solution. It is then found that the signal currents through the two tubes can be made equal to one another if the resistor r is selected according to the relationship

$$ r = \frac{1}{g_m} + \frac{2R_L}{\mu} \tag{3-57} $$

In a typical amplifier the tube selected might be the 6BX7 double triode. This tube may be operated at a quiescent current of the order of 50 ma and has $g_m = 7.6$ millimhos, $\mu = 10$, and $r_p = 1,300$ ohms. For $R_L = 37.5$ ohms, we compute $r = 132 + 7.5 \cong 140$ ohms.

If we proceed as indicated above, we find that, if r is selected as in Eq. (3-57), the gain of the stage with the load connected is then given by

$$ A = -\frac{\mu^2}{\mu+1}\frac{R_L}{R_L + r_p/2} \tag{3.58} $$

If $R_L \ll r_p$ and $\mu \gg 1$, then

$$ A \cong -2g_m R_L \tag{3-59} $$

For the 6BX7 tube we have $|A| = 0.54$.

It is, of course, possible that the value of r required by Eq. (3-57) is not appropriate to provide the correct bias for the tube section T_2. In this case provision must be made for a separate adjustment of bias as, for example, in the circuit of Fig. 3-31. Another form of the totem-pole amplifier is given in Prob. 3-32.

3-18. Cathode Interface Resistance.[11] In many vacuum tubes there develops with use a *cathode interface layer* between the base metal of the cathode and the active emitting surface of the cathode, as shown in Fig. 3-32. The interface compound is a semiconductor compound formed as a result of the chemical interaction between the oxide-emitting material and the base metal or with some reducing constituent of the base metal. The resistance of the interface layer may lie in the range from several ohms to several hundred ohms and may therefore have an appreciable influence on tube operation. Additionally the emitting surface and the cathode base metal serve as the electrodes of a capacitor, the cathode interface layer acting as a leaky dielectric between these electrodes. The over-all effect of the interface layer is to introduce into the cathode a parallel resistance-capacitance combination whose time constant, it is found experimentally, normally lies in the approximate range 0.2 to 2.0 μsec.

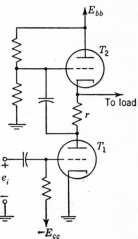

Fig. 3-31. A form of the totem-pole amplifier which permits adjustment of the bias of T_2 independently of the value of r.

In video amplifiers the effect of cathode interface resistance may well be serious. For a signal whose period is very large in comparison

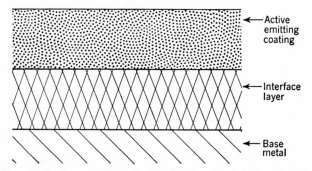

Fig. 3-32. Cross section of cathode, showing interface layer.

to the interface time constant, the principal effect is a loss in gain since the effective transconductance of the tube will be reduced from g_m to $g_m/(1 + g_m R_i)$, R_i being the interface resistance. An abrupt discontinuity applied to the tube grid will appear at the output similarly reduced in amplitude but accompanied by an overshoot at the leading edge of the pulse.

Interface resistance is present to some extent in all tubes with oxide-coated cathodes but is usually particularly pronounced in tubes whose cathode base material contains a large amount of silicon. Interface resistance is inversely proportional to cathode area and is therefore more serious in tubes with small cathode areas. Since, also, the effect of interface resistance is to reduce the effective transconductance by the factor $1 + g_m R_i$, high g_m tubes are particularly sensitive to interface effects. Interface resistance increases with the total number of hours that the cathode has been heated and the end of the useful life of a tube may be the result of interface resistance rather than loss in cathode emission.

We shall have occasion to return to this matter of interface resistance in connection with the binary circuit (Sec. 5-12). At that point we shall see the motivation which has suggested the term *sleeping sickness* to characterize the effects of interface resistance.

A second disease which is often characteristic of video amplifier tubes has the popular designation *slump*. The term is applied to a tube which behaves as though there were present in the cathode a parallel resistance-capacitance combination with a time constant in the range of several seconds. The response of such a tube to an input negative step is an output positive step which gradually slumps to a lower voltage level. The origin of *slump* is not well understood. The effect is often a source of difficulty in the design of d-c amplifiers for cathode-ray oscilloscopes.

REFERENCES

1. Gray, T. S.: "Applied Electronics," 2d ed., chaps. VIII and IX, John Wiley & Sons, Inc., New York, 1954.
2. Bedford, A. V., and G. L. Fredendall: Transient Response of Multistage Video-frequency Amplifiers, *Proc. IRE*, vol. 27, pp. 277–284, 1939.
3. Kallmann, H. E., R. E. Spencer, and C. P. Singer: Transient Response, *Proc. IRE*, vol. 33, pp. 169–195, 1945.
4. Palmer, R. C., and L. Mautner: A New Figure of Merit for the Transient Response of Video Amplifiers, *Proc. IRE*, vol. 37, pp. 1073–1077, 1949.
5. Seeley, S. W., and C. N. Kimball: Analysis and Design of Video Amplifiers, *RCA Rev.*, vol. 3, pp. 290–308, 1939.
6. Design of Video-amplifier Peaking Circuits for Optimum Transient Response, *RCA Industry Service Lab. Rept.* LB-930.
7. Valley, G. E., Jr., and H. Wallman: "Vacuum Tube Amplifiers," Massachusetts Institute of Technology Radiation Laboratory Series, vol. 18, chap. 2, McGraw-Hill Book Company, Inc., New York, 1948.
8. Larsen, M. J.: Low-frequency Compensation of Video-frequency Amplifiers, *Proc. IRE*, vol. 35, p. 666, 1945.

9. Valley, G. E., Jr., and H. Wallman: "Vacuum Tube Amplifiers," Massachusetts Institute of Technology Radiation Laboratory Series, vol. 18, sec. 2.3, McGraw-Hill Book Company, Inc., New York, 1948.

10. Peterson, A., and D. B. Sinclair: A Single-ended Push-pull Audio Amplifier, *Proc. IRE*, vol. 40, pp. 7–11, January, 1952.
Yeh, Chai: Analysis of a Single-ended Push-pull Audio Amplifier, *Proc. IRE*, vol. 41, pp. 743–747, June, 1953.

11. Dukat, F. M., and I. E. Levy: Cathode-interface Effects in TV Receivers Design, *Electronics*, vol. 26, pp. 169–171, April, 1953.
Eisenstein, A.: The Leaky-condenser Oxide Cathode Interface, *J. Appl. Phys.*, vol. 22, pp. 138–148, February, 1951.

CHAPTER 4

NONLINEAR WAVE SHAPING

In Chaps. 2 and 3 we considered the response, to nonsinusoidal input waveforms, of circuits containing linear elements. Many interesting and useful wave-shaping operations can be performed if nonlinear elements are added to the circuits. In the present chapter we shall first discuss briefly the nonlinear characteristics of thermionic diodes, crystal diodes, and triodes (with some emphasis on the positive grid region). Some of the most important wave-shaping circuits using these elements will then be considered.

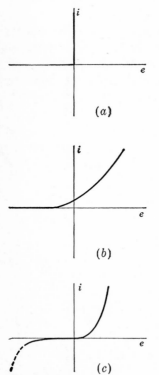

FIG. 4-1. Diode volt-ampere characteristics. (a) Ideal, (b) thermionic, and (c) crystal.

4-1. Diode Characteristics.[1] An ideal diode is defined as a two-terminal circuit element having the volt-ampere characteristic shown in Fig. 4-1a. When the diode conducts, the ratio of the applied voltage to the current e/i, called the *forward resistance R_f*, is zero. For negative voltages, the ratio e/i, called the *back resistance R_b*, is infinite. The ideal diode has characteristics which are independent of the temperature. Additionally, in an ideal diode, the capacitance shunting the diode is assumed negligible. Thermionic-diode and crystal-diode volt-ampere characteristics are sketched, respectively, in Fig. 4-1b and c. These real diodes differ from the ideal diode in the following respects:

1. The forward resistance is not zero. For thermionic diodes, R_f lies in the approximate range 100 to 1,000 ohms. For crystal diodes, R_f lies in the range 1 to 500 ohms.

For a thermionic diode, e is the plate voltage e_b and i is the plate current i_b. The forward resistance $R_f = e_b/i_b$ is called the *static plate resistance.* Sometimes it is more convenient to use the *dynamic* plate resistance r_p, which is defined by de_b/di_b.

2. The forward resistance is not constant but depends upon the voltage across the diode.

3. The back resistance is not infinite. For tubes, R_b may attain hundreds or even thousands of megohms. For germanium crystals, values of R_b of the order 100 K to 1 Meg are more usual, provided the operating temperature remains below about 75°C. For higher temperatures, the value of R_b drops rapidly and crystals can not be used (see Sec. 18-4). It should also be noted that for some types of crystal diodes the peak inverse voltage is much smaller than that of most vacuum tubes.

4. The *break* in the characteristic (the division between the low and high resistance regions) is not sharp and may not occur at zero voltage. For a thermionic diode, the current is not zero at zero applied voltage because of the finite velocity of emission of electrons from the cathode. When the distribution of velocities is taken into account, the result, for small currents, is that the plate current is related to the plate voltage by[2]

$$i_b = I\epsilon^{e_b/E_T} \tag{4-1}$$

in which I is the current at $e_b = 0$ and $E_T = T/11{,}600$, T being the absolute temperature of the cathode. The dynamic plate resistance is given by

$$\frac{1}{r_p} = \frac{di_b}{de_b} = \frac{I}{E_T}\epsilon^{e_b/E_T}$$

or

$$r_p = \frac{E_T}{I}\epsilon^{-e_b/E_T} \tag{4-2}$$

Since there is no longer an abrupt change in diode resistance, let us arbitrarily define the uncertainty in the break as that region of voltage Δe_b over which r_p changes by some large factor, say 1,000. Thus, $\epsilon^{\Delta e_b/E_T} = 10^3$. A reasonable value of T for an oxide-coated cathode is $T = 1{,}000°\text{K}$ and corresponding to this value we have, since $\ln 10 = 2.30$,

$$\Delta e_b = \frac{1{,}000}{11{,}600} \times 2.30 \times 3 = 0.6 \text{ volt}$$

Thus, the uncertainty in voltage over which the *break* in a thermionic diode occurs is of the order of ± 0.3 volt. The location of the *break* is uncertain but lies between -0.25 and -0.75 volt for most diodes.

The uncertainty of the break of a crystal diode is also found to be of the order of magnitude of ± 0.1 to ± 0.3 volt.

5. The volt-ampere characteristic is a function of temperature. For a thermionic diode there is a perceptible shift in the characteristic with filament temperature. Experiment reveals the shift to be about 0.1 *volt for a* 10 *per cent change in heater voltage*. The higher the filament voltage,

the more the curve shifts to the left, because the increase in the initial velocities of the electrons with increase in temperature results in higher currents at a given voltage. The shift with tube replacement or tube aging is found in practice to be of the order of ± 0.25 volt.

The volt-ampere characteristic of a crystal diode is a function of the operating temperature.

6. The shunt capacitance across a thermionic diode is of the order of magnitude of 5 $\mu\mu f$, while the capacitance of a point-contact crystal rectifier is about 1 $\mu\mu f$. To these values must be added the wiring capacitances introduced when the diodes are inserted in a circuit.

7. If a square wave is impressed upon either a point contact or a p-n junction germanium diode, it is found that the resistance does not change instantaneously from its forward value to its back value, or vice versa.[3] A delay, called the *recovery time*, is required for this change to take place. This recovery time varies with the diode and with the circuit in which it is used. The delay ranges from millimicroseconds to tens of microseconds. The forward recovery time is usually not of great importance, because the forward resistance reaches a low value almost instantly even though the time to reach the final forward resistance might be relatively long. The back recovery time is usually more important because the back resistance builds up gradually, approaching its final value exponentially with time.

4-2. Triode Characteristics.[4]   Typical triodes used in pulse applications, as well as in other types of circuits, are the 12AU7 or its equivalent the 5963 or the 5814, the 12AT7, the 12AX7, and the 5965. These are miniature tubes and each contains two triode sections in one envelope. The 6SN7 is a nonminiaturized type similar to the 12AU7 and was the most commonly used tube in the pulse type equipment used in World War II. The 5963 and 5965 were designed for use in high-speed digital computers. The volt-ampere characteristics of the above tubes are given in the Appendix or in this section. The curves for the 5965 are given in Figs. 4-2 and 4-3. In these latter characteristics, curves for positive grid voltages have been included because, as we shall see, the grid of a tube is often driven positive in pulse circuits. If the region near small plate voltages is ignored, then the positive grid curves are very similar in shape and spacing to those for negative grid values. Hence if the grid signal is supplied from a source of low impedance, so that the loading effect on the source due to the flow of grid current may be ignored, the tube will continue to operate linearly even if the grid signal makes an excursion into the positive grid region. This linearity will continue so long as the grid current is a small fraction of the total cathode current.

In pulse applications, large voltage swings are often encountered and the small signal equivalent circuit of Sec. 1-1 is meaningless because the

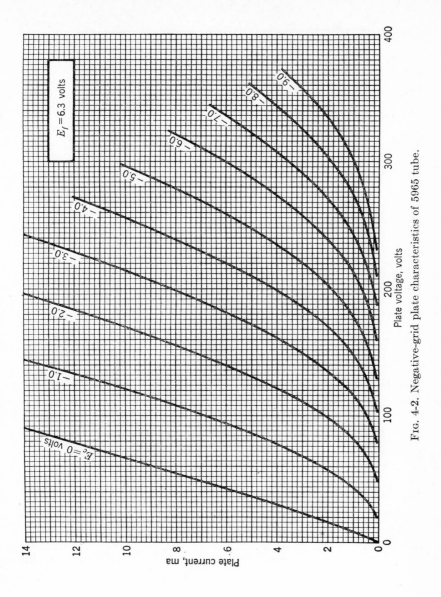

FIG. 4-2. Negative-grid plate characteristics of 5965 tube.

107

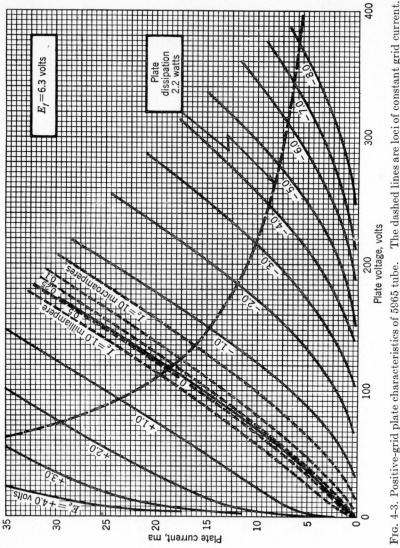

FIG. 4-3. Positive-grid plate characteristics of 5965 tube. The dashed lines are loci of constant grid current.

108

tube parameters μ, r_p, and g_m are *not* constant. The variation of these parameters with plate current is given in Fig. 4-4.

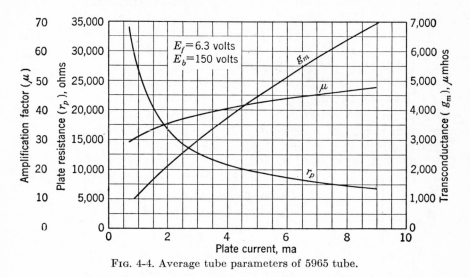

FIG. 4-4. Average tube parameters of 5965 tube.

The grid volt-ampere characteristics of the 5965 tube are given in Fig. 4-5. At a given plate voltage the grid circuit behaves as a diode. In analogy with the definition of the dynamic plate resistance, the *dynamic grid resistance* r_g is given by de_c/di_c, where e_c and i_c are the instantaneous values of grid voltage and current, respectively. The *static grid resistance* r_c is defined as the ratio e_c/i_c. From Fig. 4-5 it appears that the difference in values between the static and dynamic resistances is not great, except possibly for small grid voltages. Furthermore, the value of the grid resistance r_c is not a sensitive function of plate voltage. From Fig. 4-5 we find that for the 5965 tube, 250 ohms is a reasonable value for r_c. For other tubes, the grid resistance

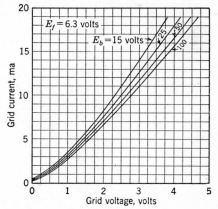

FIG. 4-5. Average volt-ampere grid characteristics of 5965 tube.

may be much more variable than indicated above. For example, for a 12AU7 the static r_c has values ranging from about 500 to 1,500 ohms, depending upon the values of grid and plate voltages (see the grid current curves of Fig. A-8).

The grid current at zero grid-to-cathode voltage, and even for slightly negative grid voltages, is often large enough to have an appreciable effect on the operation of a circuit. We estimate from Fig. 4-3 that the grid current is 400 μa at $e_c = 0$, 10 μa for $e_c = -0.5$ volt, and 0.25 μa at $e_c = -1$ volt. Consider then that a grid-leak resistor is connected from grid to cathode of the 5965. If this grid-leak resistor is, say, $R_g = 1/0.25$ Meg = 4 Meg, then a negative bias of 1 volt will be developed. At a plate voltage of 100 volts, the plate current corresponding to the 1-volt bias is seen from Fig. 4-2 to be 7 ma. If we were to neglect the effect of the grid current and assume that $e_c = 0$, we would expect a current of 15 ma, or more than twice the value actually obtained. Even if the grid leak were reduced to 50 K, the bias due to grid current would be -0.5 volt, since $(5 \times 10^4)(10 \times 10^{-6}) = 0.5$, and the plate current would be about 11 ma, which is still appreciably less than the zero grid-bias value of 15 ma.

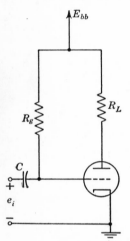

FIG. 4-6. A triode with the grid leak R_g connected to the E_{bb} supply.

If, as indicated in Fig. 4-6, the grid leak is tied to the E_{bb} supply voltage instead of to the cathode, then the grid-to-cathode voltage will approach nominal zero for values of R_g which are large compared with r_c. For example, if $R_g = 1$ Meg and $E_{bb} = 300$ volts, then the grid current will be approximately 300 μa. From Fig. 4-3, we find that the grid voltage corresponding to this grid current is about -0.1 volt. (If we assume that the value of $r_c = 250$ ohms is valid at low grid voltages, then the calculated value of e_c is $0.3 \times 0.25 = +0.075$ volt.) In many pulse circuits it is common to use this connection of the grid leak to a high positive voltage. Under such circumstances where the grid is held at the cathode voltage because of the flow of grid current, we shall refer to the grid as being *clamped* to the cathode. Alternatively, the tube is said to be *in clamp*.

If the grid voltage is made a few volts negative, it is found that the direction of the grid current reverses.[5] This negative current is due to the positive ions which are attracted to the grid. Since the positive-ion current comes from the residual gas in the "vacuum" tube, it is very variable from tube to tube, and is usually a small fraction of a microampere. Negative grid current can also result from thermionic or photoelectric emission from the grid.

The characteristics given in Figs. 4-2 to 4-5 are average values as supplied by the manufacturer, and the curves for a specific tube may differ appreciably from these published values. The Joint Army-Navy

Specification, JAN-1A, for Electron Tubes gives the limits of variability which may be expected in a given tube type.

The volt-ampere characteristics vary with filament temperature and with aging of the tube. As for a diode, so for a multielement tube, the temperature effect is found experimentally to be equivalent to a 0.1-volt shift in cathode voltage (relative to the other electrodes) for each 10 per cent change in filament voltage.

4-3. Clipping or Limiting Circuits. Clipping circuits are used when it is desired to select for transmission that part of an arbitrary waveform which lies above or below some particular reference voltage level. Clipping circuits are also referred to as *voltage selectors* or *amplitude selectors*. Some of the more commonly employed clipping circuits are now to be described.

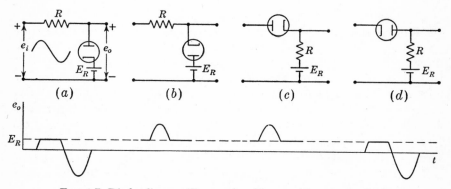

FIG. 4-7. Diode clippers (E_R may be either positive or negative).

Diode Clippers. Circuits employing diodes are shown in Fig. 4-7a to d. Assume initially that the diodes are perfect, with zero forward resistance. In Fig. 4-7a and d the output follows the input when $e_i < E_R$, and $e_o = E_R$ when $e_i > E_R$. These circuits are called *peak clippers*. In Fig. 4-7b and c, $e_o = e_i$ when $e_i > E_R$, and $e_o = E_R$ when $e_i < E_R$. These circuits are called *base clippers*. The circuits in Fig. 4-7 are, of course, essentially the same and differ only in the polarity with which the diode is inserted and in whether the voltage is taken across the diode or the resistor.

Because of the characteristics of real diodes described in Sec. 4-1, the discontinuities in slope in the waveforms of Fig. 4-7 are found, on close examination, not to be sharp, and this lack of sharpness is particularly apparent if the amplitude of the input waveform is comparable with the range over which the plate characteristic has a marked curvature (about 0.6 volt). For any particular tube, the output voltage can be found from the intersection with the plate characteristic[6] of the load line corresponding to the input e_i and the resistor R.

If the input voltage is large enough so that the lack of sharpness of the break in the characteristic can be ignored, but if the forward resistance R_f is not negligible compared with the resistance R, then there will again be a departure from the ideal waveforms of Fig. 4-7. Assuming that R_f is a constant, the output can be calculated from Kirchhoff's voltage law.

We have assumed that the diodes do not conduct in the reverse direction. This is true for thermionic diodes; but if crystals are used, the finite value of back resistance must be taken into consideration. For good limiting, the resistance R must be chosen very large compared with R_f and very small compared with R_b. These two requirements may sometimes be incompatible. Hence, a figure of merit F of a crystal for such applications is $F \equiv R_b/R_f$. The larger the value of F, the better will be the crystal in a clipper circuit.

In the clipper circuits in which the diode appears as a shunt element, the input and output are separated by a large impedance during the time when the signal is transmitted. In the series circuits the connection is direct. For this reason the series circuits are sometimes preferred to the shunt circuits. The series circuits, on the other hand, have the disadvantage that at high frequencies or for abrupt waveforms the capacitance across the diode may provide a coupling path when the diode is cut off. Another inconvenience of the series circuit arises when the heater power for the diode is furnished by a grounded filament transformer. In this case the heater-cathode insulation must withstand the full signal voltage, which may attain values of several hundred volts. On the other hand, in the series circuits the impedance of the reference voltage E_R need not be kept low, since R is usually large, and E_R may in this case be derived from a tap on a bleeder.

When a diode clipper is used with fast waveforms, the capacitances associated with the circuit may not be neglected.

EXAMPLE. The clipper of Fig. 4-8a is to be used with the input waveform indicated. This input may represent a pulse or half a cycle of a square wave. The capacitance C_1 is the total effective capacitance shunting the diode (for which 5 $\mu\mu f$ is a reasonable value), while C_2 is the total capacitance shunting the output load resistor R ($\gg R_f$). The value $C_2 = 20$ $\mu\mu f$ is nominally the input capacitance of an oscilloscope probe which we might be using. Find the output waveform.

Solution. If the diode were perfect and the capacitances were neglected, the output waveform would be as shown in Fig. 4-8b.

Assume that a steady-state condition has been reached in which the input is -5 volts and the output is zero volts. Now let the input rise abruptly by 10 volts. If the source impedance is negligible, an impulsive current results and the initial output voltage rise is determined entirely by the capacitors. Since $C_2 = 4C_1$, only one-fifth of the input rise will appear across C_2; hence the output will jump abruptly by 2 volts. The voltage across the diode is now 3 volts and in the direction to make the diode conduct. The output e_o will rise to its final value of 5 volts with a time constant $\tau_1 = (C_1 + C_2)R_f$, where R_f is the forward resistance of the diode. Similarly, when the input voltage drops by 10 volts, the output voltage will drop abruptly by 2 volts. The cathode of the diode is now at $+3$ volts and the plate is at -5 volts. The diode will not conduct, and the decay of the output signal to zero will take place with a time constant $\tau_2 = (C_1 + C_2)R$. The resultant waveform is shown in Fig. 4-8c. Typically $R_f \cong 200$ ohms, so that $\tau_1 = 0.005$ μsec, which may well be small enough to be negligible. On the other hand, $\tau_2 = 25$ μsec, and if, say, $t_p \cong 50$ μsec, the slow decay on the trailing edge of the signal will be very apparent.

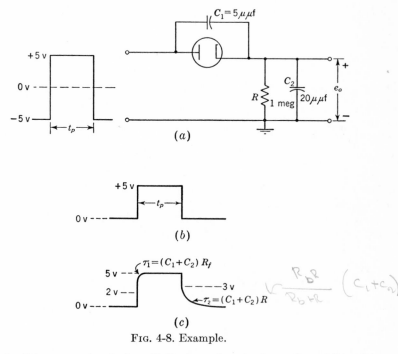

FIG. 4-8. Example.

Triode Clippers. A triode will limit a signal when the grid is driven beyond cutoff. The nominally infinite input impedance of a triode circuit as in Fig. 4-9a and the fact that the tube will also provide gain are often advantages of this circuit over that of the diode limiter. A typical dynamic transfer characteristic for a triode, the input voltage, and the load resistor current are shown in Fig. 4-9b. The sharpness of the break of the transfer characteristic in a triode is a function of the plate voltage. (High μ triodes give a sharper break than low μ triodes.) The break is less sharp as the plate voltage increases, and, except for very low plate voltages, is less sharp than in a diode. The break in a diode is appreciably more stable with respect to tube replacements than is the case with triodes.

If a resistor R is placed in series with the grid in Fig. 4-9a and if R is large compared with the grid resistance r_c, then limiting will occur whenever the applied voltage is such as to cause the flow of grid current. As discussed in Sec. 4-2, the break occurs within a few tenths of a volt of zero. Under these conditions we have said that the grid is clamped to the cathode and the corresponding plate current (I in Fig. 4-9) is the clamped current. Again it must be emphasized that the break is not due to any discontinuity in the transfer characteristic of the tube. It is

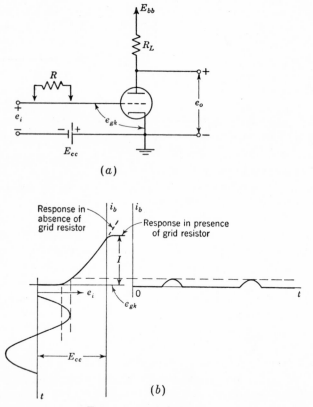

FIG. 4-9. A triode limiter.

due rather to the fact that, when the grid starts to draw current, the voltage at the grid is no longer the signal e_i. The sharpness of the break is comparable to that in a diode.

The circuit may be considered as being a combination of diode clipper together with a triode amplifier. If the series grid resistor is large enough ($\cong 1$ Meg), the sharpness of clipping at the occurrence of grid current may well be better than the sharpness obtained at cutoff. Further advantages of grid-current limiting over cutoff limiting are the following. Assume that the cathode temperature of the triode has increased. If the grid-to-cathode voltage remained the same, the plate current would increase. However, if the grid is drawing current, this current will simultaneously increase and, because of the resistance R, the grid-to-cathode voltage decreases. As a consequence the plate current remains more nearly constant. The resultant stability of the break associated with grid current permits this break to be used in precision circuits. Furthermore, when the tube is conducting, the output impedance is the parallel combination of r_p and R_L, while in the case of cutoff clipping the output impedance is R_L. The effect of capacitive loading on fast waveforms is therefore less for grid-current limiting than for cutoff limiting. On the other hand, the input capacitance is greater when the tube conducts and amplifies than when it is cut off and the gain is zero. Hence, the capacitive input impedance of a grid-current limiter will produce more distortion in a fast signal than will a cutoff limiter.

There is a third type of limiting possible with a triode. Consider the circuit of Fig. 4-9a, but without the series grid resistor which is necessary for grid-current limiting. The largest possible plate current is E_{bb}/R_L. If we apply to the grid, from a low impedance source, a signal large enough to make the plate current nearly equal to E_{bb}/R_L, limiting will take place. For example, if the tube is a type 5965 with $E_{bb} = 300$ and $R_L = 30$ K, the current will be about 10 ma and the break will be at $+2$ volts at the grid instead of zero (see Fig. 4-3). Such clipping is sometimes referred to as *plate-current saturation*, but it is not to be confused with any effect associated with maximum cathode emission. This type of limiting is also referred to as *bottoming*, since it results when the plate voltage has gone as low as it can and yet leave some tube voltage to supply the tube current. This type of limiting is not particularly stable, but it is still useful where precision is not required.

A cathode follower may also be used as limiter. The circuit has a low output impedance for the selected waveform. The input impedance is very high and essentially capacitive as long as grid current is not drawn. If the input swing is large enough to drive the grid-to-cathode voltage to zero or to a positive value, then the input impedance is essentially resistive and equal to $r_c/(1 - A)$, where A is the gain of the cathode follower. For example, for $r_c = 1$ K and $A = 0.95$, the input resistance is 20 K.

Pentode Clippers. Pentodes may be used as grid-current, cutoff, or saturation limiters. If a high value of plate load resistance is used so that the load line intersects the plate characteristics at the knee of the curves, then the bottoming takes place while the grid voltage is still negative. For example, for a 6AU6 tube with $E_{bb} = 300$, $R_L = 100$ K, and a screen voltage of 150 volts, the plate characteristics in **Fig. A-1** show that the limiting takes place at -2 volts on the grid.

As a cutoff limiter, a pentode with a fixed screen voltage may provide a sharper break than a triode. In a triode when the grid voltage changes from a value just below cutoff to a value just above cutoff, the plate voltage drops because of the plate resistor. The change in plate current is therefore smaller than in the case of a pentode with fixed screen voltage.

Clipping at Two Levels. The range of grid voltage for a triode or pentode between cutoff and zero grid voltage is referred to as the *grid base.* If the grid base is adjusted (by suitable choice of E_{bb} or screen

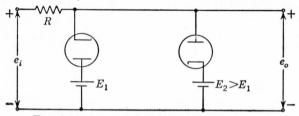

FIG. 4-10. A circuit for clipping at two levels.

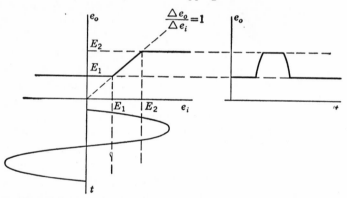

FIG. 4-11. Transfer characteristic of a double-ended limiter.

voltage) to be smaller than the peak-to-peak value of the input signal, then it is possible to clip both the positive and the negative extremes of the waveform. At the positive extremity, the clipping may be due either to grid clamping or plate bottoming. An amplifier operating under these conditions is said to be *overdriven.*

The diode clippers of Fig. 4-7 may be combined in pairs to perform the operation of double-ended limiting. A parallel, a series, or a series-parallel arrangement may be used. The parallel circuit is indicated in Fig. 4-10. Its transfer characteristic is given in Fig. 4-11, and is described by the following equations:

If $e_i < E_1$, $\qquad\qquad e_o = E_1$

If $e_i > E_2$, $\qquad\qquad e_o = E_2$ $\qquad\qquad$ (4-3)

If $E_1 < e_i < E_2$, $\qquad\qquad e_o = e_i$

This circuit has been referred to as a *slicer*, because the output contains a slice of the input between the two reference levels, as is indicated in Fig. 4-11.

This circuit has been used as a means of converting a sine wave into a square wave. In this application E_1 is negative and is made numerically equal to E_2. The transfer characteristic passes through the origin under this condition and the wave is clipped symmetrically top and bottom. If the peak of the sine wave is large compared with the reference levels then the output will be *squared*. More precise squaring circuits are described in Sec. 15-12.

A cathode-coupled clipper is indicated in Fig. 4-12. A sufficiently large positive excursion of e_i will cut off T_2, while a sufficiently large

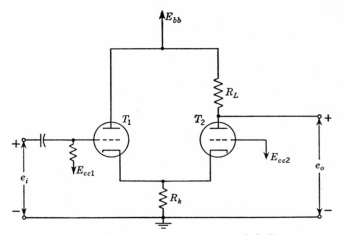

FIG. 4-12. A cathode-coupled double-ended clipper.

negative excursion of e_i will cut off T_1. Between the two clipping levels the circuit is a linear amplifier without inversion. The circuit has the advantage of high input impedance. E_{cc1} and E_{cc2} may be either positive or negative. If R_k is large, the input swing can be large without drawing grid current. By properly choosing E_{cc1} and E_{cc2} the input may be clipped symmetrically with respect to ground. Because of these features the circuit of Fig. 4-12 is an excellent double-ended clipper.

4-4. Compensation for Cathode-temperature Changes in Selectors.[7] It is possible to compensate for the shift of the volt-ampere characteristics of a diode caused by changes in heater voltage. As mentioned in Sec. 4-1, this effect is equivalent to a 0.1-volt lateral displacement in the characteristic for a 10 per cent change in heater voltage. Thus, the result can be simulated by adding a battery E_H in series with the cathode, the magnitude of E_H increasing with temperature, as in Fig. 4-13. It is seen that the selected voltage (the level at which limiting occurs) depends upon heater potential. Thus, assuming that $R_f \ll R$, where R_f is the diode forward resistance, we have

$$e_o = E_R \text{ if } e_i < E_R - E_H \quad \text{and} \quad e_o = e_i + E_H \text{ if } e_i > E_R - E_H \quad (4\text{-}4)$$

Compensation may be obtained by adding a second diode as indicated in Fig. 4-14. In order that the two fictitious batteries have the same

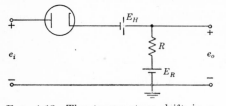

magnitude E_H, it is important that both diodes be in the same envelope or that they have a common heater supply. The circuit of E' and R' is chosen so that T_2 is always conducting. If $e_i < E_R$, T_1 does not conduct and $e_o = E_R$. If $e_i > E_R$, T_1 conducts and $e_o = e_i$. Note that these results are independent of the heater temperature.

FIG. 4-13. The temperature drift in a diode is represented by a fictitious battery E_H in series with the cathode.

In practice, it is found that the compensation is not perfect but can reduce the temperature dependence by a factor of 5 or 10.

The necessity for a separate ungrounded power supply E' can be avoided by using the circuit of Fig. 4-15a. If T_2 is in the conducting

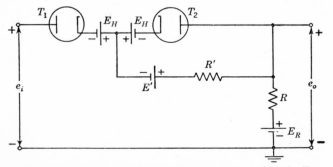

FIG. 4-14. T_2 compensates for the temperature drift in T_1.

state, then $e_o = E_R + E_H$. The diode T_1 will be in the nonconducting state if $e_i + E_H < e_o$. Hence,

$$e_o = E_R + E_H \quad \text{if } e_i < E_R \quad (4\text{-}5)$$

Similarly, when T_1 conducts, $e_o = e_i + E_H$ and T_2 will become nonconducting if $e_o > E_R + E_H$. Hence,

$$e_o = e_i + E_H \quad \text{if } e_i > E_R \quad (4\text{-}6)$$

The two tubes switch simultaneously from conducting to nonconducting states when the input voltage reaches the reference voltage independently of the heater temperature. An alternative arrangement in which the diode T_2 conducts continuously is shown in Fig. 4-15b.

It should be noted that the output voltage does depend upon the temperature (because e_o contains E_H). Often, however, the principal emphasis is on the constancy of the level at which selection takes place

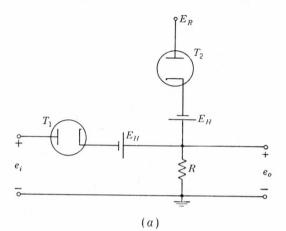

(a)

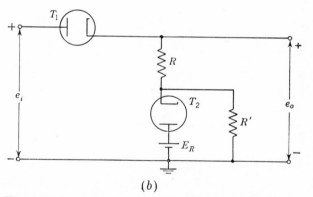

(b)

FIG. 4-15. T_2 compensates for the temperature drift in T_1.

(see Chap. 15 on Voltage Comparators) and this level was demonstrated above to be independent of E_H.

4-5. Clamping Circuits. Whenever a circuit point becomes connected through a low ($\cong$ zero) impedance to a reference voltage E_R, we say that the point has been *clamped* to E_R, since the voltage at the point will not be able to depart appreciably from E_R. The diode limiting circuit of Fig. 4-7a is an example of such a clamping circuit since the output voltage is clamped to E_R whenever the input voltage exceeds E_R. Since, in this case, the clamping prevents only an increase of the output voltage and not a decrease, the circuit is referred to as a *one-way clamp*.

Clamping is also used where it is required that a recurrent positive or negative extremity of a waveform be established at some fixed d-c level. A circuit which achieves this desired function without materially altering the waveform is sometimes referred to more specifically as a *d-c restorer*. Such d-c restoration or clamping is often required after a signal has passed through a capacitive coupling and has consequently lost its d-c component.

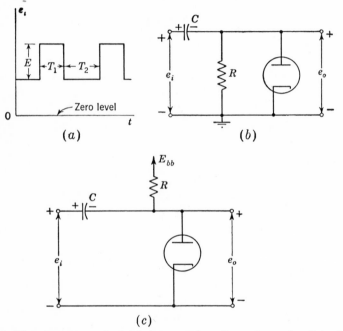

Fig. 4-16. The square wave in (*a*) is impressed on the restorer circuit in (*b*) or (*c*).

Consider that the waveform in Fig. 4-16*a* is applied to the input of the circuit of Fig. 4-16*b*. If the diode were not present, the d-c level of the output would be zero independently of the d-c level of the input. The output e_o would make excursions to voltages both positive and negative with respect to ground. In the presence of the diode, however, every time the voltage e_o would otherwise become positive, the output terminal is clamped to ground.

Current will flow in the diode, leaving the capacitor C with a charge as indicated by the polarity marking. If the resistor R were absent, the capacitor would charge, after a few cycles, to whatever voltage is required so that the maximum positive excursion of the signal leaves the diode just short of conducting. The output waveform would then appear as in Fig. 4-17, i.e., the maximum positive excursion has been fixed at zero volts. If now, however, the amplitude of the input signal should decrease in amplitude, and the maximum positive excursion is still to remain nominally zero, then the resistor R must be included to permit the capacitor to discharge. (For a crystal diode, the finite back resistance R_b of the crystal may serve as the resistor R.) In this case, however, the positive excursion must extend slightly into the positive region so that the diode may conduct and

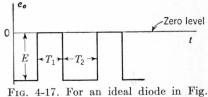

Fig. 4-17. For an ideal diode in Fig. 4-16, the output has its positive extremity clamped to ground.

supply the charge which will leak off the capacitor during the interval T_2.

The precision of operation of a d-c restorer depends, among other things, on the abruptness of the discontinuity of the volt-ampere characteristic of the diode. If the resistor R is very large, the quiescent current may be very small and the rate of change of slope of the volt-ampere characteristic of the diode (see Fig. 4-1b) may be smaller than would result if the quiescent current were larger. The quiescent current may be increased by returning the resistor R to some positive voltage

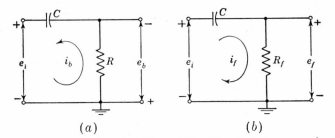

(a)   (b)

Fig. 4-18. The equivalent circuits of Fig. 4-16b. The diode is nonconducting in (a) and conducting in (b).

E_{bb} as in Fig. 4-16c. The level to which the peaks of the signal are restored will then be closer to zero voltage.

The equivalent circuit when the diode is nonconducting is given in Fig. 4-18a; that when the diode conducts, in Fig. 4-18b. We have assumed $R_b \gg R$ and $R \gg R_f$. If these inequalities are not valid, then we must replace the resistor in Fig. 4-18a by R and R_b in parallel and the resistor in Fig. 4-18b by R and R_f in parallel.

For the square-wave input of Fig. 4-16a, the resultant output waveform will appear as in Fig. 4-19. The equations from which to determine the four quantities E_1, E_1', E_2, and E_2' indicated in this figure are

$$E_1' = E_1 \epsilon^{-T_1/R_fC} \qquad E_1' - E_2 = E$$
$$E_2' = E_2 \epsilon^{-T_2/RC} \qquad E_1 - E_2' = E \qquad (4\text{-}7)$$

Note that these are identical with Eqs. (2-4) except that the first equation above contains R_f, whereas the first equation in Eq. (2-4) has R. This is an important physical difference because the charging time constant R_fC is very much shorter than the discharge time constant RC.

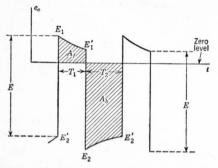

FIG. 4-19. The output from the circuit of Fig. 4-16 for a diode of finite forward resistance.

We shall now demonstrate that the area A_f under the output voltage curve in the forward direction (when the diode conducts) is related to the area A_b in the back direction (when the diode does not conduct) by the relationship

$$\frac{A_f}{A_b} = \frac{R_f}{R} \qquad (4\text{-}8)$$

If $e_f(t)$ is the output waveform in the forward direction, then the capacitor charging current $i_f = e_f/R_f$ (see Fig. 4-18b). Therefore the voltage acquired by the capacitor in the forward direction is

$$\frac{1}{C} \int_0^{T_1} i_f \, dt = \frac{1}{CR_f} \int_0^{T_1} e_f \, dt = \frac{A_f}{CR_f}$$

Similarly if $e_b(t)$ is the output voltage in the back direction, then the current which discharges the capacitor is $i_b = e_b/R$ and the voltage lost by the capacitor when the diode is nonconducting is

$$\frac{1}{C} \int_0^{T_2} i_b \, dt = \frac{1}{CR} \int_0^{T_2} e_b \, dt = \frac{A_b}{CR}$$

Under steady-state conditions the net voltage change per cycle across the capacitor is zero. Hence,

$$\frac{A_f}{CR_f} = \frac{A_b}{CR}$$

and Eq. (4-8) is justified. This proof did not assume that the input was a square wave. We can summarize the above most important conclusion as follows: *For any input waveform the ratio of the area under the output-voltage curve in the forward direction to that in the reverse direction must equal the ratio R_f/R.*

Let us return to the square-wave input of Fig. 4-16a. If $R_fC \gg T_1$, and $RC \gg T_2$, then the tilts indicated in Fig. 4-19 are negligible and the output will be a square wave. The zero level of the output square wave is determined by the above theorem.

EXAMPLE. *a.* The parameters in Fig. 4-16 are as follows: $E = 10$ volts, $T_1 = 1$ msec, $T_2 = 1$ μsec, $R_f = 500$ ohms, and $R = 500$ K. Assume that C is large enough so that the output is a square wave. Find the zero level of the output.

b. If the waveform is inverted so that $T_1 = 1$ μsec and $T_2 = 1$ msec, find the zero level of the output.

c. If the diode is inverted, but the input is as in part *b*, find the zero level of the output.

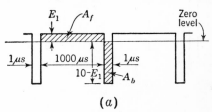

(a)

Solution.a. In Fig. 4-20a, $A_f = 1,000E_1$ and $A_b = 10 - E_1$ volts $\times$ μsec. From Eq. (4-8), we have

$$\frac{A_f}{A_b} = \frac{1,000E_1}{10 - E_1} = \frac{R_f}{R} = \frac{500}{500 \times 10^3} = 10^{-3}$$

and we find that $E_1 = 10^{-5}$ volt. This example illustrates that clamping to the baseline of a narrow negative pulse is excellent since only one-millionth of the amplitude of the input pulse is above the zero level.

b. In Fig. 4-20b, $A_f = E_1$ and

$$A_b = (1,000)(10 - E_1) \text{ volt} \times \mu\text{sec}$$

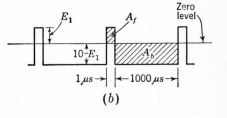

(b)

From Eq. (4-8), we have

$$\frac{E_1}{1,000(10 - E_1)} = 10^{-3}$$

or $E_1 = 5$ volts. The zero level is halfway up on the pulse amplitude, and the

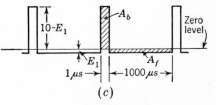

(c)

FIG. 4-20. Example.

circuit has acted as a very poor clamp. This example illustrates that it is extremely difficult to clamp to the top of a narrow positive pulse.

c. Positive voltages are now in the back direction and negative voltages are now in the forward direction, because the diode has been inserted in the circuit with the polarity oppositive to that indicated in Fig. 4-16b. Comparing Figs. 4-20c and a, we see that one is the negative of the other and hence $E_1 = 10^{-5}$ volt as in part a.

We note that the d-c level of the input did not enter into these calculations and hence has no effect on the output level.

We can summarize the results of this example by saying that it is very difficult to achieve d-c restoration to the peak (either positive or negative) of a narrow pulse, but we can very effectively clamp to the broad baseline. Application of such d-c restorers to radar and television pulses are common.

In the above example, a prohibitively large capacitor is needed to make the forward time constant R_fC large compared with 1,000 μsec. Because

R_f is very small and R is very large, it most frequently turns out that $R_fC \ll T_1$ and $RC \gg T_2$. Thus, typically a pulse-type waveform after restoration appears as in Fig. 4-21. During the interval T_2 there is a small tilt, while at the beginning of the interval T_1 a sharp spike appears. The capacitor recharges through the diode in a very short time, and during the remainder of the time T_1 no appreciable diode current flows.

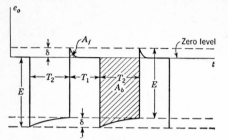

FIG. 4-21. The output from the circuit of Fig. 4-16b if $R_fC \ll T_1$ and $RC \gg T_2$.

The discussion above has neglected the output impedance R_o of the driving source. The restorer equivalent circuits including R_o are shown

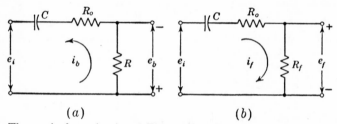

(a)   (b)

FIG. 4-22. The equivalent circuits of Fig. 4-16b taking the output impedance R_o of the source into account. The diode is nonconducting in (a) and conducting in (b).

in Fig. 4-22a and b. Typically the output impedance of vacuum-tube circuits varies from several hundred ohms to several thousand ohms. The shunt resistor R is usually of the order of megohms. Thus when the diode does not conduct, R_o is negligible in its influence on the output. However, when the diode conducts, as in Fig. 4-22b, there is an attenuation by a factor $R_f/(R_f + R_o)$, which may be appreciable. The finite output impedance thus has the effect of causing distortion, because the forward portion of the waveform is attenuated while the back portion is not. This is illustrated in Fig. 4-23 for a ramp voltage. The slope of the output above the zero output level is $R_f/(R_f + R_o)$ times the slope below the axis. It is assumed that $R_fC \gg T_1$ and $RC \gg T_2$ so that the only distortion is that due to the attenuation described above. The relationship $A_f/A_b = R_f/R$ is valid *independently*

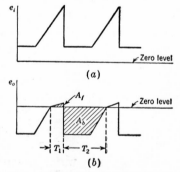

FIG. 4-23. (a) A sweep input to a restorer and (b) the output taking into account the finite source output impedance.

of the value of R_o, as can be verified by retracing the steps in the deriva-tion of Eq. (4-8).

If the diode in Fig. 4-16b is reversed, it is shown in the above example that the negative rather than the positive extremity of the signal will be established at zero. If the circuit is modified to include a fixed

voltage E_R, as in Fig. 4-24, the positive extremity (or negative ex-tremity, if the diode is reversed) will be established at E_R. This should be clear from Fig. 4-24c which gives the equivalent circuit in the forward direction. If $R_f = 0$, then the output is clearly E_R. In the reverse direction (Fig. 4-24b), the output is negative with respect to E_R. If the time constant RC is large enough, no appreciable distor-tion is introduced but the d-c level has been shifted so that the top of the wave is at E_R. If $R_f \neq 0$, then the clamping is not perfect. For example, if a square-wave input is applied to the circuit of Fig. 4-24, the output will be given by Fig. 4-19 with the difference that the line marked "zero level" is now at E_R volts with respect to ground.

Clamping may be accomplished in the grid circuit of a multielement tube (triode or pentode) as in Fig. 4-25a. The operation is identical to that described above, the grid and cathode of the tube serving as the elements of the diode. The

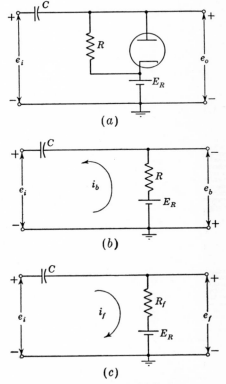

FIG. 4-24. (a) A circuit which clamps to a voltage E_R. (b) The equivalent circuit if the diode is nonconducting and $R_b \gg R$. (c) The equivalent circuit if the diode conducts and $R \gg R_f$.

circuit has an interesting application. Suppose that it is intended to use the circuit as a conventional amplifier but that circumstances exist which make it inconvenient to use bias of any sort. The clamping action in the circuit will adjust the d-c level of the signal between grid and cathode to be negative except for a very small part of the cycle when the grid draws current. That is, the circuit has provided its own bias. During the small part of the cycle when grid current flows the signal may be somewhat distorted if the signal source impedance is high, but this distortion may be kept very small by making R_g very large.

The circuit of Fig. 4-25b results if the resistor R_g at the grid is returned to the other side of the capacitor instead of to ground. This circuit is the self-biasing arrangement commonly used in oscillator circuits. If the resistor R_g is returned to the E_{bb} supply voltage as indicated in Fig. 4-25c, we have the clamping arrangement mentioned in Sec. 4-2 in connection with the discussion of grid-current characteristics. This circuit is very commonly used in pulse applications. The three circuits of Fig. 4-25 are essentially alike in behavior. In the forward direction the grid is clamped to ground (if $R_f = 0$). Hence, under steady-state conditions, the capacitor acquires a voltage equal to the positive maximum value of the input signal with respect to ground. This capacitor voltage acts as a self-bias. In the reverse direction the capacitor discharges only very slightly through R_g, provided that the time constant R_gC is large compared with the period of the input signal.

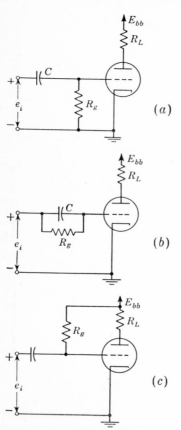

FIG. 4-25. Three methods of obtaining self-bias by clamping the grid to ground.

4-6. Synchronized Clamping. The d-c restorers discussed above are examples of clamping circuits in which the time during which the clamping is effective is controlled by the signal itself. Useful features result when the time of clamping is not determined directly by the signal but is determined rather by an auxiliary voltage called a *control signal* which occurs synchronously with the signal. For example, suppose the waveform of Fig. 4-26a is to be used to displace the beam of a cathode-ray tube linearly with time, first in one direction and then in the other direction from some fixed initial point. If the signal is transmitted through an a-c coupling network whose low-frequency time constant is not very long in comparison with the interval T_1, the signal will distort into the form shown in Fig. 4-26b. The principal defect in the waveform is that the two displacements will start from different places (A and B). In addition the d-c level E_R has been lost. If, however, the signal is passed through the circuit of Fig. 4-27 and if switch S is closed during time T_2 and is open during time T_1, the waveform will appear as in Fig. 4-26c.

The pips which appear when the voltage returns to the level E_R will be reduced to infinitesimally narrow spikes as the resistance of the switch (R_f) approaches zero.

It is, of course, required that the switch S be open for all the time interval T_1, but it is not necessary that the switch be closed for the entire interval T_2. It is only required that the switch be closed for a period long enough to allow the capacitor C to acquire or lose enough charge to bring the output terminal to the reference level E_R.

It is not possible to use synchronized clamping with a signal of arbitrary waveform. For example, if the waveform were sinusoidal, it would necessarily be distorted every time the switch S closed. Synchronous clamping may be used whenever the signal has intervals, which occur periodically, during which the input waveform is quiescent. Where synchronized clamp-

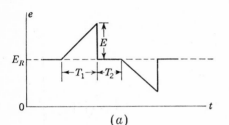

(a)

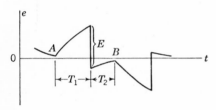

(b)

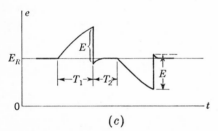

(c)

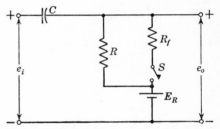

Fig. 4-26. Illustrating the necessity for synchronized clamping for a signal which may vary in both directions from some reference level.

Fig. 4-27. Switch S closes in synchronism with the signal during those intervals when it is desired that the output be clamped to E_R.

ing is feasible, it may be used to provide d-c restoration even when the positive and negative excursions of the signal fluctuate from cycle to cycle.

The switch S in Fig. 4-27 can be simulated with the double triode arrangement[8] given in Fig. 4-28. The grids are tied through a large resistance R' to the E_{bb} supply voltage. Assume that no control signal is applied to these grids. Tube T_2 prevents the output from going positive with respect to E_R, while tube T_1 prevents the output from going negative with respect to E_R. The output is restrained from departing in either direction from the reference voltage E_R. Hence this circuit is referred to as a *two-way clamp.*

If now a negative gate is applied to the grids so as to release the clamping action, $e_o = e_i$ and the input is transmitted to the output. The control signal in Fig. 4-28 must be exactly synchronous with the signal in

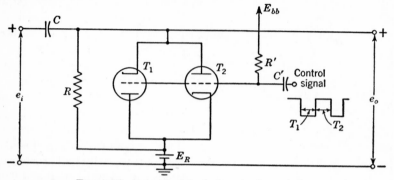

FIG. 4-28. A synchronized clamp using triodes.

Fig. 4-26. In practice, this synchronization offers no difficulty because the sweep voltage of Fig. 4-26 is generated from the control square wave itself (see Chaps. 7 and 8).

There are two chief difficulties encountered with the circuit of Fig. 4-28. The first is that during the interval T_2 the control signal will cause grid current to flow through tube T_1 and into the output. The

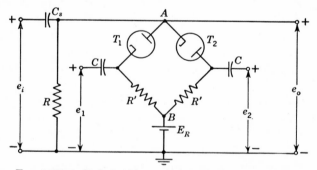

FIG. 4-29. A diode bridge used as a synchronous clamp.

second difficulty is that the control voltage is coupled to the output through the interelectrode capacitances of the tubes. Hence, the output will contain pips or spikes at the beginning and end of the control interval.

The above difficulties are avoided in the circuit of Fig. 4-29 which uses diodes in a balanced bridge arrangement. Two control signals e_1 and e_2 which have the symmetrical form indicated in Fig. 4-30 are required for proper operation of the circuit. These waveforms can be obtained from any of the phase-inverter circuits in Chap. 1. The d-c level of the signals e_1 and e_2 may be arbitrary. During the interval T_n the diodes are nonconducting and the output is free to follow the input so that $e_o = e_i$. During the interval T_c the diodes conduct, and because of the symmetry of the circuit, point A is at the same potential as point B. The output is clamped to E_R through an effective resistance equal to the sum of a diode resistance and the control-source signal impedance R_o (assuming that $R' \gg R_o$).

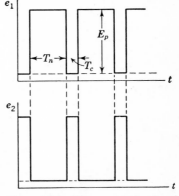

More details on the above circuit are given in Sec. 14-13. Other gating circuits which can be used as synchronous clamps are given in Chap. 14.

4-7. Tubes Used as Switches. Amplifier tubes (triodes and pentodes) are often used in applications where they act essentially as switches. In these applications the tube is periodically driven either to cutoff (switch open) or to clamp (switch closed). Such tube circuits are often called "overdriven amplifiers." Diodes are also often used as switches to change

Fig. 4-30. The control signal waveforms required for the clamp in Fig. 4-29.

the impedance between two points from a low to high value, and vice versa. These switching circuits not only are of interest in themselves but also serve as further examples of wave shaping with nonlinear elements. The principles established above in connection with clipping and clamping circuits are useful in analyzing these circuits.

Tube Switch with Resistive Load. In Fig. 4-31a is shown a triode with a resistive plate load. To the grid of this tube is applied the square wave of arbitrary d-c level, as shown in Fig. 4-31b. The square wave is to be used to turn the tube on and off periodically. With respect to the waveform at the grid the situation here is identical to that discussed in connection with Fig. 4-21. The grid waveform is shown in Fig. 4-31c. Note that the overshoot in the grid waveform is reflected in the undershoot of the plate waveform shown in Fig. 4-31d.

In any particular case the numerical values of the levels attained by the waveforms are easily calculated. Suppose that the square-wave amplitude is E. At the beginning of the interval T_2 the voltage e_{gk} will be at $-E$ but will start to rise exponentially toward E_{bb} with a time constant $\tau = (R_g + R_o)C$. Since the output impedance R_o of the source is usually small compared with the grid leak R_g, then $\tau \cong R_g C$. At the end of the interval T_2 the voltage attains the level $-E'$. If it were not for grid clamping, the overshoot would be $E - E'$. However, because of the

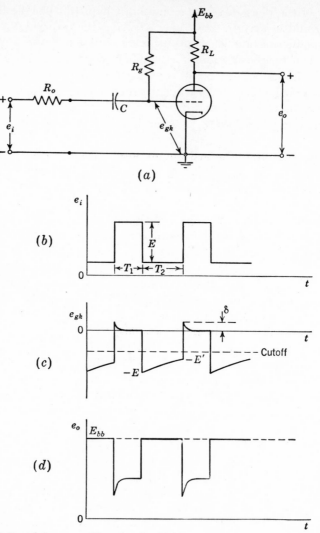

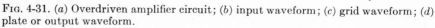

FIG. 4-31. (a) Overdriven amplifier circuit; (b) input waveform; (c) grid waveform; (d) plate or output waveform.

drop through R_o due to the grid current, the overshoot δ will be smaller and is equal to

$$\delta = (E - E') \frac{r_c}{r_c + R_o} \tag{4-9}$$

in which r_c is the grid-to-cathode resistance. The undershoot in the plate waveform is determined by the intersection of the load line for R_L with the volt-ampere characteristic curve for the tube corresponding to the grid voltage δ at the overshoot. This load line will of course have to be drawn on a set of tube characteristics in which curves are given for positive grid voltages.

If the overshoot should be objectionable in a particular application, it could be made smaller if r_c could be reduced.   Since r_c is usually not

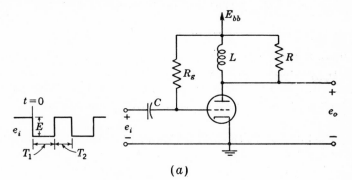

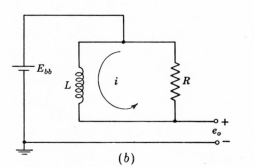

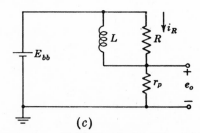

FIG. 4-32. (a) A peaking circuit.   (b) The equivalent circuit when the tube is cut off. (c) The equivalent circuit when the tube is in clamp.

adjustable, the overshoot may be reduced by making the time constant $R_g C \gg T_2$, since under these conditions $E' \cong E$.

Tube Switch with Inductive Load (Peaking).   The circuit of Fig. 4-32 shows a peaking coil L shunted by a damping resistor R in the plate circuit of a tube, the grid of which is initially clamped to the cathode. In the quiescent state the plate current I_0 corresponding to $e_c \cong 0$ and

$e_b = E_{bb}$ flows through the inductor. During the time interval T_1 a negative step of magnitude E cuts the tube off. The equivalent circuit in this interval is indicated in Fig. 4-32b, and the instantaneous current i must decrease exponentially with the time constant L/R. Since the initial current is I_0, the output voltage is

$$e_o = E_{bb} + I_0R\epsilon^{-Rt/L} \tag{4-10}$$

This voltage is indicated as the positive spike in Fig. 4-33. The peak of the pulse attains a value $E_{bb} + I_0R$ which may become very large if R is large. In practice, the peak may be limited by stray capacitance, but even so peak values several times larger than the supply voltage may be attained.

During the interval T_2 the grid is clamped to the cathode and the tube behaves like a resistor r_p, the plate resistance corresponding to $e_c = 0$. The equivalent circuit is indicated in Fig. 4-32c. Since r_p is not truly

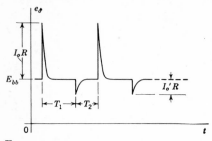

FIG. 4-33. The plate voltage of Fig. 4-32. The interval T_1 starts at $t = 0$.

constant, the current i_R in the damping resistor at the instant $t = T_1+$ is best found by a graphical construction rather than from the equivalent circuit. Since the current through the inductor cannot change instantaneously, it acts as an open circuit at $t = T_1+$. Hence a load line is drawn on the plate characteristics corresponding to R and E_{bb} and the intersection of this line and the plate curve for $e_c = 0$ gives the current I_0' at $t = T_1+$. This current then decreases exponentially to zero with a time constant given by L/R', where R' is the parallel combination of R and r_p. If t' is measured from the instant $t = T_1$, then the output is given by

$$e_o = E_{bb} - I_0'R\epsilon^{-R't'/L} \tag{4-11}$$

This voltage is indicated as the negative spike in Fig. 4-33. Since I_0 corresponds to a zero-resistance load line whereas I_0' corresponds to a resistance R, then the negative peak is always less than the positive peak. The voltage at the peak of the negative spike is the voltage corresponding to the intersection of the load line for the resistor R and the tube characteristic for $e_c = 0$. This voltage will always be positive with respect to ground. The negative pulses decay slower than do the positive pulses because R' is always less than R. This output should be compared with the voltage obtained from this peaking circuit (see Fig. 2-22) when it is operating linearly (i.e., with an input square wave of small amplitude).

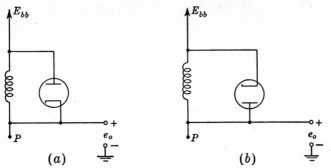

Fig. 4-34. (a) The damper diode allows the output only to go positive with respect to E_{bb}. (b) The diode allows the output only to go negative with respect to E_{bb}.

The above discussion has neglected the capacitance shunting the output terminals. If this capacitance is taken into account, we can have responses similar to those discussed in Sec. 2-7. For example, if the

circuit is underdamped, each pulse in Fig. 4-33 will be converted into a train of oscillations. Because the damping is greater when the tube conducts than when it is noncon- ducting, it is possible to have oscil- lations near $t = 0$ instead of the positive peak and at the same time a single negative pip near $t = T_1$.

In the above discussion we as- sumed that the clamping action at the grid was perfect. If the finite value of r_c is taken into account and the grid time constant is not large enough, there will be a slight over- shoot in grid voltage above the value $e_c = 0$ at $t = T_1+$ and I'_0 will correspond to this positive grid voltage.

Damper Diodes. If, in the peak- ing circuit just discussed, it is de- sired to have only positive output pulses, we can connect a diode across the coil as indicated in Fig. 4-34a. If the output voltage tries

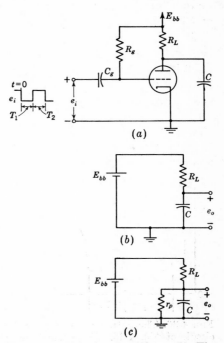

Fig. 4-35. (a) An amplifier. (b) The equivalent circuit when the tube is cut off. (c) The equivalent circuit when the tube is in clamp.

to fall below E_{bb}, the diode conducts and the small forward resistance of the diode quickly damps out this portion of the waveform. If, in Fig. 4-33, there were oscillations in the vicinity of $t = 0$, the diode of Fig.

4-34a would allow only the *first* positive peak to appear in the output because of the heavy damping which it imposes on the ringing circuit. This action accounts for the name *damper diode.*

If the damper diode is inserted across the peaking coil with the polarity indicated in Fig. 4-34b, then the output will contain a *single* negative peak in the vicinity of $t = T_1$. In this case the diode conducts whenever the output voltage tries to rise above E_{bb}.

Tube Switch with Resistor-Capacitor Load. Consider the amplifier circuit of Fig. 4-35. The total capacitance from plate to ground is designated by C. The tube is in clamp, and the quiescent plate current I_0 is found from the intersection of the load line (corresponding to E_{bb} and R_L) and the plate characteristic for $e_c = 0$. At $t = 0+$ the tube is cut off by the negative input step of magnitude E which is larger than the grid base of the tube. The equivalent circuit is indicated in Fig. 4-35b, and the output will rise exponentially with a time constant $R_L C$ to the plate-supply voltage E_{bb}. During the interval T_2 the tube is in clamp and the equivalent circuit is given in Fig. 4-35c, where r_p represents the plate resistance for zero grid voltage. The time constant of the circuit is now $R'C$, where R' is the parallel combination of R_L and r_p. Since R' must be smaller than R_L, the output falls faster than it rises, as indicated by the solid curve in Fig. 4-36. For a pentode this difference in time constants may be negligible because r_p is usually very much greater than R_L, but for a triode there will be an appreciable difference in rise and fall times.

If the finite value of r_c is taken into account and the grid time constant is not large enough, there will be an overshoot in grid voltage at $t = T_1+$ and the output voltage may fall below $E_{bb} - I_0 R_L$ and then increase toward this value, as indicated by the dashed curve in Fig. 4-36.

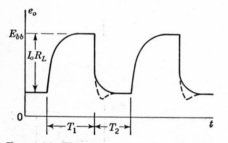

In drawing the waveform of Fig. 4-36, we have implicitly assumed that the plate time constants were small compared with the period of the square wave. If instead of this condition we assume that $R_L C$ is much greater than T_1, then the exponential rise can be approximated by a linear increase. The circuit behaves as an integrator and the output is a ramp voltage. This sweep circuit is discussed in detail in Chap. 7.

Fig. 4-36. The output waveform for the circuit of Fig. 4-35. The dashed curve takes imperfect clamping into account.

Plate-catching Diode. The effective rise time of the output of Fig. 4-35 can be shortened by clipping off the top of the wave. The diode which is used for this purpose (T_1 in Fig. 4-37) is called a *plate-catching diode* because it catches the plate at the voltage E_2 which is lower than the voltage E_{bb} to which the plate would return if the diode were not present. For example, if the output swing is reduced 20 per cent by the clipping action, the rise time is approximately one-half its original value.

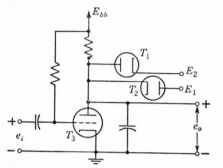

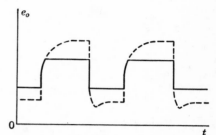

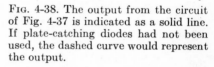

FIG. 4-37. Plate-catching diodes added to the circuit of Fig. 4-35. E_1 and E_2 are d-c bias voltages, with $E_2 > E_1$.

FIG. 4-38. The output from the circuit of Fig. 4-37 is indicated as a solid line. If plate-catching diodes had not been used, the dashed curve would represent the output.

A second diode T_2 is added at the plate in Fig. 4-37 with its polarity reversed from that of T_1 and with its plate at the voltage E_1. This second plate-catching diode will not allow the output voltage to drop below the clipping level E_1. The output voltage is now sensibly square

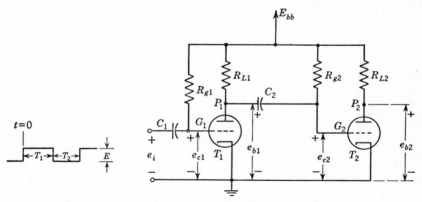

FIG. 4-39. An overdriven two-stage RC coupled amplifier.

as indicated in Fig. 4-38. This arrangement is similar to the double-ended clipper of Fig. 4-10.

4-8. An Overdriven Two-stage RC Coupled Amplifier. The circuit of this cascaded amplifier is shown in Fig. 4-39. We shall assume that all shunt capacitances are negligible, since we have already considered their effect in connection with Fig. 4-35. Furthermore, we shall assume that the clamping at G_1 is perfect, since we have already taken into account the finite value of r_{c1} in Fig. 4-36. We shall also assume that at $t = 0-$ the voltage at G_1 is $e_{c1} = -E$, where E is larger than the grid base $|E_{co1}|$ of T_1. Hence at $t = 0-$ the voltage at P_1 is $e_{b1} = E_{bb}$; at G_2 the voltage

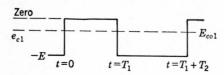

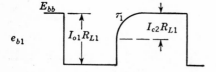

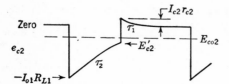

is $e_{c2} = 0$; at P_2 the voltage is $e_{b2} = E_{bb} - I_{02}R_{L2}$, where I_{02} is the clamped plate current in tube T_2. These voltages are indicated in Fig. 4-40.

At $t = 0+$, e_{c1} returns to zero and tube T_1 is in clamp. The plate P_1 drops in potential. This causes G_2 to fall and cut off T_2. The equivalent circuit for computing e_{c2} at this instant is indicated in Fig. 4-41. If the current in R_{g2} is neglected in comparison with that in R_{L1}, then the current in R_{L1} will be the clamped current I_{01}. The voltage at P_1 drops by $I_{01}R_{L1}$, and

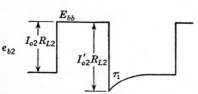

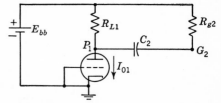

Fig. 4-40. The waveforms for the circuit of Fig. 4-39.

Fig. 4-41. Equivalent circuit of Fig. 4-39 when T_1 is in clamp and T_2 is cut off.

since the voltage across C_2 cannot change instantaneously, the voltage at G_2 must drop by this same amount, as indicated in Fig. 4-40. Since T_2 is now cut off, $e_{b2} = E_{bb}$.

From Fig. 4-41 we see that for $R_{g2} \gg R_{L1}$ the time constant τ_2 with which the voltage at G_2 changes is approximately given by $\tau_2 = R_{g2}C_2$. At $t = 0+$, $e_{c2} = -I_{01}R_{L1}$ and if permitted to do so e_{c2} would approach E_{bb} asymptotically. Hence, the grid voltage is given by

$$e_{c2} = E_{bb} - (E_{bb} + I_{01}R_{L1})\epsilon^{-t/\tau_2} \tag{4-12}$$

At $t = T_1-$, $e_{c2} = E'_{c2}$. We shall assume that $T_1 \ll \tau_2$ so that E'_{c2} is below the cutoff voltage E_{co2} of tube T_2.

At $t = T_1+$, e_{c1} drops to $-E$ and cuts off tube T_1. The voltage at P_1 tries to rise and in so doing causes G_2 to be driven positively. The equivalent circuit for the calculation of e_{c2} under these conditions is indicated in Fig. 4-42.   The grid current is made up of two components: i_{c2} which flows through the load resistor R_{L1} and is of the order of magnitude of milliamperes and i' which flows through the grid resistor R_{g2} and is of the order of magnitude of micro-amperes.   We shall neglect i' compared with i_{c2} and then the calculation of i_{c2} is very simple.   From Kirchhoff's voltage law, we have

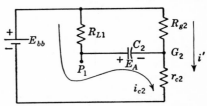

$$-E_{bb} + i_{c2}R_{L1} + E_A \\ + i_{c2}r_{c2} = 0 \quad (4\text{-}13)$$

FIG. 4-42. Equivalent circuit of Fig. 4-39 when T_1 is cut off.

where E_A is the capacitor voltage. The voltage E_A at $t = T_1-$ is $E_{bb} - I_{01}R_{L1} - E'_{c2}$. Since the voltage across a capacitor cannot change instantaneously, then, at $t = T_1+$,

$$E_A = E_{bb} - I_{01}R_{L1} - E'_{c2} \qquad (4\text{-}14)$$

Substituting this value of E_A into Eq. (4-13), we obtain at $t = T_1+$,

$$i_{c2} = \frac{I_{01}R_{L1} + E'_{c2}}{R_{L1} + r_{c2}} \equiv I_{c2} \qquad (4\text{-}15)$$

The voltage at P_1 at $t = T_1+$ is $e_{b1} = E_{bb} - I_{c2}R_{L1}$.   The voltage at G_2 at $t = T_1+$ is $I_{c2}r_{c2}$ and is of the order of a few volts positive.   If the plate current of tube T_2 corresponding to this grid voltage is I'_{02}, then $e_{b2} = E_{bb} - I'_{02}R_{L2}$ at $t = T_1+$.

For $t > T_1$, e_{c1} rises exponentially toward E_{bb} with a time constant C_1R_{g1}.   If $C_1R_{g1} \gg T_2$, then at $t = T_1 + T_2$, $e_{c1} \cong -E$, which we have assumed to be below the cutoff voltage of tube T_1.   From Fig. 4-42 we see that the time constant τ_1 for the grid current of T_2 is given approximately by

$$\tau_1 = (R_{L1} + r_{c2})C_2$$

Hence, e_{b1}, e_{c2}, and e_{b2} all vary exponentially with the time constant τ_1 toward the steady-state values indicated in Fig. 4-40.   The waveforms are drawn on the assumption that $T_2 \gg \tau_1$.

Incidentally, since the voltage across C_2 cannot change instantaneously, then the jump in voltage at G_2 must equal the jump in voltage at P_1 at $t = T_1$, or

$$I_{c2}r_{c2} - E'_{c2} = I_{01}R_{L1} - I_{c2}R_{L1} \qquad (4\text{-}16)$$

This equation is equivalent to Eq. (4-15).

Since at $t = (T_1 + T_2)-$ the voltages in Fig. 4-40 are the same as the corresponding values at $t = 0-$, then this figure depicts one steady-state cycle of waveforms.   Hence, the above analysis completes the solution.

4-9. Cathode Follower with Capacitive Load. A cathode follower with a capacitive load is shown in Fig. 4-43a. We may easily verify from the 12AT7 tube characteristics in Fig. A-5 that, neglecting the effect of the capacitor, the allowable input grid swing from cutoff to the point of grid-current flow is approximately from -107 to $+92$ volts. When the input signal is a fast waveform, the effect of the capacitance is to reduce the allowable input swing to the grid base, as will now be shown.

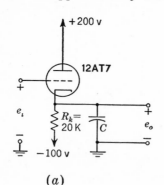

(a)

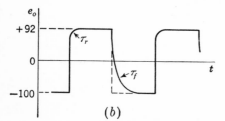

(b)

FIG. 4-43. (a) Cathode follower with capacitive load; (b) output waveform.

Suppose that the tube is biased initially at zero grid-to-cathode voltage ($e_i = 92$ volts) and that a negative step is applied which is larger in amplitude than the grid base. Because of the presence of the capacitor C the cathode can not instantaneously follow this abrupt drop in grid voltage, and as a result the tube will be driven to cutoff. The capacitor C must now start an exponential discharge toward -100 volts with a time constant R_kC. If, typically, $R_k = 20$ K and $C = 100$ $\mu\mu$f, the time constant of the fall will be $\tau_f = 20 \times 10^3 \times 100 \times 10^{-6}$ μsec $= 2$ μsec. If the negative step is larger than $107 + 92 = 199$ volts, the tube will remain cut off as the cathode falls. If the applied negative step is smaller than 199 volts, the tube will enter its grid base before the cathode voltage attains its asymptotic limit of -100 volts, and the last part of the decay will occur with a time constant R_oC, R_o being the output impedance of the cathode follower.

Similarly, suppose that the tube is initially biased at cutoff ($e_i = -107$ volts) and that a positive step is applied at the grid which is larger than the grid base. Then, again, the cathode will not be able to respond instantaneously to the grid signal, and the grid will be driven positive with respect to the cathode. The capacitor C will now charge from an impedance that is the parallel combination of R_o and r_c, where r_c is the grid-to-cathode resistance. If the input-signal amplitude is less than 199 volts, the last part of the rise of cathode voltage will occur with a time constant R_oC. The rise of cathode voltage will be more rapid than the fall, but the usefulness of the cathode follower for a fast positive-going signal is limited because of the flow of grid current.

The waveform of Fig. 4-43b shows the response of the cathode follower to a square-wave signal e_i which makes positive excursions above 92 volts and negative excursions below -107 volts and whose period is comparable to the time constant R_kC.

REFERENCES

1. Chance, B., et al.: "Waveforms," Massachusetts Institute of Technology Radiation Laboratory Series, vol. 19, pp. 58–81, McGraw-Hill Book Company, Inc., New York, 1949.
2. Millman, J., and S. Seely: "Electronics," 2d ed., p. 108, McGraw-Hill Book Company, Inc., New York, 1951.
3. Shulman, R. G., and M. E. McMahon: Recovery Currents in Germanium p-n Junction Diodes, *J. Appl. Phys.*, vol. 214, pp. 1267–1272, October, 1953.
   Firle, T. E., M. E. McMahon, and J. F. Roach: Recovery Time Measurements on Point-contact Germanium Diodes, *Trans. IRE (Professional Group on Electron Devices)*, vol. ED-1, no. 2, pp. 27–33, April, 1954.
4. Ref. 2, chap. 16.
5. Valley, G. E., Jr., and H. Wallman: "Vacuum Tube Amplifiers," Massachusetts Institute of Technology Radiation Laboratory Series, vol. 18, p. 418, McGraw-Hill Book Company, Inc., New York, 1948.
6. Ref. 2, p. 336.
7. Ref. 1, p. 333.
8. Ref. 1, p. 377.

CHAPTER 5

THE BISTABLE MULTIVIBRATOR

A bistable multivibrator or binary* is a two-tube regenerative circuit which can exist indefinitely in either of two stable states and can be caused to make an abrupt transition from one state to the other. The binary finds extensive application in pulse circuitry. It is used not only

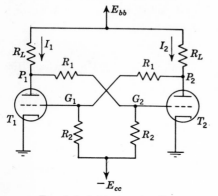

FIG. 5-1. A binary circuit.

for the generation of square waves from pulses but also for the performance of certain digital operations, such as counting.

5-1. The Stable States of a Binary.[1] The circuit diagram of a binary is shown in Fig. 5-1. Note that each tube is an amplifier, the plate of which is d-c coupled to the grid of the other tube. The plate load resistor R_L is usually of the order of magnitude of the plate-circuit resistor to be found in a conventional amplifier, i.e., several times the plate resistance of the tube. Since the fraction of the plate signal which is coupled across to the grid depends only on the ratio of the resistors R_1 and R_2, these resistors are usually made large enough to avoid loading the amplifier output excessively. In a typical case, for a type 5965 vacuum tube, R_L will lie in the range 10 to 50 K, while R_1 and R_2 are of the same order of magnitude and lie in the range 100 to 500 K.

Because of the symmetry of the circuit we might expect that the quiescent current in each of the tubes will be the same. Such would indeed be the case if both tubes were cut off or both were in clamp.

* The bistable multivibrator is also known as the Eccles-Jordan circuit (after the inventors) and as the "flip-flop" circuit. The authors suggest that, if colloquial expressions are to be used, the designation "flip-flip" is more appropriate for the bistable multivibrator and that the term "flip-flop" be reserved for the monostable multivibrator (Chap. 6). In this text we shall, however, refer to the circuit as a "binary" since this latter term is short and suggests the essential character of the circuit. The word "binary" will be used as a noun and will be understood to mean "two-vacuum-tube bistable circuit."

These cases are, however, of no interest to us. The important case is the one in which both tubes would be operating normally (with the grid voltage within the grid base) if the currents were identical. In such a circumstance, it is possible to find tube currents $I_1 = I_2$ which are consistent with the tube characteristics and with Kirchhoff's laws and hence such a state of the binary is an equilibrium state. This state, however, is one of *unstable* equilibrium, as may be seen from the following considerations.

Suppose that there should be the most minute fluctuation in the current I_1. If I_1 increases, the voltage at the plate P_1 will decrease, the voltage change at P_1 will be amplified and inverted in polarity by tube T_2, and the grid of T_1 will become more positive. As a consequence the current I_1 increases still further and the cycle of events repeats itself. The current I_1 continues to increase, while the current I_2 continues to decrease, the circuit moving progressively further away from its initial condition. This action takes place because of the regenerative feedback incorporated in the circuit, and will occur only if the loop gain of the circuit is larger than unity. The speed with which the regenerative action takes place is limited by the shunt capacitances. These capacitances are neglected for the present since we are interested now only in the stable states.

From the above discussion it is clear that a *stable* state of a binary is one in which the currents and voltages satisfy Kirchhoff's laws and are consistent with the tube characteristics and in which, in addition, the condition is satisfied that the loop gain is less than unity. The condition with respect to the loop gain will certainly be satisfied if either of the two tubes is below cutoff or if either of the two tubes is tightly clamped as would be the case if the grid draws current which must flow through a resistance which is large in comparison with the grid-cathode resistance r_c. In principle, in order that the binary be in a stable state, it would be sufficient *either* that one of the tubes be below cutoff *or* that one of the tubes be in clamp. Actually, for certain practical reasons to be discussed shortly, the arrangement almost invariably employed is one in which one of the tubes is in clamp *and* the other is below cutoff.

The procedure for calculating the circuit currents and voltages in a stable state is particularly simple if we take advantage of the fact that R_1 and R_2 are large in comparison with R_L and large also in comparison with the grid-to-cathode resistance r_c. In such a case the tube which is in clamp will be tightly clamped and we shall not make a serious error if we consider that the grid-to-cathode voltage is zero. Furthermore, in such a case the tube currents may be considered to be identical to the currents through the load resistors R_L. A typical calculation is given in the following illustrative example.

EXAMPLE. Compute the stable-state currents and voltages for the binary circuit of Fig. 5-2. The triodes are the two sections of a type 5965 vacuum tube (Fig. A-11).

Solution. Assume that tube T_1 is cut off and tube T_2 is in clamp with a grid-to-cathode voltage equal to zero. The plate voltage of T_1 is calculated from the equivalent circuit of Fig. 5-3a. We find that $E_{b1} = 250 \times 220/(220 + 47) = 206$ volts.

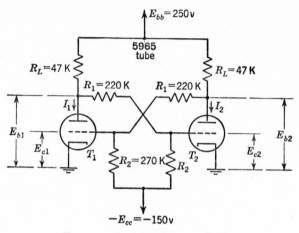

FIG. 5-2. A typical binary circuit.

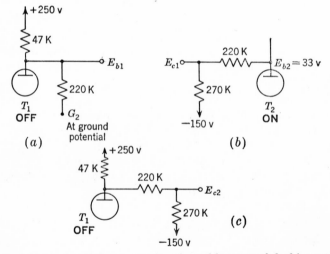

FIG. 5-3. Equivalent circuits for computing the stable states of the binary circuit with the parameters given in Fig. 5-2.

To find the plate voltage at T_2, we neglect the loading of R_1 and R_2 and draw a load line corresponding to 47 K on the plate characteristics of the tube. The plate current and voltage for $E_{c2} = 0$ are found to be $E_{b2} = 33$ volts and $I_2 = 4.6$ ma.

We must now check to see whether or not T_1 is indeed cut off and T_2 is in clamp. The grid voltage of T_1 is calculated from the equivalent circuit of Fig. 5-3b. The voltage E_{c1} is calculated by superposition to be

$$E_{c1} = 33 \frac{270}{220 + 270} + (-150) \frac{220}{220 + 270} = -49 \text{ volts}$$

Since, at a plate-to-cathode voltage of 206 volts, cutoff occurs at -8 volts, T_1 is well below cutoff. If the grid of T_2 were not drawing grid current, then, from the equivalent circuit drawn in Fig. 5-3c, the voltage E_{c2} would be

$$E_{c2} = 250 \frac{270}{220 + 270 + 47} + (-150) \frac{220 + 47}{220 + 270 + 47} = 50 \text{ volts}$$

This 50 volts is applied to the grid of T_2 from a source whose Thévenin equivalent impedance is essentially equal to the parallel combination of R_1 and R_2. This equivalent impedance is 122 K. If we calculate the grid voltage by considering that the grid-to-cathode resistance is $r_c = 250$ ohms (see Sec. 4-2), we have

$$E_{c2} = 50 \frac{0.250}{122} = 0.10 \text{ volt}$$

This same result can be obtained by multiplying the short-circuit current by the impedance from G_2 to ground. Thus

$$E_{c2} = (^{250}\!\!/\!_{267} - {}^{150}\!\!/\!_{270})(0.250) = 0.10 \text{ volt}$$

Hence T_2 is indeed in clamp and we have made only a very small error in assuming that the grid-to-cathode voltage is zero. Similarly if the loading of R_1 and R_2 is taken into account the value of E_{b2} is found to be 32 volts instead of 33 volts. These errors may well be smaller than the error involved in applying the *average* tube characteristics to a *particular* tube. To summarize, in the stable state we have approximately

$$I_1 = 0 \qquad E_{b1} = 206 \text{ volts} \qquad E_{c1} = -49 \text{ volts}$$
$$I_2 = 4.6 \text{ ma} \qquad E_{b2} = 33 \text{ volts} \qquad E_{c2} = 0 \text{ volt}$$

Tube T_1 in being at cutoff keeps tube T_2 in clamp, while T_2 in being in clamp keeps T_1 at cutoff.

The binary has *two* stable states. In one state T_1 is cut off and T_2 is in clamp. In the second state T_2 is cut off and T_1 is in clamp. The principal importance of the binary results from the fact that it is possible, by a variety of means, to transfer the binary from one stable state to the other. Suppose, for example, that initially T_1 is conducting (*on*), while T_2 is not conducting (*off*). If tube T_1 were removed from its tube socket, T_2 would go *on* and the voltage at the tube socket grid pin of T_1 would go negative. If the tube T_1 is now replaced in its socket, it would remain cut off. A *permanent* transition between states will have been accomplished. Or suppose that the grid of the *off* tube were momentarily shorted to ground. This *off* tube would go *on* and in so doing would turn *off* the tube that was initially *on*. This condition would again persist permanently even after the short circuit is removed. These means of transferring conduction are, however, only of academic interest. More practically useful methods will be considered later.

The useful plate signal, called the *output* or *plate swing*, from the binary is usually the voltage change at one or the other plate corresponding to a transition from one stable state to the other. This signal is customarily large and for large R_L may be comparable to the plate-supply voltage. The plate swing E_s in the illustrative example above is nominally $206 - 33 = 173$ volts.

It was pointed out above that a stable state is possible even if *one* of the tubes is permitted to operate as a normal amplifier, with its grid neither clamped nor below cutoff. An initial disadvantage of such an arrangement is that the plate swing is reduced. A more important difficulty has to do with the reliability of operation of the binary. Suppose that in Fig. 5-2 the negative supply voltage is set at -260 volts. Then one tube will be cut off, while the *on* tube, say T_2, will have a grid voltage

$$E_{c2} = 250 \frac{270}{270 + 220 + 47} + (-260) \frac{220 + 47}{270 + 220 + 47}$$
$$= 125.7 - 129.3 = -3.6 \text{ volts}$$

This resultant grid voltage is the small difference between two large numbers. The grid voltage and consequently the tube current will change by a large percentage if either of the coupling resistors changes even slightly. For example, if the resistors R_2 should change by only about 1 per cent from 270 to 267 K, the grid voltage will become -5.0 volts instead of -3.6 volts. The corresponding plate swing would then change by 36 volts. A larger change in the coupling resistors might then easily cause the supposedly *on* tube to be below cutoff. In such a case there would be only one stable state for the binary and the circuit would be useless.

In practice, we should like to be able to assemble these binary circuits using components which are held to a tolerance no better than, say, 10 per cent. And we should like to feel confident that the binary will continue to operate as the tubes age or are changed and despite reasonable variations in supply voltages. For these reasons the binary is usually adjusted so that in a stable state one tube is well in clamp while the other is well below cutoff.[1]

5-2. The Self-biased Binary. The need for a negative supply as in Fig. 5-2 may be eliminated by using a common cathode resistor R_k to provide self-bias as in Fig. 5-4. The procedure for calculating the stable states is in principle the same as is employed for the fixed-bias binary.

EXAMPLE. Find the currents and voltages corresponding to the stable states for the self-biased binary of Fig. 5-4.

Solution. Assume T_1 is cut off and T_2 is clamped with a grid-to-cathode voltage equal to zero. The clamped current of T_2 is determined by drawing on the plate characteristics a load line which passes through the supply voltage $E_{bb} = 175$ volts and has a slope corresponding to a load resistor of $47 + 15 = 62$ K. The intersection of this load line with the curve for zero grid voltage gives a tube current of 2.5 ma. The cathode-to-ground voltage is, therefore, $E_{kn} = 15 \times 2.5 = 37.5$ volts. The plate-to-ground voltage of T_2 is $E_{bn2} = 175 - 47 \times 2.5 = 57$ volts. The grid-to-ground voltage of T_1 is $E_{cn1} = 57 \times (^{150}/_{480}) = 17.8$ volts. The grid-to-cathode voltage of T_1 is $E_{ck1} = 17.8 - 37.5 = -19.7$ volts. The cutoff voltage is about

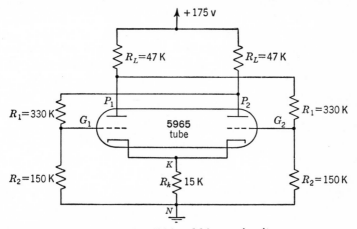

FIG. 5-4. A self-biased binary circuit.

−7 volts so that T_1 is well below cutoff, as was assumed at the start. In the absence of grid current, the voltage at the grid of T_2 would be

$$E_{cn2} = 175 \times \frac{150}{47 + 330 + 150} = 49.7 \text{ volts}$$

Since T_2 clamps when $E_{cn2} = 37.5$ volts, the assumption that T_2 is clamped is seen to be justified. The plate-to-ground voltage of T_1 is

$$E_{bn1} = 37.5 \times \frac{47}{330 + 47} + 175 \times \frac{330}{330 + 47} = 158 \text{ volts}$$

Hence the plate swing is $158 - 57 = 101$ volts.

In the calculation above a number of approximations have been made. We have again neglected the loading effect of the coupling resistors and have assumed that at clamping the grid-to-cathode voltage is zero. Furthermore, in computing the drop across the cathode resistor, we have neglected the fact that the cathode resistor carries not only the plate current but also the grid current. But again, since we must work from average tube characteristics and since voltage levels in a binary never need to be known with precision, a more detailed calculation is hardly warranted.

The drop across the cathode resistor is nominally the same for the two stable states. However, during the course of a transition, the current through R_k will vary and may even drop to zero. To keep the cathode voltage constant during the transition, R_k is bypassed with a capacitor. Typically a transition is completed in a time of the order of a microsecond. Since R_k is of the order of 10 K, a capacitor $C_k = 0.01$ µf will provide a cathode time constant of 100 µsec, which is large enough in comparison with the transition time to maintain an essentially constant cathode voltage. The stable states are, of course, not affected by the presence of the cathode capacitor, but the ease of inducing a transition between states and the rapidity with which the binary settles into its new state may be adversely affected if the capacitor is omitted.

5-3. Commutating Capacitors. A binary will remain in one of its stable states until caused to make a transition by a "triggering" signal such as a pulse applied from some external source. Often these triggering signals are of short duration, and in order that the binary shall be able to respond to each of these triggering signals it is necessary that the binary make its transition abruptly. Otherwise it is possible that the triggering pulse will have passed before the binary is able to complete its response.

Suppose, for example, that a transition is to be induced in a binary by applying in series with the grid of the conducting tube a short-duration negative pulse of sufficient amplitude to drive the tube beyond cutoff. Refer to Fig. 5-2. If the tube T_1 is driven to cutoff, the plate P_1 will rise toward E_{bb} at a rate determined by the plate load resistor and the shunt capacitance between plate and ground. This rising plate voltage must now be transmitted through the attenuator consisting of R_1 and R_2. The rising voltage at G_2 will be further delayed since the capacitance effectively shunting G_2 to ground must charge through a resistance which is essentially equal to the parallel combination of R_1 and R_2. Because of the over-all delay in the rise of voltage at G_2 it may well be that the applied pulse at G_1 will have passed before T_2 can be brought out of cutoff. As a result the binary will not respond to the applied pulse.

To ensure a transition, it is not enough that the grid G_2 shall just pass the cutoff point. It is necessary also that the plate P_2 shall fall sufficiently to keep T_1 cut off even after the input pulse passes. Hence the grid G_2 must rise somewhat into the region where T_2 acts as an amplifier. In this region the input capacitance of the triode, because of the Miller effect, may easily attain values of the order of 50 $\mu\mu f$. In a typical case, as in Fig. 5-2, the impedance through which this capacitance must charge may be of the order of 100 K, in which case the charging time constant is about 5 μsec. The charging time constant at the plate of T_1 is smaller than this amount and hence the principal delay will occur in the grid coupling circuit. It is therefore required that the coupling attenuator be *compensated* (Sec. 3-10) by shunting the resistors R_1 by small capacitances C_1, as in Fig. 5-5, such that $R_1C_1 = R_2C_2$, where C_2 is the effective capacitance across R_2. If capacitances C_1 are large enough to provide compensation when the Miller effect is operative, the attenuator will be very much overcompensated when the tube is beyond cutoff. Such a situation is quite acceptable in the present case since we are not so much concerned with preserving a waveshape as we are with obtaining, at a grid, an abrupt response to a voltage change at a plate. The larger

C_1, the faster will be the response at G_2 due to a change in P_1. However, we shall find in Sec. 5-5 that a large C_1 has other adverse effects upon the operation of the binary. The exact value of C_1 is not critical, but it should be chosen so that the attenuator R_1 and R_2 is approximately compensated. For a triode, C_1 is ordinarily of the order of 50 $\mu\mu$f. Since these capacitors, C_1, are used to assist the binary to make an abrupt transition between states they are known variously as *commutating*, *transpose*, or *speed-up* capacitors.

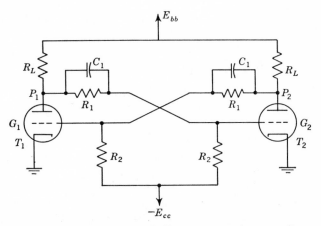

Fig. 5-5. A binary circuit including commutating capacitors.

5-4. Regeneration in a Binary.[2]   The situation in which both tubes of the binary are operating as amplifiers and in which both tubes are carrying the same current is one of *unstable* equilibrium.   If the circuit is displaced from this initial state, it will continue to move in the direction in which it was displaced until further excursion is limited by tube nonlinearities. We may get some rough idea of the rapidity of this *regenerative* action from the following considerations.

Let us assume, for simplicity, that the commutating capacitors in Fig. 5-5 have been selected to compensate exactly the coupling attenuator. In this case the impedance seen looking into the attenuator consists exactly of a parallel combination of a resistor and a capacitor.   The resistance has a value equal to $R_1 + R_2$ and the capacitance has a value equal to the series combination of C_1 and the grid input capacitance.   An equivalent circuit for the binary which applies so long as the binary continues to operate linearly is given in Fig. 5-6.   The gain A is the nominal gain of the amplifier, neglecting all capacitive loading, including, however, the attenuation and loading of the coupling network, R_1 and R_2.   The resistance R is what the output impedance of a stage would be if the signal were taken from the plate including also the loading effect of the coupling network. Finally, C is the parallel combination of the capacitance seen looking into the coupling attenuator and any other plate-to-ground capacitance.

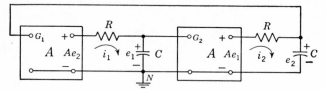

FIG. 5-6. Approximate equivalent circuit for a binary when both tubes are operating as amplifiers.

If e_1 and e_2 are, respectively, the voltages on the two capacitors with the polarities as in Fig. 5-6, Kirchhoff's voltage law yields

$$RC\frac{de_1}{dt} + e_1 - Ae_2 = 0 \qquad RC\frac{de_2}{dt} + e_2 - Ae_1 = 0 \qquad (5\text{-}1)$$

Substituting solutions of the form $e_1 = B_1\epsilon^{pt}$ and $e_2 = B_2\epsilon^{pt}$, we find, using $\tau = RC$, that the two values of p are

$$p_1 = \frac{A-1}{\tau} \qquad p_2 = \frac{-(A+1)}{\tau} \qquad (5\text{-}2)$$

In the first case ($p = p_1$) we find that $B_1 = B_2 \equiv D$, while in the second case ($p = p_2$), $B_1 = -B_2 \equiv F$. Hence,

$$e_1 = D\epsilon^{\frac{A-1}{\tau}t} + F\epsilon^{-\frac{A+1}{\tau}t} \qquad (5\text{-}3)$$

$$e_2 = D\epsilon^{\frac{A-1}{\tau}t} - F\epsilon^{-\frac{A+1}{\tau}t} \qquad (5\text{-}4)$$

In Eqs. (5-3) and (5-4) e_1 and e_2 are the departures of the grid voltages from those potentials which correspond to the state of unstable equilibrium. For if $e_1 = e_2 = 0$ at $t = 0$, then $e_1 = e_2 = 0$ permanently since in this case $F = D = 0$. And the only state in which the circuit will remain "permanently" is this state of unstable equilibrium.

The gain A in Eqs. (5-3) and (5-4) is a negative real number. The exponent in the first term of each of these equations is therefore always negative. However, if the *magnitude of the gain is larger than unity* the exponent of the second term is *positive*. Here then is the reason for the regenerative departure of the binary from its unstable equilibrium state. Suppose, for example, that both grids should be displaced in the *same* direction from the equilibrium state by means of external voltage sources which are then abruptly removed. In this case $F = 0$ and the binary simply decays exponentially back to its equilibrium state. If, however, the grids are displaced by equal amounts E in opposite directions and then released, the regenerative action will take place. In this case $D = 0$, $F = E$, and

$$e_1 = E\epsilon^{\frac{|A|-1}{\tau}t} \qquad e_2 = -E\epsilon^{\frac{|A|-1}{\tau}t} \tag{5-5}$$

If E is positive, e_1 increases and e_2 decreases rapidly with time, and we have verified the statement previously made that if the circuit is displaced from its initial state it will continue to move in the direction in which it was displaced until further excursion is limited by nonlinearities which reduce the loop gain below unity.

The rapidity of the regenerative action is measured by the quantity $(|A| - 1)/\tau \cong |A|/\tau = |A|/RC$. We may easily verify that $|A|/R = ag_m$ in which $a \equiv R_2/(R_1 + R_2)$, is the attenuation of the coupling resistors and g_m is the tube transconductance. Hence $|A|/RC = ag_m/C$. Since the capacitance C_1 of the attenuator is usually about 50 $\mu\mu$f and a reasonable value for a is $a = \frac{1}{2}$, the capacitance at the plate due to the attenuator is about 25 $\mu\mu$f. Let us, then, take the total plate capacitance $C = 35$ $\mu\mu$f. For a tube such as the type 5965 for which the average g_m is about 4 millimhos, $ag_m/C \cong 6 \times 10^7$ sec^{-1}.

We may now make an estimate of the speed with which regenerative action will carry a binary through the region where both tubes are operating as amplifiers. Suppose that we consider a situation in which the grids of the binary are released from a point which is 0.1 volt different from the grid voltages corresponding to unstable equilibrium. Suppose that one or the other grid can swing an additional 10 volts before the regenerative action must stop because a tube goes into either cutoff or clamp. From Eq. (5-5) the time of regenerative action T may be computed from $10 = 0.1 \exp (6 \times 10^7 T)$. We find that

$$T \cong 8 \times 10^{-8} \text{ sec} = 0.08 \ \mu\text{sec}$$

The value of the resistance R_L does not enter explicitly into the calculation of the regeneration time. Actually, when the tubes are triodes, the load R_L may have some bearing on the regeneration time. The reason for this circumstance is that the grid input capacitance increases with increasing gain and hence increases with increasing R_L. If the tubes employed were pentodes, however, the regeneration time would be quite independent of R_L.

We shall look shortly into the matter of how long a time is required to complete a transition from one stable state to the other. We shall find that in very many cases the time required is so much longer than the regeneration time that the regeneration time may be entirely neglected. More than this, we shall find, frequently, that a binary will make a transition without at any time being in a region where regeneration is possible.

5-5. Resolving Time in a Binary. An exact and general analysis of the transition between states in a binary triggered in an arbitrary fashion would be extremely complicated. It will be worthwhile, however, to examine in some detail a particular example to get some idea of the time required for the transition to be completed. The shortest interval between triggering pulses for which the binary will operate reliably is called the *resolving time*. This time is made up of several components, each of which will now be considered separately.

Let us consider the binary circuit of Fig. 5-7. The generator E is to be used to trigger the transition. The tubes are the two sections of a type 5963 (see the curves in Fig. A-7). The electrode voltages in one of the stable states are indicated in the figure. For simplicity, the voltages

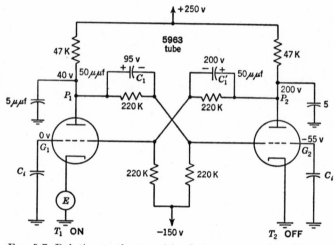

FIG. 5-7. Relating to the transition between states in a binary.

are given only approximately. In order to allow for stray capacitances, we have assumed that a capacitance of 5 $\mu\mu$f is shunted from plate to ground of each tube. Again allowing for stray capacitance, we may consider that, so long as a tube is cut off, the input capacitance at the grid, C_i, is approximately 10 $\mu\mu$f. When the tube is within its grid base, we shall consider that the Miller effect increases C_i to about 50 $\mu\mu$f so that the coupling attenuator is approximately compensated. The gain, grid to plate, is about 17, so that assuming the Miller capacitance to be 40 $\mu\mu$f allows for a total grid-to-plate capacitance, both internal and external to the tube, of about 2.2 $\mu\mu$f.

Now let us consider that the generator E provides an abrupt positive step large enough to cut off tube T_1. The plate of T_1 and the grid of T_2 will rise and the plate of T_2 will fall so that eventually, when the positive step passes, the tube T_1 will remain cut off and a transition is accomplished. Note particularly that at no time are both tubes operating as amplifiers and hence there will be no regeneration.

For simplicity, let us assume that, when T_2 is cut off, the commutating capacitor C_1 is large enough in comparison with C_i so that any voltage change at the plate T_1 appears unattenuated at the grid of T_2. To the same order of approximation we shall assume that the total capacitance shunting the plate of T_1 is $5 + C_i = 15 \mu\mu f$. The cutoff voltage of T_2 is about 15 volts; hence the plate of T_1 will rise the first 40 volts with a time constant $\tau_1 = 47 \times 10^3 \times 15 \times 10^{-12} \cong 0.75 \mu sec$. During this time the voltage across the capacitor C_1 will not have changed appreciably. As the voltage at the grid of T_2 increases from -15 volts to zero, the attenuator is compensated. The capacitance of the attenuator is now $25 \mu\mu f$ and the capacitance at the plate T_1 is $30 \mu\mu f$. Hence, the voltage at this plate rises the next 30 volts with a time constant

$$\tau_2 = 47 \times 10^3 \times 30 \times 10^{-12} = 1.5 \mu sec$$

The voltage across C_1 will also have changed by 15 volts to make the capacitor voltage equal to 110 volts. Finally, as T_2 goes into clamp, the plate of T_1 rises from 110 volts to 200 volts. During this time the total capacitance at the plate is $55 \mu\mu f$ which will charge with a time constant approximately equal to $\tau_3 = 47 \times 10^3 \times 55 \times 10^{-12} = 2.5 \mu sec$.

Next consider the coupling from the plate of T_2 to the grid of T_1. For simplicity, let us neglect the finite rise time of the grid of T_2. The plate of T_2 will eventually drop to 40 volts. Since T_2 is conducting, the impedance through which the plate capacitance charges is the parallel combination of R_L and the plate resistance r_p. The plate resistance is roughly 7 K so that the capacitors discharge essentially through this 7 K resistance. The plate P_2 drops from 200 volts to 40 volts with a time constant $\tau_4 \cong 7 \times 10^3 \times 15 \times 10^{-12} \cong 0.11 \mu sec$. Again, considering that C_1' is large enough so that the signal at P_2 is transmitted unattenuated to G_1, the grid G_1 drops from zero to -160 volts. The voltage across C_1' must discharge from 200 volts to 95 volts. Also C_1' and C_i must charge through a resistance which is essentially equal to the parallel combination of the two 220-K coupling resistors. The time constant for this discharge is $\tau_5 = 110 \times 10^3 \times 60 \times 10^{-12} \cong 6.6 \mu sec$.

We may note also that the principal delays involved in establishing the binary in its new stable state are the delays due to the need for the capacitors C_1 and C_1' to charge to a new voltage level. Capacitor C_1 charges on grid-current flow through the load resistor R_L, while C_1' charges through the parallel combination of the coupling resistors.

Since so large a time relatively is involved in recharging the commutating capacitors, we might stop to reconsider in somewhat more detail the function of these capacitors to see whether or not they do more good than harm.   For this purpose let us divide the total cycle of events involved in a complete change from one state into the other state into two parts.   The first of these we shall call the *transition time*, while the second is to be called the *settling* or *recovery time*.   The transition time is to be the time which must elapse before the grid G_1 just drops below cutoff so that even if the input step E should then return to zero (the input signal constituting, then, a pulse) the binary would continue the rest of the way unaided by any external signal.   The settling time is the additional time which must pass before the binary has completely established itself in its new state.   This recovery time is essentially the time required for the commutating capacitors to recharge.   Removing the commutating capacitors would certainly reduce the recovery time but would at the same time lengthen the transition time because of the long delays associated with the uncompensated attenuators.   As a result the pulse applied to effect the transition would have to be appreciably longer in duration, while the sum of the transition time and recovery time would not have been materially reduced.   In many cases the signal available for inducing the transition is not a flat-topped pulse but rather a spike-type voltage such as results from the differentiation of an abrupt voltage step.   In such a case a small transition time is more important than a short recovery time.

We will find an even more important reason for retaining the commutating capacitors in the following discussion.   Let us consider that the commutating capacitors have been removed and that the input pulse E is not large enough to drive T_1 to cutoff but only large enough so that the plate of T_1 rises to 100 volts.   (We assume that G_1 remains fixed, temporarily at least, at zero volts with respect to ground because of the shunt capacitance at this grid.)   There will be an abrupt change of 60 volts at P_1, the signal transmitted to G_2 will be less than 30 volts in amplitude, and T_2 will not come out of cutoff.   When the triggering pulse passes, the binary will find itself in its original state.   If, however, capacitor C_1 were present and were large in comparison with C_i, the signal transmitted through the attenuator would be large enough initially to drive T_2 into the conducting region.

In the case where the signal E is not large enough to cut off T_1, a part of the cycle involved in the transition will be regenerative.   However, no appreciable extra time is required for the circuit to complete by regenerative action that part of the cycle which would already be completed if E were large enough to cut off tube T_1.

5-6. Methods of Improving Resolution.   A first step in the direction of decreasing the resolution time of a binary is clearly to reduce all stray capacitances to a minimum.   Beyond this, it is necessary to reduce the sizes of all the resistors R_L, R_1 and R_2.   The reduction of R_L will improve the rise time of the waveforms at the tube plates and will reduce also the recharging time of the commutating capacitor connected between the plate of the *off* tube and the clamped grid. The reduction of R_1 and R_2 will reduce the recharging time of the other commutating capacitor.

The price that must be paid for these improvements in resolution time is, in the first place, increased dissipation of power in the circuit since, because of the smaller resistors, the current drain from the supply voltages will increase. Second, unless it is possible to increase the tube current in proportion, as the load resistor is reduced, the plate swing will become smaller. Hence, not only will the useful output signal be reduced but the total grid swing will be reduced and it may be difficult to maintain d-c stability in the binary. When the grid swing is reduced, it may become necessary to use 5 per cent or perhaps even 1 per cent components.

Let us compare the binary circuits of Fig. 5-8a and b. The binary in Fig. 5-8a is used in the Berkeley model 705A counter. It has a resolution time of approximately 5 μsec and is used in an application where it must respond to evenly spaced pulses which occur at a rate of 100,000 per second. The binary in Fig. 5-8b is used in the Hewlett-Packard model 524A counter in an application where it must respond to regularly spaced pulses which occur at a rate of 1 Mc. In both circuits approximate values of quiescent voltages are given.

Note that in going from Fig. 5-8a to b there is a substantial reduction in R_L and in the value of the parallel combination R_1 and R_2. The smaller load resistor also reduces the Miller capacitance at the grid and hence permits a reduction in the size of the commutating capacitors from 50 to 25 $\mu\mu$f. A further factor that speeds up the transition is that in Fig. 5-8a the change in the voltage across the commutating capacitor is 90 volts while in Fig. 5-8b the change is only 24 volts. On the other hand, the output swing in the binary of Fig. 5-8a is 110 volts against 40 volts in that of Fig. 5-8b. The total dissipation in the binary of Fig. 5-8a (exclusive of heater power) is about 0.8 watt against 1.9 watts in that of Fig. 5-8b.

At the expense of appreciably increased complexity the resolution time may be improved further. Figure 5-9 shows the circuit used in the Hewlett-Packard 524A counter which responds to a 10-Mc signal. The grid excursion is from grid clamp to −2 volts, being limited in the negative direction by the 1N34 crystal diode in the grid circuit. Here is an example of a binary operating with one tube in clamp and the other *part on* instead of below cutoff. The grid need never recover from a large negative voltage, and the d-c stability that would normally be provided by having one tube below cutoff is provided instead by the crystal diode clamp. The plate loads are large but the plate swing is again limited by plate-catching diodes (see Fig. 4-37) to a total excursion of 20 volts. The advantage of the plate clamping arrangement as against the use of small plate resistors is made clear by Fig. 5-10.   Suppose that, corresponding to the grid swing allowed, the plate-current change is ΔI.   For a small resistor, the exponential rise of plate voltage due to the shunting capacitance is shown by the solid curve in Fig. 5-10a.   The resistor would be selected to be somewhat larger than necessary to provide the minimum

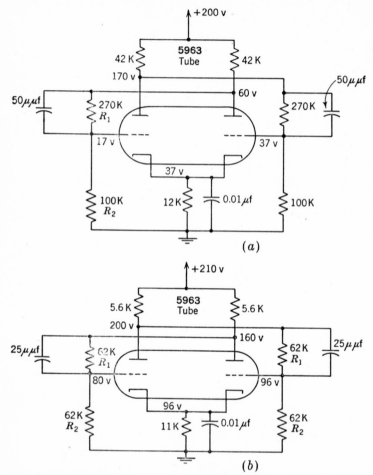

Fig. 5-8. (a) A 100-kc binary (10 per cent components); (b) a 1-Mc binary (5 per cent components).   The voltage valves indicated are nominal.

plate swing required as an output signal and to ensure that there is adequate voltage to swing the grids over the required range.   Suppose now that as the tube ages its cathode emission falls.   Then, as shown by the dotted curve in Fig. 5-10a, the plate swing may fall below the minimum acceptable value.   In Fig. 5-10b the situation depicted is one in which the plate resistor is much larger than in a.   Now, if ΔI should

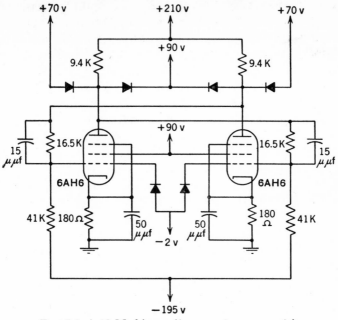

FIG. 5-9. A 10-Mc binary (1 per cent components).

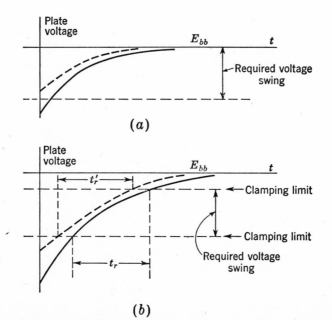

FIG. 5-10. Rise in plate voltage for a tube (a) with a small plate load resistor, (b) with a large plate load resistor.

decrease as indicated by the dotted curve in Fig. 5-10b, the plate swing will remain unaltered. Also, the time t_r' need not be appreciably longer than t_r. To make the rise and fall times at the plate equal, the clamped region is placed approximately midway between the limits of the unclamped excursion.

An important point to note is that in the present circuit the commutating capacitors need not charge at the end of a transition through the plate resistor or coupling resistors. Instead, one of the capacitors will discharge through the grid-to-cathode resistance and through the crystal diode connected to the +90-volt source. The other capacitor will charge through the grid crystal diode and the diode connected to the +70-volt source. The recovery time will therefore be very small, since the diode resistances are only of the order of 200 ohms.

Finally, we may note the use of high g_m pentodes. The high g_m reduces the regeneration time and also results in a large (unclamped) plate swing for a small grid-voltage swing. The use of pentodes virtually eliminates the Miller effect and allows the use of smaller commutating capacitors. Also, since the plate swing gets progressively smaller as we go from the circuit of Fig. 5-8a to b to Fig. 5-9, we are not surprised to find that the first of these circuits uses 10 per cent components, the second 5 per cent components, and the last 1 per cent components.

5-7. Triggering of the Binary. The triggering signal which is usually employed to induce a transition from one state to the other is either a pulse of short duration or the step voltage. This pulse or step may be introduced in such a manner that will produce either *symmetrical* or *unsymmetrical* triggering. In unsymmetrical triggering the triggering signal is effective in inducing a transition in only one direction. A second triggering signal from a separate source must be introduced in a different manner to achieve the reverse transition. In symmetrical triggering each successive triggering signal induces a transition independently of the state in which the binary happens to be. Unsymmetrical triggering, using two triggering sources, is found frequently where the binary is to be used as a generator of a gate whose width equals the interval between triggers. Symmetrical triggering is used in binary counting circuits (Sec. 11-1). Decade counting circuits (Sec. 11-3) employ a combination of symmetrical and unsymmetrical triggering. We shall consider in this present section only the method of triggering unsymmetrically.

A positive step voltage, of sufficient amplitude, applied through a capacitor to the grid of the *off* tube of a binary will cause a transition. Similarly a negative step applied to the grid of the *on* tube will induce a transition. It is important to understand that *ordinarily the sensitivity of the binary to the negative step will appreciably exceed the sensitivity to a positive step.* For the sake of being specific, let us consider a binary in which the grid base of a tube extends from 0 to −10 volts and in which, in the stable state, one grid is in clamp while the other grid is at −25 volts. Assume also that the nominal gain of a stage from grid to grid is 10. A negative step of amplitude 1.5 volts applied to the *on* grid will bring the *off* grid to the point of cutoff. A negative step of amplitude 2.5 volts will bring the initially *off* grid to zero voltage. A step of somewhat smaller amplitude than 2.5 volts will be sufficient to leave the binary in a situation in which the current in the initially *off* tube is larger than the current in the initially *on* tube, and we may expect the binary to complete the transition through regenerative action. If the coupling attenuator is overcompensated, the response at the initially *off* grid will be larger and the negative step required to induce a transition will be correspondingly smaller. Now consider a positive step applied to the *off* grid. Since the tube is 15 volts below cutoff, no response is to be anticipated until the step voltage exceeds 15 volts in amplitude. The binary will therefore respond to a smaller negative step voltage than to a positive step.

Suppose that a positive *pulse* is applied to the grid of the *off* tube. The pulse is a combination of a positive step and a delayed negative step. The result to be anticipated is therefore a combination of the response of the binary to a positive step applied to the *off* grid followed by a negative step applied to the *on* grid. Because of the greater sensitivity to the negative step, a positive pulse applied to the grid of the *off* tube will flip the binary at the leading edge of the input pulse and flip it right back again at the trailing edge of the input pulse.

Next consider a negative *pulse* applied to the *on* grid. Since the binary responds to a smaller negative step than positive step, we may adjust the pulse amplitude to prevent the binary from making a reverse transition on the trailing edge of the pulse. For the binary described above, the negative pulse amplitude may lie in the range roughly from somewhat less than 2.5 volts to somewhat less than 15 volts. The binary is more sensitive to a negative step applied to the *on* grid than to a positive step applied to the *off* grid. Therefore, to achieve a transition without a reversal, the negative step must precede the positive step.

It is possible to arrange a permanent binary transition through the use of a positive pulse, provided that the positive pulse is applied to the grid of the *on* tube. The leading edge of the positive pulse, applied to the *on* grid through a capacitor, will raise the voltage of the grid and additional grid current will flow, charging the input capacitor. This capacitor will charge rapidly through the low grid-to-cathode resistance and the voltage at the grid side of the input capacitor will decay rapidly back to zero. So far, then, all that has happened is that the conducting tube has been driven temporarily to conduct more current than in the quiescent state. Now, however, at the occurrence of the negative-going trailing edge of the input pulse the grid will be driven negative by an amount equal to the amplitude of the pulse. And since the binary is very sensitive to a negative step applied to the *on* grid, a transition may result. As a matter of fact if we consider as above that the grid-to-grid gain is 10 and that the grid of the nonconducting tube is 15 volts below cutoff, a positive pulse of somewhat more than 1.5 volt amplitude will suffice. It is to be noted particularly, however, that the transition, when it does occur, occurs at the *trailing edge* of the triggering pulse.

Up to the present we have neglected, for simplicity, the finite imped-ance to be seen looking into the grid to which the triggering signal is applied, and we have assumed that the triggering pulses had arbitrarily steep leading and trailing edges. Let us consider qualitatively how these two factors affect the conclusions arrived at above with respect to triggering. In the first place, the capacitive input impedance may well be comparable to the capacitance of the trigger input capacitor whose value typically may be of the order of 50 $\mu\mu f$. In this case the two capacitors will form a voltage divider, and if a signal of particular amplitude is required at the grid to cause triggering, the input signal may have to be appreciably larger. Next consider the case in which a positive pulse is applied to the grid of the *on* tube. We saw that if the pulse has a sharp leading and trailing edge a transition will result. But suppose that instead the pulse

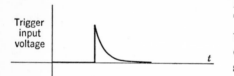

Trigger
input
voltage

t

FIG. 5-11. A binary triggering waveform.

has the form shown in Fig. 5-11. The sharp leading edge will charge the input capacitor by drawing grid current. If the pulse now falls slowly and the voltage drop across the input capacitor can decrease at about the same rate as the pulse falls, the grid-to-cathode voltage will never become negative and no transi-tion will take place. Similarly, if a pulse form as in Fig. 5-11 is applied to turn on the initially *off* tube in a binary, it may be that the slow falling portion of the pulse will not reverse the transition. Quite generally, as a matter of fact, since the input capacitor transmits preferentially fast wave-forms, a slow portion of a waveform may not affect the binary.

The application of a triggering signal directly to a grid through a capacitor has two important disadvantages. First, the presence at the grid of the additional trigger input capacitor will slow down the transi-tion between states. Second, the circuit may respond at the termination of a positive pulse applied to the *on* grid. Both these disadvantages may be eliminated if the input trigger is applied not directly through a capaci-tor but instead through a series combination of a capacitor and a large resistor. Or, equivalently, the trigger source may be a source of high resistive output impedance. Typically, the series resistor may be of the order of several hundred kilohms while the capacitor may again be of the order of 50 $\mu\mu$f. Of course, under these circumstances, because of the finite impedance seen looking into the grid, the trigger-source voltage will have to be appreciably larger than is required when the signal is applied directly through the capacitor. This larger signal is required not only because of the attenuation of the signal but also because the capacitance at the grid will cause the trigger signal at the grid to rise more slowly.

The series resistor will have no material effect on the response of the binary to a positive pulse applied to the *off* grid or a negative pulse applied to the *on* grid. But suppose a positive pulse is applied to the *on* grid. The input capacitor will now charge with a time constant equal, say, to 50 $\mu\mu$f $\times$ 200 K = 10 μsec. If the input pulse has a duration of only several microseconds, the input capacitor may not have charged appreciably and it is probable that no transition will take place at the trailing edge of the pulse.

The triggering signal may be applied at the plate of one of the tubes of the binary rather than at the grid, again preferably through a resistor and capacitor. Any signal so applied will immediately appear at the grid of the other tube, being transmitted directly through the commutating capacitor. The presence of the series resistor will serve to accentuate even further the sensitivity of the binary to a negative pulse. This extra sensitivity results because the positive step would have to be introduced at a point where the signal looks directly or through a coupling capacitor at the plate of a tube which is conducting. For example, in Fig. 5-7 a positive step must be applied at P_1 in an attempt to bring G_2 out of cutoff. At the plate P_1, however, the impedance presented to the triggering signal is low. A negative signal would be introduced, on the other hand, at the plate of a cutoff tube (P_2 in Fig. 5-7).

The discussion in this section may be summarized as follows: *The most reliable method for triggering a binary unsymmetrically is to apply a negative pulse from a high-impedance source to the plate of the nonconducting tube.* In the next section the advantages of introducing the triggering pulse through an auxiliary diode (or triode) are discussed.

5-8. Unsymmetrical Triggering Through a Triggering Tube. A very effective and reliable triggering method is shown in Fig. 5-12. The triggering tube T_3 has a sufficient negative bias so that the tube will be in the region beyond cutoff even when T_1 is not conducting so that the plate voltage of T_3 is high. Independently of which state the binary is in, a negative pulse or step applied to the grid of T_3 will have no effect. If, however, the binary is in the state in which T_1 is not conducting, a positive input pulse will drop the plate voltage at P_1 and a transition will occur. The situation is essentially the same as obtains when a negative pulse is applied at P_1 except that the resistor R_L will serve also as a plate resistor for T_3. Hence T_3 will provide gain, and the input trigger may be correspondingly reduced in amplitude. It will usually not be necessary to couple together the plates of T_3 and T_1. Depending on how large a current flows through T_3, it may be possible to connect the plate of T_3 to a point on R_L closer to the supply voltage, as indicated by the dotted alternative connection. The extent to which the triggering tube interferes with the fast action of the binary, because of the additional capacitance at the plate, will become progressively smaller as the tap point moves closer to the supply voltage.

If the binary is in the state in which T_1 is conducting, a positive input trigger will only drop further the plate P_1 and drive the grid G_2 further into cutoff.

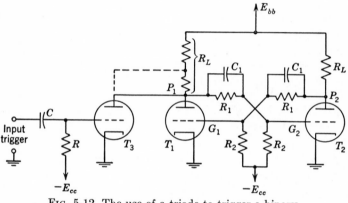

FIG. 5-12. The use of a triode to trigger a binary.

Recalling the discussion of Sec. 5-7, we note that, when a triggering pulse is impressed directly, the possibility exists that the binary will respond to either negative or positive pulses and that, when positive pulses are applied, the binary may respond independently of the state in which the binary is initially situated. In the present case we find that the binary will respond only to a positive pulse and only when the binary is in a particular state. This last feature is a result of the unilateral action of the triggering tube and, where the gain of the triggering tube is not required, may be achieved through the use of a diode (thermionic or crystal). Diode triggering is shown in Fig. 5-13a. When T_1 is conducting, the plate of the diode is negative with respect to the cathode and the diode will not transmit a triggering signal. When T_1 is off, the diode drop is zero. The diode will still fail to transmit a positive-going trigger but will transmit a negative step or pulse to the grid of T_2. Observe that here, as in the case also of the triggering triode, the signal to which the binary responds is the signal which effectively applies a negative signal to the on grid, to which signal the binary is most sensitive. The time constant RC of the input circuit is not critical, but should be small enough so that any charge which accumulates on C during the time T_3 conducts shall have time to decay during the interval between pulses. An alternative diode triggering arrangement is shown in Fig. 5-13b. Here the negative signal is applied through T_3 directly to the grid of the *on* tube T_1. The resistor R is returned to ground (corresponding to the grid voltage at clamp) rather than to the supply voltage.

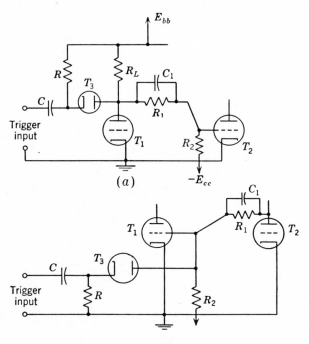

FIG. 5-13. (a) Trigger injected at plate through a diode. (b) Trigger injected at grid through diode.

5-9. Symmetrical Triggering.[3] Symmetrical triggering may be accomplished with any of the circuits of Fig. 5-14. For example, in Fig. 5-14a neither diode will conduct unless the input signal is negative. A negative input signal will be transmitted only to the clamped grid. The diodes serve exactly the same function as described in Sec. 5-8 in connection with Fig. 5-13a. The only difference is that, since there are two diodes, the binary will transfer at *each* successive negative input pulse. The circuit will also respond to either a negative pulse or step but will not respond to a positive pulse or step. We shall see in Chap. 11 the very important application which is made of the fact that it is possible to trigger a binary with a signal applied symmetrically and to have the binary respond for only one polarity of triggering signal. It turns out to be possible to accomplish this same end without the aid of auxiliary unilateral devices, and we shall examine now the mechanism by which this result is accomplished.

Consider the binary circuit of Fig. 5-15. This circuit differs from the binary circuits previously encountered only in that an additional resistor has been included directly in series with the supply voltage. Of

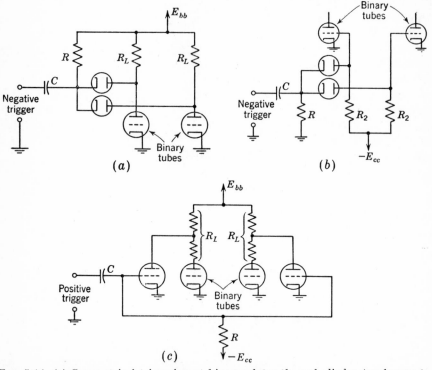

FIG. 5-14. (a) Symmetrical triggering at binary plates through diodes (analogous to the unsymmetrical triggering method of Fig. 5-13a). (b) Symmetrical triggering at binary grids through diodes (analogous to Fig. 5-13b). (c) Symmetrical triggering using triode triggering tubes (analogous to Fig. 5-12).

course, to allow for the drop in this resistor a higher supply voltage is required. Note, however, that the effective supply voltage (the drop between point A and ground) is nominally the same for the two states of the binary so that the presence of this extra resistor does not materially complicate the calculation of the stable states.

The voltage levels of the plates and grids and the voltage across the commutating capacitor corresponding to a stable state are given in the figure. For simplicity, we have taken $R_1 = R_2 = R$. We have also assumed that the coupling resistors are large enough so that their loading effect at the tube plates is negligible. The response of the circuit depends importantly on the presence of the commutating capacitors. To see this effect without extensive complication, let us neglect all other capacitances which may be present.

Now let us apply a negative input step of amplitude 90 volts and assume that the input step has dropped so rapidly that the commutating capacitors have not been able to discharge appreciably. If we now further assume that, as a consequence of the applied step, both binary tubes are cut off, the voltages at the various electrodes are easily computed. Since neither tube is conducting, the plate voltages are equal and are equal also to the voltage at point A. This voltage is 60 volts, being 150 volts minus the 90-volt input step. The voltage at G_2 is equal to the voltage at P_1 minus the drop across the commutating capacitor connected between P_1 and G_2. Hence G_2 is at -15 volts. Similarly, the voltage at G_1 is -90 volts. Since these grid voltages are well below the cutoff voltage of -12 volts, we have verified the assumption that both tubes have been cut off by the input step.

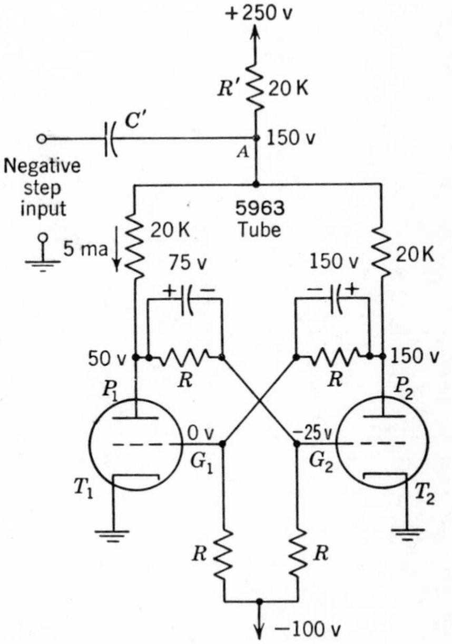

FIG. 5-15. A symmetrical triggering arrangement which does not employ auxiliary triggering diodes or triodes.

The negative step applied at A will now start to decay and the voltage at A will start to rise exponentially toward the supply voltage. So long as the tubes remain cut off, the plates, both of which start at 60 volts, will rise together. If we assume also that the commutating capacitors continue to hold their charge, then both grids will also rise at the same rate. Since G_2 starts at -15 volts while G_1 starts at -90 volts, it is clear that G_2 will reach the cutoff level first. Hence when point A returns to its quiescent level, we shall find that T_2 is conducting while T_1 is cut off; i.e., a transition has taken place. After the transition has been completed, the commutating capacitors will interchange voltages in the manner described in Sec. 5-5 in connection with the recovery time of the binary.

Suppose that the commutating capacitors were absent. The predominant capacitance present would then be the effective capacitance present at the tube grids. When the plates drop to 60 volts in response to the applied step, the grids will decay toward their quiescent value, which in this case is -20 volts for both grids. The grid G_2 therefore starts to rise from -25 to -20 volts, while G_1 starts to change exponentially from 0 to -20 volts. Since the cutoff voltage is -12 volts, tube T_2 remains *off*. Tube T_1 may go off for a short interval of time (if its grid falls below -12 volts), but as the input step decays and both the plates and grids start to rise, tube T_1 will again conduct. *The result is that no transition can take place if the commutating capacitors are removed from the circuit.*

An important point to note in connection with the circuit of Fig. 5-15 is that it is appreciably more sensitive to a negative step than to a positive step. To see in a general way how this sensitivity arises, consider that the input negative step is only 1 volt in amplitude. The plate P_2 will drop to 149 volts and the grid G_1 will drop to -1 volt. The principal change at P_1 will be due to the grid-voltage change and the plate P_1 will jump (as determined from the tube characteristics) to about 62 volts. The grid G_2 will then jump to -13 volts, which is just about the cutoff voltage of T_2. If, therefore, the step input were slightly larger, tube T_2 would start to conduct, dropping P_2 and G_1 even further and in turn raising P_1 and G_2. Of course, since we have neglected the other capacitances associated with the circuit, we may not conclude that a 1-volt signal is adequate to ensure a transition. This discussion is useful only for the purpose of comparing the effect of the step polarity. For next consider that the step is positive. The positive step transmitted to P_2 and from P_2 to G_1 will only serve to drive G_1 further into the positive grid region. The positive step which is transmitted to P_1, and from P_1 to G_2, is first of all attenuated owing to the fact that T_1 is conducting. The plate resistance of the tube is about 7 K so that the step at point A appears at P_1 and G_2 attenuated by the factor $7/27 \cong 0.26$. One may now estimate that, even if it is assumed that G_1 does not go appreciably positive a 50-volt step, roughly, will be required to bring T_2 up to the cutoff voltage.

Two additional triggering schemes similar in principle of operation are shown in Fig. 5-16a and b. It may be found that to ensure reliable triggering the commutating capacitors may have to be made larger than is consistent with a short recovery time. Hence the methods of Figs. 5-15 and 5-16 are normally not employed where resolution times are required which are shorter than about 10 μsec. Where shorter resolution times are important, the schemes of Fig. 5-14, using auxiliary unilateral devices, are more common.

5-10. The Cathode-coupled Binary.[4] A cathode-coupled binary circuit (also known as the Schmitt circuit after its inventor) is shown in

Fig. 5-17. This binary differs from the binary considered previously in that one plate-to-grid coupling attenuator has been replaced by a coupling connection through an unbypassed common cathode resistor R_k. We will be able to appreciate the usefulness of this circuit by considering its response as the voltage e is varied.

Consider that in Fig. 5-17, $e = 0$. Then we shall be able shortly to verify that T_1 will be cut off and, neglecting the loading effect of the coupling attenuator, P_1 will be at 250 volts. Let the attenuator ratio a $[\equiv R_2/(R_1 + R_2)]$ be selected so that the grid-to-cathode voltage of T_2 is -1 volt. It may then be verified from the tube characteristics

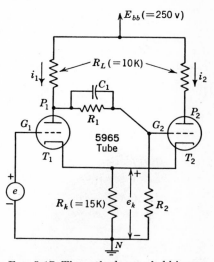

(a)

(b)

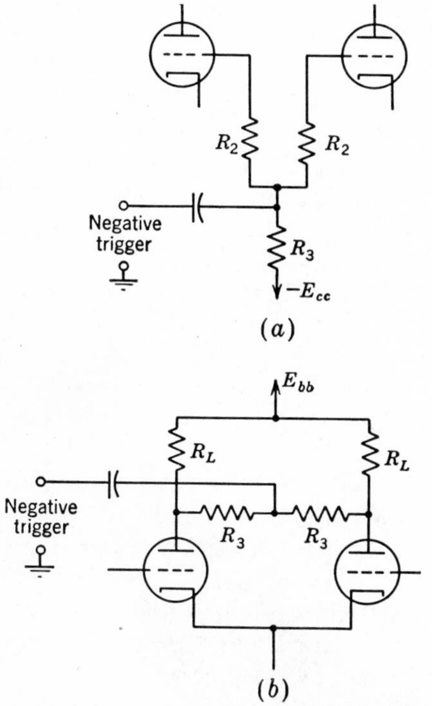

FIG. 5-16. Alternative symmetrical triggering arrangements which do not require the use of auxiliary diodes or triodes.

FIG. 5-17. The cathode-coupled binary.

that $i_2 = 6.2$ ma so that the cathode voltage $= 6.2 \times 15 = 93$ volts and T_1 is indeed cut off. The voltage at G_2 is $93 - 1 = 92$ volts and $a = {}^{92}\!/_{250} = 0.37$. Now as the voltage e is increased, the circuit will not respond until T_1 comes out of cutoff. Note that the plate-to-cathode drop of T_1 is $250 - 93 = 157$ volts, for which voltage cutoff occurs at a bias of -6 volts. Hence, when $e = -6 + 93 = 87$ volts, T_1 starts to conduct. At this moment P_1 will drop and G_2 will drop. The signal at G_2 is transferred to T_1 through the cathode circuit and reappears at P_1 with the same polarity as at G_2. The signal at P_1 is now transferred again to G_2 and if the loop gain exceeds unity a regenerative action will take place driving T_2 to cutoff.

Assuming then that T_2 is cut off and $e = 87$ volts, we find $i_1 = 5.9$ ma (see Sec. 1-7). The voltage at G_2 is $(250 - 5.9 \times 10) \times 0.37 \cong 70.7$ volts, while the cathode voltage is $5.9 \times 15 = 88.5$. The grid-to-cathode voltage of T_2 is $70.7 - 88.5 = -17.8$ volts, which verifies that T_2 is cut off.

So long as R_k is large enough so that the voltage drop across R_k is large in comparison with the grid base of the tube, the results above may be stated approximately in the following manner. Initially G_2 is at $E_{bb}a$ and the cathode is approximately at the same voltage. A transition will take place when e rises approximately to $E_{bb}a$ (provided that T_2 is not in clamp). When T_1 conducts, its current i_1 will be nominally the same as i_2 and the cathode voltage will change only slightly.

The output signal is customarily taken from P_2 and consists of a negative step of amplitude $i_2 R_L$ ($= 62$ volts in Fig. 5-17). Observe that the resistor R_L in the plate circuit of T_2 is not actually required for the operation of the circuit. This resistor may then be adjusted over a wide range to adjust the output signal amplitude. Furthermore, capacitive loading at P_2 will not slow the regenerative action, although such capacitance will slow the waveform at P_2.

If an output pulse instead of a step is desired, the plate load resistor of the right-hand tube may be replaced by an inductor or by a transformer (see Sec. 2-6).

The grid G_1 is free to receive the triggering signal and the impedance of the triggering signal source will have no influence on the operation of the circuit. After the circuit has been triggered, further increase of e has no influence on the voltage at P_2.

It will now be shown that this circuit exhibits *hysteresis* or *backlash*. In other words, the value of voltage at which triggering occurs depends upon whether e is increasing or decreasing. Let us call the value for increasing e (T_1 going from *off* to *on*) E^+ and the decreasing value (T_1 going from *on* to *off*) E^-. The value of e ($= 87$ volts) calculated in the above illustration is E^+. If e has increased above E^+ and then decreased again to slightly below E^+, the circuit will *not* flip back. The reason for this hysteresis is that, whereas the cathode voltage is approximately its previous value, the grid-to-ground voltage of T_2 is much lower than its previous value, and T_2 stays cut off. In order to bring T_2 into conduction, e must be decreased further. This decreases i_1 and the cathode voltage e_k and increases the grid-to-ground voltage at G_2. Finally, the grid-to-cathode voltage of T_2 exceeds the cutoff voltage E_{co2} corresponding to plate voltage $E_{bb} - e_k$. To find E^-, we first find the current I_1^- in T_1 just at cutin of T_2 from the equation $(E_{bb} - I_1^- R_L)a - I_1^- R_k = E_{co2}$, from which we find

$$I_1^- = \frac{E_{bb}a - E_{co2}}{R_L a + R_k} \tag{5-6}$$

In Eq. (5-6) E_{co2} is not known because it is the cutoff voltage corresponding to a plate voltage $E_{bb} - I_1^- R_k$ and I_1^- is unknown. However, as a first approximation E_{co2} may be set equal to some value between zero and the cutoff voltage corresponding to E_{bb}. Using this assumed value of E_{co2}, Eq. (5-6) gives the first approximation to I_1^-, say I_0^-. Then E_{co2} corresponding to $E_{bb} - I_0^- R_k$ is found from the plate characteristics. This value of E_{co2} is then used to find the new value of I_1^-. This process converges very rapidly. Knowing I_1^- (corresponding to E^-), it is a simple matter to find E^-. A load line corresponding to E_{bb} and a resistance $R_L + R_k$ is drawn and I_1^- is located on this load line. The corresponding grid-to-cathode voltage E_{c1}^- is read, and then

$$E^- = E_{c1}^- + I_1^- R_k \qquad (5\text{-}7)$$

If e falls below E^-, T_2 starts to conduct and the circuit flips back to its original state with T_2 on. If e continues to decrease, T_1 remains cut off and the output remains constant.

If the above calculations are carried out for the numerical values given in Fig. 5-17, the results are $I_1^- = 5.27$ ma, $E_{c1}^- = -1.6$ volts, and $E^- = 77$ volts. The hysteresis voltage E_h is defined as the difference between E^+ and E^-:

$$E_h \equiv E^+ - E^- \qquad (5\text{-}8)$$

For the circuit under consideration, $E_h = 87 - 77 = 10$ volts.

In the illustrative circuit described above, the quiescent conditions were adjusted so that, when T_1 is cut off, T_2 is within its normal grid base rather than in clamp. If instead T_2 had been in clamp, the regeneration would start not when G_1 passes cutoff but rather when G_2 comes out of clamp sufficiently so that the loop gain equals unity. Because of the presence of the commutating capacitor C_1, the regeneration point will then be a function of the speed of the input waveform since the response at G_2 to a fast waveform will be greater than for a slow waveform. When it is required that the triggering level E^+ be more independent of input waveshape, it is therefore necessary to adjust circuit parameters so that G_2 is initially within its grid base. Now, however, since the d-c stability of clamping is no longer available, it may be required that R_1 and R_2 be stable wire-wound resistors.

A large cathode resistor introduces into the circuit a number of worthwhile features of stability. To achieve this high effective cathode resistance without a correspondingly large cathode voltage, it is common to use in the cathode a constant-current device such as a pentode or the plate impedance of a triode with a moderately large resistor in the cathode of the triode (see Sec. 1-10). As we shall see (Sec. 15-13), the constant-current source minimizes the effect of heater-voltage variation on the effective cutoff voltages of the tubes. Second, it keeps constant the drop I_1R_L independently of variations of tube T_1. Both these features serve to stabilize the triggering voltages E^+ and E^-.

From the above description of the action of the circuit, it is clear that one application is as a *squaring circuit*. This means that the output will be a square wave independently of the shape of the input voltage waveform. The duration of the positive portion of the square wave corresponds to the interval between the time when the input voltage exceeds E^+ and the time when e decreases to E^-. This application is illustrated in Fig. 5-18. Note that the output amplitude is independent of input amplitude and that the output waveform may have much faster leading and trailing edges than the input waveform. The circuit is also used as a *regenerative amplitude comparison circuit* (see Sec. 15-10).

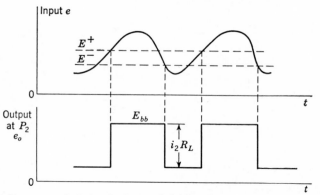

Fig. 5-18. Response of the cathode-coupled binary to an arbitrary input signal.

Thus the circuit responds only to signals whose amplitude exceeds a definite value E^+. In another application the circuit is triggered between its two stable states by alternate positive and negative pulses. Thus, if the grid of T_1 is biased to a voltage E' between E^- and E^+ and a positive pulse (whose amplitude is larger than $E^+ - E'$) is RC coupled to G_1, then T_1 will conduct and T_2 will be driven to cutoff. If now a negative pulse is applied (whose amplitude is in excess of $E' - E^-$), the circuit will flip back to the state where T_1 is off and T_2 is conducting. This behavior is the same as that of a plate-coupled multi with alternate positive and negative pulses applied to one grid. However, for the cathode-coupled multi the possible triggering difficulties discussed earlier are not encountered because the pulses are applied to the first grid which is not connected to any other point in the circuit.

5-11. Hysteresis in the Cathode-coupled Binary. In order to study the hysteresis effect in more detail, let us examine the circuit from the point of view of a feedback amplifier. Figure 5-19 shows a Schmitt circuit in which the quantity a [$= R_2/(R_1 + R_2)$] is adjustable. The resistor R_2 is returned to an adjustable voltage source so that the initial voltage at G_2 may be kept constant as the ratio a is varied.

Let us consider that the attenuation a has been adjusted so that the loop gain is less than unity. In this case a plot of output voltage e_o as a function of input voltage e would have the appearance of curve 1 in Fig. 5-20a. The voltage $e = E_1$ corresponds to cutoff in T_1 of Fig. 5-19. For $e < E_1$, $e_o = E_{bb} - I_0 R_L$, where I_0 is the current furnished by the constant-current source in the cathode. For $e > E_1$, the output increases

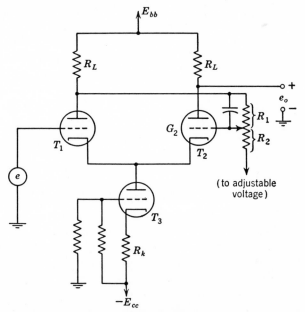

FIG. 5-19. A cathode-coupled binary with adjustable attenuator and a constant-current cathode load.

with E until tube T_2 cuts off at $e = E_2$. At this point $e_o = E_{bb}$. In the region between E_1 and E_2 both tubes operate as amplifiers and the output follows the input approximately linearly, the nonlinearity being most pronounced in the neighborhood of E_1 and E_2, where either T_1 or T_2 is near cutoff. The slope of the curve between E_1 and E_2 is $\Delta e_o / \Delta e = A$, the forward gain of the amplifier. If we assume a constant-current source in the cathode and if we continue to neglect the loading effect of the coupling attenuator, we find (from an analysis similar to that given in Sec. 1-10) that

$$A = \frac{\Delta e_o}{\Delta e} = \frac{\mu R_L}{2(R_L + r_p) - a\mu R_L} \tag{5-9}$$

If now the quantity a is increased, the gain of the amplifier will increase and correspondingly the slope in Fig. 5-20a will increase and the voltage

E_2 will move closer to the voltage E_1. Finally, the denominator in Eq. (5-6) will become zero, the gain will become infinite, and the response of the amplifier will have the appearance of curve 2 in Fig. 5-20a. The gain becomes infinite when $a = (2/\mu)[(R_L + r_p)/R_L]$. This result is con-

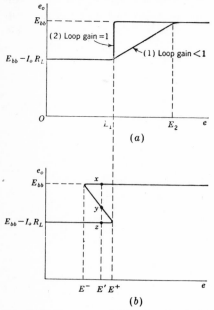

(a)

(b)

FIG. 5-20. Response of Schmitt circuit (a) for loop gain ≤ 1, (b) for loop gain > 1.

sistent with the fact that, as may be verified, the loop gain of the amplifier is

$$A \text{ (loop)} = \frac{\mu}{2} \frac{R_L a}{R_L + r_p} \qquad (5\text{-}10)$$

Hence the forward gain $A = \Delta e_o/\Delta e$ is infinite when the loop gain of the amplifier A (loop) $= 1$.

If a is increased to the point where the loop gain exceeds unity, then Eq. (5-9) indicates a negative gain and slope. This fact, together with our previous discussion in connection with hysteresis, indicates that, if a plot should now be made showing for each value of e the corresponding value of e_o which is consistent with the tube characteristics and Kirchhoff's law, the result would be as shown in Fig. 5-20b. The voltages E^+ and E^- are indicated. For a value $e = E'$, where $E^- < E' < E^+$, there are three possible consistent (hence equilibrium) values of e_o. Of these, two, x and z, are points of stable equilibrium, while one, y, is a point of unstable equilibrium. Hence, point y cannot be attained experimentally and the circuit will be in one or the other stable state, depending on the direction of approach. For example, if e is increased uniformly from zero, the output will remain at the lower value until $e = E^+$. For $e > E^+$, the only consistent output is $e_o = E_{bb}$; hence at $e = E^+$ a transition must take place. The path which the circuit takes in making the transition is determined largely by the capacitances present in the circuit and is not related to that part of the curve joining the two states in Fig. 5-20b.

The response indicated in Fig. 5-20a, curve 2, is often particularly advantageous. It indicates an abrupt transition between states whenever e passes a fixed reference voltage independently of the direction of approach. It is achieved by adjusting the loop gain of the amplifier to unity.

For the circuit of Fig. 5-17 there are several methods of eliminating hysteresis. For example, a resistor R_{k2} may be inserted into the cathode of T_2, as shown in Fig. 5-21. The value of I_1^- required to bring T_2 just out of cutoff is unaffected by R_{k2} since there will be zero voltage drop across this resistor if T_2 is nonconducting. Hence, $E^- = 77$ volts, the value calculated for $R_{k2} = 0$. For zero hysteresis, E^+ must equal this same value. Hence, R_{k2} may be found by analyzing the circuit of Fig. 5-21 subject to the condition that $e = E^+ = 77$ volts with T_1 at cutoff. However, such a calculation is only approximate because we have made the assumption that regeneration takes place when either one or the other tube just comes out of cutoff. Actually the circuit is triggered when the *off* tube is brought into conduction sufficiently so that the loop gain equals unity. Since R_{k2} introduces degeneration into the circuit, then the larger the value of R_{k2}, the greater must be the current in the tube being brought out of cutoff before the loop gain reaches unity. As the current in one tube increases, the current in the second decreases

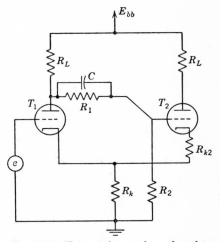

FIG. 5-21. Hysteresis may be reduced to zero by adjusting R_{k2} so that the loop gain is unity.

and hence the g_m of the first tube is increasing while that of the other is decreasing. When R_{k2} is large enough to reduce the hysteresis to zero, both tubes are conducting heavily and the gain is unity at the same input voltage whether this voltage is increasing or decreasing.

From the above discussion we can conclude that the grid voltage of T_2 must be increased over the cutoff value before hysteresis is eliminated. This condition requires an increase in the plate voltage of T_1 and a corresponding decrease in the grid voltage of T_1. Hence, the input voltage E for zero hysteresis will be somewhat smaller than $E^- = 77$ volts. Experimentally a value of $E = 75.5$ volts was found. The calculation of R_{k2} suggested above leads to a value which is about 20 per cent smaller than the value found experimentally.

A second method of eliminating hysteresis is to add a resistor R_{k1} in series with the cathode of T_1. By reasoning in a manner similar to that given above we can conclude that as a first approximation E^+ is unchanged and hence remains at the value of 87 volts found in Sec. 5-10. An approximate value for R_{k1} can be found by analyzing the circuit subject to the requirement that E^- also equal 87 volts. As already emphasized, the correct value of R_{k1} will occur when both tubes are conducting current and the loop gain is unity. The corresponding input voltage will be somewhat larger than 87 volts; experimentally a value of 88.5 volts was found.

If R_{k1} or R_{k2} is made larger than the value required to give zero hysteresis, then the loop gain will be less than unity and the circuit will not flip from one state to the other. Usually, R_{k1} or R_{k2} is chosen so that a small amount of backlash remains in order to ensure that the loop gain will remain greater than unity even if the circuit drifts somewhat (due to supply voltage changes, tube aging, etc.). Also, R_{k1} or R_{k2} is usually bypassed with a small capacitor. During the transition interval this capacitor reduces the degeneration caused by these resistors and hence a faster output pulse or step is delivered. The size of this capacitor will affect somewhat the value of R_{k1} (or R_{k2}) at which zero hysteresis is obtained.

If a value of R_{k1} (or R_{k2}) is used which is larger than required for zero hysteresis but the resistor is bypassed so that the a-c loop gain exceeds unity, then it is possible to trigger the circuit from one state to the next. Under these circumstances $E^- > E^+$ and hence *negative hysteresis* ($E_h < 0$) exists. This condition is unstable and the circuit will perform relaxation oscillations if the input voltage moves slowly between E^+ and E^-. Hence, here is another reason why the resistor R_{k1} (or R_{k2}) is so chosen as to make E_h slightly *positive*.

5-12. Cathode Interface Resistance in the Binary. Cathode interface resistance (see Sec. 3-18) which develops to some extent in tubes when used as amplifiers may be very much more serious in a tube used in a binary. The reason for this situation is that the flow of cathode current inhibits the formation of interface resistance; but in a binary one tube is normally at cutoff. Under cutoff conditions the inhibiting effect of tube current is not present and the interface resistance may become very large. When a tube has been operated with a heated cathode, but at cutoff, for many hundreds of hours, the interface resistance may become large enough, when the tube is finally turned on, to reduce the quiescent current by as much as a factor of 2. Hence when a binary has remained in one state for a long interval of time, it may well be impossible to induce a permanent transition. The problem of interface resistance is particularly serious in large-scale digital computers in which a binary may well find itself in one state for a long period.

There have been developed in recent years a series of dual triode vacuum tubes, the cathodes of which have been carefully treated to remove all impurities, such as silicon, which give rise to interface resistance. These tubes have been designed specifically for computer service. Notable among these are the types 5963, 5965, and 5844. The 5963 in other respects is not unlike the 12AU7. The types 5965 and 5844 incorporate other improvements such as better balance of cutoff in the two sections and a high zero-bias plate current to permit the use of small plate load resistors.

REFERENCES

1. Ritchie, D. K.: The Optimum DC Design of Flip-Flops, *Proc. IRE*, vol. 41, pp. 1614–1617, November, 1953.

   Pressman, R.: How to Design Bistable Multivibrators, *Electronics*, vol. 26, pp. 164–168, April, 1953.
2. Tillman, J. R.: Transition of an Eccles-Jordan Circuit, *Wireless Eng.*, vol. 28, pp. 101–110, April, 1951.

   William, E. M., D. F. Aldrich, and J. B. Woodford: Speed of Electronic Switching Circuits, *Proc. IRE*, vol. 38, pp. 65–69, January, 1950.
3. Phelps, B. E.: Dual-triode Trigger Circuits, *Electronics*, vol. 18, pp. 110–113, July, 1945.

   Potter, J. T.: A Four-tube Counter Decade, *Electronics*, vol. 17, pp. 110–113, June, 1944.

   Grosdoff, I. E.: Electronic Counters, *RCA Rev.*, vol. 7, pp. 438–447, September, 1946.
4. Schmitt, O. H.: A Thermionic Trigger, *J. Sci. Instr.*, vol. 15, pp. 24–26, January, 1938.

CHAPTER 6

MONOSTABLE AND ASTABLE MULTIVIBRATORS

The binary circuit, it will be recalled, has two stable states in either one of which it may remain permanently. The monostable multivibrator (multi) has instead only one permanently stable state and one quasi-stable state. In the monostable multi, a triggering signal is required to induce a transition from the stable state to the quasi-stable state. The multi may remain in its quasi-stable state for a time which is very long in comparison with the time of transition between states. Eventually, however, the multi will return from the quasi-stable state to its stable state, no external signal being required to induce this reverse transition.*

The astable multi has two states, both of which are quasi-stable. Without the aid of an external triggering signal the astable multi will make successive transitions from one quasi-stable state to the other.

Both these multis find extensive application in pulse circuitry. The basic application of the monostable multi results from the fact that it may be used to establish a fixed time interval, the beginning and end of which are marked by an abrupt discontinuity in a voltage waveform. The astable multi is an oscillator and is used as a generator of "square waves" and, since it requires no triggering signal, is itself often a basic source of fast waveforms.

6-1. The Plate-coupled Monostable Multi—The Stable State. The circuit of a plate-coupled monostable multi is shown in Fig. 6-1. As in the binary circuit, so also here, the plate P_2 is coupled to the grid G_1 through a resistance attenuator in which C_1 is a small commutating capacitor. The d-c coupling of the binary from P_1 to G_2 is here replaced by a-c coupling. The capacitor C is the coupling capacitor, while R is the grid-leak resistor. While the grid resistor R is shown to be returned

---

* Since after an input trigger "flips" the circuit over, it "flops" back by itself after a time T, it is known as a *one-shot*, a *single-cycle*, a *single-step multi* or a *univibrator*. Since it generates a rectangular waveform and hence can be used to gate other circuits, it is also called a *gating multi*. Furthermore, since the output can be differentiated to give a pulse at a predetermined time T after the input trigger, it is also called a *delay multi*. These names are very suggestive of the uses to which the circuit can be put.

to the plate-supply voltage, this feature of the circuit is not essential. The resistor R may be returned to any voltage in the range from zero (ground) to E_{bb}. We shall, however, at another point, discuss the advantage of returning R to the plate-supply voltage.

If the negative supply voltage $-E_{cc}$ and the coupling resistors R_1 and R_2 are adjusted so that T_1 is below cutoff, the multi will find itself in its (permanently) stable state with T_1 cut off and T_2 in clamp.

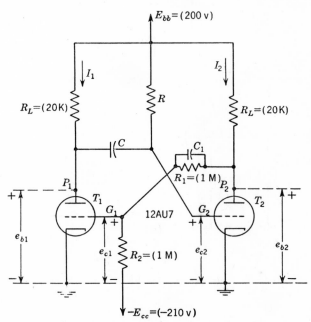

FIG. 6-1. The plate-coupled monostable multivibrator. The values of the components given in parentheses refer to the illustrative problem of Sec. 6-3.

We shall defer for discussion at a later point (Sec. 6-11) the situation which results when T_1 is not cut off. In the stable state the current in T_1 is zero and that in T_2 is I_2, corresponding to a clamped grid. The plate P_1 is at E_{bb} and the plate P_2 (neglecting the loading effect of the attenuator) is at $E_{bb} - I_2R_L = E_{b2}$. The grid G_2 is at zero (approximately) while the grid-to-ground voltage of T_1 is

$$e_{c1} = (E_{bb} + E_{cc} - I_2R_L)a - E_{cc} \equiv E_F \qquad (6\text{-}1)$$

in which $a = R_2/(R_1 + R_2)$.

6-2. The Quasi-stable State. The multi may be induced to make a transition out of its stable state by an application of a positive trigger at G_1 or P_2 or by the application of a negative trigger at G_2 or P_1. As with the binary, diode or triode triggering may be used to advantage. It is to be emphasized that the triggering is unsymmetrical, being applied to one tube only and not to both tubes simultaneously.

Consider that a single negative trigger is applied to G_2 and that a regenerative action takes place driving T_2 completely below cutoff. The voltage at P_2 is now E_{bb} and e_{c1} is given by

$$e_{c1} = (E_{bb} + E_{cc})a - E_{cc} \equiv E_N \qquad (6\text{-}2)$$

If E_N, as computed from Eq. (6-2), is greater than zero, then T_1 is in clamp and E_N is nominally zero. It is not necessary, however, that T_1

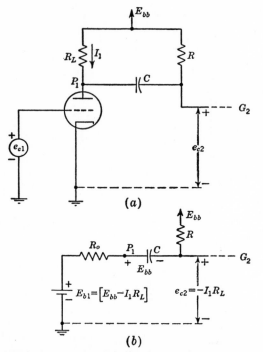

FIG. 6-2. (a) Simplified circuit for computing the voltage at G_2 during the quasi-stable state; (b) equivalent circuit. The capacitor voltage and the voltage e_{c2} are given for the instant immediately after the transition.

be in clamp. The tube may be either in clamp or within its grid base. In any event a current I_1 now flows in T_1 and the voltage at P_1 drops abruptly by an amount I_1R_L. The voltage at G_2 drops abruptly by this same amount because the voltage across C cannot change instantaneously. The multi is now in its quasi-stable state. The tube voltages are as follows: $e_{b2} = E_{bb}$, $e_{b1} = E_{bb} - I_1R_L$, $e_{c1} = E_N$ is zero, or as given by Eq. (6-2), and $e_{c2} = -I_1R_L$.

The multi will remain in this quasi-stable state for only a finite time, since the only d-c connection to G_2 is through R to E_{bb}. Eventually, therefore, G_2 will rise in voltage, and when G_2 passes the cutoff voltage of T_2, a regenerative action will take place turning T_1 off and eventually returning the multi to its initial stable state. We look now into the matter of determining the time duration of the quasi-stable state.

During the quasi-stable state T_2 is *off* and the voltage changes at G_2 may then be computed from the circuit of Fig. 6-2a in which again e_{c1} is zero or as given by Eq. (6-2). A circuit equivalent to that in Fig. 6-2a is given in Fig. 6-2b in which the tube T_1 has been replaced by a Thévenin equivalent. The voltage E_{b1} is the quiescent plate voltage

$$E_{b1} = E_{bb} - I_1 R_L$$

and R_o is the output impedance, being given by the parallel combination of R_L and the dynamic plate resistance of the tube r_p. The voltage variation at G_2 during the quasi-stable state is shown in Fig. 6-3. The transition from stable to quasi-stable state occurs at $t = 0$. For $t < 0$, $e_{c2} = 0$, while at $t = 0+$, $e_{c2} = -I_1 R_L$. The voltage will rise exponentially toward E_{bb} with a time constant $\tau = (R + R_o)C$. This exponential rise will actually continue, however, only until e_{c2} rises to the cutoff voltage E_{co}, at which time a reverse transition will occur. Since ordinarily $R \gg R_o$, we shall make little error if we consider that $\tau = RC$.

It will be recalled (Sec. 2-4) that when the voltage e at a point in a

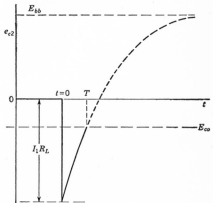

FIG. 6-3. Voltage variation of G_2 during the quasi-stable state.

circuit changes as the result of the charging of a capacitor through a resistor, then the voltage may be expressed as a function of the time by

$$e = E_f - (E_f - E_i)\epsilon^{-t/\tau} \tag{6-3}$$

Here E_i is the value of e at $t = 0$, while E_f is the final voltage value, that is, the value being asymptotically approached by e. Applying Eq. (6-3) in the present case gives

$$e_{c2} = E_{bb} - (E_{bb} + I_1 R_L)\epsilon^{-t/RC} \tag{6-4}$$

The quasi-stable state will terminate when $e_{c2} = E_{co}$ or after a time T given by

$$T = RC \ln \frac{E_{bb} + I_1 R_L}{E_{bb} - E_{co}} \tag{6-5}$$

The time T may be varied either through the time constant RC or by varying I_1. The current I_1 is controlled by e_{c1}, which may be varied by means of E_{cc}.

The duration T of a monostable multi is ordinarily not particularly stable, depending as it does on the tube characteristics through I_1 and E_{co}. The stability is somewhat better if R is returned to a high voltage such as E_{bb} rather than to ground. The reason for this feature is to be seen in Fig. 6-4. Curve 1 corresponds to returning R to E_{bb}, while curve 2 corresponds to R returned to ground. The RC time constants have been

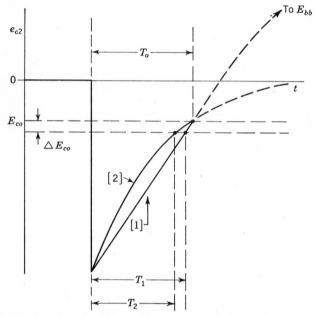

Fig. 6-4. Illustrating the advantage with respect to timing stability of returning the grid resistor to E_{bb}.

adjusted in the two cases to give the same initial time duration T_o. Suppose that E_{co} now changes by ΔE_{co} due to, say, a change in heater voltage. Then the change in timing, $T_o - T_1$, is smaller than $T_o - T_2$. This matter is discussed in more detail in Sec. 12-5.

6-3. Waveforms of Plate-coupled Multi. We shall now investigate the appearance of the waveforms at both plates and both grids from the time before a trigger is applied to the time the multi has restored itself to its initial stable state. The waveforms are shown in Fig. 6-5. The triggering signal occurs at $t = 0$ and the reverse transition occurs at $t = T$.

At $t = 0$, T_2 goes *off* and T_1 goes *on*. The voltages e_{b1} and e_{c2} drop abruptly by the same amount, $I_1 R_L$. The voltage e_{b2} rises abruptly by I_2R_L and e_{c1} rises abruptly by the amount aI_2R_L. The voltage at G_2 now starts to rise exponentially with time constant RC toward E_{bb}. Until e_{c2} reaches the cutoff voltage E_{co}, all voltages at the other electrodes remain unaltered.

Refer now to Fig. 6-5a and b. At time $t = 0$, tube T_1 was driven *on*, as a consequence of which e_{b1} and e_{c2} dropped by I_1R_L. At $t = T$, tube

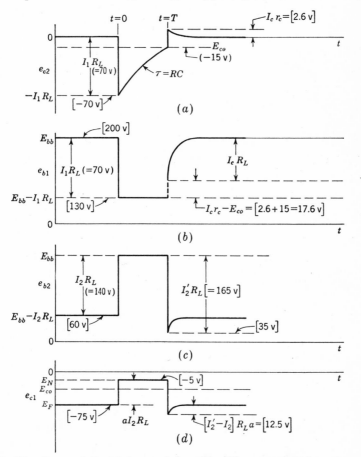

FIG. 6-5. Waveforms of the plate-coupled multi. The exponential portions of the waveforms beginning at $t = T$ all have a time constant $(R_L + r_c)C$. The numerical values in parentheses refer to the illustrative example on page 181.

T_1 will be driven back to cutoff and, if were not constrained from so doing, the plate P_1 (Fig. 6-1) would rise abruptly by I_1R_L and thus carry the grid G_2 upward by the same amount. At $t = T$, however, the grid G_2 is much closer to zero voltage than at $t = 0+$. If, therefore, the grid G_2 were driven positive by amount I_1R_L from an initial level E_{co}, the grid G_2 would go positive by the amount $I_1R_L + E_{co}$ and appreciable grid current would flow.   Since T_1 is cut off and R is much larger than R_L (in the plate of T_1), this grid current must flow predominantly through the plate load of T_1.   The voltage e_{b1} is therefore constrained from jumping upward abruptly by I_1R_L, and as a matter of fact e_{b1} will not attain E_{bb} until grid current has ceased.   Consequently, while the abrupt upward jump at G_2 is smaller than I_1R_L, the grid G_2 does not return gracefully to

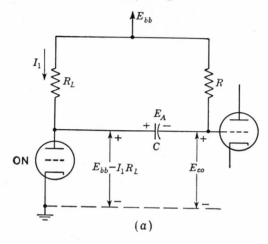

(a)

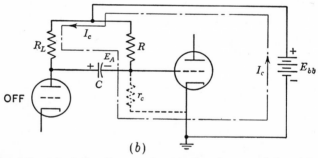

(b)

FIG. 6-6. Circuit for calculating the overshoot in the plate-coupled multi.   (a) Situation immediately before reverse transition.   (b) Situation immediately after reverse transition.

zero voltage, but instead initially overshoots its mark and then finally decays to zero.   It will be recognized that the overshoot here described is identical in origin to the overshoot shown in Fig. 4-40.   We shall now make a quantitative estimate of the magnitude of this overshoot.

The situation immediately before the reverse transition is shown in Fig. 6-6a.   The voltage drop across the capacitor is

$$E_A = E_{bb} - I_1R_L - E_{co} \tag{6-6}$$

Immediately after the reverse transition the situation is as shown in

Fig. 6-6*b*. Since the transition is abrupt, we may consider that E_A is the same in Fig. 6-6*a* and *b*. We assume that the flow of grid current may be accounted for adequately by including the resistor r_c, which is the static grid-to-cathode resistance of T_2. And since $R \gg R_L$, we may neglect the grid current through R in comparison with the current through R_L. The path of the grid current I_c is as shown in Fig. 6-6*b*. Equating to zero the sum of the voltage drops encountered yields

$$-E_{bb} + R_L I_c + E_A + r_c I_c = 0 \qquad (6\text{-}7)$$

Combining Eqs. (6-6) and (6-7) gives for the size of the grid overshoot

$$r_c I_c = \frac{(I_1 R_L + E_{co})r_c}{R_L + r_c} \qquad (6\text{-}8)$$

The total amplitude of the abrupt jump at the grid G_2 is $r_c I_c - E_{co}$. The abrupt jump at the plate P_1 is equal to the grid jump, since G_2 and P_1 are coupled by a capacitor. The overshoot decays to zero with a time constant $(R_L + r_c)C$, and as the grid overshoot decays exponentially, the plate P_1 rises exponentially to E_{bb}. Corresponding to the overshoot at G_2 there is an undershoot at P_2. The current I_2' in T_2 at the time of the overshoot may be determined by drawing a load line for R_L on the *positive* grid characteristics of the tube and noting the current corresponding to a grid voltage $r_c I_c$. The undershoot at P_2 similarly is reflected in an undershoot at G_1. Of course, all the sharp corners indicated in Fig. 6-5 are actually slightly rounded by tube and stray shunting capacitances. Ordinarily, however, this rounding is of a different order of magnitude from the rounding apparent on the trailing edge of the waveform at P_1.

The following illustrative example will indicate more specifically how one may determine the waveforms to be anticipated in a plate-coupled multi.

EXAMPLE. Compute the voltage levels for the waveforms of Fig. 6-5 for a plate-coupled multi whose components and supply voltages are as given in Fig. 6-1. The tubes employed are the two halves of a type 12AU7.

Solution. Drawing a load line for $R_L = 20$ K and $E_{bb} = 200$ volts on the negative-grid plate characteristics for the type 12AU7 (Fig. A-7), we find $I_2 R_L = 140$ volts and $E_{bb} - I_2 R_L = 60$ volts. From Eq. (6-1), we find $E_F = -75$ volts. From Eq. (6-2), we have $E_N = -5$ volts, corresponding to which

$$I_1 R_L = 70 \text{ volts} \quad \text{and} \quad E_{bb} - I_1 R_L = 130 \text{ volts}$$

Beginning immediately after $t = 0$, the grid waveform rises from -70 volts exponentially toward 200 volts with a time constant which is essentially $\tau = RC$. The quasi-stable state persists until e_{c2} reaches the cutoff voltage $E_{co} = -15$ volts, during which time all other voltage levels remain constant.

We must now compute the amplitude of the grid overshoot, for which we may use Eq. (6-8), provided that we are able to decide on a reasonable value of r_c. Examine now the positive-grid tube characteristics for the 12AU7 given in Fig. A-8. Observe that over quite a range of plate voltage, the grid current is 10 ma for a grid voltage of 10 volts. We therefore tentatively accept for r_c the value $r_c = 1,000$ ohms. The grid overshoot is therefore

$$r_c I_c = \frac{(70 - 15) \times 1,000}{20,000 + 1,000} = \frac{1}{21} \, 55 = 2.6 \text{ volts} \tag{6-9}$$

The abrupt portion of the rise of the plate voltage e_{b1} has a magnitude

$$r_c I_c - E_{co} = 2.6 + 15 = 17.6 \text{ volts}$$

The remainder of the approach to the supply voltage occurs with a time constant $(R_L + r_c)C$, which is also the time constant with which the overshoot decays.

To find $I_2' R_L$, we draw the load line for 20 K and $E_{bb} = 200$ volts on the positive grid characteristics, finding approximately that corresponding to $e_{c2} = +2.6$ volts $I_2' R_L = 165$ volts. At the overshoot, then, the voltage e_{b2} drops to 35 volts. The amplitude of the undershoot in e_{c1} is $(I_2' R_L - I_2 R_L)a = (165 - 140) \times \frac{1}{2} = 12.5$ volts.

The least certain feature of the above calculation has to do with the overshoot amplitude. This difficulty results from the fact that the static grid resistance r_c is not constant but is rather a function of the plate voltage, decreasing with decreasing plate voltage. We may, however, note that r_c does remain fairly constant, provided the plate voltage remains large in comparison with the grid voltage. This result is borne out by the curves of Fig. A-8, where it appears that for high plate voltage in comparison to grid voltage $r_c = 1,000$ ohms. In our present case we require to know the value of r_c under the circumstance that $e_{c2} = 2.6$ volts and $e_{b2} = 35$ volts; hence we may reasonably consider $r_c = 1,000$ ohms.

The matter is usually further complicated by the fact that normally tube characteristics do not furnish very precise data in the neighborhood of small positive grid voltages. The curves of Fig. A-8 are typical. If more detailed plate and grid-current curves should happen to be available, the calculation of the overshoot may be improved by the following procedure. We select first some reasonable value for r_c and compute, as above, the grid and plate voltage corresponding to the overshoot. Corresponding to this first approximation for grid and plate voltages we note from the tube characteristics a better value for r_c. We may now recalculate the overshoots, leading to a still better value of r_c, etc. Normally, however, the first approximation gives sufficiently good results and successive calculations are not warranted.

In the general discussion above of the monostable multi waveforms as well as in the illustrative example, we have, in the interest of simplicity, made two approximations which may not always be well justified in practice. The first of these approximations has to do with the fact that we have neglected the loading effect of the attenuator consisting of

R_1 and R_2 on the voltage which appears at the plate of T_2. The effect of this loading is clearly to reduce somewhat the voltage at P_2 and is more pronounced when T_2 is *off*, during the quasi-stable state, than during the stable state when T_2 is *on*.

The second approximation may be seen by referring again to Fig. 6-2, which indicates the charging path for the capacitor C during the quasi-stable state. The current which charges the capacitor flows also through the output impedance R_o toward the voltage source E_{b1}. As a result of this current the voltage at P_1 is slightly larger than $E_{bb} - I_1 R_L$ by the amount of the voltage drop across R_o. Furthermore, during the time of the quasi-stable state, the capacitor-charging current decreases and as a result the voltage at P_1 decreases. Altogether, then, the waveform of e_{b1} in Fig. 6-5b is slightly incorrectly drawn. At time $t = 0+$, the waveform voltage should be slightly higher than $E_{bb} - I_1 R_L$ and the nominally flat portion of the waveform between $t = 0$ and $t = T$ should as a matter of fact exhibit a slight downward tilt.

6-4. The Influence of Tube Current I_1 on Waveforms. The tube current I_1 determines the initial drop $I_1 R_L$ at P_1 and G_2. This initial drop is conveniently adjustable through the negative supply voltage E_{cc}. The current I_1 has an effect not only on the duration of the quasi-stable state T, as is apparent from Eq. (6-5), but also on the general appearance of the waveforms.

First, let us note that there is a minimum allowable value of I_1, $I_1 = I_1(\text{min})$, which is required in order that there shall be a quasi-stable state. This current $I_1(\text{min})$ is clearly determined by the condition that the drop $I_1(\text{min}) R_L$ shall be sufficient to drive G_2 below cutoff. Hence $I_1(\text{min}) R_L = |E_{co}|$ or $I_1(\text{min}) = |E_{co}|/R_L$. This result is consistent with Eq. (6-5) since this condition makes $T = 0$. Corresponding to $I_1(\text{min})$ there is a maximum value $E_{cc}(\text{max})$ of the bias supply. Similarly, there is a minimum value $E_{cc}(\text{min})$ dictated by the consideration that in the stable state tube T_1 must be at cutoff. If E_{cc} is adjusted so that T_1 may not be at cutoff, then the multi has no permanently stable state. In this case, as will be described in Sec. 6-11, the multi becomes astable and will switch back and forth between two quasi-stable states.

In Fig. 6-7 are to be seen the waveforms at G_2 and P_1 for two cases. In one case $I_1 = I_1'$, which is only slightly larger than $I_1(\text{min})$. In the second case, $I_1 = I_1''$, which is very much larger than $I_1(\text{min})$. The time T'' corresponding to I_1'' is of course larger than T' corresponding to I_1'. This difference in timing is, however, not the essential feature to be noted here, since, by adjusting appropriately the time constant RC in the two cases, the times may be made the same. Rather, it is to be noted that in the case $I_1 = I_1'$ the waveforms are much more nearly rectangular than for $I_1 = I_1''$. The overshoot is smaller, as is to be expected, since from Eq. (6-8) the overshoot depends on the quantity $I_1 R_L + E_{co}$, which is the amount by which the voltage e_{c2} drops below the cutoff level. Similarly, the exponential rise in e_{c2} is much less pronounced for I_1' than for I_1''.   Again in the waveforms for e_{b1} the abrupt portion of the rise is a much larger fraction of the total jump for I_1' than for I_1''. The waveforms at G_1 and P_2 will also be more rectangular for I_1' since the overshoot will be smaller than for I_1''.

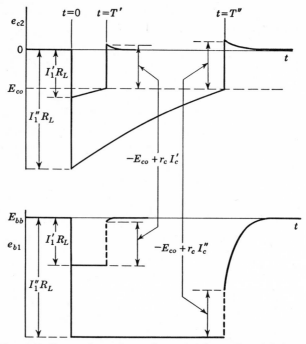

FIG. 6-7. Comparison of waveforms for I_1 small and I_1 large.

It will be clear from an examination of the grid waveforms of Fig. 6-7 that an adjustment of I_1 for a nearly rectangular waveform carries with it the disadvantage of poor stability of multi time duration.   The duration is determined by the interval during which the grid of T_2 remains below cutoff.   Initially, at $t = 0$, the grid is below cutoff by the amount $I_1 R_L + E_{co}$.   If $I_1 R_L + E_{co}$ is small in comparison with E_{co}, a small percentage change in I_1 will make a large percentage change in $I_1 R_L + E_{co}$, with a correspondingly large percentage change in timing.

6-5. Recovery Time in a Monostable Multi.   After the formation of the gate of duration T, the multi will not have completely returned to its stable state until all overshoots have decayed to zero.   The decay time of these overshoots is called the *recovery time*.   The recovery time depends on the time constant $(R_L + r_c)C$, while T depends on RC.   Where a short recovery time is of importance, a fixed required time constant RC is attained by making R as large as possible and C correspondingly small. A practical upper limit for R is of the order of 10 Meg and is set by the same considerations which limit grid-leak-resistor sizes generally (see Sec. 3-5). Additionally, if R is large and C small, the effective imped- ance between G_2 and ground will be large during the interval when G_2 is not in clamp and the circuit may become excessively sensitive to stray

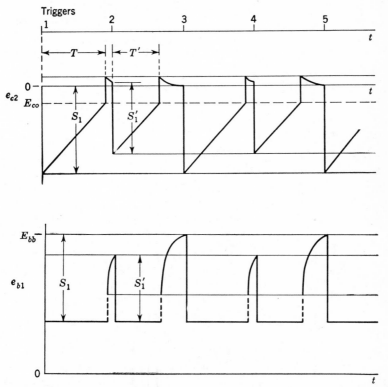

Fig. 6-8. Waveforms of multi when interval between triggers does not allow complete recovery.

fields. The advantage of a short recovery time may be seen from the following discussion.

Consider what might happen if regularly spaced triggers are to gen- erate gates which are as wide as possible (T to be nearly equal to the interval between pulses). At the end of the time T the capacitance C must recharge through R_L before the next trigger comes along. Suppose that C is not completely recharged and hence that P_1 has not reached E_{bb} before the next trigger is injected. This next impulse will trip the cir- cuit and P_1 will drop to its clamped-on value. The change in voltage S_1' at P_1 is less than the full swing $S_1 = I_1 R_L$ because the plate did not reach E_{bb}. This new smaller increment S_1' appears at G_2, as shown in Fig. 6-8. Furthermore, the voltage at G_2 will not have decayed to zero when the second trigger arrives.   The result is that, after this second trigger, G_2 starts at a more positive voltage than after the first trigger.   Therefore the length of the quasi-stable state T' after the second trigger is less than T after the first trigger.   Hence, there is a longer time available for C to charge before the third trigger appears.   Thus the drop in G_2 at this third

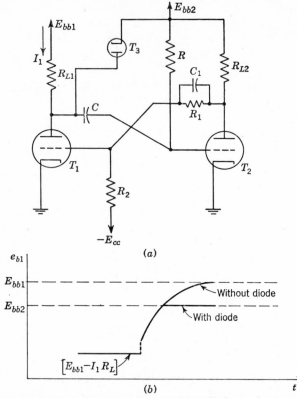

(a)

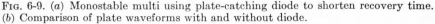

(b)

FIG. 6-9. (a) Monostable multi using plate-catching diode to shorten recovery time. (b) Comparison of plate waveforms with and without diode.

impulse may again be the original S_1.   If so, then at the fourth trigger it will be S_1'.   This will lead to the peculiar situation pictured in Fig. 6-8 in which not all cycles are alike, but rather alternate cycles have the same character.

There are a number of steps which may be taken if it should become important to reduce the recovery time.   The most straightforward method is to reduce the size of the plate load resistance of tube T_1.   It may then become necessary, however, to replace the tube T_1 by a larger tube since the tube dissipation will increase.   Thus, for a given swing at P_1, the current I_1 must increase as R_L is decreased.

A second method is illustrated in Fig. 6-9, which displays the use of a plate-catching diode to eliminate the slow portion of the rise at the plate of T_1. Note that in this case the plate resistor of T_1 must be returned to a higher supply voltage than the plate resistor of T_2.

After these first two methods have been employed, some further improvement may result if an additional diode is shunted from grid to cathode of T_2 in order to reduce r_c. Finally, we may use a cathode follower to couple the plate P_1 to the grid G_2. Since the plate P_1 is

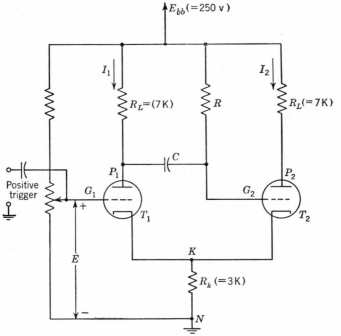

FIG. 6-10. A cathode-coupled monostable multi. Components and supply voltage specified refer to the illustrative example of Sec. 6-7.

coupled directly to the grid of the cathode follower, it is required that the cathode-follower supply voltage be higher than the multi supply voltage. The timing capacitor is connected between the cathode of the cathode follower and the grid G_2. The timing capacitor will now be able to recharge through the low output impedance of the cathode follower. The use of a cathode follower or of a small plate load resistance for tube T_1 will reduce the recovery time as already noted, but the amplitude of the overshoots will be greater than before [see Eq. (6-8)].

6-6. The Cathode-coupled Monostable Multi Waveforms. An alternative form of the monostable multi, the cathode-coupled multi, is shown in Fig. 6-10. This circuit bears the same relation to the plate-coupled monostable multi as the Schmitt circuit bears to the plate-coupled binary. Observe that the coupling from P_2 to G_1 is lacking and that in its place has been substituted a common cathode resistor R_k. No negative supply is required. The signal at P_2 is not directly involved in the regenerative loop. Hence, the plate P_2 makes an ideal point from which to obtain an output voltage. The grid G_1 is an ideal point at which to

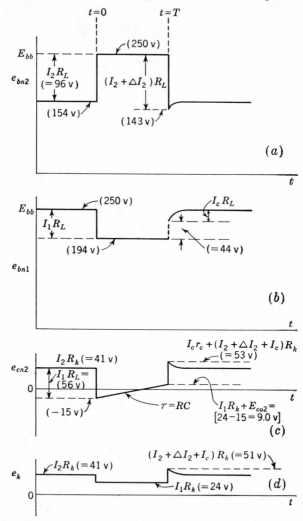

Fig. 6-11. Waveforms of the cathode-coupled monostable multi. Numerical values in parentheses correspond to the illustrative example of Sec. 6-7.

inject the triggering signal, since this grid is coupled to no other point in the circuit. Hence, the trigger source cannot load the circuit. It also turns out that the width of the multi gate is an accurately linear function of the d-c bias voltage E on G_1, and hence this circuit makes an excellent gate generator whose width is easily and linearly controllable.

The waveforms of the cathode-coupled multi are shown in Fig. 6-11. The waveform at G_1 is now of no interest since it consists only of the triggering pulse. In its place, however, we have a waveform at the cathode. Initially, tube T_2 in Fig. 6-10 carries a current I_2 corresponding to a clamped grid. The grid of T_2 and the common cathode are at a voltage $I_2 R_k$. It is, of course required here as in the case of the plate-coupled multi, that T_1 be cut off when T_2 is conducting. Hence, the bias voltage E on the grid of T_1 must be less than $I_2 R_k$ by at least the cutoff voltage E_{co1} of the tube T_1. We may therefore note that the maximum allowable value for E is

$$E_{max} = I_2 R_k + E_{co1} \qquad (6\text{-}10)$$

When a triggering signal causes a transition from the stable to the quasi-stable state, the current in T_2 becomes zero and a current I_1 flows in T_1. This current may be determined by the value at which E has been set. Hence in Fig. 6-11, immediately after $t = 0$, P_2 rises abruptly by $I_2 R_L$, while P_1 and G_2 drop abruptly by $I_1 R_L$. The cathode voltage changes from $I_2 R_k$ to $I_1 R_k$.

In order that there shall be a quasi-stable state, the current I_1 must be large enough to drive T_2 below cutoff. This minimum required current I_0 is easily calculated as follows. At $t = 0+$, the grid G_2, which was at a voltage $I_2 R_k$ with respect to ground, drops by $I_1 R_L$ volts. Hence, at $t = 0+$, the grid-to-ground voltage of tube T_2 is

$$e_{cn2} = I_2 R_k - I_1 R_L$$

At this time also the cathode-to-ground voltage is

$$e_k = I_1 R_k$$

It is required that e_{cn2} be less than e_k by at least the cutoff voltage E_{co2} of tube T_2. Hence I_0 is given by the condition that at $t = 0+$

$$e_{cn2} - e_k = E_{co2}$$

or
$$I_2 R_k - I_0 R_L - I_0 R_k = E_{co2}$$

so that*
$$I_0 = \frac{I_2 R_k - E_{co2}}{R_L + R_k} \qquad (6\text{-}11)$$

---

* In Eq. (6-11) as in (6-10), the cutoff voltages E_{co2} and E_{co1} correspond to the actual plate-to-cathode voltages E_{pk} of the tubes, which voltages are smaller than E_{bb} because of the drop across the cathode resistor. In Eq. (6-10), $E_{pk} = E_{bb} - I_2 R_k$, and I_2 is known. Hence E_{co1} may be determined directly from the tube characteristics. In Eq. (6-11), E_{co2} corresponds to $E_{pk} = E_{bb} - I_0 R_k$, in which I_0 is not known. We may, however, find E_{co2} by successive approximations. We assume initially that E_{co2} corresponds to E_{bb} and use this value in Eq. (6-11) to find a first approximation to I_0. Using this value for I_0, we may determine E_{co2} more precisely. Ordinarily, however, the error involved is small and the more detailed calculation is not warranted.

The voltage E on G_1 must not be less than a value E_{min} corresponding to the current I_0. And the waveforms of Fig. 6-11 apply only, of course, for the case $E_{max} > E > E_{min}$.

After the initial abrupt jump in all the waveforms, the voltage at G_2 starts to rise exponentially toward E_{bb}. All other voltages remain constant until e_{cn2} rises to the cutoff voltage of T_2, which occurs, as indicated in Fig. 6-11, when $e_{cn2} = I_1R_k + E_{co2}$. At this point the quasi-stable state is terminated, and as in the plate-coupled multi, there is an overshoot in the waveform at G_2 before the waveform finally settles to the quiescent level I_2R_k. Associated with this overshoot there are overshoots in the waveforms at P_2 and at the cathode and a delay in the attainment of the final level E_{bb} by the waveform at P_1.

The computation of the overshoot in the cathode-coupled multi is somewhat more involved than the calculation of the overshoot in the case of the plate-coupled multi. This complication results in the former case from the presence of the cathode resistor. In Sec. 6-7 we inquire into the overshoot, and we shall then be able to complete the discussion of the waveforms of Fig. 6-11.

6-7. Overshoots in Cathode-coupled Multi. The amplitude of the overshoot may be calculated from the circuit shown in Fig. 6-12a, since at the instant of the overshoot T_1 is *off* and T_2 is *on*. Neglecting the small current through R, we may replace a by b. In b, E_d is the difference between the supply voltage E_{bb} and the voltage E_A across the capacitor. The voltage E_A is the capacitor voltage immediately before the overshoot and may be determined from c, which depicts the situation just at the time when T_2 reaches cutoff. We have

$$E_A = (E_{bb} - I_1R_L) - (I_1R_k + E_{co2})$$

and
$$E_d = E_{bb} - E_A = I_1(R_L + R_k) + E_{co2} \tag{6-12}$$

If, in Fig. 6-12b, E_d were equal to I_2R_k, then there would be no overshoot. For the purpose then of computing the amount by which the grid voltage exceeds the quiescent level I_2R_k, we may use the circuit shown in Fig. 6-12d, in which

$$E_d' = E_d - I_2R_k = I_1(R_L + R_k) + E_{co2} - I_2R_k$$
$$= (I_1 - I_0)(R_L + R_k) \tag{6-13}$$

where use has been made of Eq. (6-11). Since here we are interested in a case in which the grid goes positive with respect to the cathode, the resistor r_c has been included to account for the flow of grid current.

Since the overshoot is ordinarily small, we may use the linear equivalent circuit of the vacuum tube as in Fig. 6-12e, to find the departure of

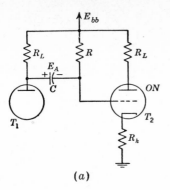

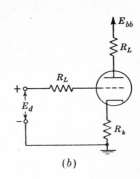

(a)

(b)

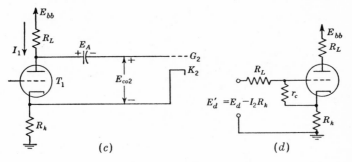

(c)

(d)

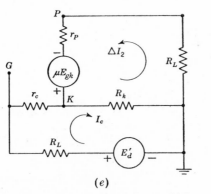

(e)

FIG. 6-12. Development of an equivalent circuit from which to calculate the overshoot in a cathode-coupled monostable multi.

voltages and currents from the quiescent condition. The quiescent condition is the one in which $e_k = e_{cn2} = I_2 R_k$ and the grid current is zero. The change in plate current is ΔI_2, and the change in grid current is $\Delta I_c = I_c - 0 = I_c$. The mesh equations of Fig. 6-12e are

$$R_k(\Delta I_2 + I_c) + (R_L + r_p)\Delta I_2 = \mu E_{gk} = \mu r_c I_c$$
$$(R_L + r_c)I_c + R_k(I_c + \Delta I_2) = E_d'$$

It may now easily be verified that, in terms of the symbol γ defined by

$$\gamma \equiv \frac{\mu r_c - R_k}{R_k + R_L + r_p} \tag{6-14}$$

that $\qquad I_c = \dfrac{E_d'}{R_L + r_c + (1 + \gamma)R_k} \qquad$ and $\qquad \Delta I_2 = \gamma I_c \tag{6-15}$

Equation (6-15) also indicates that the coupling capacitor C charges from an effective voltage E_d' through a resistance $R_L + r_c + (1 + \gamma)R_k$. The time constant of the decay of the overshoot will accordingly be $[(R_L + r_c + (1 + \gamma)R_k]C$.

In terms of the grid current I_c and the increment in plate current ΔI_2 the waveforms of the cathode-coupled multi may now be completed with the results indicated in Fig. 6-11. An illustrative example follows.

EXAMPLE. Compute the voltages $E_{\max}$ and $E_{\min}$ for the cathode-coupled multi whose components and supply voltage are as given in Fig. 6-10. For a value of E approximately midway between $E_{\max}$ and $E_{\min}$, calculate the voltage levels of the waveforms of Fig. 6-11. The tubes employed are the two half sections of a type 12AU7 tube.

Solution. Drawing a load line corresponding to $R_L + R_k = 10$ K and $E_{bb} = 250$ volts on the negative grid-plate characteristics for the type 12AU7 (Fig. A-7), we find $I_2 = 13.7$ ma. Hence $I_2 R_L = 7 \times 13.7 = 96$ volts and $I_2 R_k = 3 \times 13.7 = 41$ volts. The voltage $E_{\max}$ is given by Eq. (6-10) in which E_{co1} is the cutoff voltage corresponding to a plate-to-cathode voltage of $250 - 41 = 209$. We find $E_{co1} = -15$ volts so that $E_{\max} = 41 - 15 = 26$ volts.

To find $E_{\min}$, we must first find I_0 from Eq. (6-11). Assuming tentatively that E_{co2} is also equal approximately to -15 volts, we find

$$I_0 = \frac{41 + 15}{7 + 3} = 5.6 \text{ ma}$$

It appears, then, that E_{co2} is actually the cutoff voltage corresponding to a plate-to-cathode voltage of $250 - 3 \times 5.6 = 233$, so that E_{co2} is more nearly equal to -17 volts. However, the precision with which tube characteristics apply to an individual tube hardly warrant applying this correction. We find now from the tube characteristics that a current $I_0 = 5.6$ ma flows when the grid-to-cathode voltage is -8 volts. Hence

$$E_{\min} = E_{c1} + I_0 R_k = -8 + 5.6 \times 3 = 8.8 \text{ volts}$$

Now let us compute the voltage levels in Fig. 6-11 for $E = 18$ volts. Using the method of Sec. 1-7, we find that corresponding to $E = 18$ volts $I_1 = 8.0$ ma, giving $I_1 R_L = 56$ volts and $I_1 R_k = 24$ volts. Also, as noted above, $I_2 R_L = 96$ volts and $I_2 R_k = 41$ volts. These voltage levels are indicated in parentheses in Fig. 6-11.

At the current corresponding to grid clamping ($I_2 = 13.7$ ma) and at a plate voltage of $250 - 96 - 41 = 113$ volts, we have (see Fig. A-9) $\mu = 18$, $r_p = 6$ K. If we assume as before that $r_c = 1,000$ ohms, we find, from Eq. (6-14), that

$$\gamma = \frac{18 - 3}{3 + 7 + 6} = 0.94$$

Combining Eqs. (6-13) and (6-15), we have

$$I_c = \frac{(I_1 - I_0)(R_L + R_k)}{R_L + r_c + (1 + \gamma)R_k} = \frac{(8.0 - 5.6)(7 + 3)}{7 + 1 + 1.94 \times 3} = 1.7 \text{ ma}$$

and
$$\Delta I_2 = \gamma I_c = 0.94 \times 1.7 = 1.6 \text{ ma}$$

Hence at the overshoot the cathode voltage rises to

$$(I_2 + \Delta I_2 + I_c)R_k = (13.7 + 1.6 + 1.7)3 = 51 \text{ volts}$$

and the voltage at G_2 rises to $51 + I_c r_c = 51 + 1.7 = 53$ volts. It is now easily verified that the remaining voltages indicated in Fig. 6-11 are given correctly.

6-8. Linearity of Delay of Cathode-coupled Multi.

A useful feature of the cathode-coupled monostable multi is the fact that the delay is quite accurately linearly related to the voltage E (Fig. 6-10) on grid G_1. If, therefore, a delay or a gate duration is required which is proportional to an electrical control signal, this signal need only be applied to G_1. Similarly, if manual control of the delay is intended, then the voltage E may be derived from a *linear* potentiometer.

The linearity results from the facts that the tube current I_1 is linearly related to the voltage E and that the duration of the delay is linearly proportional, in turn, to I_1. The linearity of I_1 with E is to be expected from the discussion of Sec. 1-6, where it is pointed out that the presence of the cathode resistor introduces negative feedback which serves to make the current I_1 vary more linearly with E. To see that the delay T is fairly linear with I_1, we proceed as follows.

Let us apply Eq. (6-3) to the exponentially rising portion of G_2 (see Fig. 6-11c). Then $E_f = E_{bb}$, $E_i = I_2R_k - I_1R_L$, and when $t = T$, $e = I_1R_k + E_{co2}$. Substituting these values into Eq. (6-3) and solving for $T/\tau = T/RC$, we find

$$\frac{T}{RC} = \ln \frac{E_{bb} + I_1R_L - I_2R_k}{E_{bb} - E_{co2} - I_1R_k} \tag{6-16}$$

It is convenient to introduce the variable $I_{10} \equiv I_1 - I_0$, I_{10} being the departure of the tube current from the current corresponding to $E_{\min}$. Also let

$$E' \equiv E_{bb} + I_0R_L - I_2R_k \tag{6-17}$$

Using Eq. (6-11) for I_0, we also find

$$E' = E_{bb} - E_{co2} - I_0R_k \tag{6-18}$$

In arriving at Eq. (6-18), we have neglected the fact that E_{co2} in Eq. (6-16) actually depends somewhat on I_1, while E_{co2} in Eq. (6-11) corresponds to a value $I_1 = I_0$. Using Eq. (6-17) in the numerator of Eq. (6-16) and Eq. (6-18) in the denominator, we have

$$\frac{T}{RC} = \ln \frac{E' + I_{10}R_L}{E' - I_{10}R_k} = \ln \frac{1 + I_{10}R_L/E'}{1 - I_{10}R_k/E'} \tag{6-19}$$

From the expansion $\ln(1 + x) = x - x^2/2 + x^3/3 - \cdots$, we find approximately, for $I_{10}R_L$ and $I_{10}R_k$ both small in comparison with E', that

$$\frac{T}{RC} \cong \frac{I_{10}(R_L + R_k)}{E'} \left(1 - \frac{I_{10}(R_L - R_k)}{2E'}\right) \tag{6-20}$$

We may therefore expect linearity so long as $I_{10}(R_L - R_k) \ll 2E'$. For the circuit of Fig. 6-10, it is easily computed that $E' = 248$ volts and that the maximum value of $I_{10}(R_L - R_k) = 18$ volts. Hence the correction term in the parentheses in the above equation is never larger than

$$\frac{18}{2 \times 248} = 0.03$$

If we select $R_L = R_k$, then Eq. (6-20) gives a zero correction and we should then carry out the expansion to a higher order (see Prob. 6-15).

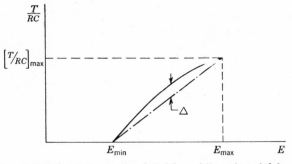

Fig. 6-13. Pertaining to the definition of linearity of delay.

The linearity of delay T with input voltage E depends on the linearity with which I_1 follows E (see Prob. 6-16). Experimentally it has been determined that it is possible to adjust the cathode-coupled multi to provide a linearity error of 1 per cent. The definition of linearity error ϵ employed here is given in connection with Fig. 6-13 as

$$\epsilon = \frac{\Delta}{(T/RC)_{\max}} \tag{6-21}$$

in which Δ is the maximum discrepancy between an experimental plot of $T/(RC)$ vs. E and a straight line joining the beginning and end points of the plot (see Prob. 6-14). From Prob. 6-14, we have

$$\epsilon = \frac{I_{10}(R_L - R_k)}{8E'}$$

The delay T is a sensitive function of supply-voltage variations. For example, if the E_{bb} supply changes by 10 per cent, we may expect about a 5 per cent change in delay. Another type of delay circuit which is much less dependent upon supply-voltage variations than this multi is described in Sec. 7-7.

6-9. The Influence of E on Waveforms. The gate width T of the cathode-coupled multi is determined by E and the product RC, assuming that all other parameters are held constant. As E is varied from $E_{\min}$ to $E_{\max}$, the logarithmic term in Eq. (6-16) varies from zero to a maximum, M. The maximum delay $T_{\max}$ is given by $T_{\max} = RCM$. A given delay can be obtained by using either a small E and a large RC or a large E and a small RC. If E is near $E_{\min}$ (so that I_1 is near I_0), then the overshoots in waveform will be small, whereas if E is near $E_{\max}$ (large I_1), the overshoots will be emphasized. This situation corresponds to the analogous state of affairs for the plate-coupled multi discussed in Sec. 6-4.

If RC is held fixed and E is slowly increased from zero, then the following events will take place. For voltages below $E_{\min}$, the circuit cannot be triggered. For $E > E_{\min}$, the waveforms will change from a narrow gate with little overshoot (analogous to those indicated to the left in Fig. 6-7) to wider and wider gates with progressively higher and higher overshoots (analogous to those indicated to the right in Fig. 6-7). When E reaches $E_{\max}$, the circuit becomes an astable instead of a monostable multi and it continues to operate even when the triggers are removed (as discussed in Sec. 6-11).

The above assumes that the triggers are widely spaced compared with the maximum multi width. If this is not true, then the above sequence of events takes place until the multi width approaches the time between triggers. Then the situation pictured in Fig. 6-8 takes place, where alternate cycles have different waveforms. As a matter of fact this anomalous situation may be obtained even at narrow widths if the recovery time constant is comparable to the time between pulses. This emphasizes the importance of keeping C as small as possible, just as with the plate-coupled monostable multi.

6-10. Triggering of the Monostable Multi. The monostable multi may be triggered by applying a positive pulse to the normally *off* grid G_1. The pulse must be at least large enough to bring G_1 out of cutoff. For example, in the cathode-coupled multi, the trigger amplitude when added to $E_{c1} = E - I_2 R_k$ must exceed the value E_{co1}. Hence for any value of E the trigger E_T required must have an amplitude of at least

$$E_T = I_2 R_k - E + E_{co1}$$

Using Eq. (6-10), we find

$$E_T = E_{\max} - E \qquad (6-22)$$

The largest trigger amplitude $E_T = E_T(\max) = E_{\max} - E_{\min}$ will be required when

$$E = E_{\min}$$

If triggers of amplitude less than E_T (max) are employed, then the multi will trigger when E is set for large delays but not when E is set for short delays. Thus, if E is initially near E_{max} and then progressively decreased, the multi will operate properly with progressively shorter delays until finally a critical value of E will be attained where the multi will fail to respond. At this point if the trigger size is increased the multi will once again function properly.

In the plate-coupled multi, if the trigger is introduced at G_1 through a capacitor, the capacitance must be small, since a signal appears at G_1 due to the regeneration in the multi. The remarks made earlier (Sec. 5-7) in connection with the triggering of a binary with a positive pulse through a small capacitor apply equally well in the present case. If the input time constant is small in comparison to the triggering pulse duration and if the pulse is rectangular in form, the multi may well make a reverse transition at the trailing edge of the trigger. Furthermore, if the trigger source impedance is low, the input capacitor may charge due to grid current and again a reverse transition may occur at the trailing edge of the trigger. This grid current may result if the pulse amplitude is large enough temporarily to drive the grid positive or if the quasi-stable state is one in which the grid G_1 is normally in clamp. In the cathode-coupled multi the input capacitor may be quite large and it is easier to avoid the reverse transition.

However, even in the case of the cathode-coupled multi there is a difficulty that arises when the triggered grid is permitted to draw grid current. As a result of the grid current the input capacitor charges and decreases the average value of the grid voltage, and the time of the quasi-stable state is correspondingly reduced. This shortening of the delay becomes more pronounced as the width of the triggering pulse increases.

A negative pulse applied to the *on* grid G_2 (or equivalently at the plate P_1) has, as in the binary, the advantage that the multi responds more sensitively. Also, as in the binary, there is less likelihood of a reverse transition occurring at the trailing edge of the trigger since, after the initial transition, G_2 is well below cutoff.

The triggering arrangement shown in Fig. 6-14 has a twofold advantage. First, it takes advantage of the improved sensitivity of the multi to a negative signal applied to G_2. Second, at the instant of the transition the plate of T_1 drops, the diode no longer conducts, and the multi is unresponsive to the triggering signal until the quasi-stable state is completed. This second feature is particularly important in a case where the input signal is not a short trigger but is rather a continuous waveform, say a sine wave. An application of this triggering scheme will be seen in Sec. 7-3 in connection with the synchronization of a vacuum-tube sweep circuit.

6-11. The Monostable Circuit Adjusted for Free-running Operation.
The monostable multi circuit has a permanently stable state only if
the tube T_1 is able to remain permanently cut off. We inquire now
into the matter of what happens when the bias on T_1 is adjusted so
that T_1 is not able to remain cut off. For this purpose consider the
circuit of Fig. 6-15. The form of the circuit is the same as for the
cathode-coupled monostable multi. However, since the return for both
grids is the same ground point, it is clear that it is not possible for the
tube current I_2 to keep tube T_1 permanently cut off. This circuit has no
stable state but instead has two quasi-stable states between which the
multi makes transitions periodically without the aid of external triggers.

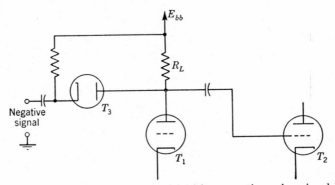

FIG. 6-14. Triggering of a monostable multi with a negative-going signal through a
diode.

We shall look now qualitatively into the waveform which will appear
at the grid G_2. In a particular case the waveform voltage levels may be
determined quantitatively by the methods given above, as may also the
waveforms and voltage levels at other points in the circuit. The discussion below will be directed at the circuit of Fig. 6-15, but the results will
apply in a general way to any monostable circuit similarly adjusted.
For example, the cathode-coupled multi with $E > E_{\max}$ will behave in an
astable manner similar to that discussed below.

Referring to Fig. 6-15a and b, we consider the grid G_2 waveform beginning at a time $t = 0$. Assume that at this time, because of the past
history of the circuit, the tube T_1 is carrying a current I_1 while T_2 is
below cutoff. The voltage at G_2 is rising exponentially toward ground
voltage. This exponential rise continues until e_{cn2}, the grid-to-ground
voltage of G_2, passes the cutin point of T_2, which occurs at

$$e_{cn2} = I_1 R_k + E_{co2}$$

At this point a regenerative transition occurs since now both tubes may
operate as amplifiers. The voltage at G_2 jumps to a high value because

the change in voltage at P_1, as T_1 goes *off*, is transferred through C to G_2. So long as e_{cn2} remains appreciably higher than ground voltage, the increased current through T_2 will be large enough to keep T_1 cut off because of the common cathode resistor. The capacitor C charges initially through the flow of grid current, and then at $t = t_1$ the grid current falls

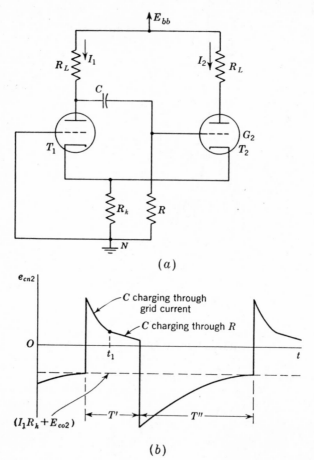

FIG. 6-15. (*a*) A monostable type circuit which has no stable state.   (*b*) The waveform at the grid G_2.

to zero and C continues to charge through R. The initial decay of e_{cn2} is therefore rapid, the remainder relatively slow. Sometime before e_{cn2} drops to zero the current I_2 is no longer adequate to keep T_1 cut off. This is the premise with which we started. When this condition is attained, the reverse transition occurs, driving T_2 to cutoff. We have now returned to our starting point. Ordinarily the partial period T' is appreciably smaller than T''. Usually a more symmetrical waveform is of advantage, and when a free-running multi is required the symmetrical circuit form discussed in Sec. 6-12 is more commonly employed.

If R_L or R_k or both are selected to be quite small, it may happen that neither tube is able even temporarily to keep the other tube cut off. In such a case the circuit will behave approximately as a sinusoidal oscillator. The frequency of oscillation will be determined by the stray capacitances associated with the circuit. These circumstances would correspond to the case in which the loop gain of the circuit is not much in excess of unity.

6-12. The Astable Plate-coupled Multi.[2] The circuit diagram of an astable plate-coupled multi is shown in Fig. 6-16. Since the coupling, in this case, is entirely capacitive, it is clear that neither tube can remain permanently cut off. This multi has, therefore, no stable state but has instead two quasi-stable states between which the circuit will make periodic transitions.

We discuss now the waveforms at the plates and grids of the astable multi of Fig. 6-16. These wave-forms are shown in Fig. 6-17a to d. We consider that at the time immediately before $t = 0$, tube T_2 is at grid clamp and carrying correspondingly a current I, while tube T_1 is below cutoff. The capacitor C_1 charges through resistor R_1, and at $t = 0$ the grid G_1 reaches the tube cutoff voltage E_{co}. Tube T_1 goes *on*, driving T_2 to cutoff and causing the plate of T_2 to start to rise to E_{bb}. The voltage rise at plate P_2 is trans-

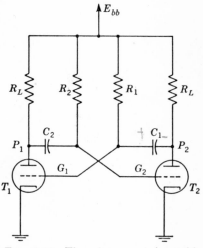

FIG. 6-16. The plate-coupled astable multi.

ferred to G_1, causing the customary grid overshoot at G_1. The amplitude of this overshoot is calculated in precisely the same manner as the grid overshoot which occurs in the plate-coupled monostable multi of Fig. 6-1. The amplitude of the overshoot is given by Eq. (6-8) as

$$r_c I_c = \frac{(I R_L + E_{co})r_c}{R_L + r_c}$$

in which we have replaced I_1 by I since the clamped current for both tubes of Fig. 6-16 is the same.

If the tube current at the moment of the overshoot is I', then the corresponding undershoot at the plate P_1 will carry the plate from E_{bb} (at $t = 0-$) to $E_{bb} - I'R_L$ (at $t = 0+$), while G_2 will change from zero (clamp) to $-I'R_L$. The abrupt portion of the rise at P_2 is the same in amplitude as at the grid G_1 and therefore is of magnitude $r_cI_c - E_{co}$. The overshoot at G_1 and the undershoots at G_2 and P_1 decay with a time constant $(R_L + r_c)C_2$, which is the time constant also with which e_{b2} eventually attains the level E_{bb}. After the overshoot has decayed, the

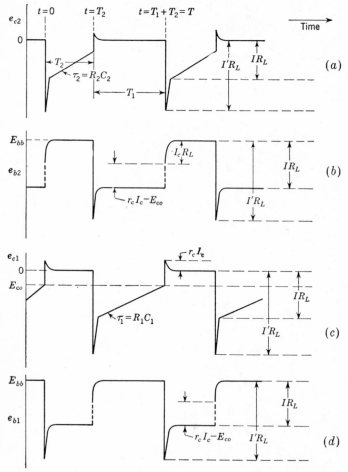

FIG. 6-17. Waveforms of the plate-coupled multi of Fig. 6-16.

grid G_2 is left at the voltage $-IR_L$ from which point it rises toward E_{bb} with the time constant R_2C_2. When G_2 reaches the cutoff level, the reverse transition occurs. The second part of the cycle produces the same waveshapes as does the first part described above except for the fact that if the grid time constants are different the duration of the individual portions of a complete cycle are different.

The time durations of the overshoots are ordinarily very small in comparison with the times required for C_1 to charge through R_1 and C_2 to charge through R_2. Using Eq. (6-5), we find that the time required for a complete cycle is, neglecting the overshoot times,

$$T = T_1 + T_2 = (R_1C_1 + R_2C_2) \ln \frac{E_{bb} + IR_L}{E_{bb} - E_{co}} \qquad (6\text{-}23)$$

We may neglect E_{co} in comparison with E_{bb}. Then for values of plate swing IR_L which vary all the way from $\frac{1}{4}$ to $\frac{3}{4}$ of E_{bb}, the logarithm in Eq. (6-23) varies only between 0.25 and 0.55. Hence as a rough but useful general approximation

$$T \cong \frac{R_1C_1 + R_2C_2}{2} \cong RC \qquad (6\text{-}24)$$

in the symmetrical case when $R_1C_1 = R_2C_2 = RC$.

Since the plate characteristic for $E_c = 0$ can be approximated by a straight line through the origin, IR_L is roughly proportional to E_{bb}. To a first approximation, $-E_{co} = E_{bb}/\mu$. Under these circumstances the factor E_{bb} can be canceled in the numerator and the denominator of Eq. (6-23). Thus, the frequency of the multi will vary only of the order of several per cent for a supply-voltage variation of the order of 100 volts.

REFERENCES

1. Chance, B., et al.: "Waveforms," Massachusetts Institute of Technology Radiation Laboratory Series, vol. 19, chap. 5, McGraw-Hill Book Company, Inc., New York, 1949.
   von Tersch, L. W., and A. W. Swago: "Recurrent Electrical Transients," chap. 9, Prentice-Hall, Inc., New York, 1953.
2. Shenk, E. R.: The Multivibrator, Applied Theory and Design, pt. I, *Electronics*, vol. 17, pp. 136–141, January, 1944; pt. II, *ibid.*, vol. 17, pp. 140–145, February, 1944; pt. III, *ibid.*, vol. 17, pp. 138–142, March, 1944.

CHAPTER 7

VOLTAGE TIME-BASE GENERATORS

A linear time-base circuit is one that provides an output waveform, a portion of which exhibits a linear variation of voltage with time. An application of first importance of such a waveform is in connection with a cathode-ray oscilloscope. The display on the screen of a scope* of the variation with respect to time of an arbitrary waveform requires that there be applied to one set of deflecting plates a voltage which varies linearly with time. Since this waveform is used to *sweep* the electron beam horizontally across the screen, it is called a *sweep voltage*. There are in addition many other important applications for time-base circuits such as in radar and television indicators, in precise time measurements, and in time modulation.

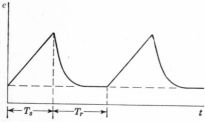

Fig. 7-1. A general sweep voltage. The sweep time is T_s, and the return time is T_r.

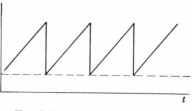

Fig. 7-2. A saw-tooth voltage.

7-1. General Features of a Time-base Signal. The typical form of a time-base voltage is as shown in Fig. 7-1. Here it appears that the voltage, starting from some initial value, increases linearly with time to a maximum value, after which it returns again to its initial value. The time required for the return to the initial value is called the *restoration time*, the *return time*, or the *flyback time*. Very frequently the shape of the waveform during the restoration time and the restoration time itself are matters of no special consequence. In some cases, however, a restoration time is desired which is very short in comparison with the time occupied by the linear portion of the waveform. If it should happen

---

* It is customary to refer to a cathode-ray oscilloscope simply as a *scope*.

that the restoration time is extremely short and that a new linear voltage
is initiated at the instant the previous one is terminated, then the waveform will appear as in Fig. 7-2.   This figure suggests the designation
saw-tooth generator or *ramp generator*.   It is customary to refer to waveforms of the type indicated in Figs. 7-1 and 7-2 as *sweep* waveforms even
in applications not involving the deflection of an electron beam.

We shall see that generators of time-base signals do not ordinarily
provide sweep voltages which are precisely linear.   Additionally a
nominally linear sweep may be distorted in the course of transmission
through a coupling network (see Secs. 2-1 and 2-4).   The three most
useful ways of expressing the deviation from linearity, and the correlation
between them, are given in the following.

The Slope or Sweep Speed Error ϵ_s.   In the case of a general-purpose
cathode-ray oscillograph an important requirement of the sweep is that
the sweep speed (i.e., the rate of change of sweep voltage with time) be
constant.   A reasonable definition of the deviation from linearity is

$$\epsilon_s \equiv \frac{\text{difference in slope at beginning and end of sweep}}{\text{initial value of slope}}$$

The Displacement Error ϵ_d.   In connection with other timing applications a more important criterion of linearity is the maximum difference

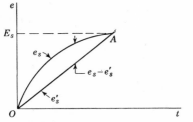

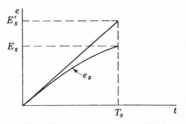

FIG. 7-3. Relating to the definition
of displacement error.

FIG. 7-4. Relating to the definition
of transmission error.

between the actual sweep voltage and linear sweep which passes through
the beginning and end points of the actual sweep as in Fig. 7-3.   Here
we may define

$$\epsilon_d \equiv \frac{(e_s - e_s')_{\max}}{E_s}$$

The Transmission Error ϵ_t.   If a ramp voltage is transmitted through
a high-pass RC network, the output falls away from the input, as indicated in Fig. 2-10a and in Fig. 7-4.   The *transmission error* is defined
as the difference between the input and output divided by the input.
Thus, with reference to Fig. 7-4, we have (at time $t = T_s$)

$$\epsilon_t = \frac{E_s' - E_s}{E_s'}$$

If the deviation from linearity is small so that the sweep voltage may be approximated by the sum of a linear and a quadratic term in t, then it can be shown from the above definitions that

$$\epsilon_d = \tfrac{1}{8}\epsilon_s = \tfrac{1}{4}\epsilon_t \tag{7-1}$$

7-2. The Thyratron Sweep Circuits. We consider first the sweep circuit using a thyratron tube, the schematic of which is shown in Fig. 7-5. The circuit lacks much of the versatility of sweep circuits employing vacuum tubes and is limited in its ability to provide sweeps of high speed. However, because of its simplicity it is employed commonly in many general-purpose laboratory oscilloscopes.

In order that the arc of a thyratron[1] be ignited, the plate-to-cathode voltage must first attain the breakdown voltage E_d. The breakdown

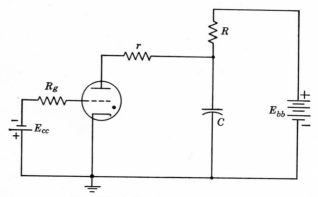

Fig. 7-5. A thyratron sweep circuit.

voltage is a function of the grid bias and for the type 884 thyratron the variation of E_d with grid bias voltage e_c is given approximately by the relationship $E_d = -8e_c$.

Once the arc has formed in a thyratron, the grid loses its ability to control the tube current. Variations in grid voltage accomplish nothing but a variation of the thickness of the positive ion sheath surrounding the grid. The arc will persist just as long as the current through the tube is large enough to maintain an adequate supply of positive ions to replace those ions which are lost through the process of recombination. If the current is large enough to maintain the ion supply and is less than the saturation current of the tube, the tube drop will remain essentially constant at the maintaining voltage E_m independently of the current. Over this range of currents, the tube current is determined by the circuit external to the tube. The arc may be extinguished only by reducing the tube current below the minimum required to maintain ionization. When the arc has been extinguished, the grid once again regains control and determines the plate voltage which must be applied to the tube to cause breakdown.

The output waveform of the circuit of Fig. 7-5 is the voltage which appears across the capacitor C. This waveform is plotted in Fig. 7-6. A negative bias E_{cc} is maintained on the grid, and the tube consequently does not conduct until the plate voltage rises to the breakdown voltage E_d which corresponds to E_{cc}. The capacitor C charges through R, approaching asymptotically the supply voltage E_{bb} as shown. When the capacitor attains the voltage E_d, the thyratron ignites. At this point the thyratron may be considered to be replaced by a battery whose terminal voltage is equal to the maintaining voltage of the tube. The capacitor C will discharge through the tube and series resistor r until the capacitor voltage drops to the maintaining voltage. The arc will extinguish itself

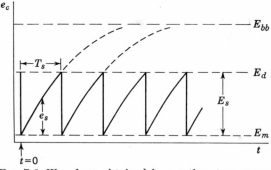

FIG. 7-6. Waveform obtained from a thyratron sweep.

at the instant the tube current is less than the minimum required to maintain the arc and the charging of the capacitor through R from the supply voltage will begin again. The resistor r is made small enough to permit a rapid discharge of the capacitor but not so small that it permits a larger discharge current through the tube than the tube can safely handle. The maintaining voltage of the 884 thyratron is about 16 volts, the minimum current required to maintain the arc is of the order of magnitude of 1.0 ma, while the maximum peak current which should be permitted to flow at the discharge of the capacitor is about 0.5 amp. To limit the positive ion grid current to a safe value, a resistor R_g ($\cong$ 10 K) is inserted in the grid circuit.

The sweep voltage $e_s = e_c - E_m$ is given by

$$e_s = E(1 - e^{-t/RC}) \qquad (7\text{-}2)$$

in which $E = E_{bb} - E_m$. If the definition of sweep-speed error is applied to the above waveform, we find that ϵ_s is given exactly by

$$\epsilon_s = \frac{E_s}{E} \qquad (7\text{-}3)$$

where $E_s = E_d - E_m$ is the sweep amplitude. From Eq. (7-1), the displacement error is given approximately by $\epsilon_d = \frac{1}{8}E_s/E$.

If $t/RC \ll 1$, it is convenient to expand the exponential in Eq. (7-2), so that

$$e_s = E \frac{t}{RC}\left(1 - \frac{t}{2RC} + \frac{t^2}{6R^2C^2} - \cdots\right) \tag{7-4}$$

Since $e_s = E_s$ when $t = T_s$, we have to a first approximation that

$$\frac{E_s}{E} = \frac{T_s}{RC} \tag{7-5}$$

Hence, if the sweep is to be reasonably linear, the time constant RC must be large compared with the sweep time T_s.

In the sweep circuit presently being considered the waveform is repetitive; one sweep is initiated immediately at the termination of the previous sweep and the circuit does not wait for some external signal to initiate the sweep. The sweep is termed *recurrent* and it is customary to calibrate the control dials of the scope in frequency rather than sweep time. The frequency is a function of E_{bb}, E_{cc} (since E_d is a function of E_{cc}), R, and C. In practice, E_{bb} and E_{cc} are kept constant and the frequency is varied through R and C. In this way the amplitude and linearity of the sweep are kept constant. Continuous variation of frequency is accomplished through varying R, while the ranges are changed by switching the value of C. The resistance R must always be large enough to prevent the supply voltage from furnishing to the tube a current large enough to maintain the arc, since in such a case the circuit will stop oscillating.

If a periodic signal of frequency f_v is applied to the vertical axis of a scope while a sweep of frequency f_s is applied to the horizontal axis, a stationary pattern of n cycles will appear if $f_v = nf_s$. A small portion of the last cycle occurs during the return time and is ordinarily not visible because of the speed with which the beam moves during the return. It is customary to apply to the grid of the cathode-ray tube a voltage derived by differentiating the sweep. This differentiated voltage consists essentially of sharp negative pulses which serve to turn off the cathode-ray tube-beam during the retrace. This process of turning off the beam is referred to as *blanking*.

To maintain the condition $f_v = nf_s$ exactly for long periods of time, it is necessary to synchronize the sweep generator to the signal. If f_v is only very slightly different from nf_s, the waveform will drift slowly across the screen. Synchronization is accomplished by applying to the grid of the thyratron the vertical deflecting signal, increased or reduced in amplitude as may be required. The process of synchronization is explained in detail in Chap. 12.

It sometimes happens that a waveform is not periodic but occurs rather at irregular intervals. In such a case it is desirable that the sweep circuit, instead of running continuously, should remain quiescent and wait to be initiated by the waveform itself. Even if it should happen that the waveform does recur regularly, it may happen that the interesting part of the waveform is short in time duration in comparison with the period of the waveform. For example, the waveform might consist of 1-msec pulses with a time interval of 100 msec between pulses. In this case the fastest recurrent sweep which will provide a synchronized pattern will have a period of 100 msec. If, typically, the time base is spread out over 4 in. (on a 5-in. CRT*), the pulse will occupy 0.04 in. and none of the detail of form of the pulse will be apparent. If, on the other hand,

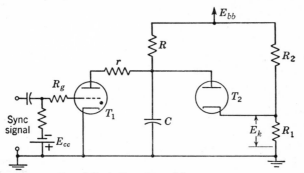

Fig. 7-7. A thyratron driven sweep.

a sweep of period 1 msec or somewhat larger could be used, the pulse would be spread across the entire screen. Therefore, what is required here is a sweep set for, say, a 1.5-msec interval which remains quiescent until it is initiated by the pulse. Such a sweep is known as a *driven* sweep or a *triggered* sweep.

The circuit for a thyratron driven sweep is shown in Fig. 7-7. The bias E_k on the cathode of the diode T_2 is adjusted by resistors R_1 and R_2. The grid bias on the thyratron is adjusted so that the firing voltage is slightly higher than the diode cathode voltage. Accordingly, as the capacitor voltage increases, a point is reached before the thyratron firing voltage is attained, where the diode begins to conduct and prevents the further rise of the capacitor voltage. Tube T_2 acts as a plate-catching diode clamp (see Sec. 4-5). Now let a signal be applied to the grid which even instantaneously raises the grid voltage to the point where the firing voltage is equal to or less than the voltage E_k. Then the capacitor will discharge abruptly and will charge again to the diode cathode voltage.

* It is customary to abbreviate *cathode-ray tube* by CRT.

Here the circuit will remain until another sweep is initiated by a sync* signal applied to the thyratron grid.

Figure 7-8 shows the operation of a triggered sweep for a case in which the waveform to be observed on the scope consists of a train of pulses. This signal e_v is applied to the vertical-deflection amplifier of the scope and is used also to trigger the sweep circuit. Observe that at the occurrence of the leading edge of a pulse the circuit capacitor first discharges, after which a linear sweep occurs. Note also that the sweep speed has been adjusted so that the pulse will be spread out over a large portion of the sweep trace.

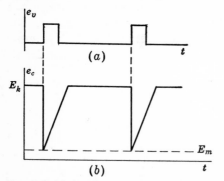

FIG. 7-8. (a) A pulse waveform. (b) The driven sweep triggered by the waveform in (a).

A typical thyratron sweep circuit for a general-purpose scope (Du Mont type 304) is shown in Fig. 7-9. T_1 is used for adjustment of the polarity and amplitude of the sync signal. T_2 is a sync signal amplifier. T_3 is the thyratron sweep tube. T_4 is the diode clamp used when the circuit is set for driven sweep. T_5 is a buffer stage which is used as a cathode follower not only to provide a low output impedance but also because it can handle the relatively large amplitude of the sweep signal. Observe that T_5 has no grid-leak resistor. The 22-$\mu\mu f$ capacitor and 15-K resistor in the cathode circuit of T_5 generate the blanking pulse. T_6 is an amplifier for the blanking pulse. The pulse is applied to the CRT cathode so that the CRT grid may be available at a front-panel terminal for external intensity modulation (called Z axis modulation). The 5-Meg potentiometer is used for fine frequency control, and, to change frequency ranges, the capacitor C is changed by switching (not shown). The bias for the 6Q5G thyratron is applied to the cathode and is derived from a bleeder. For recurrent operation, switch S is closed and the diode T_4 never conducts. For driven sweep operation, S is open and R is adjusted so that the cathode voltage of T_4 is just slightly less than the peak sweep voltage. The circuit will operate reliably up to sweep repetition rates of about 30 kc. Operation at high frequencies is inconvenient because of the time required between sweeps for the thyratron to deionize.

7-3. Vacuum-tube Sweep Circuit. The basic circuit of a vacuum-tube sweep generator is shown in Fig. 7-10a. The grid is clamped to the cathode and the capacitor voltage is held at a low value, say, E_m. If the

* It is customary to refer to a synchronizing signal as the *sync* signal.

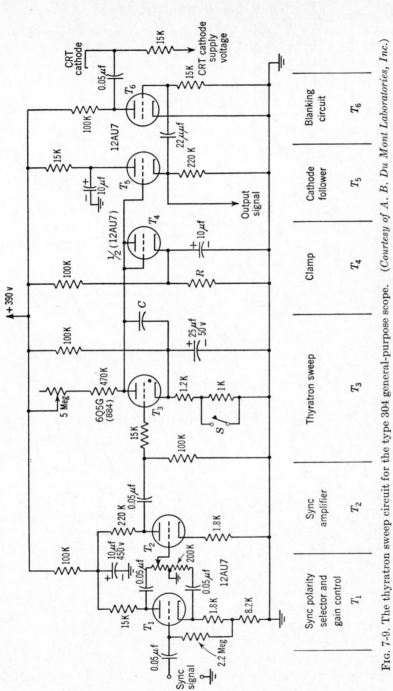

FIG. 7-9. The thyratron sweep circuit for the type 304 general-purpose scope. (*Courtesy of A. B. Du Mont Laboratories, Inc.*)

209

"gating" waveform e_i of Fig. 7-10b is applied to the grid so as to cut the tube off for a time T_s, then C charges through R. The initial charging current is $(E_{bb} - E_m)/R \equiv E/R$. Hence, the sweep amplitude is given approximately by

$$E_s = \frac{ET_s}{RC} \tag{7-6}$$

For the thyratron sweep, the amplitude is equal to the difference between the breakdown and maintaining voltage of the thyratron. For the vacuum sweep, the amplitude is almost independent of the tube (there is a slight dependence because E_m is determined by the tube, but E_m can be made much smaller than E_{bb}). The displacement error is determined, as before, by $\epsilon_d \cong \frac{1}{8}E_s/E \cong \frac{1}{8}T_s/RC$.

At the end of the sweep time T_s, the tube is in clamp again and the capacitor discharges through the tube to its quiescent value E_m, as indicated in Fig. 7-10c. If the time constant $R_g C_g$ is not very large compared with T_s, there will be an overshoot at the grid at the end of the gate which will drive the grid positive (see Sec. 4-7) and aid in discharging C all the more rapidly.

A practical vacuum-tube sweep circuit such as is used in the Tektronix type 511 and 514 scopes is shown in Fig. 7-12. Switching arrangements and certain other details have been omitted to avoid excessive complexity. The circuit is more complicated, but is also more versatile than a gas-tube sweep and is capable of the much higher sweep speeds

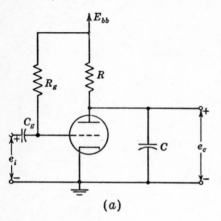

(a)

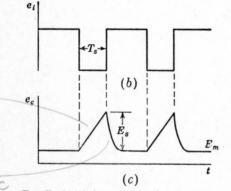

(b)

(c)

Fig. 7-10. (a) A vacuum-tube sweep circuit. (b) The input gating waveform. (c) The output sweep voltage.

which are required in a high-frequency oscilloscope. The sweep circuit is intended to be used as a triggered or driven sweep at all times. High g_m pentodes are used in almost every case for good high-frequency response. The type 514 scope vertical amplifier response extends from 0 to 10 Mc (rise time equals 0.04 μsec) and the sweep speed is continuously adjustable from 0.01 sec/cm to 0.1 μsec/cm.

The sync or triggering signal is applied to the grid of tube T_1 (Fig. 7-12). Switch S is used to select proper polarity whenever the sync signal is very unsymmetrical, as in case of a pulse. Tube T_2 amplifies the sync voltage and applies it to the triggering diode T_3. Tubes T_4 and T_5 constitute a plate-to-grid coupled monostable multivibrator which is used as a gate generator. T_6 is the "time-base former"; capacitor C_2 charges through R_2 to provide the sweep voltage when T_6 is cut off. In the quiescent condition the plate of T_4 is at E_{bb} and the grid of T_6 is clamped at zero. The swing at the plate of T_4 when the multi is triggered is large enough to drive T_6 well into cutoff. The sweep speed is determined by R_2C_2, while the gate width is determined by R_1C_1. If the sweep amplitude is to remain nominally constant, the gate width controls R_1 and C_1 must be adjusted whenever the sweep speed controls R_2 and C_2 are varied. Capacitors C_1 and C_2 are switched simultaneously to change the range of sweep speed, and resistor R_2, which is used for continuous variation of sweep speed, is ganged to R_1. No attempt is made to maintain constant amplitude with any precision. The sweep amplitude is deliberately made so large that the end of the sweep occurs at a point well off the CRT screen, so that variations of amplitude are not observed.

The magnitude of the sync signal which is applied to the grid of T_5 through diode T_3 and capacitor C_1 is controlled by the bias on T_2. The negative bias on T_2 is adjusted by the potentiometer labeled "trigger amplitude." A sync signal large enough to bring T_2 out of cutoff causes the plate of T_2 to fall. This drop in voltage is transmitted through the diode. As soon as the multi is triggered, the plate of T_4 falls abruptly, and unless the sync signal is extremely large in amplitude, the multi is disconnected from the sync voltage during the formation of the gate. The distortion of the sync signal produced by the limiting amplifier T_2 is of no consequence since the sync voltage serves only to initiate the gate. Varying the amplitude of the sync signal by adjusting cutoff makes a compensated sync signal attenuator unnecessary. The "sweep-stability" control permits an adjustment of the bias of T_4 so that the tube is only slightly below cutoff and consequently only a small sync signal is required to trigger the multi. Since the ratio of sweep time to time between sweep is variable, a d-c restorer (T_7) and a d-c amplifier are used to ensure that each sweep starts at the same place on the CRT screen.

In a case in which the sweep time is short in comparison to the time between sweeps the CRT beam will remain in one place most of the time. If the intensity is reduced to prevent screen burns, the fast trace will be very faint. To intensify the trace during the sweep, a positive gate, at the cathode of T_8, which is derived from the plate of T_5 is applied to the CRT grid. As a matter of fact in the presence of this "unblanking signal" the beam intensity may be adjusted so that the spot is initially invisible and the trace will become visible as soon as the sweep starts.

In operation the "trigger-amplitude" control is initially set at maximum negative bias so that no sync signal reaches the multi. The arm on the "sweep-stability" control is initially set at ground so that the multi is astable and a trace appears on the CRT screen. The bias on T_4 is now increased just beyond the point where the trace disappears. The multi is now monostable; that is, T_4 is cut off. At this point the bias on T_2 is reduced to just beyond the point where the sweep reappears and the sweep speed controls are adjusted until a stationary pattern is observed. It is possible to use the circuit under circumstances where the gate generator operates as a synchronized free-running multi but under these conditions the operation is not so clean-cut as in the triggered case.

The sweep voltage is applied to a paraphase-inverter amplifier of the type described in Sec. 1-10. The push-pull output sweep voltages from this amplifier are d-c coupled to the CRT horizontal deflection plates. In order to improve the linearity, some degeneration is introduced into each amplifier cathode and then a small cathode bypass capacitor is used in order to improve the rise time so as to be able to pass the fastest sweep without appreciable distortion.

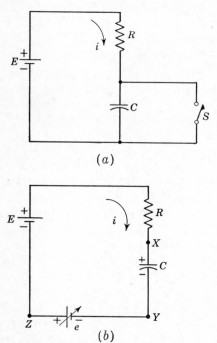

7-4. Circuits to Improve Sweep Linearity. In general-purpose scope sweeps E_s/E is usually of the order of $\frac{1}{10}$, giving a slope error of 10 per cent and a displacement error of about 1.25 per cent. In many timing applications a much higher precision sweep is required.

Fig. 7-11. In (a) the current varies exponentially with time, whereas in (b) it remains constant, provided that e is equal to the instantaneous voltage across C.

The basic sweep circuit is shown in Fig. 7-11a in which S opens to form the sweep. If, as in Fig. 7-11b, an auxiliary variable generator e is introduced and if e is always kept equal to the voltage drop across C, the charging current will be kept constant at $i = E/R$ and perfect linearity will have been achieved. Methods of simulating the fictitious generator e with an amplifier will now be given.

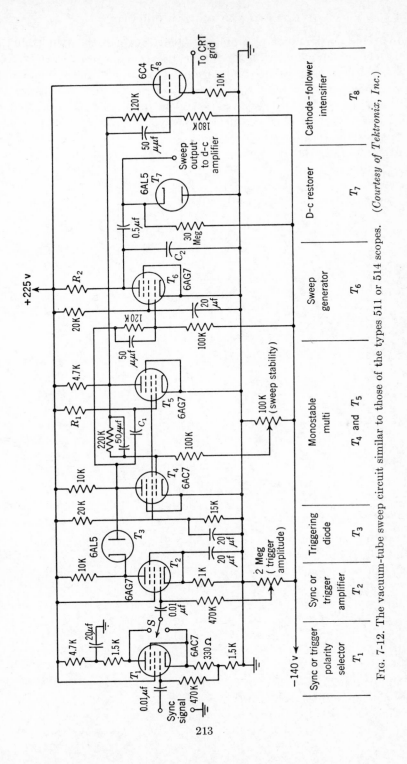

Fig. 7-12. The vacuum-tube sweep circuit similar to those of the types 511 or 514 scopes. (*Courtesy of Tektronix, Inc.*)

213

It is common practice to build electronic circuits on a metallic chassis and to have one point in the circuit electrically connected to the chassis. The chassis is then referred to as *ground*, and customarily the voltage at any point in the circuit is given with respect to ground. Differences in the point selected to be grounded yield different descriptions of the mechanism whereby the linearity is improved. Suppose that the point Z of Fig. 7-11b is grounded as in Fig. 7-13a. A linear sweep will appear between Y and ground and will increase in the negative direction. Let

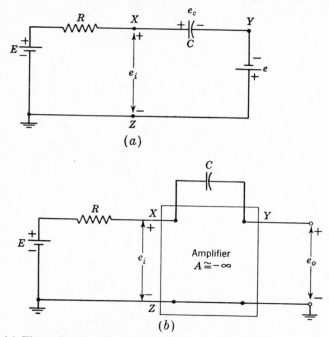

(a)

(b)

Fig. 7-13. (a) Figure 7-11b with point Z grounded. (b) The same circuit simulated with an operational (Miller) integrator with $A \cong -\infty$.

us now replace the fictitious generator by an amplifier with output terminals YZ and input terminals XZ as in Fig. 7-13b. Since we have assumed that the magnitude of the generator voltage e equals the voltage e_c across the capacitor at every instant of time, then the input e_i to the amplifier is zero. In other words, point X behaves as a virtual ground, and in order to obtain a finite output, the amplifier gain A should ideally be infinite. Figure 7-13b should be recognized as the operational integrating amplifier of Sec. 1-13 and is customarily referred to as a *Miller integrator*.

Suppose that point Y of Fig. 7-11b is grounded as in Fig. 7-14a. A linear sweep will appear between Z and ground and will increase in the positive direction. Let us now replace the fictitious generator by an amplifier with output terminals ZY and input terminals XY as in Fig. 7-14b. Since we have assumed that $e = e_c$ ($e_o = e_i$), then the amplifier

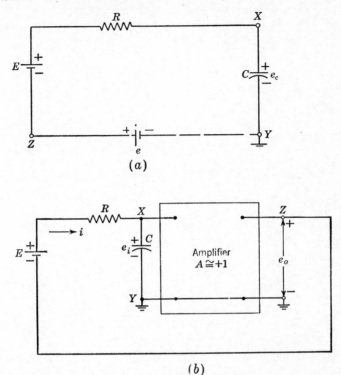

(a)

(b)

FIG. 7-14. (a) Figure 7-11b with point Y grounded. (b) The same circuit simulated with a noninverting unity-gain amplifier (a *bootstrap integrator*).

gain A must equal unity. The circuit of Fig. 7-14b is referred to as a *bootstrap sweep*, since the voltage E is lifted, as it were, by its own bootstraps.

Since the mechanism of linearity improvement is, in both cases, the same, it may seem strange that two such radically different amplifiers are required, one with a gain $-\infty$ and the other with a gain $+1$. It may be shown that actually these amplifiers are identical, i.e., that given one and the same amplifier, the gain may be changed from unity to $-\infty$ by simply redefining the input and output terminals. The amplifiers of Figs. 7-13b and 7-14b have three independent terminals X, Y, and Z, as in Fig. 7-15. Suppose that Z is taken as the terminal common to input and output, then take e_{xz} to be the input, e_{yz} to be the output, and let the gain be $A = e_{yz}/e_{xz}$, as in Fig. 7-13b. Next, as in Fig. 7-14b, take Y to be

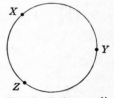

FIG. 7-15. An amplifier has three independent terminals X, Y, and Z.

the common terminal, and let e_{xy} be the input, e_{zy} be the output, and let the gain $A' = e_{zy}/e_{xy}$. Then

$$A' = \frac{e_{zy}}{e_{xy}} = \frac{-e_{yz}}{e_{xz} + e_{zy}} = \frac{-e_{yz}}{e_{xz} - e_{yz}} = \frac{-e_{yz}/e_{xz}}{1 - e_{yz}/e_{xz}} = \frac{-A}{1 - A}$$

If $A = -\infty$, $A' = +1$, as anticipated.

The effect of a finite value of A on the linearity of a Miller sweep is now to be investigated. In accordance with the principle of the virtual

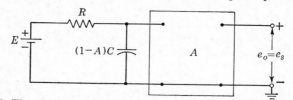

FIG. 7-16. The equivalent circuit of the Miller integrator for finite gain A.

ground explained in Sec. 1-12 the equivalent circuit is as drawn in Fig. 7-16. The output or sweep voltage is given by

$$e_s = AE(1 - \epsilon^{-t/RC(1-A)})$$

$$\cong E\frac{A}{1-A}\frac{t}{RC}\left[1 - \frac{t}{2RC(1-A)} + \cdots\right]$$

$$\cong -\frac{Et}{RC}\left(1 - \frac{t}{2RC|A|} + \cdots\right) \tag{7-7}$$

since A is large and negative. Comparison of Eq. (7-7) with Eq. (7-4) shows that, for a fixed sweep amplitude E_s relative to the supply voltage E [see Eq. (7-5)], the deviation from linearity of the Miller sweep is $1/|A|$ times that of the uncompensated time base.

The effect of a deviation of A from 1 for the bootstrap sweep is now to be investigated. Referring to Fig. 7-14b, we have

$$E = iR + e_i - e_o = iR + e_i(1 - A) \tag{7-8}$$

because $e_o = Ae_i$. Dividing by $1 - A$, gives

$$\frac{E}{1 - A} = i\frac{R}{1 - A} + e_i \tag{7-9}$$

Remembering that e_i is the voltage across capacitor C, Eq. (7-9) leads to the equivalent circuit of Fig. 7-17. The output or sweep voltage is given by

$$e_s = \frac{AE}{1-A}(1 - \epsilon^{-\frac{t(1-A)}{RC}})$$

$$\cong AE\frac{t}{RC}\left[1 - \frac{t(1 - A)}{2RC} + \cdots\right] \tag{7-10}$$

Since A is close to unity, we see, by comparing Eq. (7-10) with Eq. (7-4), that the deviation from linearity of the bootstrap circuit is $(1 - A)$ times that of the uncompensated time base. It follows from this dis-

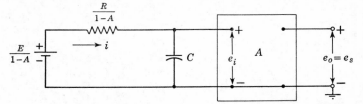

FIG. 7-17. The equivalent circuit of the bootstrap sweep.

cussion that a Miller amplifier (of gain A_M) will give the same amplitude, sweep speed, and deviation from linearity as a bootstrap amplifier (of gain A_B), provided that $|A_M| = 1/(1 - A_B)$. For example, a boot-strap circuit with a gain of 0.95 is equivalent to a Miller circuit with a gain of 20. The decision between these two circuits is often difficult to make. Some practical considerations are given in the following sections. Other fine points are brought out in Chap. 16 in connection with the use of these sweep circuits for precision time modulation.

7-5. The Miller Sweep.[2] A simple Miller sweep is shown in Fig. 7-18a. The negative bias should not be so large that the tube is cut off. Observe that E_{bb} is used both to charge C and to supply tube current. When S opens, a negative-going sweep will appear at the plate. However, as indicated in Fig. 7-18b, the sweep will be preceded by a positive jump. The jump results from the finite output impedance of the amplifier which

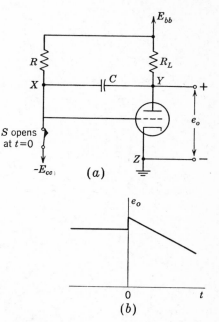

FIG. 7-18. A Miller sweep with the gate applied to the grid. (a) Circuit; (b) output waveform.

has heretofore been neglected (see Prob. 7-13). This jump can be eliminated by the addition of a resistor $r = 1/g_m$ in series with the capacitor C (see Prob. 7-14).

A Miller sweep with symmetrical outputs is indicated in Fig. 7-19. The triode T_1 with its grid clamped to ground acts as the closed switch S

of Fig. 7-18. A negative gate applied to the grid cuts T_1 off and allows C to charge from E_{bb} through R and the Miller tube T_2. The output e_{o1} from the plate of T_2 is a negative-going sweep. This voltage is applied to the grid of T_3 through the resistor R_2 and an equal resistor R_2 is used for feedback from plate to grid of T_3. Hence, T_3 acts as an operational phase inverter (see Sec. 1-13) and the output e_{o2} is a positive-going sweep. The symmetrical voltages e_{o1} and e_{o2} drive the CRT horizontal plates. It should be noted that the negative bias of Fig. 7-18 has been replaced by the voltage across the cathode resistor R_k. This resistor does *not* introduce degeneration because the current through it remains constant. Thus, as the current in T_2 increases, the symmetrical current in T_3

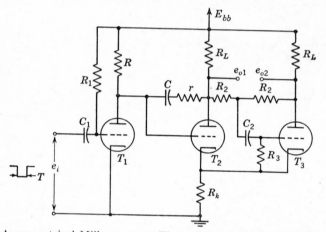

Fig. 7-19. A symmetrical Miller sweep. The switch tube is T_1, the Miller integrator is T_2, and the operational inverter is T_3.

decreases by the same amount, leaving the current in R_k unchanged. The grid leak for T_3 is R_3 and the blocking capacitor C_2 keeps the high plate voltage of T_2 from reaching the grid of T_3. The time constant R_3C_2 must be large enough to introduce negligible transmission error (see Sec. 7-1).

A total sweep voltage equal to the supply voltage can be obtained by choosing $e_{o1} = -E_{bb}/2$ and hence $e_{o2} = +E_{bb}/2$. From the theory developed in Sec. 7-4 the displacement error under this condition is $\epsilon_d \cong \dfrac{1}{8} \dfrac{E_s}{E_{bb}} \dfrac{100}{|A|} = \dfrac{100}{16|A|}$ per cent. It is not difficult to obtain a gain $|A|$ of 15 with a triode (say, a 12AU7 tube), and then $\epsilon_d \cong 0.4$ per cent for a total swing of E_{bb} volts. The sweep speed is E_{bb}/RC volts/sec.

At the end of the sweep time the capacitor C must discharge and return to its quiescent voltage. The discharge path is through the amplifier output impedance and through a switching tube such as T_1 in Fig.

7-19. If fast retrace time is important, then C should be kept as small as possible and R chosen sufficiently large to give the desired sweep speed. For practical reasons it is advisable not to permit R to exceed several megohms. A high-current switching tube and, additionally, the use of a cathode follower interposed between the capacitor C and the amplifier output will reduce the recovery time still further. The recovery may also be hastened by selecting the time constant R_1C_1 (Fig. 7-19) to be comparable to the width of the gating signal, since under these circumstances there will be a pronounced overshoot at the grid at the termination of the gate. A Miller sweep using a cathode follower to speed recovery and using a pentode amplifier for higher gain is shown in Fig. 7-20. Note that the low output impedance of the cathode follower makes the resistor r in series with C (Fig. 7-19) unnecessary.

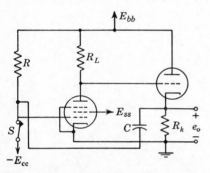

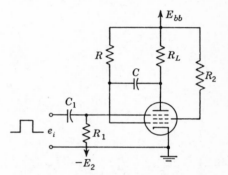

FIG. 7-20. A Miller sweep using a cathode follower in order to reduce the retrace time. Note that a negative-going sweep is obtained at the low impedance output of the cathode follower.

FIG. 7-21. A suppressor-gated Miller time-base generator.

7-6. Pentode Miller Sweep with Suppressor Gating.

If a pentode is used as the amplifier tube of a Miller sweep, then the gating voltage may be applied to the suppressor grid instead of to the control grid. A suppressor-gated Miller integrator is indicated in Fig. 7-21. A tube with a sharp cutoff suppressor characteristic is used, such as the types 6AS6, 7AK7, 5915 (RCA), 6CS6 (Raytheon), and 6BH6 (Tungsol). The 6SA7 converter tube[3] has also been used in this application. Initially the suppressor grid is biased to plate current cutoff, while the control grid is clamped to the cathode. All the cathode current flows to the screen and hence the screen voltage is low. The waveforms at all the electrodes are given in Fig. 7-22. A positive gate applied to the suppressor drives this electrode either slightly positive or to clamp. Clamping may occur either because the impedance of the driving source is large in comparison with the suppressor-cathode resistance or because a diode is added to the circuit from suppressor to ground. This increased suppressor voltage permits plate current to flow and the plate voltage drops. Since the voltage across the Miller capacitor C cannot change instantaneously, the grid voltage must drop by the same amount E_1 that the plate falls. The grid voltage is now $-E_1$, the tube finds itself operating above cutoff, and a negative-going sweep forms at the plate. The load resistor R_L is large so that bottoming will take place (see Sec. 4-3). The load line is drawn on the plate characteristics in Fig. 7-23. Since $-E_1$ is very close to the cutoff bias, we have considered that the tube characteristic corresponding to the grid voltage $-E_1$ is coincident with the abscissa.

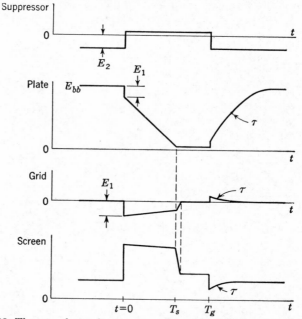

FIG. 7-22. The waveforms for a suppressor-gated Miller sweep generator.

For a type 6AS6 tube, the order of magnitude of E_1 is 5 volts and bottoming begins when the grid has increased by only one or two volts. For example, if $E_{bb} = 300$ and the amplifier gain is 150, then the grid will increase by $300/150 = 2$ volts for complete "run-down."

When the grid voltage drops from zero to $-E_1$, the cathode current falls, the screen current drops, and hence the screen voltage rises as indicated in Fig. 7-22. During the formation of the sweep the grid rises slightly, as noted above, and the increased screen current results in a slight decrease in screen voltage. When the plate voltage bottoms, the grid voltage increases to zero with a time constant RC, the space current and hence screen current increases, and the screen voltage drops, as indicated in Fig. 7-22. The screen voltage does not quite fall to its value for $t < 0$

because some of the cathode current is now being collected by the plate, whereas for $t < 0$ all the space current goes to the screen.

At the end of the gate the suppressor again cuts off the plate current. The capacitor C whose voltage has fallen almost to zero recharges toward E_{bb} through R_L and the grid-cathode resistance r_c with a time constant $\tau = (R_L + r_c)C \cong R_L C$. The grid voltage will be driven positive by approximately $r_c E_{bb} / R_L$ volts. This positive grid voltage will increase the cathode current above its value for $t < 0$, and hence there will be a dip in screen voltage below its value for $t < 0$. The overshoot in grid voltage and undershoot in screen voltage are indicated in Fig. 7-22.

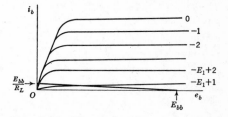

FIG. 7-23. Illustrating bottoming in a pentode and the fact that the grid voltage changes by only a few volts during the entire sweep voltage.

At $t = 0+$, the voltage across R is $E_{bb} + E_1$, and since the current through R passes through C, the initial sweep speed is $(E_{bb} + E_1)/RC$ volts/sec. As long as the amplifier gain remains high, the sweep speed remains essentially constant. Hence, a linear ramp results for almost the entire plate voltage rundown except near the very bottom.

If the gate width T_g is less than the time T_s for the capacitor to discharge completely, then there will be no bottoming and the flat portions of Fig. 7-22 between T_s and T_g are missing. The screen voltage is itself a gating voltage, and, if the sweep is being used in connection with a scope display, can be used as an intensifier to brighten the CRT trace during the sweep time and to cut off the CRT beam during the retrace time. The recovery time may be made quite small by driving the capacitor C from a cathode follower as in Fig. 7-20. Under these circumstances the recovery time constant is $\tau = (C)(R_o + r_c)$, where R_o is the output impedance of the cathode follower and r_c is the grid-cathode resistance.

The step in the plate voltage at $t = 0+$ *cannot* be eliminated by adding a resistor r in series with C in Fig. 7-21, as was done for the grid-gated Miller integrator. The use of the resistor r is effective because the amplifier of the grid-gated circuit is initially biased within its grid base. The suppressor-gated circuit, however, is held beyond cutoff in the quiescent condition. When the gate is applied, the tube must draw some plate current, and hence the plate voltage must drop somewhat.

7-7. Phantastron Circuits.[4] The screen waveform of Fig. 7-22 is a positive step for the interval of the linear rundown. Hence, it is possible to start the sweep by means of a narrow pulse or trigger and to couple the output from the screen to the suppressor so that the positive gate needed

at the latter grid is supplied internally.   A circuit in which a Miller time
base is initiated with a trigger and the circuit then supplies its own gate
is called a *phantastron*.*

The screen-coupled phantastron is drawn in Fig. 7-24.   This circuit
differs from the suppressor-gated Miller sweep (Fig. 7-21) only in that the
screen and suppressor voltages are obtained from a bleeder arrangement
R_1-R_2-R_3.   These resistors are so chosen that in the quiescent state the
suppressor grid is sufficiently negative (say, $-E_2$) so that no plate current
flows, all the space current going to the screen.   Assume now that a
positive trigger is applied at $t = 0$ to the suppressor so as to allow the
plate to draw current.   The plate voltage drops, the grid voltage drops
the same amount (say, E_1), the cathode current falls, and the screen

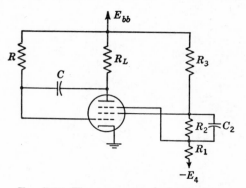

FIG. 7-24. The screen-gated phantastron.

voltage rises.   This causes the suppressor voltage to rise because it is
obtained from the same bleeder as the screen potential.   The capacitor C_2
is a speed-up capacitor (see Sec. 5-3).   The action described above is
regenerative and the tube is rapidly driven from cutoff to its normally *on*
condition and the Miller sweep is initiated.

The waveforms at all the electrodes are given in Fig. 7-25 and are
identical with those in Fig. 7-22 except that the flat portions at the end
of the run-down are missing.   As soon as the tube bottoms and the plate
can fall no further, the plate side of C in Fig. 7-24 remains at a fixed
potential.   Hence, the grid side of C must rise with respect to ground
(with a time constant RC) because current continues to flow from E_{bb}
through R through C into the tube plate.   As the grid rises, the cathode
current increases, the screen current increases, and the screen voltage
drops.   Because of the action of the bleeder arrangement the suppressor
voltage also falls and the plate current decreases.   A reduction of plate
current means an increase in plate voltage which in turn causes the grid

* The British considered the operation of this circuit as *fantastic* and dignified it
with the name *phantastron*.

to rise still further. This action is regenerative and the suppressor voltage is rapidly driven negative. The waveshapes for $t > T_s$ in Fig. 7-25 are explained in exactly the same manner as the waveshapes for $t > T_g$ in Fig. 7-22. There is one difference between these two figures in the region under consideration. Since the suppressor voltage comes from the same bleeder as the screen voltage, there will be an undershoot at the suppressor, as indicated in Fig. 7-25.

Triggering may also be done with negative pulses applied to the plate and hence fed to the grid through the capacitor C. A negative trigger so applied reduces the cathode current and consequently raises the screen

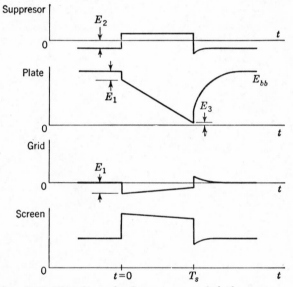

FIG. 7-25. Waveforms in the screen-coupled phantastron.

voltage. The rise of screen voltage is transmitted to the suppressor to bring the suppressor above the point of plate current cutoff. The trigger size should be large enough to start the regenerative action but not so large as to cut off the tube current. If the tube should be driven below cutoff, the grid voltage will rise initially with a time constant RC into the conducting region and there will be a delay between the application of the trigger and the start of the sweep.

The phantastron circuit has a recovery time constant $\tau = R_L C$. If a shorter retrace time is desired, then a cathode follower can be interposed between the plate of the amplifier and the capacitor C, as was done for the externally control-grid-gated Miller sweep of Fig. 7-20. Since the sweep voltage at the plate of the pentode starts near E_{bb} and since this voltage is applied directly to the grid of the cathode follower, a separate supply

E'_{bb} must be used for the cathode follower with $E'_{bb} > E_{bb}$. The magnitude of the overshoots and undershoots is greatly increased (perhaps by a factor of 10) if a cathode follower is used. The reason for this feature is that the plate of the amplifier is no longer loaded down by the low grid-cathode resistance r_c which allowed the grid to overshoot to only $r_c E_{bb}/R_L$ volts. With a cathode follower in the circuit, when the plate rises at the end of the sweep it carries the grid of the cathode follower way up with it and hence the grid of the pentode can be driven several volts positive.

The sweep speed is, as with the simple Miller integrator, $(E_{bb} + E_1)/RC$ volts/sec and can be adjusted by changing E_{bb}, R, or C. If the rundown proceeds to within E_3 volts of ground (see Fig. 7-25), then the amplitude of the sweep is $E_{bb} - E_1 - E_3$. The sweep time T_s is the amplitude divided by the speed, so that

$$\frac{T_s}{RC} = \frac{E_{bb} - E_1 - E_3}{E_{bb} + E_1} \tag{7-11}$$

If $E_{bb} \gg E_1 + E_3$, then $T_s \cong RC$, a result which is independent of variations in E_{bb}. The next approximation is obtained by dividing the numerator in Eq. (7-11) by the denominator with the result

$$x \equiv \frac{T_s}{RC} = 1 - \frac{2E_1 + E_3}{E_{bb} + E_1} \cong 1 - \frac{2E_1 + E_3}{E_{bb}} \tag{7-12}$$

Taking the derivative, we find

$$\frac{dx}{x} \cong \frac{2E_1 + E_3}{E_{bb}} \frac{dE_{bb}}{E_{bb}} \tag{7-13}$$

For example, if $E_1 = E_3 = 5$ volts and $E_{bb} = 150$ volts, then a 10 per cent change in supply voltage ($dE_{bb}/E_{bb} = 0.1$) gives

$$\frac{dx}{x} = \frac{15}{150} \times 0.1 = 0.01$$

or a 1.0 per cent change in sweep time.

A diode (T_2 in Fig. 7-26) may be used to clamp the suppressor to ground during the time when the time base is being formed. Hence the negative supply $-E_4$ plays no part in determining conditions during the interval T_s. The voltage $-E_4$ is needed only to ensure plate-current cutoff before the circuit is triggered. Variations in the negative supply have negligible effect on the sweep time T_s.

Variations in filament voltage should affect E_1 and E_3 to some extent. Experimentally it is found that a 10 per cent change in filament voltage results in only a few tenths of a per cent change in T_s and in a direction opposite to the change due to a plate supply variation. If tubes are changed, then T_s may change by a few per cent because $2E_1 + E_3$ varies from tube to tube.

Comparing Eq. (7-7) with Eq. (7-4), it follows that

$$\epsilon_d = \frac{1}{8} \frac{T_s}{RC} \frac{1}{|A|} \cong \frac{1}{8} \frac{1}{|A|} \tag{7-14}$$

If the amplifier gain is 100, then $\epsilon_d \cong 0.13$ per cent. (Incidentally, if linearities under 1 per cent are to be realized, then the capacitance C must be independent of voltage to this precision. A mica capacitor is usually satisfactory, whereas a paper capacitor may not be.) Here, then, is a circuit possessing many fine characteristics: excellent linearity of sweep and a time-base duration whose value is not very sensitive to positive, negative, or filament supply voltages and whose sweep speed

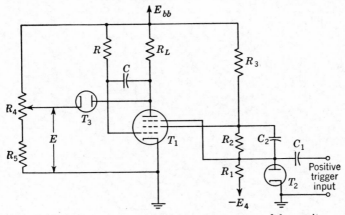

FIG. 7-26. The screen-coupled phantastron as a delay unit.

is readily adjusted. With a trigger input a square-wave output is obtained at the screen, in addition to the linear output at the plate, and hence the circuit is analogous to the plate-coupled monostable multi discussed in Chap. 6. One of the principal applications of the phantastron is as a delay unit. If the output at the screen is differentiated (peaked), then a negative output pulse is obtained, delayed T_s sec from the triggering pip. The delay is adjusted by controlling the voltage E from which the run-down begins. A plate-catching diode T_3 is ideal for this purpose and the complete circuit is shown in Fig. 7-26. The waveforms are given in Fig. 7-25 except that the plate voltage starts at E rather than E_{bb}. The overshoot at the grid is approximately $E_{bb}r_c/R_L$, where r_c is the static grid-cathode resistance and is independent of E and therefore T_s. This characteristic is different from the corresponding one for the plate-coupled multivibrator where the overshoot increases with delay. The delay T_s is a linear function of E except for small delays where curvature due to bottoming becomes important. Incidentally, T_3 also serves the useful purpose of reducing the recovery time because it catches the plate which is rising toward E_{bb} when it reaches E (see Fig. 7-28).

Analogous to the cathode-coupled monostable multi a cathode-coupled monostable phantastron can be constructed as indicated in Fig. 7-27. In the quiescent state the suppressor potential (the voltage E_2 across R_1) is much lower than the cathode voltage so that the plate current in T_1 is zero. The grid is clamped to the cathode and the plate is clamped to the control voltage E. A positive trigger of large enough magnitude is applied to the suppressor so that plate current commences to flow. This current causes the plate to fall, and because of the capacitive coupling the grid falls an equal amount. This drop in grid voltage decreases the

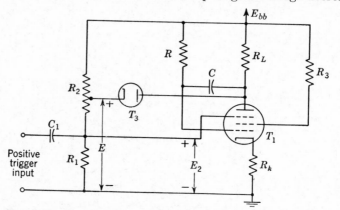

Fig. 7-27. The cathode-coupled phantastron as a delay circuit.

cathode current and the cathode potential falls. Hence, the suppressor voltage increases relative to the cathode and more plate current is drawn, etc. This explanation shows that the circuit is regenerative, and at $t = 0+$ normal plate current flows and the Miller run-down commences.

The waveforms are indicated in Fig. 7-28. Because of cathode-follower action the grid and cathode waveforms are almost identical. Since the grid follows the cathode drop at $t = 0+$, the plate, which is tied to the grid through C, must drop the same amount. Hence, the initial fall in plate potential E_1 may be larger by a factor of about 10 than the corresponding drop in the screen-coupled phantastron. The overshoots at the grid and cathode and the undershoot at the screen can be minimized by using a grid-catching diode connected with its plate at the grid of T_1 and its cathode at a tap on R_2 such that the voltage at this point is 1 or 2 volts less than the quiescent cathode potential. The exponential voltage at the plate during the retrace time ends abruptly at E because of the plate-catching diode. This abrupt termination of the plate waveform is reflected in the other waveforms in Fig. 7-28, as indicated. The vertical sides in Fig. 7-28 are actually of the order of 1 μsec in duration. These waveforms should be compared with the analogous ones in Fig. 6-11 for the cathode-coupled monostable multi.

The cathode-coupled phantastron has the following advantages over the screen-coupled circuit. No negative supply is needed. The screen is a free (unloaded) electrode from which a positive gate is obtained. A negative gate is available at the cathode. The principal disadvantages

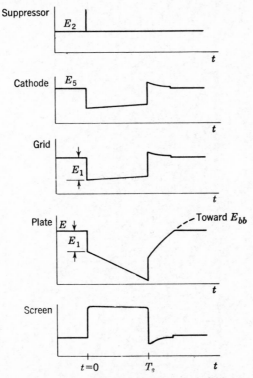

FIG. 7-28. Waveforms in the cathode-coupled phantastron.

are that there is a larger initial step in plate voltage and the gain of the amplifier is smaller because of the cathode degeneration introduced by R_k. This decreased gain means that the linearity is somewhat poorer.

The phantastron has the advantage over the cathode-coupled multi in that the former is much less sensitive to tube characteristics and to supply-voltage variations than the latter. For example, if the E_{bb} supply changes by 10 per cent in a multi circuit, we may expect the delay to change by perhaps 5 per cent, which is five or ten times what can be expected in the phantastron circuit. Also, the phantastron delay can be made more linear than that of the multi if sufficient gain is used. An astable phantastron circuit is suggested in Prob. 7-16.

The phantastron circuit is limited to the generation of linear sweeps of duration of the order of 10 μsec or longer because of the effect of the stray capacitance to ground at the various tube electrodes. Williams

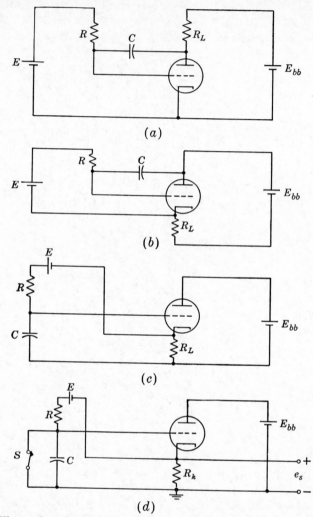

Fig. 7-29. Illustrating that a Miller integrator and a bootstrap sweep are different forms of the same circuit.

and Moody[3] describe circuits of the Miller type, called *sanatron* or *sanaphant*, which are capable of giving precise delays as short as 1 μsec. These circuits are essentially phantastrons in which a separate tube is used to generate the necessary gate from the input trigger.

7-8. The Bootstrap Sweep. In Fig. 7-29a the Miller sweep of Fig. 7-18 has been redrawn. The switch S has been omitted, no ground connection is indicated, and the tube supply voltage has been separated from the capacitor-charging voltage. Figure 7-29b is equivalent to Fig. 7-29a. In Fig. 7-29c one terminal of C has been moved from one side of E_{bb} to the other. This change will have no effect on signal voltages. In Fig. 7-29d one point has been grounded, output terminals have been selected, and R_L has been relabeled R_k. The switch S which clamps the circuit at some initial level until opened is located in different positions in this last circuit and in Fig. 7-18. Because of this new switch location

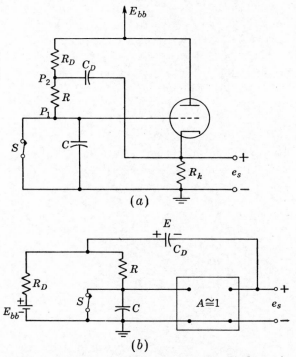

FIG. 7-30. (*a*) A practical form of the bootstrap sweep; (*b*) the equivalent circuit.

there will be no jump in the output voltage when S is opened. The circuit of Fig. 7-29d has the form given in Fig. 7-14b for the *bootstrap* sweep. The above discussion illustrates once more that the Miller integrator and the bootstrap sweep are two forms of the same circuit. The sweep voltage may be calculated from Eq. (7-10).

The practical disadvantage in Fig. 7-29 is that neither side of the supply E is grounded. This disadvantage may be remedied essentially by replacing E by a charged capacitor C_D, as shown in Fig. 7-30. It is necessary that C_D be large enough so that the voltage across C_D does not change appreciably during the sweep time. If the voltage across C_D were truly constant and if the cathode follower had exactly unity gain, then point P_2 in Fig. 7-30 would exactly follow point P_1. Hence, the voltage difference between P_2 and P_1 would remain constant and the current through R would remain constant. Under these conditions the current through capacitor C (which equals that through R) is constant and the sweep is truly linear.

In the equivalent circuit of Fig. 7-30b, if we neglect the small initial drop across the cathode resistor, $E = RE_{bb}/(R + R_D)$. If the output impedance of the amplifier (cathode follower) is small in comparison to R_D, the branch consisting of R_D and E_{bb} may be neglected in Fig. 7-30b and the resultant circuit is identical to that of Fig. 7-14b. The nominal sweep speed is $E/RC = E_{bb}R/(R + R_D)RC = E_{bb}/(R + R_D)C$ so that the sweep speed is the same as if C charged through $R + R_D$ directly from E_{bb}. The amplifier gain in the presence of the load is $A' \equiv AR_D/(R_o + R_D)$, in which R_o is the amplifier output impedance. From the discussion in Sec. 7-4 it follows that the displacement error is

$$\epsilon_d = \frac{1}{8}\frac{E_s}{E}(1 - A') = \frac{1}{8}\frac{E_s}{E_{bb}}\frac{R + R_D}{R}\left(1 - \frac{AR_D}{R_o + R_D}\right) \quad (7\text{-}15)$$

where E_s is the sweep amplitude.

This equation shows that for best linearity R_D should be chosen small compared with R and very large compared with R_o. For example, if $R_D = 0.1R$, the error is multiplied by 1.1. However, if $R_D = 10R_o$ and $A = 0.95$, then $1 - A = 0.05$ and

$$1 - \frac{AR_D}{R_o + R_D} = 1 - 0.95 \times \frac{10}{11} = 0.135$$

so that the error is multiplied by $0.135/0.05 = 2.7!$ This numerical example illustrates the fact that R_D/R_o must indeed be very large if the displacement error is to be kept small.

At the termination of the sweep, C_D must recharge through a resistance which is equal to the parallel combination of R and R_D. In a repetitive sweep, if the restoration time is not long enough to permit the capacitor C_D to recharge fully, the sweep speed will be a function of the restoration time and hence of the repetition rate. Much of the difficulty associated with R_D is eliminated in the circuit of Fig.

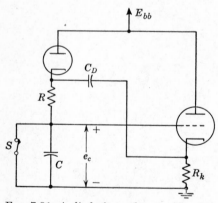

Fig. 7-31. A diode is used to replace R_D of Fig. 7-30 in order to decrease the retrace time.

7-31, in which the resistor is replaced with a diode.

Initially the voltage at the cathode of the diode is only slightly negative with respect to the plate since the diode need supply only the small current E_{bb}/R. At the instant S opens the cathode voltage rises and the diode is cut off. The current to recharge C_D flows through the low-resistance diode and the low output impedance of the cathode follower. Since the cathode voltage of the diode must rise a few tenths of a volt before its resistance becomes very large compared with the output impedance R_o of the cathode follower, then the beginning ($\cong 0.2$ volt) of the sweep will be nonlinear.

We now estimate how large C_D must be in order that it have negligible influence on linearity. From Fig. 7-31 we find (see Prob. 7-21) that

$$e_c = E_{bb}\frac{C'}{C}(1 - \epsilon^{-t/RC'}) \cong \frac{E_{bb}t}{RC}\left(1 - \frac{t}{2RC'} + \cdots\right) \qquad (7\text{-}16)$$

in which $\dfrac{1}{C'} = \dfrac{1}{C_D} + \dfrac{1-A}{C}$. The term $\dfrac{t}{2RC'} = \dfrac{t}{2RC}\left(1 - A + \dfrac{C}{C_D}\right)$ and the factor by which the linearity is multiplied is $\left(1 - A + \dfrac{C}{C_D}\right)$ rather than $1 - A$. Therefore it is required that $C_D \gg C/(1 - A)$. Too large a value of C_D will mean a very long restoration time and the circuit will be sensitive to changes in the repetition rate. Hence C should be chosen small (so that C_D will not be too large) and the sweep speed is adjusted to the desired value by the proper choice of R. The maximum value of R is limited to a few megohms by practical considerations. For sweep lengths of, say, 0.01 sec and longer, C will be of the order of magnitude of 0.2 μf and C_D should be much larger than this value. Even if R_D is a diode, the restoration time may be several thousand microseconds.

A method[5] of avoiding the use of large capacitors and of making the sweep speed independent of the repetition rate is to replace C_D in Fig. 7-30a by a ⅟₂₅-watt neon lamp. This lamp has a voltage drop E_L of about 65 volts which remains constant over the current range from 30 to 300 μa. The sweep speed is now almost independent of the supply voltage, since it is given by $(E_L + E_k)/RC$, where E_k is the quiescent cathode voltage. Very slow sweeps (of the order of 40 sec) have been obtained with retrace times as short as 10 μsec! The restoration time is now determined by how fast C can be discharged through the resistance of the switch.

Instead of a cathode follower we could use a noninverting amplifier and adjust the gain to be exactly unity. The linearity would then be perfect. However, as the gain varied in the neighborhood of unity due to tube aging, temperature effects, line-supply variations, etc., the output would vary as shown in Fig. 7-32. To minimize the drift in gain, we might use a two-stage negative-feedback amplifier. This circuit would have to be stabilized so that it would not oscillate.   Also the amplifier bandwidth

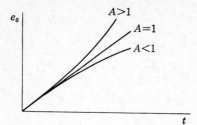

would have to be large enough so as to pass the sweep undistorted. As we have mentioned before, this latter requirement is not an easy one to fulfill. Several modifications of the simple bootstrap circuit are discussed in the problems.

FIG. 7-32. If the amplifier gain in a bootstrap circuit is different from unity, the sweep voltage curves away from the ideal linear sweep.

7-9. Additional Methods of Linearity Improvement.

In addition to the feedback methods discussed above, there are a number of other circuits which improve the linearity over that which is obtained by the simple exponential charging of a capacitor.

A Compensating Network. If a distorted sweep voltage of the form $e_s = A_1 t - A_2 t^2 + A_3 t^3 - \cdots$ is put into an integrating network, the output is of the form $e_o = B_2 t^2 - B_3 t^3 + \cdots$. If the integrator output is added to the original voltage and if the network parameters are chosen so that $A_2 = B_2$, then the result is

$$e_s + e_o = A_1 t + (A_3 - B_3)t^3 + \cdots$$

This voltage is much more linear than the original sweep because the quadratic term is missing. This type of compensation is easily applied to improve the bootstrap linearity.[6]

Use of an Inductor. If an inductor L is added in series with the resistor R_L in the plate circuit of a Miller-type sweep amplifier, then an improvement in linearity results because the gain of the amplifier is thereby increased.

An inductor L may also be used to improve the linearity of a simple RC sweep, as indicated in Fig. 7-33. The inductor also allows a sweep to be obtained whose amplitude is larger than the supply voltage because of the oscillatory nature of the circuit. Assuming that the switch S opens at $t = 0$, the solution for e_s is

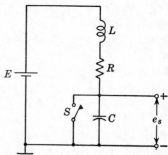

FIG. 7-33. A large inductance L will improve the sweep linearity because an inductor tries to keep constant current flowing through it.

$$\frac{e_s}{E} = 1 + \epsilon^{-Rt/2L}(A \sin \omega t - \cos \omega t) \qquad (7\text{-}17)$$

where $\quad A = \dfrac{1}{\omega}\left(\dfrac{1}{RC} - \dfrac{R}{2L}\right) \quad$ and $\quad \omega = \sqrt{\dfrac{1}{LC} - \left(\dfrac{R}{2L}\right)^2} \qquad (7\text{-}18)$

The voltage may be expanded in a power series in t with the result

$$e_s = \frac{E}{RC} t \left[1 - \frac{1}{6} \left(\frac{t}{\sqrt{LC}} \right)^2 + \frac{1}{12} \left(\frac{t}{\sqrt{LC}} \right)^2 \frac{t}{2L/R} - \cdots \right] \quad (7\text{-}19)$$

If enough inductance has been added to make the circuit oscillatory, then $1/\sqrt{LC}$ is larger than $R/2L$ and $t/\sqrt{LC}$ is larger than $t/(2L/R)$. If, therefore, $t/\sqrt{LC} \ll 1$, then the third term in Eq. (7-19) is less than $\frac{1}{12}(t/\sqrt{LC})^3$. We may then write as a good approximation

$$e_s = \frac{E}{RC} t \left(1 - \frac{t^2}{6LC} \right) \quad (7\text{-}20)$$

The improvement in linearity results from the fact that there is no quadratic term in Eq. (7-20).

The value of L for critical damping is $L_c = R^2 C/4$. For $L = nL_c$,

$$e_s = \frac{E}{RC} t \left[1 - \frac{2}{3n} \left(\frac{t}{RC} \right)^2 \right] \quad (7\text{-}21)$$

Equation (7-21) applies if $n \geq 1$. If $n = 0$, $e_c = \frac{E}{RC} t \left(1 - \frac{t}{2RC} \right)$. From Prob. 6-15, the displacement error under the conditions that Eq. (7-21) is valid is given by

$$\epsilon_d = 0.385 \left[\frac{2}{3n} \left(\frac{T_s}{RC} \right)^2 \right] \quad (7\text{-}22)$$

Even if n is only equal to 1, a considerable improvement in linearity results. For example, if $T_s/RC = 0.1$, then ϵ_d for the circuit without the inductor is $T_s/8RC = 1.25$ per cent, and for $n = 1$,

$$\epsilon_d = 0.385 \times 0.667 = 0.26 \text{ per cent}$$

If n is larger than 1, ϵ_d varies inversely with n.

It is possible to trade linearity for amplitude. For example, let us keep the displacement error at the uncompensated value, discussed above, of 1.25 per cent. If we use $n = 100$, then, from Eq. (7-22), $T_s/RC = [0.0125 \times 300/(0.385 \times 2)]^{1/2} = 2.2$, so that the sweep amplitude is 2.2 times the supply voltage. A value of $n = 100$ may mean an inductance equal to several hundred henrys, but it is feasible to obtain such inductors today because the inductor current is small and because of the presently available high-permeability magnetic cores. In other types of sweep circuits it is possible to trade linearity for sweep amplitude only so long as the amplitude remains reasonably small in comparison with the supply voltage. In the feedback sweep circuits, when the sweep amplitude becomes comparable to the supply voltage, the vacuum tubes in the circuit begin to operate nonlinearly.

The inductor current is smaller at the end of the sweep period than at the beginning. The initial inductor current depends on the restoration period allowed between sweeps and therefore the sweep speed will be a function of the repetition rate of the sweep. The time constant associated with the restoration period is L/R, but, on the other hand, the percentage difference in the inductor current between beginning and

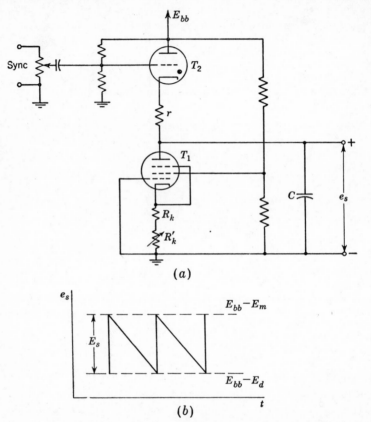

(a)

(b)

Fig. 7-34. (a) A sweep circuit using the constant-current characteristics of a pentode for linearization. (b) The output waveform. E_m and E_d are, respectively, the maintaining and breakdown voltages of the thyratron.

end of the sweep is small. Therefore the restoration period need not be large in comparison with L/R to make the initial inductor current approximately independent of repetition rate.

The Use of a Pentode. The plate current in a pentode, for fixed screen-to-cathode voltage, is largely independent of plate voltage except for quite low voltages. Therefore a capacitor charging from a supply voltage through a pentode will charge at approximately constant current. For example, in a 6AU6, if the supply voltage is 300 volts, the grid bias

−2 volts, and the screen voltage 150 volts, the initial charging current is 5.8 ma (Fig. A-1). When the capacitor voltage is 200 volts, the tube voltage is 100 volts, and the charging current is 5.7 ma. The percentage slope error is therefore $100(5.8 - 5.7)/5.8 \cong 2$ per cent. Without the pentode the slope error would be $100 \times {}^{200}\!\!/\!{}_{300} = 67$ per cent.

A thyratron sweep circuit using a pentode for linearization is shown in Fig. 7-34a. A thyratron is used for the switch tube. The capacitor C charges rapidly through the thyratron until the difference between the supply voltage and the capacitor voltage drops to less than the thyratron maintaining voltage E_m. The sweep voltage is formed as the capacitor discharges through the pentode. The cathode resistor stabilizes the quiescent tube current, and the rheostat adjusts the nominal tube current and hence the sweep rate. Coarse frequency changes are accomplished by changing the capacitor C. The sweep at the output terminals is negative-going as indicated in Fig. 7-34b. The amplitude of the sweep may be adjusted as in a conventional thyratron sweep circuit by adjusting the thyratron bias.

REFERENCES

1. Millman, J., and S. Seely: "Electronics," 2d ed., pp. 302–308, McGraw-Hill Book Company, Inc., New York, 1951.
2. Chance, B., et al.: "Waveforms," Massachusetts Institute of Technology Radiation Laboratory Series, vol. 19, pp. 278–285, McGraw-Hill Book Company, Inc., New York, 1949.
3. Williams, F. C., and N. F. Moody: Ranging Circuits, Linear Time-base Generators and Associated Circuits, *J. IEE*, vol. 93, pt. IIIA, pp. 1188–1198, 1946.
   Close, R. N., and M. T. Lebenbaum: Design of Phantastron Time Delay Circuits, *Electronics*, vol. 21, pp. 101–107, April, 1948.
4. Ref. 2, pp. 195–204 and 285–288.
5. Miller, R. E., and W. R. Kincheloe, Jr.: Neon Lamps as Bootstrap Circuit Elements, *Tech. Rept.* 10, Electronics Research Laboratory, Stanford University, Calif., June 25, 1952.
6. Ref. 2, pp. 274–278.

CHAPTER 8

CURRENT TIME-BASE GENERATORS

For some applications it is necessary to provide for deflection of the beam of a cathode-ray tube by the use of a magnetic coil rather than through the use of electrostatic plates. A set of coils is arranged with an axis perpendicular to the desired direction of deflection. The beam deflection angle is proportional to the coil current[1] and for a linear sweep. it is, of course, required that the coil current increase linearly with time.

8-1. The Generator Waveform. Consider that a current generator is used to drive the deflection coil. In Fig. 8-1, L is the deflection coil inductance, R_L is the coil resistance, and C is the effective distributed capacitance of the coil. The resistor R is a *damping* resistor which has been included for a purpose that will appear shortly.

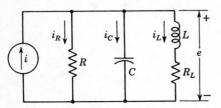

FIG. 8-1. A current generator i feeds a magnetic deflection coil.

We shall now find the waveform of the current i which the generator must supply in order that the inductor current i_L shall increase linearly with time. We assume that the inductor current is $i_L = kt$, in which k is a constant. The drop across L and R_L in series equals the voltage across R and C in parallel. This voltage is

$$e = L\frac{di_L}{dt} + R_L i_L = kL + kR_L t \qquad (8\text{-}1)$$

Hence, the current taken by the damping resistor is

$$i_R = \frac{e}{R} = \frac{kL + kR_L t}{R}$$

The sweep is to begin at $t = 0$. The capacitor is uncharged at $t = 0-$ and, as indicated by Eq. (8-1), the capacitor voltage must jump to kL at $t = 0+$. Hence, a current i_C must be furnished by the generator which will charge the capacitor to the voltage kL in zero time. This current must be infinite in magnitude but must last for only an infinitesimal time duration and must have the property that $(1/C)\int i_C\, dt = kL$ or

$$\int i_C\, dt = kLC$$

236

Also, an additional capacitor current must flow which is equal to kR_LC so that the voltage across the capacitor will continue to rise at the same rate at which the voltage e is rising.

It is convenient to introduce the *unit impulse* or *delta* function $\delta(t)$ defined by $\delta(t) = \infty$ when $t = 0$, $\delta(t) = 0$ when $t \neq 0$, and

$$\int_{-\infty}^{+\infty} \delta(t)\, dt = 1$$

We may now write that

$$i = i_L + i_R + i_C = kt + (kL + kR_Lt)\frac{1}{R} + kR_LC + kLC\ \delta(t)$$

or

$$i = kLC\ \delta(t) + \frac{kL}{R}\left(1 + \frac{RR_LC}{L}\right) + kt\left(1 + \frac{R_L}{R}\right) \tag{8-2}$$

Altogether the current generator must furnish a current which consists of an impulse, a step, and a linear rise as indicated in Fig. 8-2.

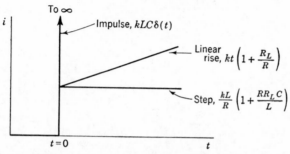

FIG. 8-2. In order to obtain a linear sweep, a current generator must supply three components of current: an impulse, a step, and a linear rise.

At the termination of the sweep the energy stored in the inductor must be dissipated. It is usually desired that the decay of inductor current shall not be accompanied by an oscillation in the circuit. The resistor R serves to provide damping for the circuit and is usually adjusted so that the circuit is either critically damped or overdamped. If we neglect the effect on the damping of the small resistance R_L (see Prob. 8-1), the value of R for critical damping is $R = \frac{1}{2}\sqrt{L/C} \equiv R_c$. The parameters for some typical deflection coils are given in Table 8-1.

TABLE 8-1. DEFLECTION-COIL PARAMETERS[2]

Core	L, mh, at 1,000 cps	R_L, ohms	C, $\mu\mu f$	$R_c = \frac{1}{2}\sqrt{\dfrac{L}{C}}$, ohms	$\sqrt{LC}$, μsec	$\dfrac{R_cR_LC \times 10^3}{L}$
Iron....	280	340	200	19,000	7	5
Iron....	70	73	250	8,000	4	2
Air.....	97	408	25	31,000	1.5	3

8-2. Effect of the Omission of the Impulsive Component of Current.
It is physically impossible to generate exactly the impulse term in Eq.
(8-2). Let us investigate the effect of omitting it completely. If i is
given by Eq. (8-2) except that the term $kLC\,\delta(t)$ is missing, the differential equation for i_L for the circuit of Fig. 8-1 is found to be

$$Ri = RLC\frac{d^2i_L}{dt^2} + (RR_LC + L)\frac{di_L}{dt} + (R + R_L)i_L$$
$$= kL + RR_LCk + (R + R_L)kt \tag{8-3}$$

The solution of the inhomogeneous equation is $i_L = kt$, as is to be anticipated. The transient part of the solution is to be found by setting
the right-hand member of Eq. (8-3) equal to zero. Consider first that R

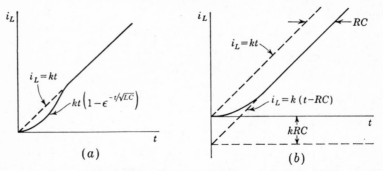

Fig. 8-3. The coil current resulting from the omission of the impulsive current term
in Eq. (8-2). In (a) R equals the critically damped value R_c, and in (b) $R \ll R_c$.

has been selected for critical damping, $R = R_c$. Then $RR_LC \ll L$ and
also $R_L \ll R$ (see Table 8-1) so that

$$RLC\frac{d^2i_L}{dt^2} + L\frac{di_L}{dt} + Ri_L = 0 \tag{8-4}$$

The single root of Eq. (8-4) for critical damping is $p = -1/\sqrt{LC}$ and the
form of the complete solution is

$$i_L = (A + Bt)\epsilon^{-t/\sqrt{LC}} + kt \tag{8-5}$$

At $t = 0$, the coil current i_L is zero and the capacitor voltage e is zero.
Since $e = L\,di_L/dt + R_Li_L = 0$, then the initial conditions are $i_L = 0$ and
$di_L/dt = 0$. Subject to these conditions we find that

$$i_L = kt(1 - \epsilon^{-t/\sqrt{LC}}) \tag{8-6}$$

which is plotted as a solid line in Fig. 8-3a. The maximum deviation
between the actual sweep and the ideal sweep is $0.37k\sqrt{LC}$ and occurs
at a time $t = \sqrt{LC}$. The sweep is temporarily delayed for an interval
which is several times $\sqrt{LC}$. Values of $\sqrt{LC}$ are tabulated in Table 8-1.
    Consider the extreme case of very heavy damping. Since now R is

even smaller than R_c, then certainly $RR_LC \ll L$, but it may not be that $R_L \ll R$. Replacing the term Ri_L in Eq. (8-4) by $(R + R_L)i_L$, we find for the roots

$$p = -\frac{1}{2RC} \pm \frac{1}{2RC} \sqrt{1 - \frac{4(R + R_L)RC}{L}} \qquad (8\text{-}7)$$

If R is smaller than one-tenth R_c, then, for the typical coil parameters in Table 8-1, the second term under the square root sign is less than 0.01. Neglecting this term compared with unity, we have for the two roots

$$p_1 = -\frac{1}{RC} \qquad \text{and} \qquad p_2 = 0$$

The form of the complete solution is

$$i_L = A + Be^{-t/RC} + kt$$

Subject to the initial condition $i_L = di_L/dt = 0$ at $t = 0$, we find for the complete solution

$$i_L = kt + RCk(e^{-t/RC} - 1) \qquad (8\text{-}8)$$

The current i_L is plotted (solid line) in Fig. 8-3b, where it is seen that the sweep is permanently delayed by a time RC. The time delay will be smaller than the delay in the case of critical damping. For example, say, R is reduced to $R_c/10 = 1,900$ ohms for the first entry in Table 8-1. Then the delay is of the order of 0.38 μsec rather than several times 7 μsec.

This result is to be expected since C may now charge from a lower impedance source.

The effective capacitance across a deflection coil should, of course, always be kept as low as possible by using a type of winding which gives the minimum distributed capacitance and by keeping stray circuit capacitances at a minimum. One very effective procedure is to reduce the number of turns on the coil,

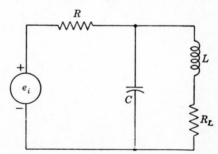

FIG. 8-4. A voltage generator used to drive a deflection coil.

but in this case the deflection produced per unit coil current is correspondingly low. In applications where fast sweeps are required, it is not uncommon to use small transmitting tubes to provide the necessary current.

Alternatively, we may use the circuit of Fig. 8-4 in which the current generator of Fig. 8-1 is replaced by a voltage generator e_i. The series combination of the voltage generator e_i and the series resistor R is completely equivalent to the combination of a current generator i shunted by a resistor R, provided that e_i and i are related by $e_i = iR$. Therefore it is required that $e_i = iR$, where i is given by Eq. (8-2). Thus,

$$e_i = kRLC\ \delta(t) + k(L + RR_L C) + (R + R_L)kt \quad (8\text{-}9)$$

8-3. Current Drivers. The deflection coil is usually placed in series with a tube which is used to supply the current and is called the *current driver*. The coil may be placed either in the plate or cathode circuit. A signal voltage which has the form shown for the current in Fig. 8-2 (but without the impulse) is applied to the grid of the current driver. The circuits of either Fig. 8-1 or Fig. 8-4 may then be used to analyze the result, depending on whether the tube approximates more nearly a current source or a voltage source.

The trapezoidal voltage waveform required is generated by a voltage sweep circuit, modified, as in Fig. 8-5a, by the inclusion of a resistor R_1 in series with the sweep

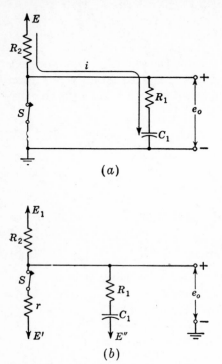

(a)

(b)

Fig. 8-5. (a) A circuit for generating a trapezoidal waveform. (b) A more general circuit.

capacitor C_1. If the switch S opens at $t = 0$, the output e_o is given by

$$e_o = E - \frac{R_2 E}{R_1 + R_2} \epsilon^{-t/(R_1+R_2)C_1} \quad (8\text{-}10)$$

This equation is consistent with the facts that at $t = \infty$, $e_o = E$, and at $t = 0$, $e_o = ER_1/(R_1 + R_2)$. Expanding the exponential, we find

$$e_o \cong \frac{R_1 E}{R_1 + R_2}$$

$$+ \frac{R_2 E}{R_1 + R_2} \frac{t}{(R_1 + R_2)C_1} \left[1 - \frac{t}{2(R_1 + R_2)C_1} + \cdots \right] \quad (8\text{-}11)$$

Since usually $R_2 \gg R_1$, then

$$e_o \cong \frac{R_1 E}{R_2} + \frac{Et}{R_2 C_1} \left(1 - \frac{t}{2R_2 C_1} + \cdots \right) \quad (8\text{-}12)$$

As long as $t/R_2 C_1 \ll 1$, then e_o is trapezoidal as required.

A more general form of a trapezoidal waveform generator is shown in Fig. 8-5b. Here a switch resistance r has been included and the switch and capacitor C_1 have been returned to arbitrary voltages E' and E'', respectively. Equations (8-10) to (8-12) continue to apply, however, provided that E is taken to be the quiescent voltage across R_2 and e_o is interpreted as the departure of the output voltage from its quiescent value.

EXAMPLE. In Fig. 8-6 a cathode follower is used as a current driver for the deflection coil. Assume that the coil is the one described in the first entry in Table 8-1. Let the gating tube T_1 be a 6J5, while T_2 is a 6F6, triode connected. Take $E_{bb} = 300$ volts. Let it be required that the sweep duration be 10^{-3} sec during which time the

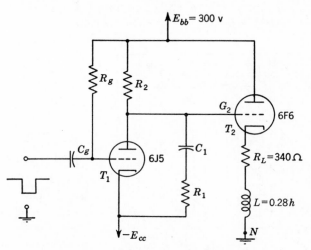

FIG. 8-6. An illustrative problem. The 6J5 is equivalent to one section of a 6SN7 (see Fig. A-2).

coil current is to change by 50 ma so that $k = 50$ amp/sec. Choose reasonable values for R_2, E_{cc}, R_1, and C_1. Also find the waveform at G_2 and the waveform of the coil current.

Solution. Initially the grid of T_1 is clamped to the cathode and the sweep starts when T_1 is driven beyond cutoff by the application to the grid of a negative gate, as shown. We arbitrarily select R_2 to be 1 Meg so that with T_1 in clamp the plate voltage of T_1 is close to the cathode voltage. From the 6F6 triode tube characteristics of Fig. 8-7a we find that T_2 will be cut off when the grid voltage is about -50 volts. We bias T_2 at -25 volts *with respect to ground.* We then find that, in the presence of the 340-ohm cathode resistance, the tube current is about 20 ma. In this way the tube nonlinearity at low current is avoided. The drop through R_2 must then be 325 volts so that the current in T_1 is about 0.3 ma. At zero grid-to-cathode voltage T_1 will conduct 0.3 ma when the plate-to-cathode voltage is about 5 volts. Accordingly we set $-E_{cc} = -30$ volts. The quiescent voltage across C_1 is 5 volts.

The equivalent circuit for the cathode follower T_2 is given in Fig. 8-7b in which e_o is the voltage applied to the grid of T_2. The plate resistance of the 6F6 is $r_p = 2,600$ ohms and $\mu = 6.8$. $R = r_p/(\mu + 1) = 330$ ohms, while $\mu/(\mu + 1) = 0.87$. Hence from Eq. (8-9), with the impulse voltage missing,

$$e_i = \frac{\mu e_o}{\mu + 1} = k(L + RR_LC) + (R + R_L)kt \tag{8-13}$$

Substituting $k = 50$ amp/sec, $L = 0.28$ henry, $R = 330$ ohms, $R_L = 340$ ohms, $C = 200$ $\mu\mu$f, and $\mu/(\mu + 1) = 0.87$, we find

$$e_o = 16.1 + 38.5 \times 10^3 t \tag{8-14}$$

This equation must be compared with Eq. (8-12).   Hence,

$$\frac{R_1}{R_2} E = 16.1 \qquad \text{and} \qquad \frac{E}{R_2 C_1} = 38.5 \times 10^3$$

Since the quiescent voltage across R_2 is 325 volts, then $E = 325$ volts.   For this value of E and $R_2 = 1$ Meg, we find $R_1 = 50$ K and $C_1 = 0.0084$ μf.

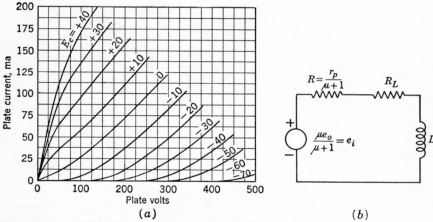

FIG. 8-7.   (a) The 6F6 triode plate characteristics.   (b) Equivalent circuit (for changes from the quiescent value) of the 6F6 cathode follower in Fig. 8-6.

Because we have omitted the impulsive component of current there is a delay in the start of the sweep.   In Sec. 8-2 we showed that, for a heavily damped coil, this time is $RC = 330(200 \times 10^{-12})$ sec $= 0.06$ μsec.   This delay is so small that it is evident that this circuit would also be suitable for use at very much faster sweep speeds.

The grid-to-ground voltage of tube T_2, e_{cn2} equals $-25 + e_o$, because the quiescent voltage is -25 volts and e_o represents the increase from the quiescent value.   Assuming that the trapezoidal voltage given in Eq. (8-14) is a sufficiently good approximation to the true exponential of Eq. (8-10), then e_{cn2} rises linearly from $-25 + 16.1 = -8.9$ volts at $t = 0+$ to $-25 + 16.1 + 38.5 = 29.6$ volts at $t = 1$ msec.   This voltage is plotted in Fig. 8-8a.   The coil current is 20 ma in the quiescent condition and increases linearly at the rate of 50 amp/sec to 70 ma at $t = 1$ msec, as indicated in Fig. 8-8b.

We shall now investigate the grid voltage of T_2 at the end of the sweep.   At $t = 1$ msec, the capacitor will be charged to $38.5 + 5 = 43.5$ volts.   The equivalent circuit of T_1 at this instant is indicated in Fig. 8-9, where we assume that the current in the 1-Meg load remains approximately 0.3 ma. From Kirchhoff's law we find

$$-43.5 + 50(i_b - 0.3) + e_b = 0 \qquad \text{or} \qquad e_b + 50i_b = 58.5 \qquad (8\text{-}15)$$

If this load line is plotted on the plate characteristics of the 6J5, the intersection with the $e_c = 0$ characteristic is found to be at $e_b = 12$ volts. Hence, from Fig. 8-9, $e_{cn2} = -30 + e_b = -30 + 12 = -18$ volts at $t = 1 +$ msec. This value is plotted in Fig. 8-8a. The grid decreases to the quiescent value of -25 volts with a time constant $(R_1 + r_p)C_1 \cong 0.5$ msec. Actually there will probably be an overshoot to the grid waveform of T_1 so that the abrupt drop in Fig. 8-8a will be even larger.

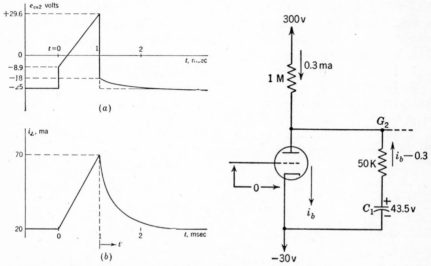

FIG. 8-8. (a) The grid-to-ground voltage of T_2, and (b) the coil current in the illustrative problem of Fig. 8-6.

FIG. 8-9. Equivalent circuit for calculating the voltage at G_2 at the end of the sweep.

We shall assume, for simplicity, that the grid of T_2 drops to its quiescent (-25 volt) level immediately at the termination of the gate, as indicated by the broken line portion of the waveform of Fig. 8-8a. The equivalent circuit to describe the decay of current in the inductor is now as shown in Fig. 8-7 except with the generator shorted. If t' is the time measured from the end of the sweep, then the instantaneous coil current is given by

$$i_L = 50\epsilon^{-\left(\frac{R+R_L}{L}\right)t'} + 20 \qquad \text{ma} \qquad (8\text{-}16)$$

The current decays with a time constant $L/(R + R_L) = 0.28/670 = 0.42$ msec, as indicated in Fig. 8-8b.

If the circuit had been critically damped, $R_c = 19$ K, then the recovery time constant would have been $0.28/19 \times 10^3 = 15$ μsec. In this case the start of the sweep would have been delayed by several times $\sqrt{LC} = 7$ μsec. Altogether then we conclude that critical damping gives a relatively large delay and small recovery time, whereas heavy damping gives a short delay and large recovery time.   The waveform across the deflection coil (the voltage at the cathode of T_2) will have a backswing at the end of the sweep as the voltage across the coil changes sign.   This waveform is given in Prob. 8-8.

The deflection coil may be placed in the plate circuit of Fig. 8-6 instead of in the cathode circuit.   A pentode or beam power tube is used for T_2 and an external damping resistor R is added across the coil.   The calculation of voltage and current waveforms and of the required component values may be carried out in a straightforward manner, as in the illustrative problem above.

8-4. Methods of Linearity Improvement.[3]   The simple sweep circuits discussed in Sec. 8-3 will not provide precisely linear sweeps for the following four essential reasons.

1. The impulse term required by Eq. 8-2 is lacking.

2. The driver tubes which provide the inductor currents do not operate with sufficiently linearity, especially over the large current ranges required.

3. The nominally linear portion of the trapezoidal waveform provided by the circuit of Fig. 8-5 is actually exponential in form.

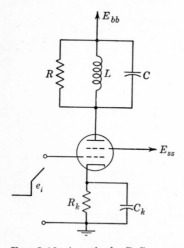

FIG. 8-10. A cathode R_kC_k combination is used to approximate an impulsive component of current.

4. The inductance of an iron-core coil varies with current.   This nonlinearity of the iron is avoided by using an air-core coil.   The first three nonlinearities mentioned above will now be discussed.

Circuits for Generating an Impulse.   In Fig. 8-10 is shown a pentode driver for the deflection coil which is in the plate circuit.   A resistor R_k bypassed with a small capacitor C_k is placed in the cathode circuit.   The input voltage is a trapezoidal voltage e_i, as shown.   The degenerative effect of the cathode resistor R_k will not make itself felt until C_k has charged.   The output current i of the pentode will appear as in Fig. 8-11.   During the relatively slow rise of the linear part of the trapezoidal voltage the presence of C_k will have little influence on the output current and the effect of C_k may be neglected.   The time constant R_kC_k is taken of the order of magnitude of the sweep delay resulting from the omission of the impulse.   Since the spike in Fig. 8-11 is only a crude approximation to an impulse, the final value of C_k is obtained experimentally for optimum linearity.

Alternatively, instead of adjusting the current driver so that it provides a current spike, we may instead produce a spike in the voltage applied to the driver tube. For example, we may invert the gating square wave in Fig. 8-6, differentiate it with a small RC circuit (see Sec. 2-2), and apply the resultant positive pip at the beginning of the sweep across R_1. The voltage at G_2 will then have the waveshape depicted in Fig. 8-11. Another circuit which produces the same result is given in Prob. 8-14.

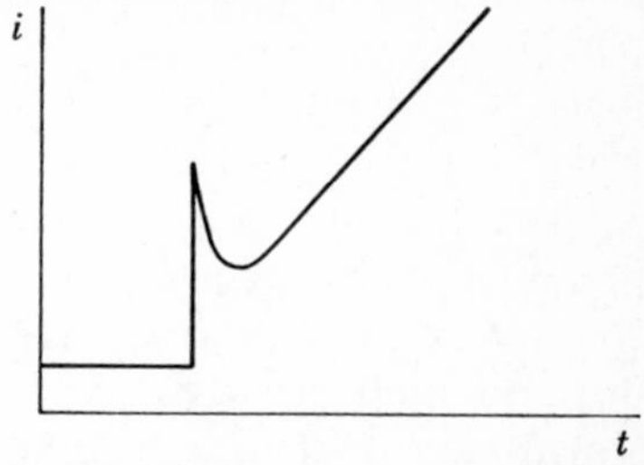

FIG. 8-11. The plate current in Fig. 8-10 contains a *spike* because of the small R_kC_k time constant.

Improvement of Linearity of Current Driver for Deflection Coil. The obvious remedy for the nonlinearity of the current driver for the deflection coil is the use of negative feedback. A method of incorporating inverse feedback is illustrated in Fig. 8-12a. The coil (L, R_L, C) together with its damping resistance R is arranged to be the load on the amplifier with current feedback. The amplifier has a gain A, output impedance

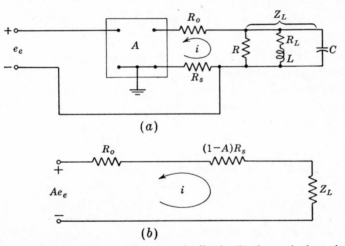

(a)

(b)

FIG. 8-12. (a) An amplifier with current feedback; (b) the equivalent circuit.

R_o, and the feedback impedance is the resistor R_s. The effect of current feedback is to leave unchanged the gain of the amplifier but to increase the output impedance of the amplifier by the term $(1 - A)R_s$ (see Sec. 1-3). Hence, we may replace Fig. 8-12a by the equivalent circuit in Fig. 8-12b. Now, if $(1 - A)R_s \gg |R_o + Z_L|$ and if $|A| \gg 1$ then

$$i \cong \frac{-Ae_e}{(1 - A)R_s} \cong \frac{e_e}{R_s} \tag{8-17}$$

and the resultant current is independent of the amplifier characteristics. The negative current feedback has transformed the amplifier into a device which acts as a current generator whose output current is proportional to the applied input signal e_e. The coil current will vary linearly with time, provided that the input voltage is given by $e_e = iR_s$, where i is given in Eq. (8-2).

The amplifier of Fig. 8-12 will usually consist of several stages of preamplification together with an output current driver. The deflection coil may then be placed either in the cathode circuit of the current driver or in the plate circuit. In the latter case the current driver is invariably a pentode. It is usually advantageous to use the plate circuit connection since in this case the driver tube contributes to the overall amplification.

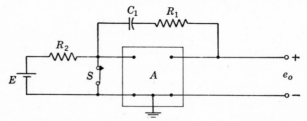

Fig. 8-13. An operational amplifier used to generate a trapezoidal waveform.

Alternatively, of course, voltage feedback may be used. In this case, it will be recalled (see Sec. 1-2) that the equivalent generator seen looking back into the output terminals is $Ae_e/(1 - \beta A) \cong -(e_e/\beta)$ if $|\beta A| \gg 1$ so that again the equivalent voltage generator is independent of the amplifier characteristics. The output impedance is $R_o/(1 - \beta A)$.

Linearization of Trapezoidal Voltage. Referring to Fig. 8-5, it is clear that a perfect trapezoid will be developed if the current through R_2 is kept constant. The current will be constant at E/R_2 if the top of the resistor R_2 is *bootstrapped* to the output voltage e_o. This bootstrapping is conveniently done in the case of an amplifier with current feedback. From Eq. (8-17), the voltage developed across the feedback resistor is $R_s i = e_e$, and since the output voltage in Fig. 8-5 is $e_o = e_e$, it is only necessary to bootstrap the top of R_2 to the voltage drop across the feedback resistor.

A second method for improving the linearity of the trapezoid is through the use of an operational amplifier, as shown in Fig. 8-13 (see Sec. 1-11). When the switch S opens at $t = 0$, the output is

$$e_o = - \frac{R_1}{R_2} E - \frac{E}{R_2 C_1} t \tag{8-18}$$

just as required, provided only that the gain A of the amplifier is very large.

8-5. Illustrative Current-sweep Circuits.   Because of the feedback the circuit of Fig. 8-13 not only provides an output of the correct form but, in the case of large A, has an output which is independent of tube characteristics, etc.   The deflection coil may therefore be placed directly across the output terminals.   Since the output impedance is nominally zero, the required output voltage [see Eq. (8-1)] is

$$e_o = kL + R_Lkt \tag{8-19}$$

Comparing Eqs. (8-18) and (8-19) and neglecting the arbitrary minus signs in Eq. (8-18), we may compute the required values of R_1 and C_1 as

$$R_1 = \frac{kLR_2}{E} \qquad C_1 = \frac{E}{kR_LR_2} \tag{8-20}$$

where E is the quiescent voltage across R_2.

A practical circuit which is patterned after the ideal circuit of Fig. 8-13 is shown in Fig. 8-14.   Of course, since the amplifier here is only a single

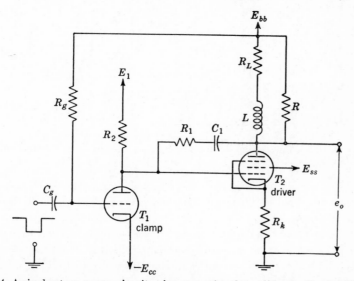

FIG. 8-14. A single-stage sweep circuit using operational amplifier feedback to linearize the trapezoidal voltage.   Current feedback through R_k makes the waveform more independent of the driver tube characteristics.

pentode, the results in Eq. (8-20) hold only approximately.   The grid of the pentode is clamped except during the sweep time so that no feedback exists after the termination of the sweep.   The output impedance is accordingly high after the sweep and a shunt damping resistor is required.   The cathode resistor R_k serves to stabilize the quiescent tube current.   If the voltage across T_1 when it is in clamp is neglected, then $E = E_1 + E_{cc}$.   The circuit of Fig. 8-14 finds wide application principally because of its relative simplicity. It has also a convenience, not shared by the circuit of Fig. 8-6, that the damping resistor R may be selected for critical damping to permit a rapid decay of the inductor current. The location of the deflection coil in the plate circuit, however, has the difficulty that the effect of power supply ripple is much more pronounced than when the coil is located in the cathode circuit.

A more elaborate circuit[3] using current feedback is shown in Fig. 8-15. A trapezoidal voltage is developed at the grid of T_2 at the opening of switch S. This signal is amplified by the two-stage amplifier T_2 and T_3 and applied to the grid of the driver tube T_4. A voltage proportional to the output current is developed across the cathode resistor R_s. The

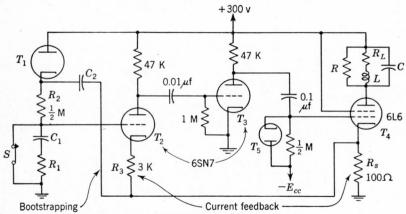

FIG. 8-15. A three-stage sweep circuit using current feedback and bootstrapping to improve the linearity.

feedback voltage is injected into the amplifier input through the cathode of T_2 since the grid of T_2 is already being used. At the same time the feedback voltage is used to bootstrap the trapezoidal voltage-forming circuit. Since the trapezoidal signal is a-c coupled to the driver tube, then a d-c restorer T_5 is used to ensure that the d-c level of the grid of T_4 is independent of repetition rate. In the quiescent state T_4 is cut off and it is brought into the conducting region by the step at the beginning of the sweep.

8-6. Television Sweep Circuit.[4] The frequency of a television horizontal sweep circuit is 15,750 cps (see Sec. 17-4) corresponding to a total time of 63.5 μsec for the combined sweep and retrace times. Since the flyback should be a small fraction of the complete cycle, one of the special problems associated with this television sweep is that of obtaining a fast retrace time (of the order of a few microseconds). Another important problem is that of conserving power. The peak energy stored in the inductance L of a deflecting coil is $\frac{1}{2}LI_m^2$, where I_m is the peak current.

Since this energy is dissipated in each cycle, the power lost in the yoke is $P = \frac{1}{2}LI_m^2 f_h$, where f_h is the horizontal scanning frequency. Typical values are $L = 30$ mh, $I_m = 300$ ma, and $f_h = 15{,}750$ cps, so that $P = 21$ watts. This value is about 10 per cent of the total power taken by the entire television set. By the simple technique of replacing the damping resistor across the deflecting coil by a damper diode the power loss is cut to about one-quarter its previous value (for the same deflection) and also the retrace time is made appreciably smaller. This method will now be explained in detail and several other interesting and valuable features of this circuit will be brought out in the discussion.

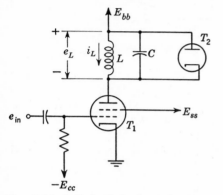

FIG. 8-16. A diode T_2 is shunted across coil L.

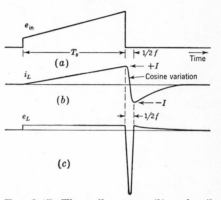

FIG. 8-17. The coil current (b) and coil voltage (c) corresponding to the sweep input voltage (a).

In Fig. 8-16 the damping resistor across the coil L is replaced by the diode T_2. Assume that the input to the grid of the amplifier T_1 is a single-stroke trapezoidal sweep lasting for a time T_s, as indicated in Fig. 8-17a. The current i_L in the coil is approximately linear (see Sec. 8-1). If the coil resistance is neglected, the voltage e_L across the coil is positive and of constant value for the interval T_s. The diode T_2 conducts a constant current during this interval. At the end of the sweep, the tube T_1 is cut off. The plate current immediately falls to zero and the coil current now flows through the capacitor C. The circuit rings (see Sec. 2-8) for one-half a cycle during which time $e_L = L\,di/dt$ is negative and the diode T_2 is cut off. The coil current changes in a cosinusoidal manner from a positive peak I to a negative value $-I$ in a time $1/2f$, where f is the resonant frequency corresponding to L and C. At the end of this half cycle the voltage e_L reverses sign (see Fig. 8-17c) and T_2 conducts again. The current i_L and the voltage e_L now decrease to zero with a time constant L/R_f, where R_f is the forward resistance of the diode.

The retrace time is $1/2f$. Since the resonant frequency of a coil used in a commercial television set is at least 70 kc, the flyback time is less than $1/(2 \times 7 \times 10^4) \cong 7$ μsec.   This calculation demonstrates that the circuit does indeed have the desired fast recovery time.

For the sake of simplicity, we assumed a single-stroke sweep in the above discussion.   For a recurrent sweep, the situation is as pictured in Fig. 8-18.   The sweep time T_s is chosen so that the period T of the input voltage is only slightly longer than $T_s + 1/2f$.   Under these circumstances tube T_1 begins to conduct again before tube T_2 stops conducting.   Hence, now the total coil current (shown dashed in Fig. 8-18) is made up of two components: the positive one is that part of the coil current which flows

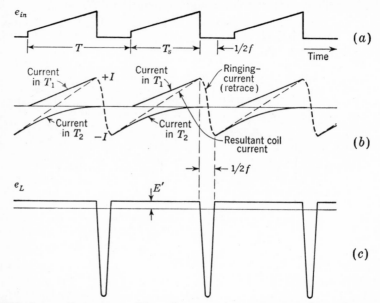

FIG. 8-18. A recurrent sweep.   The coil current is seen in (b) to be made up of the superposition of two currents.

in T_1 and the negative one is that portion of the coil current which flows in T_2.

We see also from Fig. 8-18b that the total sweep corresponds to a current of $2I$ and yet the peak energy stored in the inductor is $\frac{1}{2}LI^2$ and *not* $\frac{1}{2}L(2I)^2$.   This observation verifies our previous claim that the power loss due to the magnetic-coil energy which is dissipated each cycle can be cut to one-quarter its value by using a damper diode.

The horizontal sweep circuit of a television receiver is indicated in Fig. 8-19.   Because the kinescope is a flat-faced tube, the rate of change of yoke current must be greatest at the center of the scan and must decrease when the beam reaches the edges of the tube.   The current waveform is shaped by means of the network consisting of two capacitors C_1 and C_2 (see Fig. 8-19) and the adjustable inductor L_L resonating near the scanning frequency. Hence this combination controls the horizontal linearity of the television picture. We have also indicated in Fig. 8-19 an adjustable resistor R_W in series with the deflection coil. This resistor controls the peak coil current and hence the width of the television picture.

During the sweep time, when the diode T_2 conducts, the positive voltage E' (Fig. 8-18c) is impressed across C_2. Neglecting the d-c drop in L_L, this voltage appears also across C_1. Hence, at the junction of the capacitors C_1 and C_2 (marked "boosted d-c output" in Fig. 8-19) there

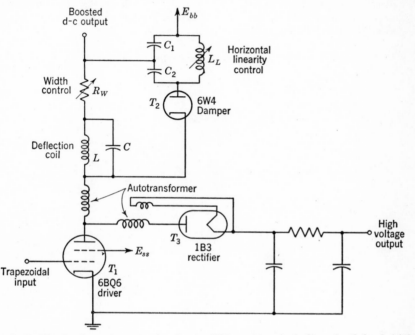

Fig. 8-19. The horizontal sweep circuit of a TV receiver, including the flyback high-voltage supply.

appears a voltage which is greater than that provided by the low voltage supply E_{bb}. This boosted voltage is the effective plate-supply voltage for the sweep driver and also for other tubes in the television set. The increase in voltage E' over E_{bb} is of the order of 50 to 350 volts.

The voltage induced across the deflection coil during the flyback time (see Fig. 8-18c) can be very high—of the order of thousands of volts. Advantage is taken of this phenomenon in order to supply the high voltages (say, 12 kv at 100 μa) required for acceleration of the electron beam. Thus, in Fig. 8-19 an autotransformer has been added with its primary in series with the deflection coil and its secondary in series with a rectifier tube T_3. The sum of the voltages induced in L, in the transformer primary, and in its secondary is rectified by T_3. This arrangement is called a *flyback* (or *kickback*) power supply.

The deflection coil may be transformer-coupled into the plate circuit of the driver tube instead of being placed directly in series with this tube as in Fig. 8-19. An autotransformer is often used for this purpose.

REFERENCES

1. Millman, J., and S. Seely: "Electronics," 2d ed., chap. 3, McGraw-Hill Book Company, Inc., New York, 1951.
2. Soller, T., M. A. Starr, and G. E. Valley, Jr.: "Cathode Ray Tube Displays," vol. 22, Appendix B, Massachusetts Institute of Technology Radiation Laboratory Series, McGraw-Hill Book Company, Inc., New York, 1948.
3. Ref. 2, chap. 10.
4. Anner, George E.: "Elements of Television Systems," chap. 4, Prentice-Hall, Inc., New York, 1951.

CHAPTER 9

PULSE TRANSFORMERS AND BLOCKING OSCILLATORS

Iron-cored transformers are used in the transmission and shaping of pulses which range in width from a fraction of a microsecond to about 25 μsec. Among the extensive applications of pulse transformers are the following:

1. To change the amplitude and impedance level of a pulse.

2. To invert the polarity of a pulse. Also to provide, with the aid of a center-tapped winding, equal positive and negative pulses simultaneously.

3. To produce a pulse in a circuit having negligible d-c resistance.

4. To effect "d-c isolation" between a source and a load. In other words, to produce a pulse in a winding whose d-c voltage level may be arbitrarily selected.

5. To couple between stages of pulse amplifiers.

6. To differentiate a pulse.

7. To act as a coupling element in certain pulse-generating circuits such as the *blocking oscillator* (considered in this chapter) and the *multiar* (discussed in Chap. 15).

In many instances the functions listed above may be accomplished as well or better by vacuum-tube circuitry. But the transformer, being a completely passive circuit element, has none of the instability normally associated with tubes and in addition avoids the inconvenience of supplying the voltages required for tube operation.

9-1. Equivalent Circuit. The schematic diagram for a transformer is indicated in Fig. 9-1. The primary inductance is L_p, the

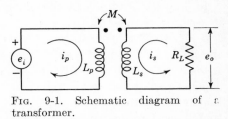

Fig. 9-1. Schematic diagram of a transformer.

secondary inductance is L_s, and the mutual inductance is M henrys. The load resistance is R_L ohms. In this section, we shall ignore the primary, secondary, and source resistances and also all capacitances. We shall also neglect core loss and the nonlinearity of the magnetic circuit. These parameters, however, will be added later to the equivalent circuit. The coefficient of coupling K between primary and secondary is defined by $K \equiv M/\sqrt{L_p L_s}$. Under the circumstances specified above, an ideal transformer is one for which L_p is infinite and $K = 1$. In this case the output e_o is an exact replica of the input e_i and the transformation ratio n is independent of the load. For the ideal transformer,

$$n = \frac{e_o}{e_i} = \frac{i_p}{i_s} = \sqrt{\frac{L_s}{L_p}} = \frac{N_s}{N_p} \tag{9-1}$$

where i_p is the primary current, i_s is the secondary current, N_p is the primary number of turns, and N_s is the secondary number of turns.

An iron-cored transformer, such as a pulse transformer, behaves as a reasonable approximation to a perfect transformer, when used in connection with the fast waveforms it is intended to handle. In such a case it is advantageous to replace the actual transformer by an ideal transformer together with additional circuit components which represent the

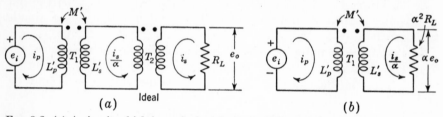

Fig. 9-2. (a) A circuit which is equivalent to that of Fig. 9-1, in which an ideal transformer T_2 having a voltage step-up ratio $1/\alpha$ is introduced. Hence, the primary current in T_2 is $1/\alpha$ times the secondary current. (b) The load impedance R_L is reflected into the primary of T_2 as $\alpha^2 R_L$.

departure of the real transformer from perfection. This representation is particularly worthwhile if we are able to compute from the geometry of the transformer the magnitude of the circuit elements which represent the imperfections.

In Fig. 9-2 is drawn a circuit consisting of an ideal transformer T_2 in cascade with a transformer T_1. The transformation ratio of T_2 is $1/\alpha$ = secondary volts/primary volts, where α is a number which will be specified later. For the ideal transformer T_2, the secondary impedance R_L may be reflected into the primary as $\alpha^2 R_L$, as indicated in Fig. 9-2b. The network of Fig. 9-2 is to be equivalent to that of Fig. 9-1 in the sense that both are to draw the same current i_p from a given source e_i and are to deliver the same current to a given load R_L. The parameters L'_p, L'_s, and M' are now to be found. For the circuit of Fig. 9-1, we may write

$$e_i = L_p \frac{di_p}{dt} + M \frac{di_s}{dt}$$
$$0 = M \frac{di_p}{dt} + L_s \frac{di_s}{dt} + i_s R_L \tag{9-2}$$

The corresponding equations for the circuit of Fig. 9-2b are

$$e_i = L'_p \frac{di_p}{dt} + \frac{M'}{\alpha} \frac{di_s}{dt}$$

$$0 = M' \frac{di_p}{dt} + \frac{L'_s}{\alpha} \frac{di_s}{dt} + \frac{i_s}{\alpha} (R_L \alpha^2)$$

(9-3)

The above two sets of equations are equivalent if

$$L'_p = L_p \qquad M' = \alpha M \qquad L'_s = \alpha^2 L_s$$ (9-4)

Finally, we replace the transformer T_1 of Fig. 9-2 by its equivalent T network and the circuit of Fig. 9-3 results. It is easily verified that the mesh equations of Fig. 9-3 agree with those of Fig. 9-2. Different equivalent circuits are obtained depending upon the value selected for

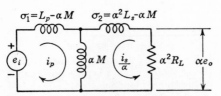

Fig. 9-3. The transformer T_1 of Fig. 9-2 is replaced by its equivalent T network.

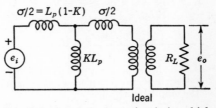

Fig. 9-4. An equivalent circuit in which the series inductance is divided into two equal parts.

$1/\alpha$. Consider, for example, the equivalent circuits which result when $1/\alpha$ is selected so that $\sigma_1 = \sigma_2 = \sigma/2$ or $\sigma_1 = 0$ or $\sigma_2 = 0$.

Case 1. $\sigma_1 = \sigma_2 \equiv \sigma/2$

$$L_p - \alpha M = \alpha^2 L_s - \alpha M \qquad \text{or} \qquad \alpha = \sqrt{\frac{L_p}{L_s}}$$ (9-5)

Then $$\frac{\sigma}{2} = L_p - \alpha M = L_p - \sqrt{\frac{L_p}{L_s}} K \sqrt{L_p L_s}$$

remembering that $K = M/\sqrt{L_p L_s}$.

Hence $$\frac{\sigma}{2} = L_p(1 - K) \qquad \text{and} \qquad \alpha M = KL_p$$ (9-6)

The equivalent circuit is given in Fig. 9-4.

Case 2. $\sigma_1 = 0$

$$L_p - \alpha M = 0 \qquad \text{or} \qquad \alpha = \frac{L_p}{M} = \frac{1}{K} \sqrt{\frac{L_p}{L_s}}$$ (9-7)

$$\sigma_2 = \alpha^2 L_s - \alpha M = L_p \left(\frac{1}{K^2} - 1 \right) \qquad \text{and} \qquad \alpha M = L_p$$ (9-8)

The equivalent circuit is given in Fig. 9-5.

Case 3. $\sigma_2 = 0$

$$\alpha^2 L_s - \alpha M = 0 \qquad \text{or} \qquad \alpha = \frac{M}{L_s} = K\sqrt{\frac{L_p}{L_s}} \tag{9-9}$$

therefore

$$\alpha M = K\sqrt{\frac{L_p}{L_s}} K\sqrt{L_p L_s} = K^2 L_p$$

and

$$\sigma_1 = L_p - \alpha M = L_p(1 - K^2) \tag{9-10}$$

The equivalent circuit is given in Fig. 9-6.

For a well-constructed pulse transformer the coefficient of coupling differs from unity by less than 1 per cent. For such a transformer ($K \cong 1$), the equivalent circuits of Figs. 9-4 to 9-6 each give very nearly

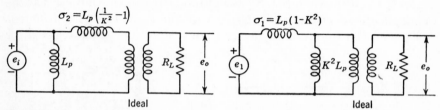

FIG. 9-5. An equivalent circuit in which the series inductance is placed to the right of the shunt inductance.

FIG. 9-6. An equivalent circuit in which the series inductance is placed to the left of the shunt inductance.

the same value for the shunt inductance and for the total series inductance. The total series inductance, called the *leakage inductance*, is

Case 1:

$$\sigma = 2L_p(1 - K)$$

Case 2:

$$\sigma_2 = L_p\left(\frac{1}{K^2} - 1\right) = L_p \frac{(1 - K)(1 + K)}{K^2} \cong 2L_p(1 - K)$$

Case 3:

$$\sigma_1 = L_p(1 - K^2) = L_p(1 - K)(1 + K) \cong 2L_p(1 - K)$$

Similarly, the shunt inductance, called the *magnetizing inductance*, is approximately L_p for all three cases if $K \cong 1$. *To summarize*, the equivalent circuit of a pulse transformer consists of a series leakage inductance $\sigma = 2L_p(1 - K)$ and a shunt magnetizing inductance L_p. These elements are in cascade with an ideal output transformer of stepup voltage ratio $n = 1/\alpha \cong \sqrt{L_s/L_p} \cong N_s/N_p$ (because the inductance is proportional to the square of the turns). The leakage inductance σ may be placed entirely to the right of L_p, entirely to its left, or split into two inductors, one to the right and the other to the left of L_p. The equivalent circuit discussed above must be modified to take the transformer losses and capacitances into account. These modifications are made in Sec. 9-5.

9-2. Transformer Inductance Parameters. The equivalent circuits derived above indicate how the leakage and magnetizing inductances may

be obtained experimentally.   From Fig. 9-6 we see that, if the secondary
is short-circuited, then the input impedance is the leakage inductance σ.
This inductance may be measured on a Q meter.   A second method of
determining σ is to short the secondary, shunt the primary with a capacitance C_1, and measure the resonant frequency f_1.   In order to eliminate
the effect of the transformer and other unknown external capacitors which
are in shunt with C_1, the above measurement is repeated with a second
capacitor C_2.   If the resonant frequency is now found to be f_2, then we
can show that

$$\sigma = \frac{f_1{}^2 - f_2{}^2}{(2\pi f_1 f_2)^2(C_2 - C_1)} \tag{9-11}$$

A simple procedure for measuring the resonant frequencies f_1 and f_2 is the
following: The transformer is placed in the plate circuit of a tube whose

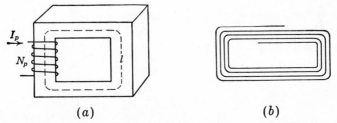

(a)   (b)

Fig. 9-7. A transformer core made by winding a continuous strip of high-permeability
iron into a rectangular shape.   The secondary winding is not indicated.

grid is clamped to its cathode.   A negative pulse (or a square wave) is
applied to the grid to cut the tube off.   The transformer will now ring
and the resonant period may be measured from the waveform, as observed
on a scope.   This method also allows the simultaneous measurement of
the effective losses in the transformer.   Thus, as explained in Sec. 2-8, if
the amplitude of the waveform falls to $1/\epsilon$ of its initial value in N cycles,
the Q of the circuit is $N\pi$.

From Fig. 9-5 we see that the input impedance consists of the magnetizing inductance L_p, if the secondary is open-circuited.   Hence, if the
above experiment is repeated with the secondary unloaded, then L_p may
be determined.

It is also possible to estimate the inductances from the geometry
of the transformer.   Figure 9-7 shows a rectangular core made from
high-permeability alloys such as Hipersil (Westinghouse), $\mu_{\max} \cong 12{,}000$,
or Permalloy (Western Electric), $\mu_{\max} \cong 80{,}000$.   In order to reduce
eddy-current losses, the iron should, of course, be laminated.   It has been
found that Hipersil and Permalloy can be rolled into strips as thin as
2 mils and cores are often formed by winding a continuous strip as indicated in Fig. 9-7b.   The permeability actually achieved in pulse transformers is much less than the maximum values indicated above.   The

principal reason for this reduction in μ is that at the instant the pulse is applied the flux in the core is confined largely to the surface (the "skin effect") because of the eddy currents that flow. The effective cross section of the core is thus reduced. As time passes, the flux penetrates deeper into the core and eventually becomes uniform. Accordingly the effective permeability of the core increases with increasing pulse duration.[1] The effective permeability of Hipersil is of the order of 400 for microsecond pulses.

The primary inductance L_p is easily calculated[2] for the simple magnetic circuit of Fig. 9-7. If l is the mean length of the magnetic path, A the cross section of the core, and N_p the number of primary turns,

$$L_p = \frac{\mu A N_p^2}{l} \tag{9-12}$$

where all quantities are expressed in mks units.

In order to see in a typical case how the leakage inductance σ depends on the geometry, consider the simple geometrical arrangement of Fig.

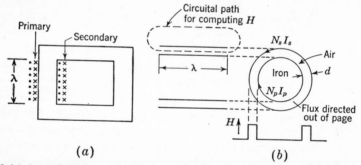

FIG. 9-8 (a) A one-layer secondary wound directly over a one-layer primary. A cross indicates current into the page, and a dot indicates current out of the page. (b) A top view of the windings considered as current sheets and the magnetic flux density between windings.

9-8a where a single-layer secondary is wound over a one-layer primary. We have already emphasized that the secondary must be short-circuited in order to find σ. For this connection the output voltage is, of course, zero. Hence the net flux in the iron is zero and the primary and secondary ampere-turns must be equal and oppositely directed, $N_p I_p = N_s I_s$. Almost all the flux appears in the space between the coils. For simplicity, we replace the coils by current sheets carrying the currents $N_p I_p$ and $N_s I_s$ ($= N_p I_p$), respectively. A top view of the concentric solenoidal windings is shown in Fig. 9-8b and the magnetic field intensity H between windings is also indicated. The current sheets are of the same length λ (in the direction perpendicular to the current flow) as the coils are long. We locate the current sheets at the point midway through the thickness of the wires of the coils. The value of H in the region between sheets is $H = N_p I_p / \lambda$. This result for H is computed by applying Ampère's circuital law to the path indicated in Fig. 9-8b. The energy density stored in the magnetic field is given by $\frac{1}{2} \mu H^2$ joules/m^3. Hence the total energy W stored is $W = \frac{1}{2} \mu_0 H^2 V$, where V is the volume between coils and where we have replaced μ by μ_0, the permeability of free space because the medium between the coils is air. The energy may also be calculated from $W = \frac{1}{2} \sigma I_p{}^2$ since this magnetic energy (with the secondary shorted) may be considered to reside in the leakage inductance σ. Equating the above two expressions for W, we obtain

$$\sigma = \frac{\mu_0 H^2 V}{I_p{}^2} = \frac{\mu_0 N_p{}^2 V}{\lambda^2} \tag{9-13}$$

where all quantities are expressed in mks units. This calculation indicates clearly that σ is due to the leakage flux, that is, the flux which links one but not both windings. Hence, σ is essentially independent of the magnetic circuit of the transformer, since the leakage flux is almost entirely in air. Note that the ratio of magnetizing to leakage inductance $L_p / \sigma = \mu A \lambda^2 / \mu_0 V l$ is independent of the number of turns and is proportional to the permeability of the iron. One of the main reasons for using high-permeability cores in pulse transformers is in order to have a large ratio of magnetizing to leakage inductance.

More accurate calculations of σ taking into account the current distribution throughout the windings and also taking into consideration multilayer windings are given in the literature[3] and in Probs. 9-3 and 9-4.

9-3. Transformer Capacitances. We shall now consider the capacitances present in a transformer. A simple calculation (see Prob. 9-6) shows that the interturn capacitance is negligibly small in comparison with the capacitance between windings and hence may be neglected. If the separation d between windings is small compared with the core thickness, then the two layers may be considered the plates of a parallel-plate capacitor and the capacitance C_o between layers is given by

$$C_o = \frac{\epsilon S \lambda}{d} \tag{9-14}$$

where S is the mean circumference, ϵ is the dielectric constant of the insulation, and all quantities are expressed in mks units. It is not evident how to include C_o into the equivalent circuit. Let us assume, therefore, that the proper capacitance to use is not C_o but rather a different value C' which is to be connected as a shunt element in the equivalent circuit. This value C' will be chosen such that the electric energy stored in C' equals the energy stored in the electric field between layers of the windings. This assumption seems reasonable and is justified because it leads to a transformer behavior which is verified experimentally. In Fig. 9-9 is shown the trace in the plane of the paper of the two windings of Fig. 9-8. We assume that the voltage distribution along a winding is linear with distance x so that the voltage difference between windings V_x at a height x measured from the bottom, is given by

$$V_x = V_{cd} + (V_{ab} - V_{cd})\frac{x}{\lambda} \tag{9-15}$$

where V_{cd} and V_{ab} are the potential differences between windings at the bottom and top, respectively. The electric field E at the height x is $E = V_x/d$. The energy stored per cubic meter is $\frac{1}{2}\epsilon E^2 = \frac{1}{2}(\epsilon V_x^2/d^2)$. If S is the mean circumference, then the element of volume is $Sd\,dx$ and the total energy W is

$$W = \int_0^\lambda \frac{1}{2}\frac{\epsilon V_x^2}{d^2}\, Sd\,dx \tag{9-16}$$

If V_x from Eq. (9-15) is substituted into Eq. (9-16) and the integral is evaluated, the result is

$$W = \frac{C_o}{6}(V_{ab}^2 + V_{ab}V_{cd} + V_{cd}^2) \tag{9-17}$$

where C_o is given in Eq. (9-14). If the adjacent ends of the windings are connected together as in Fig. 9-9b, the transformer is noninverting. If the step-up ratio is n and the input voltage is e_i, then $V_{cd} = 0$,

$$V_{ab} = (1 - n)e_i$$

and, from Eq. (9-17),

$$W = \frac{C_o}{6}(n - 1)^2 e_i^2 \tag{9-18}$$

If we now introduce the capacitance C' across the magnetizing inductance in Fig. 9-6, then the energy stored in C' is approximately $\frac{1}{2}C'e_i^2$. Actually the voltage across C' will be less than e_i by the drop across the leakage inductance. But the voltage across σ will normally be small in comparison with e_i.

If the quantity $\frac{1}{2}C'e_i^2$ is equated to W in Eq. (9-18), we have for the capacitance C', which is to be included as a shunt element in the equivalent circuit,

$$C' = (n - 1)^2 \frac{C_o}{3} \tag{9-19}$$

If opposite ends of the windings are connected together as in Fig. 9-9c, the transformer is inverting. The capacitance C' is now larger and is found, by proceeding as above, to be

$$C' = (n^2 - n + 1)\frac{C_o}{3} \qquad (9\text{-}20)$$

The symbol n in the above equations is a positive number.

For the special case of a $1:1$ noninverting transformer, $n = 1$ and Eq. (9-19) gives $C' = 0$. A more accurate equivalent circuit[4] based upon the transmission-line approximation to the transformer has been given for this special case.

The capacitance of a transformer may be measured on a Q meter. It also may be determined as a by-product of the ringing-method measurement of the inductance L_p. The result of the measurement is not only the transformer capacitance C' but it also includes all external shunting capacitance C_e. Unfortunately, C_e may often be much larger than C' and furthermore C_e may be difficult to estimate.

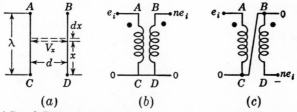

Fig. 9-9. (a) AC and BD represent the traces of the windings of Fig. 9-8 in the plane of the paper. (b) The noninverting transformer connections. (c) The inverting transformer connection.

We have taken the transformer capacitance into account by including a shunt capacitor C', which is connected on the load side of the leakage inductance. Actually the transformer capacitance is a distributed element, and no matter what location is selected for a single lumped capacitance, the result is an approximate equivalent circuit. A somewhat better approximation would result if the capacitance C' were split so that a part of it appeared on the generator side and a part appeared on the load side of the leakage inductance. Such a division, however, leads to an equivalent circuit whose extra complexity is not warranted, since a single capacitor in the equivalent circuit usually gives reasonably good agreement with experimental results.

Having decided to use a single lumped capacitor representation of the distributed capacitance, we have located this capacitance at the load end of the leakage inductance for the following reasons. First, if C' were located on the generator side, then if the generator had a nominally zero output impedance the effect of this capacitor would disappear—a result which is not in accord with experiment. Second, the external shunt-loading capacitance encountered with a pulse transformer is very frequently heavier on the output side of the leakage inductance, and this external shunt capacitance may simply be added to C'.

9-4. Ferrite Cup-core Transformers.   Cores molded from a magnetic ceramic such as sintered manganese-zinc ferrite are now available which are excellent for pulse transformers.   The maximum permeability of this material is not very great, but its resistivity is at least 10 million times that of Hipersil or Permalloy.   This high resistivity means that the skin effect due to eddy currents is very small and an effective permeability of the order of 1,000 is attained.   This value is larger than the effective permeability of strip alloys.   Also, because of this high resistivity the core loss is very small and a Q of the order of 5–15 is obtained at a frequency of 1 Mc.   Three views of one-half of a ferrite core are shown in Fig. 9-10a.   Because of its shape this element is called a "pot" or "cup" core.   The windings are placed on a circular nylon or paper bobbin which is then inserted in the core.   An end view of the complete core, assembled by butting two halves together, is indicated in Fig. 9-10b.   The two sections are held together, with a machine screw through a small hole in the center of the core and the entire assembly is dipped into a hard-setting resin.   The magnetic circuit thus completely encloses the windings.

The primary inductance of a pot core may be calculated[2] from

$$L_p = \frac{N_p{}^2}{\mathcal{R}_1 + \mathcal{R}_2 + \mathcal{R}_3 + \mathcal{R}_4} \tag{9-21}$$

where $\mathcal{R}_1$, $\mathcal{R}_2$, $\mathcal{R}_3$, and $\mathcal{R}_4$ are the reluctances of paths 1, 2, 3, and 4 of Fig. 9-10b, respectively.   Since the flux is radial along paths 2 and 4, the cross-sectional area through which it passes is not constant.   This fact must be taken into account when evaluating $\mathcal{R}_2$ ($= \mathcal{R}_4$).   The result of the calculation for a core whose dimensions are given in Fig. 9-10a is $L_p = 1.1N_p{}^2$ μh, to within about 10 per cent.   For a 100-turn primary, $L_p = 11$ mh.

The windings in a pot core may be arranged in solenoidal layers as they are for a rectangular core or instead may be put side by side in slots in the bobbin.   In the latter case, the turns pile up radially in the shape of a flat disk.   The leakage inductance is given approximately by Eq. (9-13), where V is the volume of the air between windings and λ is the radial extent of the disks.   The capacitances are given approximately by Eqs. (9-14), (9-19), and (9-20), where S is the mean circumference of the windings and d is the separation between windings.   Since d is much greater for the slot-type winding than for the solenoidal-type arrangement, σ is greater, whereas C' is smaller for the slot-type winding.

The order of magnitude of the parameters of transformers designed for pulses in the range 0.1 to 20 μsec are the following: $L_p = 0.1$ to 100 mh, $K = 0.990$ to 0.999, and $C' = 1$ to 100 $\mu\mu$f.

9-5. Rise-time Response of a Transformer. If capacitances and resistances are taken into account, the equivalent circuit of a transformer is given in Fig. 9-11. The resistance R_1 is the sum of the generator impedance (assumed resistive) and the primary winding resistance. If R_L is the load resistance and R_2' is the secondary winding resistance, $R_2 = (R_L + R_2')/n^2$. If the transformer core losses are appreciable, these

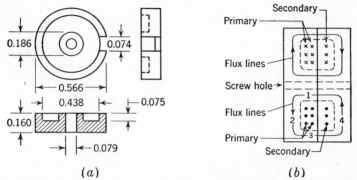

FIG. 9-10. (a) Three views of a small ferrite pot core. Dimensions are in inches. (*Courtesy of Ferroxcube Corporation of America.*)   (b) The assembled transformer.

may be represented by a resistor R_c in parallel with R_2. If C_L is the capacitance shunting the secondary terminals, then $C = n^2C_L + C'$, where C' is the effective interwinding capacitance as given by Eq. (9-19) or Eq. (9-20). The primary inductance is indicated by L. The circuit of Fig. 9-11 is represented by a third-order differential equation whose solution would be quite involved. Furthermore, this complete solution would not clearly indicate the physical behavior of the circuit. Hence,

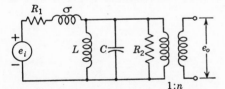

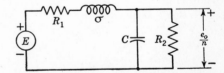

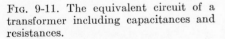

FIG. 9-11. The equivalent circuit of a transformer including capacitances and resistances.

FIG. 9-12. The approximate equivalent circuit used to calculate the rise-time response.

if the input is a pulse, it is advantageous to divide the solution into three parts; the first gives the response near the front edge of the pulse, the second gives the response during the flat top, and the third gives the response after the termination of the pulse. In this section we consider the *rise-time response* and in the following two sections the remainder of the waveform is discussed.

The response near the front edge of the pulse is given by the high-frequency equivalent circuit of Fig. 9-12, which is obtained from Fig. 9-11 by neglecting the effect of L. The magnitude of the input step is E. Writing down the differential equations for this network and assuming a solution in the form ϵ^{pt}, we find for the roots p of the characteristic equation[5]

$$p = -\left(\frac{R_1}{2\sigma} + \frac{1}{2R_2C}\right) \pm \left[\left(\frac{R_1}{2\sigma} + \frac{1}{2R_2C}\right)^2 - \frac{R_1 + R_2}{\sigma C R_2}\right]^{\frac{1}{2}} \quad (9\text{-}22)$$

Let us introduce the *attenuation* a, the *damping constant* k, and the *period* T defined by.

$$a \equiv \frac{R_2}{R_1 + R_2} \qquad T \equiv 2\pi(\sigma C a)^{\frac{1}{2}} \qquad k \equiv \left(\frac{R_1}{\sigma} + \frac{1}{R_2C}\right)\frac{T}{4\pi} \quad (9\text{-}23)$$

in which case Eq. (9-22) can be put in the form

$$p = -\frac{2\pi}{T} k \pm j \frac{2\pi}{T} (1 - k^2)^{\frac{1}{2}} \quad (9\text{-}24)$$

If $k = 0$, we see that the roots are purely imaginary, $\pm j2\pi/T$, and hence the response is an undamped sinusoid of period T. In order for k to approach zero, we must have $R_1 \to 0$ and $R_2 \to \infty$, in which case

$$T = 2\pi \sqrt{\sigma C}$$

is the free period of oscillations of the σC circuit. If $k = 1$, the two roots are equal, corresponding to the *critically damped* case. If $k > 1$, there are no oscillations in the output, and the response is said to be *overdamped*. If $k < 1$, the response will be a sinusoid whose amplitude decays with time and the response is said to be *underdamped*.

If we introduce the parameter $x \equiv t/T$, the response is given by the following:

Critical Damping, $k = 1$

$$\frac{e_o}{naE} = 1 - (1 + 2\pi x)\epsilon^{-2\pi x} \quad (9\text{-}25)$$

Overdamped, $k > 1$

$$\frac{e_o}{naE} = 1 - \frac{4k^2}{4k^2 - 1} \epsilon^{-\pi x/k} + \frac{1}{4k^2 - 1} \epsilon^{-4\pi k x} \quad (9\text{-}26)$$

If $4k^2 \gg 1$, the response may be approximated by

$$\frac{e_o}{naE} \cong 1 - \epsilon^{-\pi x/k} \quad (9\text{-}27)$$

Underdamped, $k < 1$

$$\frac{e_o}{naE} = 1 - \left[\frac{k}{(1 - k^2)^{\frac{1}{2}}} \sin 2\pi(1 - k^2)^{\frac{1}{2}}x + \cos 2\pi(1 - k^2)^{\frac{1}{2}}x\right] \epsilon^{-2\pi k x} \quad (9\text{-}28)$$

These responses are plotted in Fig. 9-13 for several values of k. If the *rise time* t_r is defined as the time interval required for the critically damped output to rise from 0.1 to 0.9 its final value, we find, from Eq. (9-25) or Fig. 9-13, that

$$t_r = 0.53T = 3.35(\sigma Ca)^{1/2} \qquad (9\text{-}29)$$

We note that in order for the output to rise rapidly, the leakage inductance and the shunt capacitance must be kept small. The rise time may also be reduced by reducing a, but a small value of a will result in a highly attenuated output voltage.

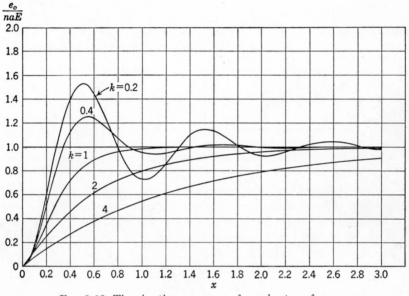

FIG. 9-13. The rise-time response of a pulse transformer.

If the derivative of Eq. (9-28) is set equal to zero, the positions x_m and magnitudes e_{om} of the maxima and minima are obtained. The result is

$$x_m = \frac{m}{2(1 - k^2)^{1/2}} \qquad \text{and} \qquad \frac{e_{om}}{naE} = 1 - (-1)^m \epsilon^{-2\pi k x_m} \qquad (9\text{-}30)$$

where m is an integer. The maxima occur for odd values of m and the minima are obtained for even values of m. By using Eq. (9-30) the waveshape of the underdamped output may be sketched very rapidly.

9-6. The Flat Top of the Pulse. The response during the top of the pulse is obtained from the low-frequency equivalent circuit of Fig. 9-14a, which is obtained from Fig. 9-11 by neglecting the effect of the leakage inductance and shunt capacitance. Applying Thévenin's theorem, we obtain Fig. 9-14*b*. The output is given by

$$\frac{e_o}{naE} = \epsilon^{-Rt/L} \tag{9-31}$$

where $R = R_1R_2/(R_1 + R_2)$. For small values of Rt/L, the output is approximated by

$$\frac{e_o}{naE} = 1 - \frac{Rt}{L} \tag{9-32}$$

Hence, the top of the output pulse will be tilted downward and the per cent tilt P is given by

$$P = \frac{Rt_p}{L} \times 100\% \tag{9-33}$$

where t_p is the pulse width. Near the beginning of the pulse there will be superposed upon the linear fall the response pictured in Fig. 9-13.

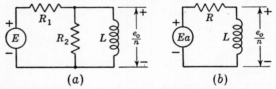

$$(a) \qquad\qquad (b)$$

Fig. 9-14. (*a*) The equivalent circuit used to calculate the flat-top response of a transformer. (*b*) The Thévenin equivalent. $a = R_2/(R_1 + R_2)$; $R = R_1R_2/(R_1 + R_2)$.

We have assumed that the inductance L is a constant. This assumption is valid as long as the iron does not begin to saturate. For a ferrite core, the permeability is fairly constant for flux densities B up to a maximum B_m of about 1,500 gauss (0.15 weber/m²). Saturation occurs if B exceeds the above value B_m. Now

$$e_o = \frac{nN_pA\,dB}{dt}$$

where n is the step-up ratio, N_p is the number of primary turns, and A is the cross-sectional area of the core. Assuming that the top of the pulse is constant and equals naE, the flux density at the end of the pulse is

$$B = \int_0^{t_p} \frac{e_o}{nN_pA}\,dt = \frac{aEt_p}{N_pA} \tag{9-34}$$

In any particular application we must be sure not to saturate the core. For example, consider that a pulse generator having an adjustable pulse width is applied to a transformer. The output pulse will be a reasonable reproduction of the input for small widths. When the input duration exceeds the value of t_p given by Eq. (9-34) with $B = B_m = 0.15$ weber/m², the output will drop rapidly. This behavior follows from the fact that, when the iron saturates, the inductance drops to a very low value.

Also, because of the skin effect mentioned earlier, it is found[4] that for certain sheet steels the effective inductance is proportional to the square root of the pulse width.

9-7. Decay-time Response of a Transformer. During the time of the pulse a current builds up in the magnetizing inductor and the nature of the output pulse decay results largely from the discharge of this current. The effect of σ is only important in the immediate neighborhood of the end of the pulse. We shall consider this region later and hence shall now neglect σ so that the equivalent circuit is given in Fig. 9-15. This parallel RLC combination is discussed in detail in Sec. 2-8 in connection with ringing

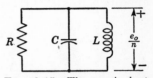

Fig. 9-15. The equivalent circuit used to calculate the decay-time response.

circuits. The response is given by Eqs. (2-47) to (2-49) and is plotted in Figs. 2-30 to 2-32. In using these equations, we must remember that

$$E_o = naE \qquad k = \frac{1}{2R}\sqrt{\frac{L}{C}} \qquad T_o = 2\pi\sqrt{LC} \qquad x = \frac{t - t_p}{T_o} \qquad (9\text{-}35)$$

The parameter Δ is defined as the ratio of the current in the inductor to the current in R at $t = t_p$. It is found that usually the response is heavily overdamped, $4k^2 \gg 1$, at the end of the pulse and the response is given by Eq. (2-48), which is repeated here for easy reference:

$$\frac{e_o}{naE} = -\left(\frac{1}{4k^2} + \Delta\right)\epsilon^{-\pi x/k} + (1 + \Delta)\epsilon^{-4\pi kx} \qquad (9\text{-}36)$$

For all values of x, except those close to $x = 0$, the second term in Eq. (9-36) is negligible compared with the first. From Eqs. (9-35),

$$\frac{\pi x}{k} = \frac{R(t - t_p)}{L}$$

and hence the response for $t > t_p$ can be approximated by

$$\frac{e_o}{naE} \cong -\left(\frac{1}{4k^2} + \Delta\right)\epsilon^{-(R/L)(t-t_p)} \qquad (9\text{-}37)$$

We thus see that for this heavily damped case the output at the end of the pulse drops to a negative value and then decays exponentially toward zero with the same time constant with which the top of the wave tilts.

In order to find Δ, we note, from Fig. 9-14b, that the inductor current i_L and voltage e_L during the flat-top response are given, respectively, by

$$i_L = \frac{Ea}{R}(1 - \epsilon^{-Rt/L}) \qquad \text{and} \qquad e_L = Ea\epsilon^{-Rt/L} \qquad (9\text{-}38)$$

The current in L at $t = t_p+$ is the same as at $t = t_p-$, because the current in an inductor cannot change instantaneously. Similarly, because the voltage across a capacitor cannot change instantaneously (remember that C is in shunt with L), the value of e_L at $t = t_p+$ is the same as that at $t = t_p-$. At the end of the pulse the input drops to zero and e_L appears across R. Hence, the ratio of inductor to resistor current is

$$\Delta = \left.\frac{i_L}{e_L/R}\right|_{t=t_p} = \frac{1 - \epsilon^{-Rt_p/L}}{\epsilon^{-Rt_p/L}} \tag{9-39}$$

or

$$\Delta = \epsilon^{+Rt_p/L} - 1 \cong \frac{Rt_p}{L} \tag{9-40}$$

if Rt_p/L is small compared with unity. From Eq. (9-33) we see that the fractional tilt during the pulse is given by Rt_p/L, which, by Eq. (9-40), equals Δ. If we desire to reproduce the pulse well, then Δ will be small, say, less than 0.2 (corresponding to 20 per cent droop).

Let us now consider the response in the neighborhood of $t = t_p$. A pulse may be considered to be the sum of a step of voltage $+E$ whose discontinuity occurs at $t = 0$ and a step of voltage $-E$ whose discontinuity occurs at $t = t_p$ (see Fig. 2-3). Hence, if the transformer response to a step E at $t = 0$ is $e_o(t)$, then the output for $t > t_p$ is $e_o(t) - e_o(t - t_p)$. The waveform $e_o(t)$ is the composite of the *rise-time response* and the *flat-top response* found above. For the underdamped case, the trailing edge of the output waveform will contain the same high-frequency oscillations as are present on the leading edge. For t greater than approximately $2t_p$, the effect of σ is negligible, the equivalent circuit of Fig. 9-15 is valid, and the response is given by Eq. (9-37), assuming heavy damping at the end of the pulse.

It should be stated that the output impedance of the pulse generator may be different at the termination of the pulse than during the time of the pulse. If this condition exists, then a different value of R_1 must be used when calculating the response for $t > t_p$ than for $t < t_p$. For example, if $R_1(t > t_p)$ is much greater than $R_1(t < t_p)$, then the high-frequency oscillations at the trailing edge will be greatly damped. However, even when the pulse is terminated by opening a generator switch, in which case σ could be omitted, at least in Fig. 9-12, oscillations often persist. The reason for this behavior is that actually the capacitance is not properly included in the circuit as a lumped element, but should really be included as an element continuously distributed between the leakage inductance and ground.

In every case the area under the pulse which is above the zero axis is equal to the area below the axis. This conclusion follows from the fact that a transformer cannot pass a d-c voltage. This feature may also be verified thus: The output voltage may be written as $e_o = n\, d(Li_L)/dt$.

where i_L is the current in the magnetizing inductor.   The total area under the output voltage waveform is

$$\int_0^\infty e_o \, dt = n \int_0^\infty \frac{d(Li_L)}{dt} \, dt = nLi_L \Big|_0^\infty = 0 \qquad (9\text{-}41)$$

since $i_L = 0$ at $t = 0$ and at $t = \infty$.   This proof does not assume that L is a constant.   Even if saturation takes place so that L is not constant, the area above the zero axis equals that below the zero axis and hence there is no shift in d-c level.

The response of a transformer of typical parameters is computed in the following illustrative example.

EXAMPLE. A pot-core transformer has the following parameters: $L = 5$ mh, $\sigma = 40$ μh, $C = 50$ $\mu\mu$f, $R_1 = 200$ ohms, $R_2 = 2$ K, $n = 1$.   Find the response to a 2-μsec 10-volt pulse.
Solution.   For the rise-time response we have, from Eq. (9-23),

$$a = \frac{R_2}{R_1 + R_2} = \frac{2{,}000}{200 + 2{,}000} = 0.909$$
$$T = 2\pi(\sigma Ca)^{\frac{1}{2}} = 2\pi(40 \times 10^{-6} \times 50 \times 10^{-12} \times 0.909)^{\frac{1}{2}} = 0.267 \; \mu\text{sec}$$
$$k = \left(\frac{R_1}{\sigma} + \frac{1}{R_2 C}\right)\frac{T}{4\pi} = \left(\frac{200}{40 \times 10^{-6}} + \frac{1}{2 \times 10^3 \times 50 \times 10^{-12}}\right)\frac{2.67 \times 10^{-7}}{4\pi}$$
$$= 0.318$$

Since $k < 1$, the response is underdamped and is given by Eq. (9-28), namely,

$$\frac{e_o}{naE} = 1 - \left[\frac{k}{(1 - k^2)^{\frac{1}{2}}} \sin 2\pi(1 - k^2)^{\frac{1}{2}} \frac{t}{T} + \cos 2\pi(1 - k^2)^{\frac{1}{2}} \frac{t}{T}\right] \epsilon^{-2\pi kt/T}$$

Substituting numerical values into this equation, we obtain

$$e_o = 9.09[1 - (0.325 \sin 22.3t + \cos 22.3t)\epsilon^{-7.48t}]$$

where t is expressed in microseconds.
From Eqs. (9-30) we find that the maxima and minima occur at

$$t_m = \frac{mT}{2(1 - k^2)^{\frac{1}{2}}} = 0.141m$$

where $m = 1, 2, 3 \ldots$, and that the magnitudes at t_m are

$$e_{om} = 9.09[1 - (-1)^m \epsilon^{-1.01m}]$$

The *flat-top response* is given by Eq. (9-31), namely,

$$e_o = naE\epsilon^{-Rt/L} = 9.09\epsilon^{-0.0364t} \cong 9.09(1 - 0.0364t)$$

where t is expressed in microseconds.   The percentage tilt of the top of the pulse is $3.64t_p = 7.28$ per cent.
At the end of the pulse the damping factor k is given by Eq. (9-35), namely,

$$k = \frac{1}{2R} \sqrt{\frac{L}{C}} = \frac{2{,}000 + 200}{2 \times 2{,}000 \times 200} \left(\frac{5 \times 10^{-3}}{50 \times 10^{-12}}\right)^{\frac{1}{2}} = 27.5$$

This value of k should not be confused with the damping factor of 0.318 which is valid during the rise-time response. Since $4k^2 \gg 1$, then Eq. (9-37) gives the response, namely,

$$\frac{e_o}{naE} = -\left(\frac{1}{4k^2} + \Delta\right)\epsilon^{-R(t-t_p)/L}$$

Since Δ equals the fractional tilt at $t = t_p$, then $\Delta = 0.0728$ and

$$e_o = -9.09 \times 0.073\epsilon^{-0.0364(t-t_p)}$$

The complete response (up to $t = 6$ μsec) is sketched in Fig. 9-16. The composite curve was constructed by first drawing the exponential (almost linear) portions at the top of the pulse and after the pulse terminates. Then the positive and negative peak overshoots, given by $e_{om}/9.09 - 1$, were superposed upon these exponentials.

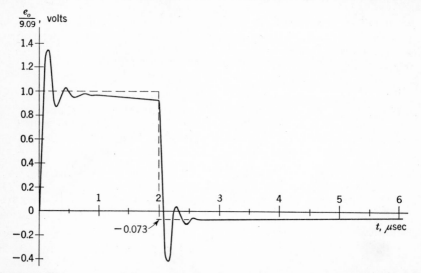

FIG. 9-16. The response of the transformer whose parameters are given in the illustrative example.

The long undershoot for $t > t_p$ should be noted. This section of the curve will slowly approach the zero axis so that, as noted above, the positive area will equal the negative area.

The high-frequency oscillations noted in Fig. 9-16 may be reduced to zero by increasing the loading on the transformer. Critical damping (at the beginning of the pulse) for the transformer of the above illustrative example is obtained when $R_2 = 400$ ohms. This result is obtained by calculating the value of R_2 for $k = 1$. The attenuation is now

$$a = \frac{R_2}{R_1 + R_2} = \frac{400}{600} = 0.667$$

whereas the attenuation for $R_2 = 2$ K was 0.909. Thus, the oscillations have been removed at the expense of increased attenuation. Also, the output will rise somewhat more slowly toward its peak value, the rise time t_r calculated from Eq. (9-29) is 0.056 μsec. On the other hand, the tilt will now be smaller than it was for $R_2 = 2$ K because $R = R_1 a$ is reduced. With $R_2 = 400$ ohms, the droop is calculated to be 5.35 per cent, which is to be compared with the value of 7.28 per cent found above for $R_2 = 2$ K.

9-8. Pulse-transformer Design Considerations. The number of factors involved in the design of pulse transformers are too numerous to permit one to set down a schedule of design procedure. The few remarks that follow are intended to serve as a general guide and the gaps must be filled in by trial and error and on the basis of past experience. Initially one must specify the pulse duration, the pulse voltage, the step-up ratio, the generator impedance, the load impedance, the allowable rise time and overshoot on the leading edge of the pulse, the allowable tilt of the pulse top, and the allowable backswing at the pulse termination.

One must first select a core material. The principal feature required of the core material is high permeability at high frequencies. As outlined in Sec. 9-4, pot cores of ferrite have excellent characteristics for pulse transformers. These cores are also very convenient to use in constructing a transformer. The smallest core on which there is room available to place the required windings should be selected.

The primary inductance required is determined by the allowable percentage tilt P. From Eq. (9-33), $L = 100 R t_p / P$. The number of primary turns are now calculated from the magnetic circuit [say, using Eq. (9-21)] so as to obtain the desired inductance. The secondary turns are, of course, calculable from the step-up ratio given. At this point it is well to check, with the aid of Eq. (9-34), that the iron is not saturated.

In a small pulse transformer, the preservation of the pulse shape is more important than efficiency of operation. The winding resistances may therefore be permitted to be quite large, often as large as 10 per cent of the load or generator resistances. Small wire sizes may therefore be used with a consequent reduction in capacities. If the interwinding and interlayer distances are kept small, the leakage inductance will be small but the effective capacity will increase. The reverse will be true if the interlayer distances are large. When the load and generator impedances are high, a large series leakage inductance may be much more readily tolerated than a large shunt capacity. In this case the windings may be spaced far apart. If the load and generator resistances are very small, a close spacing may be preferred.

Large step-up ratios are seldom used in pulse transformers, because the gain n can be obtained only at the price of increasing the rise time by the factor n. This conclusion is easily verified. If the step-up ratio is n, then load and interwinding capacitances are multiplied by approximately

n^2 [see Eqs. (9-19) and (9-20)]. Since the rise time t_r varies as $C^{1/2}$ [see Eq. (9-29)], t_r is proportional to n. If, in order to accommodate additional secondary turns, the geometry is modified so that σ also increases, then the rise time deteriorates even further.

When a tentative design has been made, the transformer response may be calculated by the methods given above and then the design may be altered as seems required by the results obtained.

9-9. The Blocking Oscillator.[6] The blocking oscillator is a circuit used for the generation of short pulses of duration from about 0.05 to 25 μsec. The circuit is indicated in Fig. 9-17 and consists of a triode (or a pentode) and a pulse transformer. The transformer has a turns ratio of the order of unity and is wired into the circuit to provide polarity inversion, as indicated in Fig. 9-17.

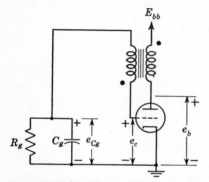

FIG. 9-17. A blocking-oscillator circuit.

Typical waveforms of plate voltage, grid voltage, and cathode current appear as in Fig. 9-18a to c. Qualitatively the operation of the circuit is as follows. Consider that initially there is a negative charge on C_g adequate to bias the tube beyond cutoff. The capacitor C_g discharges through R_g, and when the grid voltage reaches cutoff at $t = t_1$, the tube starts to draw plate current and the plate voltage drops. The drop in plate voltage causes an increase in grid voltage, which in turn results in a further decrease in plate voltage. If the a-c loop gain of the circuit is larger than unity, regeneration takes place. The plate is driven abruptly downward and the grid is driven abruptly positive. The regenerative action continues until limited by the nonlinearity of the tube so that the loop gain drops to unity and, finally, at the peak of the pulse, $t = t_2$, the loop gain has fallen below unity. The peak plate and grid currents are very large in comparison with the currents which are normally encountered in receiving-type tubes.

The plate and grid voltages cannot remain constant at the values reached at t_2 for two reasons. First, even assuming that the plate voltage were to remain constant, the grid voltage would have to drop in potential because of the finite magnetizing inductance of the transformer. This conclusion follows from the discussion of Sec. 9-6, where it is proved that a constant voltage impressed on the primary of a transformer gives an output at the secondary which decreases exponentially with time if L is finite. The second reason that the blocking oscillator output does not remain constant is that the grid current charges C_g (see Fig. 9-18d) and makes the grid voltage less positive, which in turn causes the plate current to decrease and the plate voltage to increase.   Since the loop gain is less than unity, the changes in plate and grid voltages occur relatively slowly until the circuit drifts back to a point where the loop gain once again equals unity and a regenerative action occurs in the direction to turn the tube off.

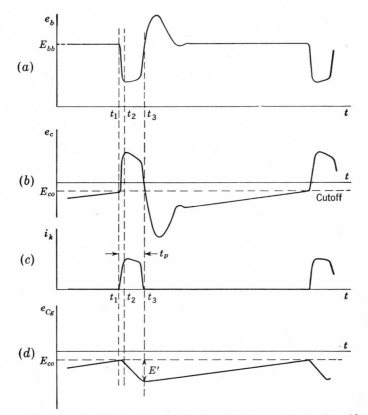

FIG. 9-18. Waveforms in the blocking oscillator.   (a) Plate voltage; (b) grid voltage; (c) cathode current; (d) voltage across C_g.

For a 1:1 inverting transformer, the voltage across the grid winding is the negative of that across the plate winding.   In this case, the waveform b of Fig. 9-18 is equal to the waveform d minus a plus the d-c voltage E_{bb}.   We can conclude, therefore, that the top of the grid waveform will be tilted more than the top of the plate waveform, particularly if C_g is small.

At the termination of the pulse there is a finite current flowing in the magnetizing inductance of the transformer.   Since the current through an inductor cannot change instantaneously, the current must continue to flow even when, at $t = t_3$, the tube current has dropped to zero. The path for the magnetizing current is through the effective capacitance of the transformer. Since the capacitance is small, the magnetizing current decays rapidly, and hence a large induced voltage appears at the plate. The rapid decay of the magnetizing current accounts for the overshoot at the plate and grid. Note in Fig. 9-18 that the overshoot or backswing at the end of the pulse occurs after the tube current has dropped to zero.

The grid current which flowed during the course of the pulse will leave the capacitor C_g with a negative voltage larger than that which existed at the beginning of the pulse (see Fig. 9-18d). The circuit now remains inoperative until C_g again discharges through R_g and the grid voltage reaches cutoff. At this point the cycle repeats itself, the interval between pulses being of the order of magnitude of the time constant R_gC_g.

If the circuit parameters are such that the circuit is underdamped, then high-frequency oscillations such as those indicated in Fig. 9-16 will be present near the beginning and immediately after the termination of the flat top of the plate and grid waveforms.

It is important to note that adequate damping of the backswing is absolutely essential to the operation of the blocking oscillator. In Fig. 9-19 the solid curve represents a typical waveform when the damping is adequate to cause the backswing to be completely damped in one half cycle. The voltage E' is the additional voltage acquired by C_g during the course of the pulse. If the damping is inadequate, the backswing may oscillate, as indicated by the dotted curve. In such a case, regeneration would start again at the point marked X and the blocking oscillator would behave more like a generator of a distorted sinusoidal waveform than a generator of separated pulses. As a matter of fact, the circuit of Fig. 9-17 differs from the circuit of a conventional tuned-plate oscillator principally in the

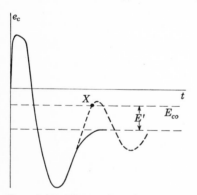

FIG. 9-19. Illustrating the necessity for adequate damping of the backswing in a blocking oscillator.

tightness of coupling between the plate and grid windings. If the core losses of the transformer are low, as they are for a ferrite core, then *an external resistor must be shunted across the transformer* in order to provide the proper damping mentioned above.

The important features in connection with the waveshapes of Fig. 9-18 are the rise time, the amplitude, the duration of the pulse, and the time interval between pulses. The amplitude and decay time of the back-swing are also of some interest. An exact analysis of the blocking oscillator is very difficult, principally because of the extremely nonlinear fashion in which the tube operates, but some useful approximate calculations will be made in the following sections.

9-10. The Blocking-oscillator Rise Time. The equivalent circuit for the purpose of calculating changes of voltage from some quiescent condition during the rise of the pulse is shown in Fig. 9-20a and b. We assume that the change in voltage across C_g is negligible during the short rise time, and hence C_g is replaced by a short circuit. The dynamic grid resistance r_g is included in the circuit to account for the grid current which flows, since during the course of the pulse the grid is driven very far into the positive grid region. If the transformer is loaded by an external

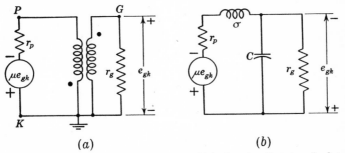

(a)   (b)

FIG. 9-20. The equivalent circuits from which the rise time is calculated.

resistor or by appreciable internal core losses, these equivalent resistors must be placed in shunt with r_g. In Fig. 9-20b the transformer has been replaced by the equivalent circuit of Fig. 9-12 which includes the leakage inductance and the total effective capacitance C. A 1:1 transformer has been assumed and r_g has been reflected from the grid into the plate side of the transformer. The winding resistance is usually small compared with the dynamic plate resistance r_p of the tube, and hence the symbol r_p is used for the total resistance in the plate circuit. Writing down the differential equation of this network and assuming a solution in the form ϵ^{pt}, we find for the roots p of the characteristic equation

$$p = -\left(\frac{r_p}{2\sigma} + \frac{1}{2r_gC}\right) \pm \left[\left(\frac{r_p}{2\sigma} + \frac{1}{2r_gC}\right)^2 + \frac{\mu}{\sigma C}\left(1 - \frac{1}{A}\right)\right]^{\frac{1}{2}} \quad (9\text{-}42)$$

where $A \equiv \mu r_g/(r_g + r_p)$ is the (low-frequency) loop gain of the circuit. If the loop gain exceeds 1, $A > 1$, then one root p_1 is a real positive number. Hence, the grid-voltage variation e_g (measured with respect to the cutoff voltage) is of the form

$$e_g = B_1\epsilon^{p_1t} + B_2\epsilon^{p_2t} \quad (9\text{-}43)$$

Since p_1 is positive, the first term increases rapidly with time, whereas, since p_2 is negative, the second term decreases quickly to zero. Hence, we shall neglect the second term with respect to the first and approximate e_g by

$$e_g = B_1 \epsilon^{p_1 t} \qquad (9\text{-}44)$$

This exponentially increasing grid voltage clearly indicates the regenerative action of the circuit when the loop gain exceeds unity. If the peak grid swing is E_{gm} and if the times when the voltage reaches $0.1E_{gm}$ and $0.9E_{gm}$, respectively, are designated by $t_{0.1}$ and $t_{0.9}$, then

$$0.1E_{gm} = B_1 \epsilon^{p_1 t_{0.1}} \quad \text{and} \quad 0.9E_{gm} = B_1 \epsilon^{p_1 t_{0.9}} \qquad (9\text{-}45)$$

the rise time t_r is defined by $t_r \equiv t_{0.9} - t_{0.1}$. Dividing the two equations in (9-45), we obtain

$$t_r = \frac{2.20}{p_1} \qquad (9\text{-}46)$$

Consider a transformer having the parameters $n = 1$, $L = 5$ mh, $\sigma = 40$ μh, and $C = 50$ $\mu\mu$f and a 6SN7 for which $\mu = 20$, $r_p = 8$ K and $r_g = 1$ K (for small positive grid voltages). Then $A = \mu r_g/(r_g + r_p) = 2.2$. The capacitance $C = 50$ $\mu\mu$f is an estimate of the sum of the transformer capacitance, the effective input capacitance at the grid, the output capacitance at the plate, and stray wiring capacitance. Substituting the above values in Eq. (9-42), we find $p_1 = 2.20 \times 10^7$ and, from Eq. (9-46), $t_r = 0.10$ μsec.

The above calculation is only approximate, particularly since the tube parameters are not constant. For example, as the grid is driven positive, the gain decreases. Hence, p_1 decreases, and the rate at which the voltage is changing decreases. We may expect, therefore, that the rise time of 0.1 μsec calculated above is too small. Experimentally a rise time of 0.25 μsec was obtained.

9-11. The Blocking-oscillator Pulse Amplitude. If both C_g and the magnetizing inductance were infinite, the pulse would rise to its full amplitude and remain there permanently. Under these circumstances the leakage inductance and stray capacitance may be neglected because the currents and voltages have stopped changing. Furthermore, at an instant immediately after the pulse has risen, the magnetizing inductance may be neglected also since the rise time is too short to have permitted any appreciable current to have built up in it. At this instant, then, the transformer may be considered to be a perfect transformer. Also because of the short rise time the voltage across C_g cannot have changed, and it will remain at E_{co}, the cutoff voltage. If E_b and E_c are the plate voltage and grid voltage, respectively, when the pulse has reached its full amplitude, then $E_{bb} - E_b$ is the change in plate voltage and $E_c - E_{co}$ is the change in grid voltage. If there are n times as many turns in the grid winding as in the plate winding, then

$$E_c - E_{co} = n(E_{bb} - E_b) \qquad (9\text{-}47)$$

For each value of E_c given on the plate characteristics of the tube, the value of E_b is calculated from Eq. (9-47) and the locus of corresponding values of E_c and E_b can be plotted on the plate characteristics.

Since the flux in a transformer cannot change instantaneously, then, neglecting the finite rise time of the pulse, the ampere-turns in the primary

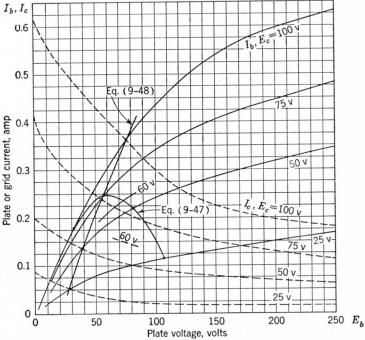

Fɪɢ. 9-21. Positive grid characteristics for a 6SN7 tube.   Illustrating the construction for obtaining the currents and voltages at the peak of the pulse.

must equal the secondary ampere-turns at the peak of the pulse.   Hence, if I_b and I_c are the peak plate and grid currents, respectively,

$$I_b = nI_c \qquad (9\text{-}48)$$

For each value of E_c given on the plate characteristic, the value of E_b may be found (by trial and error) such that Eq. (9-48) is satisfied.   The locus of the corresponding values of I_b and E_b may be plotted.   Then the intersection of the two curves which have been constructed in accord with Eqs. (9-47) and (9-48) gives the values of E_b, E_c, and I_b corresponding to the peak of the pulse.   The peak grid current is $I_c = I_b/n$.

The above-outlined construction has been carried out in Fig. 9-21 for a 6J5 (one-half a 6SN7) tube with $E_{bb} = 140$ volts and a 1:1 transformer.

Since $n = 1$, Eq. (9-48) is satisfied at that value of E_b where the plate-current curve for a given value of E_c intersects the grid-current curve for the same E_c. The result is

$$E_b = 57 \text{ volts} \qquad E_c = 75 \text{ volts} \qquad I_b = I_c = 0.25 \text{ amp}$$

and hence the cathode current is 0.5 amp. Oxide-coated cathodes such as are found in receiving-type tubes are capable of furnishing pulsed currents even up to an ampere. Of course, however, the average tube current must be kept within the rating of the tube, which, for a 6SN7 is about 5 or 10 ma. Experimentally, the following values were measured: $E_b = 50$ volts, $E_c = 75$ volts, and $I_b = I_c = 0.25$ amp.

9-12. The Blocking-oscillator Pulse Width. From Fig. 9-21 we find that at the top of the pulse $r_g = (\Delta E_c / \Delta I_c)_{E_b=57} \cong 200$ ohms and

$$r_p = \left(\frac{\Delta E_b}{\Delta I_b}\right)_{E_c=75} \cong 330 \text{ ohms}$$

The value of μ is difficult to read from the curves of Fig. 9-21, particularly since μ varies rapidly with grid voltage in the region near the peak of the pulse. If the curves for $E_c = 100$ volts and $E_c = 75$ volts are used, $\mu = (\Delta E_b / \Delta E_c)_{I_b=0.25} = 0.4$. If the curves for $E_c = 75$ volts and $E_c = 50$ volts are used, $\mu = 2.0$. Let us take μ as the average of these two values or $\mu = (0.4 + 2)/2 = 1.2$. The loop gain is $A = \mu r_g/(r_g + r_p) = 0.45$.

Thus the loop gain at the peak of the pulse is less than unity, as we already anticipated in Sec. 9-9. Hence, no regeneration takes place, and the circuit voltages may now be expected to change relatively slowly with time. Let us assume that C_g is so large that the voltage across it does not change during the pulse. The equivalent circuit for

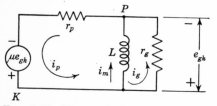

Fig. 9-22. The equivalent circuit from which the pulse duration is calculated.

calculating the *changes* in plate and grid voltages is shown in Fig. 9-22. Assuming a solution in the form ϵ^{pt}, we find for the root p of the characteristic equation

$$p = -\frac{R_o}{L} \frac{1}{1 - A} \tag{9-49}$$

where $R_o \equiv r_p r_g/(r_p + r_g) = 330 \times 200/530 = 125$ ohms is the output impedance at the top of the pulse. The grid voltage measured with respect to the cutoff voltage is

$$e_g = E_{gm}\epsilon^{pt} \tag{9-50}$$

where $E_{gm} = E_c - E_{co} = 75 + 8 = 83$ volts. Since the change in grid voltage equals the variation in plate voltage (for a 1:1 transformer), then the operating point will move along the curve marked "Eq. (9-47)" in Fig. 9-21 in the direction of increasing loop gain. When a voltage is reached for which $A = 1$, regeneration takes place and the pulse is quickly terminated. It is very difficult to find, from the curves of Fig 9-21, the exact point at which $A = 1$, but we may estimate that this takes place at $E_c = 60$ volts or $e_g = 60 + 8 = 68$. Then, from Eq. (9-50), we find, for the pulse duration,

$$t_p = -\frac{0.20}{p} \tag{9-51}$$

In order to obtain a rough approximate magnitude for t_p, let us use the value of R_o and A at the beginning of the pulse and assume that p is constant over the top of the pulse. This assumption will lead to too large a value of t_p, because the rate at which the voltage changes increases with time, since A is increasing from 0.45 to 1. We find $p = -4.5 \times 10^4$ and $t_p = 4.4$ μsec.

We shall now consider an alternative method of calculating t_p which will throw additional light upon the operation of the circuit. From Fig. 9-22, we see that the magnetizing current i_m equals the difference between the plate and grid currents. From Fig. 9-21, we find that at the end of the pulse $E_c = 60$ volts, $E_b = 72$ volts, $I_b = 0.23$ amp, and $I_c = 0.15$ amp. Note that the plate current has changed very little over the pulse width, whereas the grid current has dropped from 0.25 to 0.15 amp. The magnetizing current at the end of the pulse is

$$I_m = 0.23 - 0.15 = 0.08 \text{ amp}$$

The voltage across the magnetizing inductance is $E_{bb} - E_b = L\, di_m/dt$. If we assume E_b is approximately constant over the pulse duration, we can integrate the above equation and obtain

$$t_p = \frac{LI_m}{E_{bb} - E_b} \tag{9-52}$$

Using for E_b the average value over the pulse, namely, $(57 + 72)/2 = 65$ volts and $L = 5$ mh, $E_{bb} = 140$ volts and $I_m = 0.08$ amp, we obtain $t_p = 5.3$ μsec. Considering the crude approximations we have made, this value may be considered in good agreement with the duration of 4.4 μsec found above.

The above analysis, which has assumed that the core is not saturated, leads to the conclusion that t_p is proportional to L. However, as the number of turns are increased (for a given core), saturation will set in. Under these circumstances t_p will vary as $L^{1/2}$ rather than as the first power of L. This statement may be justified as follows. Integrating the equation $E_{bb} - E_b = N\, d\phi/dt$ leads to the result $t_p = N\phi_m/(E_{bb} - E_b)$, where ϕ_m is the magnetic flux in the core at the end of the pulse. If saturation has been reached, then ϕ_m is a constant, and we see that t_p is proportional to N. However, from Eq. (9-21), N varies as $L^{\frac{1}{2}}$, where L is the initial (low flux density) inductance. Experimentally we find that for a small pot core wound with 68 turns, which gives an inductance of 5 mh, the observed value of $t_p = 3$ μsec. By measurements made directly on the transformer (not in the blocking-oscillator circuit) it is found that saturation has begun to set in at 0.08 amp (80 ma). When transformers with more turns are used in the oscillator, it is verified experimentally that t_p does indeed vary as $L^{\frac{1}{2}}$.

The calculations made above have neglected the influence of the finite size of C_g. If C_g is small enough so that during the pulse time t_p the change in voltage across C_g is comparable to the change in e_c, then the pulse will be shorter in duration. Hence, the value of t_p given above is *the maximum value possible for a given transformer* and smaller pulse durations may be secured by reducing the size of C_g. Under these circumstances the top of the plate-voltage pulse waveform is fairly flat while the grid-voltage waveform displays a decided tilt.

The use of a delay line to control the pulse width of a blocking oscillator is discussed in Sec. 10-4.

9-13. The Blocking-oscillator Backswing.

At the termination of the pulse the grid is driven abruptly negative so that neither grid current nor plate current flows. The equivalent output circuit is indicated in Fig. 9-23. The resistor R is the load resistance placed across the transformer and also includes the transformer core losses if these are significant. Since R is usually large compared with the output impedance, it has very little effect

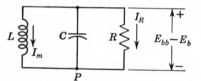

FIG. 9-23. The equivalent circuit from which the plate voltage overshoot is calculated.

on the analysis given above of the pulse size and shape. The primary inductance is L, the magnetizing current is I_m, and the net effective capacitance across the transformer is C. The analysis of the ringing circuit in Fig. 9-23 is given in Sec. 2-8. The response is given in terms of the damping parameter $k = \dfrac{1}{2R}\sqrt{\dfrac{L}{C}}$ and $\Delta = I_m/I_R$, where I_m is the inductor current and I_R is the resistor current. From Eq. (9-52), $I_m = (E_{bb} - E_b)t_p/L$ and from Fig. 9-23, $I_R = (E_{bb} - E_b)/R$. Hence, $\Delta = I_m/I_R = Rt_p/L$. In Fig. 9-19 we demonstrated the necessity for adequate damping of the grid backswing. Hence, let us now assume that R has been chosen for critical damping; $k = 1$ or $R = \frac{1}{2}\sqrt{L/C}$ and $\Delta = \frac{1}{2}t_p/\sqrt{LC}$. For $t_p = 3$ μsec, $L = 5$ mh, and $C = 50$ μμf, $\Delta = 3.0$. The response can be visualized from the curves of Fig. 2-30 and is given analytically by Eq. (2-47).   From this equation we find that the peak grid backswing is 2.2 times the pulse amplitude.   For a plate-voltage pulse amplitude of $140 - 50 = 90$ volts, this means an overshoot at the plate of $2.2 \times 90 = 200$ volts.   For the ferrite core under consideration the inductance decreases with increasing magnetizing current, as indicated in Sec. 9-12.   Hence, at the beginning of the backswing L is smaller than 5 mh, Δ is larger than 3, and we may expect a larger overshoot than the 200 volts calculated above.   Experimentally an overshoot of 290 volts was observed.

If, in any given blocking oscillator, the pulse duration is decreased by decreasing C_g, then the amplitude of the backswing will also be reduced. This result is apparent from the discussion above and also from the fact that the area under the backswing must equal the area under the pulse (see Sec. 9-7).

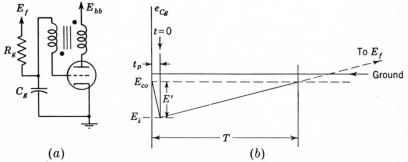

(a)   (b)

FIG. 9-24. (a) A modification of the circuit of Fig. 9-17.   (b) The waveform across C_g.

9-14. The Blocking-oscillator Period.   The circuit of Fig. 9-17 may be modified by connecting the grounded end of R_g to an auxiliary voltage E_f, as indicated in Fig. 9-24a.   The voltage e_{C_g} across C_g is shown in Fig. 9-24b and is given (in the interval outside of the pulse duration) by the expression

$$e_{C_g} = E_f - (E_f - E_i)\epsilon^{-t/R_g C_g} \tag{9-53}$$

The initial voltage E_i on C_g at the end of the pulse is $E_i = E_{co} - E'$, where $E' = \bar{I}_c t_p / C_g$ and $\bar{I}_c$ is the average grid current over the pulse time t_p.   The next pulse commences when e_{C_g} has risen to the cutoff voltage E_{co}, and hence the period T is given by

$$T = t_p + 2.30 R_g C_g \log \frac{E_f - E_{co} + E'}{E_f - E_{co}} \tag{9-54}$$

Usually t_p is negligible compared with T.   If R_g is connected to ground, then the period is given by Eq. (9-54) with $E_f = 0$.   The period may be varied by adjusting R_g and E_f without affecting the pulse shape or duration.   If C_g is varied, then both T and t_p are changed.

The period T is not particularly stable, so that the interval between pulses may vary from cycle to cycle and with aging of the tube, etc. The factors affecting the stability are given in Chap. 12. Methods for synchronizing the oscillator with pulses or sine waves on a 1:1 basis or on an $n:1$ basis (counting) are also considered in Chap. 12.

9-15. The Blocking-oscillator Output Impedance. An important characteristic of the blocking oscillator is that the impedance level of the output pulse is low. In Sec. 9-12 we found that the output impedance $R_o = r_g r_p/(r_p + r_g)$ was 125 ohms. Another method of estimating the output impedance at the plate may be made by noting the extent to which the pulse amplitude decreases when a current is delivered to an external load. Consider that a load resistor is connected across the plate winding of the transformer. The plate current is now the sum of the load current and the transformer primary current. The voltage condition given in Eq. (9-47) and the corresponding plot in Fig. 9-21 still apply. Let us assume that a value of load resistor has been selected such that the peak of the pulse corresponds to the intersection of the curve with the tube characteristic for a grid voltage of 50 volts. Then the plate voltage is 82 volts, the plate current is 220 ma, and the grid current is about 100 ma, as read from the characteristics of Fig. 9-21. For a 1:1 transformer, the current in the plate winding equals the grid current. The load current is, therefore, $220 - 100 = 120$ ma. Originally, in the absence of a load, the pulse amplitude was $140 - 57 = 83$ volts, while now it is $140 - 82 = 58$ volts. The output impedance is, accordingly, $(83 - 58)/0.12 = 210$ ohms. The discrepancy between this value and the value of 125 ohms obtained in Sec. 9-12 is due to the uncertainty with which positive grid characteristics such as those plotted in Fig. 9-21 are known. For one particular 6SN7 an experimental value of 132 ohms was obtained for the output impedance.

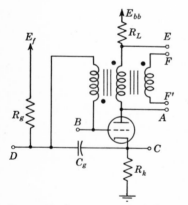

FIG. 9-25. Output terminals in a blocking oscillator.

9-16. The Blocking-oscillator Output Terminals. Many different types of output waveforms may be obtained from a blocking oscillator, depending upon the choice of output terminals. The basic circuit has been modified in Fig. 9-25 by the addition of a cathode resistor R_k and a plate resistor R_L. These resistors are ordinarily of the order of 10 to 200 ohms. In any particular application either one or the other resistor or perhaps neither one is used. Outputs at the following terminals (with

respect to ground) are now available.   At A there is the plate waveform
of Fig. 9-18a, consisting of a negative pulse with a positive overswing.
At B there is the grid waveform of Fig. 9-18b, consisting of a positive
pulse with a negative overswing and a long recovery time.   At C there
is the cathode waveform of Fig. 9-18c, consisting of a positive pulse with
no negative overshoot and at a very low output impedance.   At D there
is the capacitor waveform (assuming $R_k = 0$) of Fig. 9-18d, consisting
essentially of a sweep-type voltage.   If this point is loaded too heavily,
the pulse shape and the period may be affected.   At E a negative pulse
with no overshoot is available.   If the transformer has a tertiary winding such as FF' in Fig. 9-25, then an ungrounded output is obtained having the same waveshape as that at the plate (output A).   Either polarity
of pulse may be selected.   Also, by choosing the turns ratio appropriately,

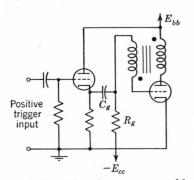

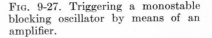

FIG. 9-26. Triggering a monostable
blocking oscillator by means of a cathode follower.

FIG. 9-27. Triggering a monostable
blocking oscillator by means of an
amplifier.

the impedance and voltage level of the output may be adjusted.   If the
overshoot is undesirable, it may be clipped with a diode.

9-17. The Monostable Blocking Oscillator.   The circuit considered
above is a *free-running* or *astable* form of blocking oscillator since pulses
are generated periodically independent of any external excitation.   If, on
the other hand, E_f is made a negative voltage, $-E_{cc}$, so that the tube is
maintained beyond cutoff, the circuit will remain quiescent until the
application of an external trigger brings the grid out of cutoff.   A blocking oscillator connected in this manner is referred to as a *monostable* or
triggered circuit.   Positive triggers may be injected at B, D, or F of Fig.
9-25, or negative triggers may be applied at A, C, E, or F'.   It is not
difficult to see that in each case the applied pulse must be provided by a
low impedance source and must be reasonably large in amplitude.   In
addition, in each case, the blocking oscillator will react back on the pulse
source.   A cathode follower may be used as an impedance-matching
device if necessary, as in Fig. 9-26.   Even in this last circuit there may

be some reaction back on the pulse source. For when the grid current of the blocking oscillator flows through the output impedance of the cathode follower, the cathode of the cathode follower may go sufficiently negative to cause the tube to draw grid current. A triggering circuit which has much to recommend it is illustrated in Fig. 9-27. Since the plate resistance of the triggering tube is large in comparison with the output impedance of the blocking oscillator, the interference with the operation of the blocking oscillator will be a minimum. In addition, in this circuit there is no possibility of a reaction back on the pulse source and also the trigger tube provides some amplification for the applied pulse. The applied trigger must have a sufficiently steep leading edge so that the induced transformer voltage brings the blocking-oscillator grid out of cutoff.

9-18. Applications of Blocking Oscillators. Among the most important applications of the blocking oscillator are the following:

1. The astable circuit is used as a master oscillator to supply triggers for synchronizing a system of pulse-type waveforms—square waves, sweep voltages, etc.

2. The monostable circuit is used to obtain abrupt pulses from a slowly varying input triggering voltage.

3. Either form of blocking oscillator is capable of generating a pulse of large peak power. For example, it is possible to obtain 0.5 amp at 100 volts or 50 watts from a receiving-type tube. Of course, the average power is small since the duty cycle (the ratio t_p/T) is low.

4. Using a tertiary winding output, pulses with neither end grounded may be obtained.

5. The use of the blocking oscillator as a frequency divider or counter is discussed in Chap. 12.

6. The blocking oscillator as a low impedance switch used to discharge a capacitor quickly is considered in Sec. 11-11.

7. The blocking-oscillator output may be used as a gating waveform with a very small *on*-to-*off* time. For example, in some television receivers the voltage across C_g is used as the gating waveform for the vertical sweep-voltage generator.

REFERENCES

1. Lee, Reuben: "Electronic Transformers and Circuits," John Wiley & Sons, Inc., New York, 1947.
2. Massachusetts Institute of Technology Staff: "Magnetic Circuits and Transformers," John Wiley & Sons, Inc., New York, 1943.
3. Glasoe, G. N., and J. V. Lebacqz: "Pulse Generators," Massachusetts Institute of Technology Radiation Laboratory Series, vol. 5, chap. 12, McGraw-Hill Book Company, Inc., New York, 1948.

4. Wimett, T. F.: "Low-power Pulse Transformers," *Rept.* R-122, Servomechanisms Laboratory, Massachusetts Institute of Technology, 1947.
5. Salvadori, M., and R. J. Schwarz: "Differential Equations in Engineering," Prentice-Hall, Inc., New York, 1954.
6. Benjamin, R.: Blocking Oscillators, *J. IEE*, vol. 93, pt. IIIA, no. 7, pp. 1159–1175, 1946.
   Ref. 3, sec. 14.2.
   Chance, B., et al.: "Waveforms," Massachusetts Institute of Technology Radiation Laboratory Series, vol. 19, chap. 6, McGraw-Hill Book Company, Inc., New York, 1949.

CHAPTER 10

ELECTROMAGNETIC DELAY LINES

Delay lines are passive four-terminal networks which have the property that a signal impressed at the input terminals appears at the output terminals at the end of a time interval t_d, called the *delay time*. Delays in the range from a few millimicroseconds to hundreds of microseconds are obtainable with electromagnetic lines. Millisecond delays may be achieved with acoustical delay lines.

If a pulse is applied to a real (nonidealized) line, the signal will not only be delayed but will also suffer attenuation and distortion. In such a line, t_d is defined as the time interval between the 50 per cent amplitude points on the rising edge of the incident and delayed pulses. The important characteristics of delay lines are the following: the time delay, the rise time, the attenuation, the distortion, the characteristic impedance, the volume occupied by the line, the maximum voltage that may be applied to the line, the stability of delay with temperature and time, the ease and accuracy of adjusting the delay, and, finally, the cost.

The applications of delay lines are numerous. For example, a CRO used for observing fast waveforms has a built-in delay line so that the signal which triggers the sweep is delayed slightly before being applied to the vertical-deflection circuit. If the sweep were not allowed to start before the signal was applied, then the first portion of the waveform might not be visible on the scope face. Other applications of delay lines are made in distributed amplifiers, in pulse coders and decoders, in precise time measurement, in radar, in television, and in digital-computer systems.

The first several sections in this chapter discuss the characteristics of both distributed-and lumped-parameter electromagnetic delay lines. The remaining sections consider a number of applications for delay lines. Other uses are found discussed throughout the text, particularly in Chap. 13.

10-1. Distributed-parameter Lines.[1] A uniform lossless transmission line, terminated in its characteristic impedance Z_o, may be used as a delay line. If a sinusoidal voltage $E_s = A\epsilon^{j\omega t}$ is impressed at the sending end of the line of Fig. 10-1, a traveling wave moves to the right along the line. The voltage as a function of the distance x down the line is given by $E_x = A\epsilon^{j(\omega t - \beta x)}$ and the voltage at the receiving end of the line is given by $E_r = A\epsilon^{j(\omega t - \beta l)}$. These facts follow from elementary transmission-line theory[2], where it is shown that $\beta = \omega\sqrt{LC}$, ω is the angular frequency, L is the inductance per meter, and C is the capacitance per meter. Since the velocity with which the wave progresses is $v = (LC)^{-\frac{1}{2}}$, then $\beta = \omega/v$. Hence

$$E_r = A\epsilon^{j(\omega t - \beta l)} = A\epsilon^{j\omega(t - l/v)} = A\epsilon^{j\omega(t - t_d)} \tag{10-1}$$

where $t_d \equiv l/v$. From this equation we see that the voltage which appears at the receiving end is the same as that which was impressed on the sending end at a time t_d earlier. Since any waveform may be resolved into a Fourier spectrum and since the velocity v is independent of frequency, it follows from Eq. (10-1) that an arbitrary waveform impressed on the input terminals will appear at the output terminals after a delay time t_d.

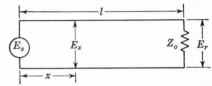

FIG. 10-1. A transmission line terminated in its characteristic impedance.

Both L and C are functions of the geometry of the cross section of the line, but it turns out that for lines with a uniform cross section the product LC is independent of the geometry[2] and equals $\mu\epsilon$, where μ and ϵ are the magnetic permeability and the dielectric constant, respectively, of the medium between the conductors of the line. For a line whose conductors are in free space, $v = (LC)^{-\frac{1}{2}} = (\mu_o\epsilon_o)^{-\frac{1}{2}}$, where $\mu_o = 4\pi \times 10^{-7}$ henry/m and $\epsilon_o = (36\pi \times 10^9)^{-1}$ farad/m so that $v = 3 \times 10^8$ m/sec. This speed is the same as that with which a wave of electromagnetic radiation travels in free space, i.e., the velocity of light. The delay per meter T is given by $T = \sqrt{\mu\epsilon} = 1/v$ and, for air, $T = (3 \times 10^8)^{-1} = 0.0033$ μsec/m. For a medium of relative dielectric constant ϵ_r, the delay is $0.0033\epsilon_r^{\frac{1}{2}}$ μsec/m. For the low-loss dielectric media which are available (polystyrene, polyethylene, or Teflon), $\epsilon_r \cong 2.3$ and $T \cong 0.005$ μsec/m. Such lines are useful in the millimicrosecond delay range, but the length of cable required is prohibitively long in the microsecond region. For example, a delay of 1 μsec requires a line 200 m long!

Before discussing the constructional modifications necessary in a conventional line in order to increase T, let us consider the characteristic impedance Z_o. For a lossless line, $Z_o = \sqrt{L/C}$ ohms and is a pure resistance independent of frequency. For the coaxial cable, the values of L and C can be calculated, and we find $Z_o = 138\epsilon_r^{-\frac{1}{2}} \log (a/b)$ ohms, where a and b are indicated in Fig. 10-2. When the attenuation in the line results principally from ohmic losses in the conductors, the loss (for a fixed a) is a minimum for $a/b = 3.6$. For this ratio and for $\epsilon_r = 2.3$, $Z_o = 51$ ohms. Most conventional lines have impedances of this order of magnitude, i.e., from 50 to 125 ohms. These lines have reasonable physical dimensions. On the other hand, a line with $Z_o \cong 1,000$ ohms would require log $(a/b) = 11$, or $a/b = 10^{11}$, which certainly is an impractical ratio. The low values of characteristic impedance obtainable in

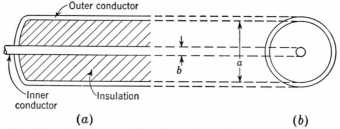

FIG. 10-2. Coaxial cable. (a) Longitudinal section; (b) transverse section.

lines of uniform cross section are often as much an inconvenience as is the short delay per meter. For example, consider that we are required to transmit a 10-volt pulse along a line. If $Z_o = 50$ ohms, the generator must supply 200-ma peak current, while if $Z_o = 1,000$ ohms only 10 ma are required. Accordingly in such applications, the higher impedance line has a distinct advantage over the lower impedance cable.

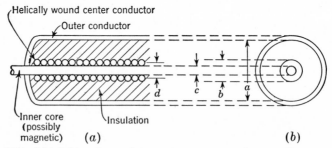

FIG. 10-3. Helical high-impedance delay cable. (a) Longitudinal section; (b) transverse section.

Since $T = \sqrt{LC}$ and $Z_o = \sqrt{L/C}$, then both T and Z_o can be increased if a constructional change is made which increases L. The method of accomplishing this increase in inductance is illustrated in Fig. 10-3, where the straight center conductor in Fig. 10-2 is replaced with a continuous coil of wire in the form of a helix. In such a cable, in which the cross section is not uniform, the product LC is no longer equal to $\mu\epsilon$. Since the center conductor is wound in a tight helix, the magnetic flux in the region between inner and outer conductors may be neglected. The inductance then equals that of a solenoid of diameter d m, with n turns per meter, or

$$L = \frac{\mu n^2 \pi d^2}{4} = \mu_r n^2 \pi^2 d^2 \times 10^{-7} \qquad \text{henrys/m} \qquad (10\text{-}2)$$

where μ_r is the relative permeability of the core on which the solenoid is wound. The capacitance is that of coaxial cylinders with a material of relative dielectric constant ϵ_r between the diameter a and b, or

$$C = \frac{2\pi\epsilon}{\ln (a/b)} = \frac{2.40 \times 10^{-11}\epsilon_r}{\log (a/b)} \qquad \text{farads/m} \qquad (10\text{-}3)$$

For a type RG-65/U cable (Federal Telephone and Radio Company) whose parameters are $a = 0.285$ in., $c = 0.11$ in., the helix is AWG No. 32 wire of diameter 0.008 in., with $n = 112$ turns per inch and a polyethylene dielectric ($\epsilon_r = 2.3$), values of $Z_o = \sqrt{L/C} = 1,100$ ohms and $T = \sqrt{LC} = 0.18$ μsec/m are calculated. These agree reasonably well with the measured values of $Z_o = 950$ ohms and $T = 0.14$ μsec/m. Note that the helical center conductor has increased the delay of the conventional polyethylene coaxial cable from 0.005 to 0.13 μsec/m, or by a factor 26, and the impedance from 50 to 950 ohms, or by a factor of about 20.

The inductance may be further increased by winding the helical inner conductor upon a ferromagnetic core.[3] The type HH-1500 (Columbia Technical Corporation) is identical with the RG-65/U cable except that a flexible, stable, low-loss magnetic core ($\mu_r \cong 2$) is used. For this line, $Z_o = 1,600$ ohms and $T = 0.23$ μsec/m, which is an improvement by a factor of $\sqrt{\mu_r} \cong 1.4$.

It follows from Eqs. (10-2) and (10-3) that if the dimension b in Fig. 10-3 is increased while maintaining a constant, then both L and C, and hence T, are increased. The General Electric Company manufactures a line (type DL1100) in which b is as large as possible, the inner and outer conductors being separated by a thin layer of insulating tape which is effectively 0.003 in. thick.[4] The helical conductor consists of No. 40 insulated wire with 277 turns per inch wound on a $\frac{3}{16}$-in.-diameter flexible plastic tubing. The outer conductor is made of a braid of *insulated* wires which are electrically connected only at the ends of the cable. If the braid were not insulated, the eddy currents would be excessive. For this line, $Z_o = 1,100$ ohms and $T = 1.8$ μsec/m.

A higher impedance may be obtained without sacrificing delay by increasing L and decreasing C. The type HH-2500 line[3] (Columbia Technical Corporation) is similar to the DL1100 line just discussed, except that L is increased by using a magnetic core ($\mu_r \cong 4$) and C is decreased by using a thicker polyethylene spacer (0.035 cm) between inner and outer conductors. For this line, $Z_o = 2,800$ ohms and $T = 2.0$ μsec/m. The

HH-4000 and HH-1600 are similar lines having characteristic impedances of 4,000 and 1,700 ohms, respectively, and each has a delay of 3.35 μsec/m. For lines of this type, in which the outer conductor is composed of insulated strands, there is unfortunately some leakage of the fields outside the line. Two lines placed in close proximity side by side will exhibit some cross coupling of signals.

Experimental lines have been reported[5] with impedances up to 10,000 ohms and delays up to 30 μsec/m. These lines are wound on a $\frac{3}{16}$-in.-diameter polystyrene core 12 in. long. The core is covered with silver conducting paint which acts as a ground strip. The silver is slotted axially into 36 thin strips in order to reduce eddy-current losses. The

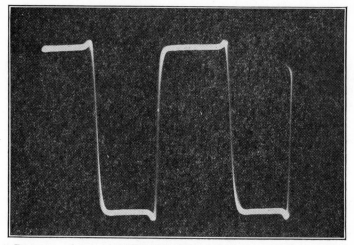

Fig. 10-4. Response of 1 μsec of HH-1600 delay cable (linearized) to a 250-kc square wave. (*Courtesy of Columbia Technical Corporation.*)

ground conductor is covered with a thin layer of insulating tape and a multilayer bank winding is placed over this insulation. From 2 to 5 layers of wire (sizes from No. 32 to No. 47) have been used. These lines have longer delays per axial inch and less attenuation for the same delay time, but have poorer rise times and more distortion due to internal reflections than the helical lines previously discussed.

The assumption that Z_o and T are independent of frequency is quite well satisfied for frequencies below a megacycle. At higher frequencies there is a substantial progressive phase shift in the current in successive turns of the helix and the inductance decreases. As a consequence both the delay and characteristic impedance decrease with frequency. In addition the attenuation of the line increases with frequency and is due principally to the dielectric loss in the insulation of the wire of the center helix. All these factors introduce distortion, the effect of the attenuation (about 6 db/μsec at 10 Mc) being particularly marked when long lengths of line must be used to provide long delays. The rise time t_r increases with the square root of the delay time t_d and the ratio $t_r/\sqrt{t_d}$ for many helical lines lies in the range 0.02 to 0.08 (with t_d and t_r in microseconds). Figure 10-4 is an oscillogram of the response of one microsecond of HH-1600 delay cable to a 250-kc square wave.

Short calibrated lengths of delay lines (with the leads brought out through plastic endcaps) are available from the manufacturers of the bulk lines.

10-2. Lumped-parameter Delay Lines.[2] A given delay can often be obtained with less attenuation and in a smaller volume (but with more distortion) with a lumped-parameter line than with a distributed-parameter line. A lumped line is made up of a cascaded series of symmetrical networks such as the T section of Fig. 10-5a. The *image* or *characteristic*

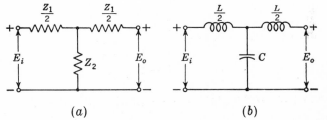

(a)   (b)

FIG. 10-5. (a) A prototype filter section. (b) A low-pass constant-k prototype section.

impedance Z_o of this section is defined as follows. If the network is terminated in Z_o, then the impedance seen looking into the input terminals is also Z_o. Applying this definition, we find

$$Z_o = \left[Z_1 Z_2 \left(1 + \frac{Z_1}{4Z_2} \right) \right]^{\frac{1}{2}} \qquad (10\text{-}4)$$

The *propagation constant* γ is defined by $E_o/E_i \equiv \epsilon^{-\gamma}$ under the condition that the impedance Z_o is connected across the output terminals. The propagation constant is given by

$$\cosh \gamma = 1 + \frac{Z_1}{2Z_2} \qquad (10\text{-}5)$$

where $\cosh \gamma \equiv \frac{1}{2}(\epsilon^\gamma + \epsilon^{-\gamma})$ is the hyperbolic cosine of γ. If (as indicated in Fig. 10-5b) the series element is an inductor $L/2$ so that $Z_1 = j\omega L$ and the shunt element is a capacitor C so that $Z_2 = -j/\omega C$, then $Z_1 Z_2 = L/C = k$, a constant, independent of frequency. Such a network is called a low-pass, constant-k prototype section. The *attenuation factor* α and the *phase factor* β are defined by $\gamma \equiv \alpha + j\beta$, where α and β are real functions of frequency. Equation (10-5) becomes, for the constant-k section,

$$\cosh(\alpha + j\beta) = 1 - \frac{\omega^2 LC}{2} \tag{10-6}$$

The passband of the filter is defined by the frequency band over which the attenuation factor is zero. Hence,

$$\cosh j\beta = \cos \beta = 1 - \frac{\omega^2 LC}{2} \tag{10-7}$$

Since β must be real, then $\cos \beta$ must have a magnitude between $+1$ and -1. Hence, $0 < \omega^2 LC/2 < 2$. The upper frequency f_c given by the above inequality is called the *cutoff frequency* and is given by

$$f_c = \frac{1}{\pi \sqrt{LC}} \tag{10-8}$$

For all frequencies between zero and f_c, the attenuation is zero and within this passband the phase factor is given by

$$\cos \beta = 1 - 2\left(\frac{f}{f_c}\right)^2 \tag{10-9}$$

Since $\cos \beta = 1 - \beta^2/2 + \beta^4/4! - \cdots$, we have the result that for $f \ll f_c$, $\beta \ll 1$ and $\beta \cong 2(f/f_c)$. For a sinusoidal input to the filter, $E_i = A \epsilon^{j\omega t}$ and

$$E_o = E_i \epsilon^{-\gamma} = A \epsilon^{j\omega t - j\beta} = A \epsilon^{j\omega(t - \beta/\omega)} = A \epsilon^{j\omega(t - 1/\pi f_c)} \tag{10-10}$$

Thus, if the Fourier spectrum of the input signal to the network consists of frequencies all of which are much less than f_c, the output signal will be a faithful reproduction of the input signal except delayed by a time

$$t_s \cong \frac{1}{\pi f_c} = \sqrt{LC} \tag{10-11}$$

The quantity t_s is called the *time delay per section of filter*. For the constant-k network, Eq. (10-4) reduces to

$$Z_o = \sqrt{\frac{L}{C}\left[1 - \left(\frac{f}{f_c}\right)^2\right]} \tag{10-12}$$

For $f \ll f_c$, the characteristic impedance is independent of frequency and equals $\sqrt{L/C}$.

A delay line is specified[6] by giving the nominal impedance Z_o, the total delay t_d, and the rise time t_r of the output voltage when an ideal step is applied at the input. The quantity t_r is related to the delay per section t_s, but steady-state filter theory can give this relationship only after a very difficult Fourier spectrum analysis. On the other hand, the response of a single section can be obtained directly by solving the differential equations of the two-mesh circuit of Fig. 10-5b. The result of such an analysis is given (Prob. 10-4) in graphical form in Fig. 10-6. The output is taken across a pure resistance R_o equal to the nominal characteristic impedance $\sqrt{L/C}$ of the filter. The solid curve a corresponds to a generator impedance equal to the output impedance R_o. The dashed curve is for a generator impedance equal to zero. We note that the peak overshoot is reduced from 22 to 8 per cent as the generator resistance is increased from zero to the R_o. Such an improvement is reasonable on the grounds that any reflection at the output termination will be absorbed at the input end.

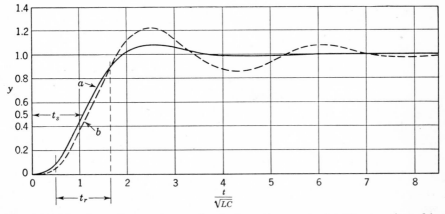

FIG. 10-6. The step voltage response of a single section constant-k filter terminated in $R_o = \sqrt{L/C}$. Curve a: the input impedance is also R_o, and $y = 2e_o/e_i$. Curve b: the input impedance is zero, and $y = e_o/e_i$.

In the discussion to follow we shall assume a termination R_o at each end of the filter. From Fig. 10-6 we find the delay per section to be $t_s = 1.07 \sqrt{LC}$. This value is to be compared with $t_s = \sqrt{LC}$ of Eq. (10-11), which is the result that would be obtained if the terminating impedance was the Z_o given in Eq. (10-12) and if all the frequency components in the input step could be considered to be small compared with f_c. The rise time per section t_{r1} is found from Fig. 10-6 to be $t_{r1} = 1.13 \sqrt{LC}$. Experimentally we find that the delay t_d of n sections is n times the delay per section, just as would be expected from filter theory.

$$t_d = nt_s \qquad (10\text{-}13)$$

Also, experimentally[7] it is found that the rise time t_r of n sections is $n^{1/3}$ times that of a single section. It is possible to provide some theoretical justification for the factor $n^{1/3}$, but the matter is involved and we shall not pursue the point.   We consider then that, approximately,

$$t_r = t_{r1} n^{1/3} \tag{10-14}$$

From Eqs. (10-13) and (10-14) it follows that

$$n = \left(\frac{t_d}{t_r}\right)^{1.5} \left(\frac{t_{r1}}{t_s}\right)^{1.5} \tag{10-15}$$

Using the value of $t_{r1}/t_s = 1.13 \sqrt{LC}/1.07 \sqrt{LC} = 1.06$, found from Fig. 10-6, we have

$$n = 1.1 \left(\frac{t_d}{t_r}\right)^{1.5} \tag{10-16}$$

This equation gives the number of sections required in order to attain the desired specified value of t_d/t_r.   If Eq. (10-16) does not yield an integer, then the next larger integer is used for n.   From the relationships $t_s = 1.07 \sqrt{LC}$, $t_d = nt_s$, and $R_o = \sqrt{L/C}$, we find

$$C = \frac{t_d}{1.07 n R_o} \quad \text{and} \quad L = \frac{t_d R_o}{1.07 n} \tag{10-17}$$

For given values of t_r, t_d, and R_o, Eqs. (10-16) and (10-17) are used to find the number of sections n required and the capacitance C and the inductance L of each section.   The exact value of characteristic impedance is often not of importance.   Hence, the standard manufactured value of C nearest the value obtained from the first of Eqs. (10-17) is used and then this equation is solved again for R_o.   Using this value of R_o, the second of Eqs. (10-17) is solved for L.   This inductance is then wound on a polystyrene cylinder or on a ferrite core.

Often the characteristic impedance required is dictated by the circuitry in which the line is to be incorporated.   If there is some freedom of choice it is advantageous to design the line for the lowest acceptable impedance. Most of the attenuation on a line results from the resistance of the inductors, and if R_o is small, L can be made small while the time delay may be kept constant by increasing the size of C.

If experiment shows that the output pulse shape is unsatisfactory (too much ringing) for a particular application, then a more conservative (smaller) value of t_s is chosen.   Of course, a smaller t_s requires a greater number of sections.   Hence, a line will result which will be more expensive, will occupy more space, and will have more attenuation than a line based upon a larger value of t_s.

We have already emphasized [see Eq. (10-10)] that if β/ω is independent of frequency the output will be an exact replica of the input but delayed by an amount $t_s = \beta/\omega$.   In Fig. 10-7 the value of t_s is seen to be far from constant over the passband of a constant-k filter.   The constancy of t_s with frequency can be improved considerably by permitting coupling to exist between the two inductors of the constant-k section. This modification leads to the *m-derived filter section*, which will now be discussed.

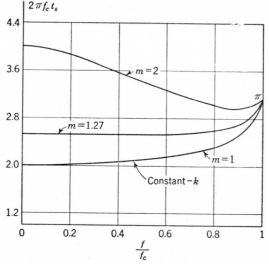

FIG. 10-7. The variation of delay t_s vs. frequency over the passband of an m-derived filter. The special case $m = 1$ corresponds to the constant-k filter.

Consider the network of Fig. 10-8 in which m is a real number. From Eqs. (10-4) and (10-5) we find that the cutoff frequency f_c and the characteristic impedance Z_o are given by the same expressions as for the prototype filter, namely, Eqs. (10-8) and (10-12), respectively. From Eq. (10-5) we find that, within the passband, β is given by

$$\cos \beta = 1 - \frac{2m^2(f/f_c)^2}{1 - (1 - m^2)(f/f_c)^2} \tag{10-18}$$

The time delay per section (at a given frequency ω) is $t_s = \beta/\omega$. Values of $\omega_c t_s$ calculated from Eq. (10-18) are plotted vs. f/f_c in Fig. 10-7 with m as a parameter. It turns out that the value of m which gives optimum constancy of $\omega_c t_s$ vs. f is $m = 1.27$. For this value of m, the delay is constant up to about $0.6f_c$, whereas for the constant-k filter (corresponding to $m = 1$) the delay already departs appreciably from constancy at $0.2f_c$. We must not,

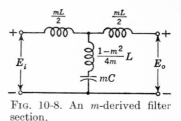

FIG. 10-8. An m-derived filter section.

however, naïvely conclude that an m-derived filter (with $m = 1.27$) will be "three times as good" as a constant-k filter. A comparison can only be made after the transient response is studied, as we shall do later.

For small values of f/f_c, Eq. (10-18) reduces to

$$\cos \beta = 1 - 2m^2 \left(\frac{f}{f_c}\right)^2 \cong 1 - \frac{\beta^2}{2}$$

or $\beta = 2mf/f_c$ and the delay per section is

$$t_s = \frac{\beta}{\omega} = \frac{\beta}{2\pi f} = \frac{m}{\pi f_c}$$

and since $f_c = 1/\pi \sqrt{LC}$,

$$t_s = m \sqrt{LC} \tag{10-19}$$

The m-derived section of Fig. 10-8 is not realizable for $m > 1$ since the shunt inductance is negative. It is, however, realizable in the form of Fig. 10-9 in which there is a mutual inductance between the series inductors. The circuit of Fig. 10-10 is identical to the circuit of Fig. 10-9, as

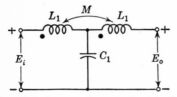

FIG. 10-9. A network equivalent to the m-derived section.

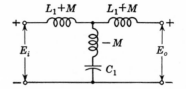

FIG. 10-10. A network equivalent to that of Fig. 10-9.

may readily be established from the mesh equations for these two circuits. Comparing Figs. 10-10 and 10-8, we have

$$M = \frac{m^2 - 1}{4m} L \qquad L_1 + M = m \frac{L}{2}$$

from which

$$L_1 = \frac{m^2 + 1}{4m} L = 0.515L \tag{10-20}$$

Also

$$C_1 = mC = 1.27C \tag{10-21}$$

and the coefficient of coupling between the inductors L_1 is

$$K = \frac{M}{L_1} = \frac{m^2 - 1}{m^2 + 1} = 0.237 \tag{10-22}$$

The step-voltage response of a single section terminated at both ends in a pure resistance $R_o = \sqrt{L/C}$ is given in Fig. 10-11. The value of t_s is found to be $1.20 \sqrt{LC}$, which is to be compared with $t_s = 1.27 \sqrt{LC}$ obtained from Eq. (10-19) for $m = 1.27$. There are two advantages of the m-derived filter (with $m = 1.27$) over the constant-k. The first is that the peak overshoot of the former is 4 per cent as against 8 per cent for the latter. The second is that $t_{r1}/t_s = 1.06$ for the constant-k, whereas for $m = 1.27$ this ratio is found from Fig. 10-11 to be 0.96, or

10 per cent smaller.   The number of sections needed is now found from Eq. (10-15) to be

$$n = 0.94 \left(\frac{t_d}{t_r}\right)^{1.5} \tag{10-23}$$

Comparing this equation with Eq. (10-16), we see that for the same ratio of delay to rise time a line with m-derived filters requires about 16 per cent fewer sections than one constructed from prototype sections.   Note, however, that an m-derived section has an *undershoot* or *preshoot* of magnitude 12 per cent.

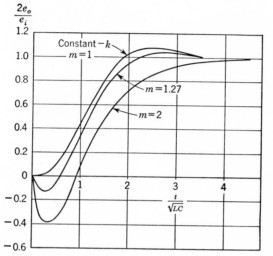

FIG. 10-11. The step-voltage response of a single-section m-derived filter terminated at each end in $R_o = \sqrt{L/C}$.

From the relationships $t_s = 1.20 \sqrt{LC}$, $t_d = nt_s$, and $R_o = \sqrt{L/C}$, we find

$$C = \frac{t_d}{1.20 n R_o} \quad \text{and} \quad L = \frac{t_d R_o}{1.20 n} \tag{10-24}$$

For specified values of t_d, t_r, and R_o, Eqs. (10-23) and (10-24) give n, C, and L.   Then Eqs. (10-20) to (10-22) give L_1, C_1, and k.   The inductances are often wound on a polystyrene cylinder and the core diameter and length of winding are chosen so as to give the required value (0.237) of the coefficient of coupling.[8]   If a delay line is to be used to reproduce a signal with a minimum of distortion, it may be necessary to use variable shunt capacitors and to adjust these individually so as to obtain the best possible step-voltage response.   Since the characteristic impedance is not constant, the line should ideally be terminated, as is the practice with filters, in a half m-derived Π section for which $m = 0.6$.   Such a termination should be used on both the input and output ends of the line.   In practice, it is often found that simpler terminations are adequate.

If the inductor is wound on a ferrite core, the coefficient of coupling is very close to unity.   If the capacitor C is connected not to the center of the inductor but rather close to the right-hand end of the coil, then a line comparable to the m-derived line results.   Still another type of structure which is used in the construction of delay lines is the so-called "bridged-tee" section.   In this section, in addition to the coupling between coils, one includes an impedance element which is bridged directly across the network from input to output.   Design formulas for these two types of lines are given in the literature.[9,10]

Figure 10-12 shows the response of a commercially available decade delay line.   A selector switch allows delays up to 11.0 μsec (in steps of 0.1 μsec) to be obtained.   Several manufacturers supply (physically) small lumped-parameter lines having fixed delays in standard values up to about 20 μsec, with impedances in the range from 50 ohms to 10 K, and with the ratio of delay to rise time of the order of 10.

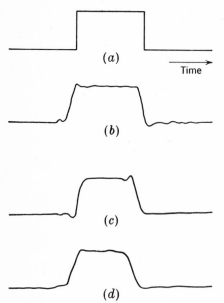

FIG. 10-12. Oscillogram traces taken with the DD-1 line.   (a) A 2-μsec input pulse; (b) output with $t_d = 0.3$ μsec; (c) output with $t_d = 3.0$ μsec; (d) output with $t_d = 11.0$ μsec.   (*Courtesy Electronic Computer Division, Underwood Corporation.*)

Quite typically, lumped-circuit delay lines, even of the most conservative design, exhibit some ringing.   In many applications this type of distortion is acceptable.   For example, in computer circuits (Chap. 13) the occurrence or absence of a pulse is of more importance than the exact form of the pulse.   And where pulses have become badly deteriorated in form, they may be reshaped.   In other applications, notably in a CRO ringing is completely intolerable.   It will be recalled that in a CRO a delay line is used to delay the signal until the sweep has started.   The remedy in this latter case is to construct a delay line whose cutoff frequency is well beyond the bandpass of the system in which it is included. This arrangement is effective because the ringing frequency is of the order of magnitude of the cutoff frequency of the line.   If, as an example, a line of cutoff frequency 60 Mc is included in cascade with a 10-Mc amplifier in a CRO, the ringing will not appear in the CRO pattern.

10-3. Reflections on Transmission Lines. It will be recalled[11] that the general solution for the voltage e and current i on an ideal (lossless) transmission line is given by

$$e = f_1\left(t - \frac{x}{v}\right) + f_2\left(t + \frac{x}{v}\right) \tag{10-25}$$

and

$$i = \frac{1}{R_o}\left[f_1\left(t - \frac{x}{v}\right) - f_2\left(t + \frac{x}{v}\right)\right] \tag{10-26}$$

The positive assumed directions of e and i are indicated in Fig. 10-13. The characteristic impedance of the line is R_o and v is the propagation velocity. The function f_1 is an arbitrary function of the argument $t - x/v$ and represents a wave traveling to the right (in the positive x direction) with velocity v. Similarly, f_2 represents a wave traveling to the left. For a wave

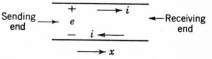

FIG. 10-13. Sign conventions for current and voltage on a transmission line.

traveling to the right, $e/i = R_o$, while for a wave moving to the left, $e/i = -R_o$. This difference in sign results simply from the fact that in both cases the assumed positive current direction is as shown in Fig. 10-13. The general solution for wave propagation on a transmission line consists in combining a wave traveling to the right with a wave traveling to the left in such a way that the boundary conditions at the sending and receiving ends are satisfied (at each end of the line the ratio e/i must equal the terminating resistance). We shall now illustrate this principle by applying it to a number of important special cases.

Infinite Line. Assume that a unit step $U(t)$ is applied to the sending end of a line which is arbitrarily long so that the conditions at the receiving end need never be considered. Then the boundary conditions are obviously satisfied by taking

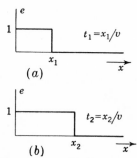

FIG. 10-14. The voltage distribution along an infinite line at two particular instances of time t_1 and t_2, with $t_2 > t_1$.

$$e = U\left(t - \frac{x}{v}\right) \qquad i = \frac{1}{R_o}U\left(t - \frac{x}{v}\right) \tag{10-27}$$

It is understood, from the definition of the unit step, that $U(t - x/v)$ is zero whenever the argument is negative. The voltage distributions along the line at two successive times are shown in Fig. 10-14. The abrupt discontinuity in voltage travels down the line with velocity v.

Finite Line Terminated in Its Characteristic Impedance. An additional boundary condition now must be satisfied at the termination where e/i

must equal R_o. But the solution given by Eq. (10-27) already satisfies this additional condition so that the voltage and current on the line remain as before (for an applied unit step). In general, a line terminated in its characteristic impedance behaves as an infinitely long line.

Finite Line Terminated in $R \neq R_o$. The boundary condition at the termination is no longer satisfied by Eq. (10-27). It is now required that at the termination the ratio e/i equal R rather than R_o. Hence, we must now find a combination of waves traveling to the right and to the

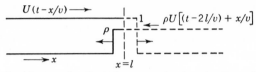

FIG. 10-15. Incident and reflected waves at a termination with $R > R_o$.

left which will satisfy the boundary condition. The circumstances which exist at the termination of the line $(x = l)$ for the case of a resistive termination $R > R_o$ are shown at a time $t > l/v$ in Fig. 10-15. The incident wave of voltage $U(t - x/v)$ has progressed to the point where the discontinuity has passed beyond the end of the line. The second or reflected wave is represented by $\rho U(t - 2l/v + x/v)$ and is one which travels from right to left and whose discontinuity passes $x = l$ at $t = l/v$. (Of course, it is understood that the dashed portions of the waves to the right of $x = l$ do not actually exist because the line ends at $x = l$.) The constant ρ is called the *reflection factor*. For times $t \geq l/v$, the net volt-

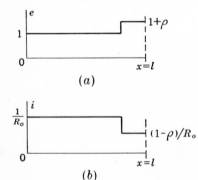

FIG. 10-16. The voltage (a) and current (b) distributions along a line with a termination $R > R_o$.

age at the termination is $1 + \rho$. The current associated with the original wave is $1/R_o$ flowing to the right. The current associated with the reflected wave is ρ/R_o flowing to the left. The net current is $(1 - \rho)/R_o$ flowing to the right. If the termination is R, then it is required that $(1 + \rho)/[(1 - \rho)/R_o] = R$ or

$$\rho = \frac{R/R_o - 1}{R/R_o + 1} \qquad (10\text{-}28)$$

This result for ρ, which measures the ratio of the amplitudes of the two waves, is consistent with our expectation that $\rho = 0$ if $R = R_o$. We also note that ρ is positive if $R > R_o$, whereas the reflected wave is inverted (ρ is negative) if the terminating resistance is less than the characteristic resistance ($R < R_o$). The voltage and current distributions along the line for a particular instant of time, $t > l/v$, are shown in Fig. 10-16.

The net voltage and current at any point on the line result from the simultaneous existence of the incident and reflected waves. The time $l/v \equiv t_d$ which it takes the wave to travel down the entire length of the line is called the *one-way delay time*.

Note, in particular, that for an open-circuited line $\rho = +1$, whereas for a short-circuited line $\rho = -1$.

Multiple Reflections. At a time $t = 2t_d$, the discontinuity of the reflected wave will reach the termination at the sending end of the line. We find that for $t \geq 2t_d$ the boundary condition at the sending end is not satisfied unless the generator impedance equals R_o. We must therefore postulate, for any other termination, the existence of a third wave which travels to the right and has a discontinuity which passes $x = 0$ at $t = 2t_d$. This wave is represented by $\rho\rho' U(t - 2t_d - x/v)$, where ρ' is the reflection factor for the sending-end termination and is given by Eq. (10-28), with R replaced by the sending-end resistance. This third wave is the

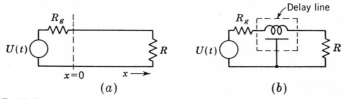

Fig. 10-17. (*a*) A generator with an output impedance R_g at the sending end of a line. (*b*) The same circuit drawn using the standard symbol for a delay line.

reflection of the second wave and will in turn produce a reflection at the receiving end, and so on indefinitely.

In the case where the generator at the sending end provides a voltage $U(t)$ and has an impedance R_g, the amplitude of the first wave is easily calculated. In Fig. 10-17, the ratio of voltage to current on the line is R_o until the discontinuity of the first wave reaches the termination R. Hence, at time $t = 0$, the impedance seen looking to the right is R_o and the amplitude of the first wave is $R_o/(R_o + R_g)$.

There is an alternative method of describing what takes place on the line which is quite convenient if the input waveform is a unit step (or a pulse). Instead of focusing our attention on the entire waveform we concentrate on the discontinuity. This edge moves down the line with a velocity v leaving the line behind it charged to unit voltage (if $R_g = 0$) and leaving behind it a current of $1/R_o$ amp. When the discontinuity reaches the end of the line, it causes a second discontinuity of magnitude ρ to go back along the line. This second discontinuity charges the line to an *additional* voltage ρ volts as it progresses and it also leaves behind it an *additional* current $-\rho/R_o$ amp. This process is repeated at each reflection from either end of the line. The resultant voltage (or current) is the algebraic sum of the individual components. If one end of the line is terminated in R_o, then when the discontinuity reaches this termination it is completely "absorbed" and no additional discontinuity arises.

A Shorted Line. Consider a generator of a step voltage E and impedance $R_g = R_o$ connected to a line which is short-circuited at the receiving end as indicated in Fig. 10-18a. What is the appearance of the voltage waveform at the sending end? At $t = 0$, a step $ER_o/(R_o + R_g) = E/2$ appears at $x = 0$. This discontinuity travels to the shorted end where a second discontinuity $-E/2$ (since $\rho = -1$) will start toward the left. When this second edge reaches the input end, it will add a voltage $-E/2$ to the voltage $+E/2$ established previously. The resultant waveform will be a pulse of amplitude $E/2$ and duration $2t_d$, as indicated in Fig. 10-18b. The advantage of producing a pulse in this manner is that the

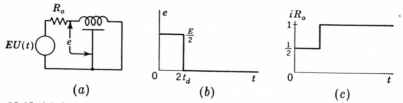

(a)   (b)   (c)

FIG. 10-18. (a) A step voltage applied to a short-circuited line from a generator whose impedance matches that of the line. (b) The resulting voltage e and (c) the resulting current i at the input of the line.

duration depends only on passive elements (the L and C of the line) and thus may have a stability not shared by pulse generators (blocking oscillators, etc.) which depend upon active elements. The initial current is $E/2R_o$. This current discontinuity is reflected as $-\rho E/2R_o = +E/2R_o$ so that at time $t \geq 2t_d$ the input current is $E/2R_o + E/2R_o = E/R_o$, as it should be, since the steady-state voltage at the input to the line is zero. The current waveform is indicated in Fig. 10-18c for $E = 1$.

Attenuation. In the above discussions we have neglected the attenuation of the line which we shall now take into account. Consider the circuit of Fig. 10-18 again. The initial discontinuity at the input end will arrive at the shorted end as $\frac{1}{2}E\epsilon^{-a}$, where $a = \alpha l$, α is the attenuation factor, and l the length of line. At $t = 2t_d$, a negative step of amplitude $\frac{1}{2}E\epsilon^{-2a}$ will appear at the input end and the resultant wave will be as in Fig. 10-19. We see that a small step voltage e' remains after the pulse.

The above result will yield an expression for α in terms of the d-c input resistance R_{dc} of the shorted distortionless line. Since for $t > 2t_d$ there are no further discontinuities, then e' may be calculated from

$$e' = \frac{ER_{dc}}{R_{dc} + R_o} \simeq E\frac{R_{dc}}{R_o}$$

in which we have taken into account the fact that on any practically useful line $R_{dc} \ll R_o$. From Fig. 10-19 we see that

$$E \frac{R_{dc}}{R_o} + \frac{E}{2} \epsilon^{-2a} = \frac{E}{2}$$

Assuming small attenuation so that $\epsilon^{-2a} \cong 1 - 2a$, we find

$$a = \alpha l = \frac{R_{dc}}{R_o} \tag{10-29}$$

Reflection of Pulses. It will be recalled (see Fig. 2-3) that a pulse of amplitude E and duration t_p may be constructed by superimposing a voltage $EU(t)$ and a voltage $-EU(t - t_p)$. Using this fact, we may conclude that the results stated above for step voltages apply equally well for pulses. *To summarize,* a voltage pulse of amplitude E is reflected as a pulse of amplitude ρE at a termination with a reflection factor ρ. A current pulse of amplitude I is reflected at the termination as a pulse of amplitude $-\rho I$. The pulse amplitude is attenuated by a factor $\epsilon^{-\alpha x}$ when the pulse travels the distance x.

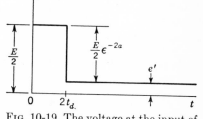

FIG. 10-19. The voltage at the input of the line in Fig. 10-18 when attenuation is taken into consideration.

In Fig. 10-20a is shown a pulse generator whose impedance R_g is less than the characteristic impedance R_o of a line which is terminated in an impedance R which is greater than R_o. Applying the above rules, we may readily verify that the waveforms at the input and output of the line are as pictured in Fig. 10-20b and c. Note, in particular, the polarities of the pulses.

Discharge of an Initially Charged Line. In Fig. 10-21a is indicated a line charged to a voltage E before the switch S is closed at $t = 0$. The Thévenin equivalent of the line with S open is a generator of voltage E in series with a resistance R_o. Hence, when S is closed, the voltage e across R is $ER/(R + R_o)$. For $t > 0$, the change in voltage

$$\frac{ER}{R + R_o} - E = -\frac{E R_o}{R + R_o}$$

travels down the line and is reflected without inversion ($\rho = +1$) at the end of the line. If $R = R_o$, the initial voltage is $E/2$ and the discontinuity $-E/2$ travels down the line, discharging it to half voltage as it progresses. We shall assume negligible attenuation in the line. At the end of the line the discontinuity $-E/2$ is reflected and it discharges the line to zero as it moves toward the beginning of the line. At $t = 2t_d$,

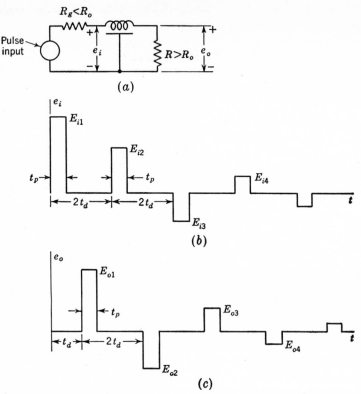

FIG. 10-20. (a) A pulse applied to a line. (b, c) The voltage waveforms at the input and output of the line, respectively.

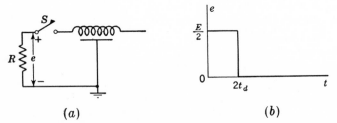

FIG. 10-21. (a) A charged line discharged through R when switch S is closed. (b) The output across R is a pulse if $R = R_o$.

the line is completed discharged. The resultant output across R is a pulse of amplitude $E/2$ and duration $2t_d$, as indicated in Fig. 10-21b. If a mercury relay or a thyratron is used for the switch S, a discharge-line-type pulse generator[12] results which delivers pulses having rise times of the order of 1 to 10 mμsec. The polarity and amplitude of the pulse depend upon the charging voltage, and the pulse width is determined by the line length.

If the resistance R does not equal R_o, then there will be multiple reflections from each end of the line. The voltage across R for the two special cases $R = 3R_o(\rho = +\frac{1}{2})$ and $R = \frac{1}{3}R_o(\rho = -\frac{1}{2})$ are indicated in Fig. 10-22.

A charged line may be used as a *pulse stretcher*.[13] Consider, for example, a constant-k line shorted at the input end and open-circuited

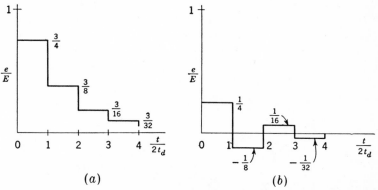

(a)   (b)

FIG. 10-22. The voltage across R in Fig. 10-21 if (a) $R = 3R_o$, (b) $R = \frac{1}{3}R_o$.

at the output end. Each capacitor is charged simultaneously from an input pulse through a cathode follower and buffer diodes. At the trailing edge of the input pulse the line starts to discharge, but the output will remain constant for a time t_d. Hence, the input width t_p has been *stretched* to t_d.

10-4. Delay-line Control of a Blocking Oscillator.[14]

An example of a shorted line used to control the pulse width of a blocking oscillator is given in Fig. 10-23. When the blocking oscillator is triggered, a positive step is generated at the input to the line. This discontinuity upon reaching the shorted end is reversed in polarity. When this reflected wave reaches the input to the line, the positive step at the plate of the tube starts the regenerative action which terminates the blocking oscillator pulse. The width of the pulse will be $2t_d$, provided that the "natural" width, as determined by the

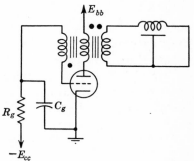

FIG. 10-23. A delay line in the plate circuit used to determine the pulse width of a blocking oscillator.

transformer magnetizing inductance, the capacitance C_g, and the tube characteristics, is greater than $2t_d$.

An alternative method of controlling the pulse width is to use an open-circuited line in the grid circuit in place of C_g, as indicated in Fig. 10-24a.

When the blocking oscillator is triggered, the grid current component I_g' which passes through R_g gives a negative voltage step $-I_g'R_g$ which travels down the line. At the open end of the line this discontinuity is reflected without change of sign, and when it reaches the input of the line again (at $t = 2t_d$) the line voltage will become $-2I_g'R_g$ (if attenuation is neglected). This additional negative voltage at the grid of the tube may be sufficient to initiate the regenerative action which terminates the pulse. The line will then discharge in a staircase manner to zero, as in Fig. 10-22a. The line waveshape is shown in Fig. 10-24b.

Delay lines may also be used to control the repetition rate in a blocking oscillator. For example, consider that the delay line in Fig. 10-23 is

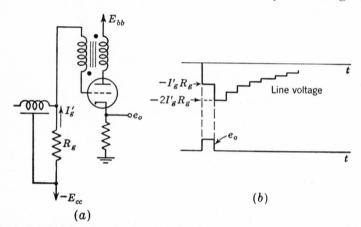

(a)   (b)

FIG. 10-24. (a) A delay line in the grid circuit used to control the pulse width of a blocking oscillator. (b) The line voltage and the output pulse.

open-circuited instead of short-circuited and that $2t_d$ is now longer than the "natural" width of the blocking-oscillator pulse. If the circuit is triggered once, it will thereafter continue to deliver pulses separated by an interval $2t_d$. This behavior is a result of the fact that the negative plate pulse travels down the line, is reflected without inversion from the open end, and retriggers the oscillator when it again reaches the plate end of the line.

A similar action to that just described is obtained from the circuit of Fig. 10-24 if the line in the grid circuit is shorted. Again we must use a line for which $2t_d$ is longer than the "natural" pulse width. If the circuit is triggered once, then the negative pulse at the input to the line (see Fig. 10-24b) travels down the line, is inverted at the shorted end, and hence reaches the grid as a positive pulse. This positive pulse retriggers the oscillator.

An alternative arrangement for delay-line control of repetition rate is indicated in Fig. 10-25. The tube T_1 is normally biased beyond cutoff by the $R_1 - R_2$ divider. The capacitor C is a large blocking capacitor. The line is terminated in its characteristic impedance. Once the circuit is triggered, the positive pulse generated at the cathode travels down the line and is applied at a time t_d to the blocking oscillator grid through the cathode follower T_2. This pulse retriggers the oscillator and a train of pulses separated by an interval t_d is obtained.

It is possible to use two delay lines with a blocking oscillator so as to combine the two actions described above and hence to control simultaneously both the pulse width and the pulse spacing.

A finite train of pulses may be obtained from a blocking oscillator for each triggering pulse as follows.[15] The oscillator tube of one of the circuits discussed above (for example, T_1 of Fig. 10-25) is now a pentode with its suppressor grid biased beyond cutoff. The input trigger generates a gate (say, by means of a monostable multi) which effectively removes the suppressor bias and thereby allows the blocking oscillator to deliver a train of pulses.

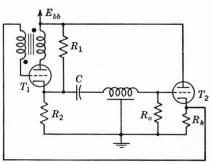

FIG. 10-25. Delay-line control of repetition rate.

At the end of the gate the suppressor voltage returns to its negative value and the oscillator is again quiescent. The result of this action is that each input trigger causes some number n (perhaps three or four) of equally spaced pulses to be obtained.

Timing markers for a scope may be obtained from the circuit just described. The signal which starts the sweep also triggers the blocking oscillator and hence delivers a train of accurately spaced pulses synchronous with the sweep. These pulses are used to intensify the trace and serve as timing markers.

Delay lines may also be used to control the gate width of a monostable multi in a manner similar to that described above. The gate width cannot be made too large, however, because an impractically long delay line would be required.

10-5. Pulse Coders.[16] Pulse-type waveforms may be distinguished from one another by some distinctive feature, called a *code*. A single pulse code consists of using, in the system under consideration, pulses of various *widths* or *amplitudes*. A multiple-pulse code may be constructed in many ways. For example, a train of equally spaced pulses may be characterized by the *number* of pulses in the group. Alternatively, the code may consist of a fixed number of pulses in the train, the distinguishing feature now being the *spacing* or *grouping* of the pulses. Digital computers (see Chap. 13) use a code which consists of a pulse train in which both the number and spacing of pulses is significant (although the spacing is always a multiple of some fixed interval). More complicated codes may be constructed by allowing all four parameters (width, amplitude, number, and spacing) to be adjustable. A pulse code can carry information or give instructions to various portions of a system. Hence, coding is useful in communications, in television, in computation, in radar identification (say, of friendly from enemy aircraft), in aerial navigation, etc.

The generation of a pulse code will now be considered. Methods for adjusting pulse amplitude are evident. Pulse width is controlled by the length of a delay line for narrow widths or by using a delay multi or a phantastron for longer durations. A circuit for obtaining a number of

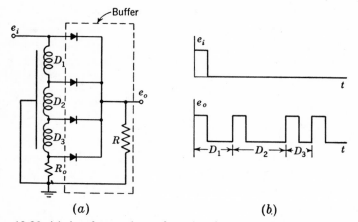

FIG. 10-26. (a) A pulse-spacing coder using delay lines; (b) the waveforms.

equally spaced pulses was discussed in Sec. 10-4. A circuit for producing a group of unequally spaced pulses is indicated in Fig. 10-26a. The delay line terminated in its characteristic impedance is tapped at delay times D_1, $D_1 + D_2$, and at the end of the line where the delay is $D_1 + D_2 + D_3$. The diodes constitute a *buffer* or *OR* circuit (discussed in detail in Sec. 13-2) which prevents interaction between pulses. The output is a four-pulse code, as indicated in Fig. 10-26b.

When the timing intervals required are longer than the spacing for which delay lines are practicable, delay multivibrators (or phantastrons) may be employed. One such circuit is shown in Fig. 10-27a. The trailing edge of each multi waveform is differentiated and the resultant spikes are reformed in the shaper (perhaps a blocking oscillator) to produce a pulse waveform not unlike the original pulse. The resultant pulses are combined in the buffer circuit to give the pulse train indicated in Fig. 10-27b.

The method of extending the circuits of Figs. 10-26 and 10-27 to any number of pulses is obvious. The type of coding used in digital computers is discussed in Chap. 13.

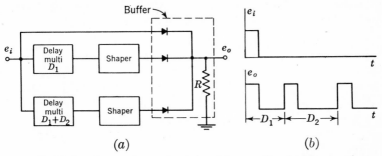

FIG. 10-27. (*a*) A pulse-spacing coder using delay multis; (*b*) the waveforms.

10-6. Pulse Decoders.[17] Circuits which respond to a particular code are called pulse decoders. We shall now discuss several decoder circuits.

Pulse-amplitude Decoders. A *comparator* (see Chap. 15) is a circuit which delivers an output pulse if the input exceeds a definite reference level E_R. Hence, a comparator is the basic element in a pulse amplitude decoder. The circuit of Fig. 10-28 will deliver an output if and only if the amplitude of the input pulse lies between two definite limits, say, E_1 and E_2 (with $E_2 > E_1$).
The first comparator delivers a pulse only if the input amplitude E exceeds the reference voltage $E_{R1} = E_1$, whereas the second comparator responds only if E exceeds the reference $E_{R2} = E_2$. The block marked *INHIBITOR* (discussed in Sec. 13-5) delivers an output if there is a

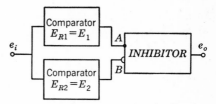

FIG. 10-28. A pulse-amplitude decoder.

pulse at input A, provided only that there is no pulse at input B. Hence, if $E_1 < E < E_2$, the circuit of Fig. 10-28 will deliver a pulse, which is the desired decoder action.

Pulse-width Decoders. An integrator-type decoder which will detect a pulse if its duration is greater than some specified minimum value t_m is illustrated in Fig. 10-29*a*. The basic elements used in this type of decoder are a time-base generator and a comparator. The pulse, negative in polarity, is applied to the grid of the sweep-forming tube T. This tube is thereby cut off and the voltage across C rises approximately linearly with time. The time constant RC and the supply voltage E_{bb} are adjusted so that the voltage across C will attain the comparator reference voltage E_R only if the pulse width t_p is at least equal to t_m. Typical waveforms are indicated in Fig. 10-29*b*.

A second type of pulse-width decoder, using as basic elements a delay line and a voltage selector, is illustrated in Fig. 10-30. The input pulse, positive in polarity, is applied to an open-circuited delay line. The line is terminated in its characteristic impedance R_o at its input end. The signal at the input of the line is connected to the grid of a tube which is

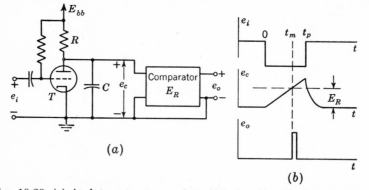

(a)

(b)

Fig. 10-29. (a) An integrator-type pulse-width decoder; (b) the waveforms.

biased beyond cutoff. This bias is made large enough so that the pulse which appears at the grid, at the instant the external signal is applied, is not large enough to bring the tube out of cutoff. The pulse will travel down the line, be reflected without inversion from the open end, and will return to the input after a time $2D$, where D is the one-way delay time of the line. If $2D$ is smaller than the pulse duration t_p, the reflected

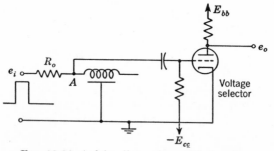

Fig. 10-30. A delay-line pulse-width decoder.

pulse will add at the input to the initial pulse. The voltage at the grid of the tube will rise to nominally twice its previous value, as indicated in the waveforms of Fig. 10-31. The bias on the tube may be adjusted so that this larger voltage is sufficient to cause conduction and an output signal results. On the other hand, if $2D > t_p$, no output will appear. The termination R_o at the input is required so that the pulse reflected from the open end of the line will not be again reflected from the sending end.   The output pulse may be used to trigger a regenerative device if a larger output signal is required.   Alternately, the biased tube may be replaced by a comparator whose reference level is set, say, midway between $E/2$ and E.

The basic principle of a circuit which will respond only to a pulse width t_p which lies between a specified minimum and a maximum value

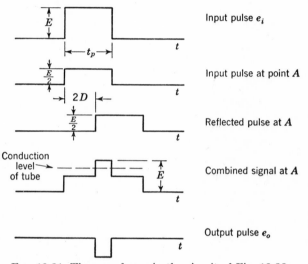

Input pulse e_i

Input pulse at point A

Reflected pulse at A

Combined signal at A

Output pulse e_o

FIG. 10-31. The waveforms in the circuit of Fig. 10-30.

is illustrated in Fig. 10-32.   Two delay lines and a comparator or voltage selector are required.   The two-way delay of the first line is $2D_1$ and of the second line is $2D_2$.   We shall now show that if $D_1 < D_2$, then the range of t_p which results in an output signal is $2D_2 + 2D_1 > t_p > 2D_2 - 2D_1$.   The buffer amplifier is required for isolation and phase inversion.   It is not necessary that the gain have a magnitude of 2, but

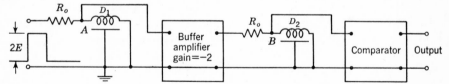

FIG. 10-32. A pulse decoder that responds to widths which are within a specified range.

it is convenient for the following discussion to assume that such is the case.

An input positive pulse of amplitude $2E$ appears at point A as a positive pulse of amplitude E.   Since the delay line is shorted, the reflected pulse which appears at A after a time interval $2D_1$ is negative.   These alternate positive and negative pulses are amplified by a factor of 2 and inverted. These pulses appear at B with amplitude E once again because of the attenuation which results from the terminating resistor R_o. The first pulse, now negative, reappears at B as a positive pulse delayed by a time $2D_2$. The second positive pulse, delayed $2D_1$ by the first line, reappears as a negative pulse with total delay $2D_1 + 2D_2$. Altogether at B there are four pulses whose polarities and delays are as indicated in Fig. 10-33. The pulse duration is t_p in every case, and each amplitude will be E if the amplifier gain is 2 and we neglect attenuation on the lines. The resultant waveform at B, and hence the comparator input, is to be determined by combining the waveforms in Fig. 10-33.

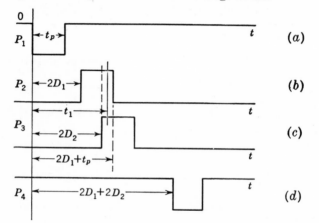

FIG. 10-33. The waveforms in the circuit of Fig. 10-32. (a) Original pulse at A (drawn inverted); also, the same pulse at B. (b) Reflected pulse of first line (drawn inverted); also the same pulse at B. (c) Reflection at B of P_1 in second line. (d) Reflection at B of P_2 in second line.

The comparator has its reference level set at a value more positive than $+E$. The input to the comparator will exceed E if there is a coincidence of the two positive pulses, provided that there is not simultaneously an overlapping of one or both of the negative pulses. For the circumstances indicated in Fig. 10-33, the voltage at B will be $2E$ for the time interval from $2D_2$ to $2D_1 + t_p$. In general, the limits on t_p are arrived at as follows. In order that there shall be at least an overlapping of P_2 and P_3, it is required that P_3 begin before P_2 ends, which means $2D_1 + t_p > 2D_2$ or $t_p > 2D_2 - 2D_1$. Furthermore, there must exist an instant of time t_1, at which a coincidence of P_2 and P_3 occurs, when simultaneously P_1 and P_4 are both zero. From Fig. 10-33 we see that this time t_1 must then satisfy the inequalities $t_1 > t_p$ and $t_1 < 2D_1 + 2D_2$. It follows from the elimination of t_1 from these inequalities that $t_p < 2D_2 + 2D_1$. These considerations verify the statement made at the beginning of this discussion that the decoder responds to pulse widths in the range $2D_2 + 2D_1 > t_p > 2D_2 - 2D_1$.

We have considered above only the simple case where the pulses have arbitrarily sharp rises and falls. In the more practical case of pulses with finite rise times, the condition of coincidence or failure to overlap will not be so sharply defined and the acceptable range for t_p will be somewhat smaller than indicated above.

The principal advantage of delay-line decoders lies in the fact that the timing is determined entirely by passive delay lines which therefore rarely require adjustment. Delay lines to provide delays in excess of 10 μsec, however, become inconveniently bulky. Where longer timing intervals are required and ease of changing the timing intervals is important, integrator-type decoders are more suitable. The integrator type has the additional advantage of being less influenced by noise that may accompany the signal. In the circuit of Fig. 10-30, for example, a short sharp

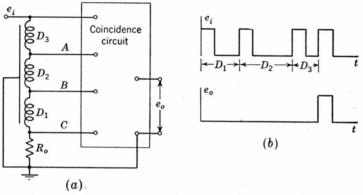

FIG. 10-34. (a) A multiple-pulse decoder; (b) the waveforms.

positive spike of noise added to the signal might easily cause the decoder to respond even when the input signal pulse is very much shorter than that for which the decoder is adjusted. However, in Fig. 10-29 the same noise spike could produce only a very small error.

Pulse Group Decoders. The pulse coder of Fig. 10-26 may be used as a decoder if the buffer block is replaced by a *coincidence* circuit, as indicated in Fig. 10-34a. Coincidence or *AND* circuits are discussed in Sec. 13-3. As the name implies, a coincidence circuit delivers an output if and only if there is a pulse at *all* its inputs simultaneously. Assume that the input train is the four-pulse system of Fig. 10-34b. It is clear that, when the first pulse appears at C, the second pulse is at B, the third is at A, and the fourth is at the input to the line. Hence, the coincidence circuit will deliver an output at this instant. If the delay-line taps D_1, D_2, and D_3 do not match the pulse spacing of the train, no output is obtained. Note that the series of delay lines in the decoder of Fig. 10-34 are connected in the reverse order from those in the coder of Fig. 10-26.

The line is terminated in its characteristic impedance so that reflections are prevented.

An alternative multiple-pulse decoder is shown in Fig. 10-35. Again let us consider that the waveform to be decoded is the one indicated in Fig. 10-34b. In the present case the delay line L_1 is adjusted so that the interval D_1 between the first and second pulse is equal to the time required for a signal to travel from the input of the line to the short-circuited termination and back to the tap. The timing of L_2 and L_3 are similarly arranged to correspond to times D_2 and D_3, respectively. The input pulses are of negative polarity and are applied simultaneously to the cathodes of all tubes. The grid bias is, however, sufficiently large to prevent conduction of the tubes. The first negative pulse travels down

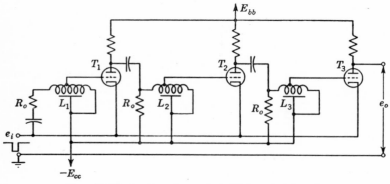

Fig. 10-35. Another form of multiple-pulse decoder.

the line L_1, where it is reflected and reappears at the tap on L_1 as a positive pulse. This positive pulse appears at the grid at the time the second negative pulse appears at the cathode. The combined effect of both pulses is to overcome the bias and to cause a negative pulse to appear at the plate of the tube. Thus the amplifier behaves as a coincidence circuit which delivers a pulse to L_2 only if the spacing between the first two pulses is correct. If the spacing between the second and third pulse is correct, then the pulse which was delivered to L_2 combines with the third pulse to give an output pulse at the plate of the second tube, and so on. Each of the delay lines is matched at its input end to avoid multiple reflections.

The circuit of Fig. 10-35 is more complex than that of Fig. 10-34 but the former has two advantages over the latter. In the first place, the amplification between the various sections of the delay makes up for the attenuation on the lines. Second, the lines themselves are used more economically since we have taken advantage of the additional delay time required for the pulse to return from the shorted end to the tap. The delay time between the input and the tap need only be somewhat larger than the pulse duration itself in order to prevent the reflected positive pulse from being canceled by the next input negative pulse.

When the timing intervals required in decoders are large, then delay multis are used in place of delay lines. The circuit is similar to that given in Fig. 10-27 for the multivibrator-type coder except that a coincidence circuit is used in place of the buffer circuit. Since the circuit is used because long time intervals are employed, it has the disadvantage of not being able to respond to a second train of pulses until the first has passed. This difficulty may be remedied by replacing each delay multi by several cascaded multis whose total delay is the required delay. In this case the first multi may well respond to the first pulse of a second train, while the cascaded multis are still delaying the first pulse of the first train.

It must not be imagined that the decoders described above are capable of distinguishing one acceptable signal from all other possible signals. As a matter of fact the decoder, say, of Fig. 10-34 would respond equally well to a single pulse whose duration is $D_1 + D_2 + D_3$. We would not find it difficult to invent an arbitrary number of acceptable "false" signals for any of the decoders described above. Still, the ability to distinguish one from a large number of available signals is an asset of considerable importance.

10-7. Distributed Amplifiers. Lumped-circuit delay lines are essential elements in a type of pulse amplifier which is referred to as a *distributed amplifier*. Distributed amplifiers will provide worthwhile gain over a bandwidth which exceeds appreciably the bandwidth attainable with conventional amplifiers.

In a conventional uncompensated amplifier stage, increased bandwidth may be achieved only at the expense of gain. When the stage gain has been reduced to unity or less, the stage is no longer useful for the purpose of *amplification*. Furthermore, since the gain of a number of stages in cascade is the product of the individual gains, no advantage accrues from cascading such stages of unity gain or less. To pursue the matter further, let us compute approximately the relationship between the gain, the bandwidth, and the number of stages in a conventional uncompensated amplifier. The gain of n stages is

$$A = (g_m R_L)^n \tag{10-30}$$

in which g_m is the transconductance and R_L the plate-circuit resistor of a stage. In Sec. 3-8 we saw that the result of cascading n amplifiers was to decrease the bandwidth approximately by the factor $\sqrt{n}$. The upper 3-db frequency of an n-stage amplifier is therefore approximately

$$f_2 = \frac{1}{2\pi R_L C_s \sqrt{n}} \tag{10-31}$$

in which C_s is the sum of the input and output capacitance in a stage. The *figure of merit* F of a tube may be defined as the product of gain and band-width and is given by

$$F = \frac{g_m}{2\pi C_s} \tag{10-32}$$

From Eqs. (10-30) to (10-32) we have

$$f_2 A^{1/n} \sqrt{n} = F \tag{10-33}$$

Now as an example of the limitations of the bandwidth capabilities of a conventional amplifier let us compute the bandwidth possible in an amplifier where the gain is required to be, say, $\epsilon^2 = (2.72)^2 = 7.4$. We shall use the type 6AK5 vacuum tube (see Table 3-1) for which the sum of the input and output capacitance is 6.8 $\mu\mu f$. We shall assume (unrealistically) that we may neglect all additional stray capacitance. The figure of merit $F = (5.1 \times 10^{-3})/(2\pi \times 6.8 \times 10^{-12}) = 120 \times 10^6$ sec^{-1}. We may compute from Eq. (10-33) that f_2 will be a maximum for a given value of gain if

$$n = 2 \ln A \tag{10-34}$$

For a gain $A = \epsilon^2$, $n = 4$ and, from Eq. (10-33), we have $f_2 = 36.4$ Mc. We have the result, then, that even using a tube of high figure of merit and assuming that every conceivable precaution is taken to reduce shunt capacitance, it is not possible to build a conventional amplifier of gain 7.4 with a bandwidth in excess of 36.4 Mc. This situation may, of course, be remedied somewhat by the use of some form of high-frequency compensation. But, as we noted in Chap. 3, a really worthwhile improvement in bandpass is achieved only with a circuit of considerable complexity with its attendant difficulties of adjustment, particularly in a multistage amplifier.

The basic limitation of the conventional cascade of amplifier stages is overcome by combining amplifier tubes in the manner indicated in Fig. 10-36. Such an arrangement is called a *distributed amplifier*.[10,18] The capacitances C_g and C_p represent, respectively, the input and output capacitances of the tubes together with the stray capacitances. A signal applied at the input travels down the grid transmission line, reaches each grid in turn, and is finally absorbed in the matched termination. Each pentode delivers current to the plate line which is matched at both ends. One-half the tube current flows to each plate-line termination. The delay per section of the plate and grid lines are adjusted to be identical. Then all the current which reaches the plate-line output termination, in response to a given input voltage, will arrive at this termination at the same time. If the characteristic impedance of the plate line is

R_{op}, then it follows that the gain of an amplifier having n sections is

$$A = \tfrac{1}{2} n g_m R_{op} \qquad (10\text{-}35)$$

The upper frequency limit of the amplifier may be considered to be determined essentially by the cutoff frequency of the delay lines. The cutoff frequencies of the plate and grid lines are the same since the delay per section is the same for both lines.

We may observe the following distinctive features. The gain of a distributed amplifier is computed by *adding* the gain provided by each tube individually. Hence, even if each tube provides a gain less than unity, the over-all gain still increases with increasing number of tubes. Further, since the cutoff frequency of a delay line is not a function of the

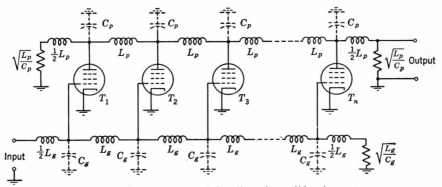

Fig. 10-36. A stage of distributed amplification.

number of sections, the upper frequency limit of the amplifier is not decreased as more tubes are added to increase the gain.

At low frequencies, where the reactances of the elements of the transmission lines are negligibly small, the amplifier of Fig. 10-36 may be viewed simply as n parallel pentodes feeding a plate load resistor $R_{op}/2$. Hence the gain is given again by Eq. (10-35). However, a simple parallel connection of n tubes would not serve a useful purpose, since in such a case the effective g_m and shunt capacitance would increase in the same proportion. The figure of merit F for a parallel combination of tubes is the same as for a single tube. The distributed amplifier arrangement, however, effectively parallels the tubes so far as transconductance is concerned, but manages to keep the capacitances separate.

The delay lines indicated in Fig. 10-36 are constructed of prototype sections and the terminations are simple resistors. Actually, of course, any of the other types of lines described earlier may be used instead, and better terminations may be used to advantage. Any improvement of the delay lines will improve the performance of the amplifier.

10-8. Distributed Amplifiers in Cascade. In Fig. 10-36 each tube with its portion of transmission line is called a *section*. The combination of n such sections is called a *stage*. Distributed amplifier stages may be cascaded in the conventional sense. Suppose that we consider a cascade of m such stages. Then the total number of tubes involved in such an amplifier is $N = nm$. We may now show that, for a given number N of tubes and for a fixed gain, there is an optimum arrangement of tubes which yields a maximum bandwidth.

When stages are cascaded, the output end of the plate line of one amplifier must be coupled into the input end of the grid line of the succeeding amplifier. Since generally the plate and grid lines will have different characteristic impedances, an impedance transformer must be interposed between the lines. An impedance transforming device which matches the grid-line impedance R_{og} to the plate impedance will simultaneously produce a voltage transformation in the ratio $(R_{og}/R_{op})^{1/2}$. Thus, from Eq. (10-35), we have the result that the gain from one grid line to the next is

$$A = \frac{ng_m}{2} R_{op} \sqrt{\frac{R_{og}}{R_{op}}} = \frac{ng_m}{2} \sqrt{R_{op}R_{og}} \tag{10-36}$$

Using Eq. (10-8), using $R_{op} = \sqrt{L_p/C_p}$, $R_{og} = \sqrt{L_g/C_g}$, and taking into account that $L_pC_p = L_gC_g$ (since the delay per section of the plate and grid lines are the same), we have

$$A = \frac{n}{f_c} \frac{g_m}{2\pi \sqrt{C_pC_g}} = \frac{nF'}{f_c} \tag{10-37}$$

Here we have introduced

$$F' \equiv \frac{g_m}{2\pi \sqrt{C_pC_g}} \tag{10-38}$$

as a figure of merit for the tubes which is more appropriate in the present instance than the figure of merit in Eq. (10-32). The gain of m stages is $G = A^m$. Replacing A by $G^{1/m}$ in Eq. (10-37) and solving for n, we have

$$n = \frac{f_c}{F'} G^{1/m} \tag{10-39}$$

and

$$N = nm = m \frac{f_c}{F'} G^{1/m} \tag{10-40}$$

For a given bandpass f_c and a given gain G we can find the minimum number of tubes by setting the derivative $dN/dm = 0$ in Eq. (10-40). The result is that N is a minimum when

$$m = \ln G \tag{10-41}$$

From Eqs. (10-39) and (10-41), we now find that

$$n = \frac{f_c}{F'} \epsilon \tag{10-42}$$

and $$A = \epsilon \tag{10-43}$$

in which $\epsilon = 2.72$. Hence the tubes are used in the optimum fashion when each stage produces a gain ϵ corresponding to 8.68 db.

Similarly, for a given number of tubes N and a given gain G we can find the maximum bandpass by setting $df_c/dm = 0$ in Eq. (10-40). For this situation we find that Eqs. (10-41) to (10-43) are also valid.

For the 6AK5 vacuum tube, the figure of merit F' is (see Table 3-1)

$$F' = \frac{5.1 \times 10^{-3}}{2\pi \sqrt{4 \times 2.8 \times 10^{-12}}} = 242 \times 10^6 \ \text{sec}^{-1}$$

From Eq. (10-42), we may calculate that for $n = 2, f_c = 177$ Mc. Hence four tubes arranged in two cascaded stages of distributed amplification will yield a gain of ϵ^2 over a frequency range up to 177 Mc. This situation is to be compared with the case discussed in Sec. 10-7 where it is shown that in a conventional amplifier the bandwidth for comparable gain was only 36.4 Mc.

10-9. Practical Considerations in Distributed Amplifiers. The discussion, so far, of distributed amplifiers has been unrealistic in that it has been assumed that the frequency range of the amplifier is limited only by the cutoff frequency of the delay lines. The fact is, however, that as the frequency increases, the impedance seen looking into the grid of the tubes exhibits not only a capacitative reactance but a resistive loading as well. The resistive loading at the grid has two sources. The first of these is due to the presence of inductance in the cathode-to-ground lead of the tube. The presence of such a cathode lead inductance results in a conductive component of admittance at the grid. For this reason, good construction practice requires that the cathode connection to ground be made as short and direct as possible. But, of course, some residual conductive component at the grid will always remain.

A second and much more important source of conductive loading at the grid results from effects due to the finite time of transit of an electron across the tube. For a sinusoidal signal, the loading due to transit time effects[19] begins to make itself felt when the period of the signal becomes small enough to be comparable to the transit time. Each of these components of conductance at the grid is proportional to the square of the frequency. The severity of this loading with increasing frequency may be noted by observing that at 400 Mc the input resistance of a 6AK5 is only 250 ohms.

An example of a stage of distributed amplification[20] is shown in Fig. 10-37. The plate and grid lines are constructed of prototype sections. They are terminated in m-derived half sections ($m = 0.6$) which serve to improve the match between the lines and the terminating resistors. The lines are designed to have a cutoff frequency of 400 Mc. The grid line has a characteristic impedance of 50 ohms. This low impedance has

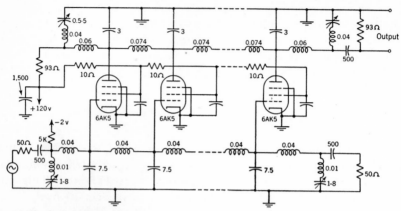

Fig. 10-37. A practical form of a distributed amplifier. Inductances are given in microhenrys, and capacitances in micromicrofarads.

been selected to minimize the effect of the loading of the grid line due to transit time effects. The general formulas

$$R_o = \sqrt{\frac{L}{C}} \quad \text{and} \quad f_c = \frac{1}{\pi \sqrt{LC}}$$

may be solved for L and C with the result

$$L = \frac{R_o}{\pi f_c} \tag{10-44}$$

$$C = \frac{1}{\pi R_o f_c} \tag{10-45}$$

The inductance per section of the grid line is calculated from Eq. (10-44) with the result $L_g = 0.04$ μh. The grid-line capacitance is calculated from Eq. (10-45) with the result $C_g = 16$ $\mu\mu$f. After the 6AK5 input capacitance, the tube-socket capacitance, and other stray capacitance have been taken into account, it is found that an additional 7.5 $\mu\mu$f must be added in the grid circuit to bring the total to the required 16 $\mu\mu$f.

It is advantageous to make the impedance of the plate line as large as possible since the amplifier gain increases with plate-line impedance. The impedance would be a maximum if the capacitance per section were kept at a minimum. Actually 3 $\mu\mu$f of capacitance has been added to each section of the line to bring the line impedance down to 93 ohms. A 93-ohm impedance is particularly convenient since there is available a commercial coaxial cable (RG-62/U) whose impedance is 93 ohms.

The amplifier uses a total of nine 6AK5 tubes. The transit-time loading of the grid line is therefore quite heavy and actually the signal level on the grid line falls appreciably as the upper frequency limit of the amplifier is approached. This effect, however, is counterbalanced by the fact that the impedance of the plate line (as viewed at the point where the tube plates are connected) increases substantially as the line cutoff frequency is approached. The result is that the gain remains reasonably uniform up to a frequency nearly equal to the cutoff frequency. The frequency response of the amplifier of Fig. 10-37 is given in Fig. 10-38. A number of other practical designs of distributed amplifiers are to be found in the literature.[21]

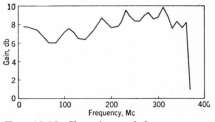

Fig. 10-38. Experimental frequency response of amplifier of Fig. 10-37.

REFERENCES

1. Blackburn, J. F. (ed.): "Components Handbook," Massachusetts Institute of Technology Radiation Laboratory Series, vol. 17, sec. 1-12 and chap. 6, McGraw-Hill Book Company, Inc., 1949.
   Kallmann, H. E.: High-impedance Cable, *Proc. IRE*, vol. 34, pp. 348–351, June, 1946.
   Anderson, J. R.: Electrical Delay Lines for Digital Computer Applications, *Trans. IRE (Professional Group on Electronic Computers)*, vol. EC-2, no. 2, pp. 5–13, June, 1953.
2. Ryder, J. D.: "Networks, Lines and Fields," Prentice-Hall, Inc., New York, 1949.
   Johnson, W. C.: "Transmission Lines and Networks," McGraw-Hill Book Company, Inc., New York, 1950.
3. Stein, D. R.: Magnetic-core Delay Cables, *Convention Paper IRE*, 1954.
4. Blewett, J. P., and J. H. Rubel: Video Delay Lines, *Proc. IRE*, vol. 35, pp. 1580–1584, December, 1947.
5. Carley, W. J.: Multilayer Distributed Constant Delay Lines, *Tele-Tech*, vol. 13, no. 5, pp. 74–76, 100–102, May, 1954.
6. Trevor, J. B.: Artificial Delay-line Design, *Electronics*, vol. 18, pp. 135–137, June, 1945.
7. Elmore, W. C., and M. Sands: "Electronics," p. 39, McGraw-Hill Book Company, Inc., New York, 1949.
8. Ref. 1, p. 211.
9. Wallis, C. M.: Design of Low-frequency Constant Time Delay Lines, *Trans. AIEE*, pt. I, vol. 71, pp. 135–139, 1952.
10. Ginston, E. L., W. R. Hewlett, J. H. Jasberg, and J. D. Noe: Distributed Amplification, *Proc. IRE*, vol. 36, pp. 956–969, August, 1948.
11. Johnson, ref. 2, chap. 1.

12. Lewis, I. A. D., and F. H. Wells: "Millimicrosecond Pulse Techniques," chap. 4, McGraw-Hill Book Company, Inc., New York, 1954.
13. Craib, J. F.: Improved Pulse Stretcher, *Electronics*, vol. 24, no. 6, pp. 129–131, June, 1951.
14. Benjamin, R.: Blocking Oscillators, *J. IEE*, vol. 93, pt. IIIA, no. 7, pp. 1159–1175, 1946.
15. Jensen, G. D.: Gated Marker Generator, *Electronics*, vol. 27, p. 177, April, 1954. Chance, B., et al.: "Waveforms," Massachusetts Institute of Technology Radiation Laboratory Series, vol. 19, p. 250, McGraw-Hill Book Company, Inc., New York, 1949.
16. Roberts, A.: "Radar Beacons," Massachusetts Institute of Technology Radiation Laboratory Series, vol. 3, chap. 10, McGraw-Hill Book Company, Inc., New York, 1947.
    Blake, R. F.: Pulse Group Coding and Decoding by Passive Networks, *Proc. Natl. Electronics Conf.*, vol. 8, pp. 760–765, 1952.
17. Ref. 16, chap. 9.
18. Ref. 12, chap. 5.
    Horton, W. H., J. H. Jasberg, and J. D. Noe: Distributed Amplifiers: Practical Considerations and Experimental Results, *Proc. IRE*, vol. 38, pp. 748–753, July, 1950.
19. Spangenberg, K. R.: "Vacuum Tubes," chap. 16, McGraw-Hill Book Company, Inc., New York, 1948.
20. Scharfman, H.: Distributed Amplifier Covers 10 to 360 MC, *Electronics*, vol. 25, pp. 113–115, July, 1952.
21. Cormack, A.: Distributed Amplification, *Electronic Eng.*, vol. 24, pp. 144–147, April, 1952.
    Copson, A. P.: A Distributed Power Amplifier, *Elec. Eng.*, vol. 69, pp. 893–898, October, 1950.

CHAPTER 11

COUNTING

In this chapter we shall discuss circuits which are used for the purpose of counting pulses. A number of important applications of the counting process will be described.

11-1. The Binary Chain as a Divider. Consider the cascade of four binaries as shown in Fig. 11-1a. Such an arrangement is called a *binary chain*. A sequence of triggering pulses is applied in a symmetrical fashion to the first binary labeled B_0. The output signal of the first binary

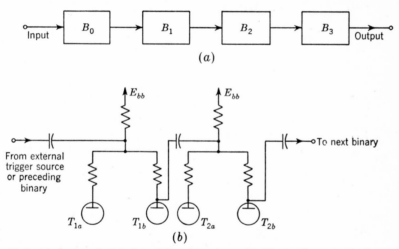

FIG. 11-1. (a) A cascade (chain) of four binaries. (b) Illustrating a typical coupling connection.

(which is the signal that appears at one of the plates) is in turn applied symmetrically to the second binary B_1. Similarly, B_1 is coupled to B_2 and B_2 to B_3. A typical coupling arrangement is indicated in Fig. 11-1b. Here the symmetrical triggering scheme of Fig. 5-15 has been employed. Of course, many other symmetrical triggering circuits may be used, including diode triggering, as in Fig. 5-14.

We shall now show that the binary chain of Fig. 11-1 may be used to *divide* the number of input pulses by a factor of 16. That is to say that

323

each time 16 pulses are applied at the input, 1 pulse appears at the output.

Each of the binaries has two stable states. Let us designate one of the states by the numeral 0 and the other state by the numeral 1. The aptness of this designation will appear shortly. The binaries under consideration are two-tube devices and the section from which the output is obtained is called the *output tube*. Let us arbitrarily agree that state 0 is the one in which current is flowing in the output tube and, hence, its plate voltage is low. Then the state 1 is the state in which the output tube is cut off and the voltage at the output plate is nominally equal to the supply voltage. Finally, let us take as our initial or reference state of the combination of the binaries the one in which all four individual binaries are in the state 0. Starting from this reference state, the waveforms which appear at the output plates of the binaries as a result of the

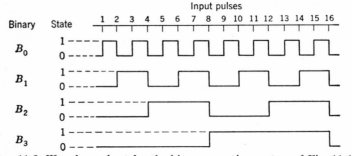

FIG. 11-2. Waveform chart for the binary counting system of Fig. 11-1.

application of 16 successive input pulses is shown in Fig. 11-2. In the state 0 the output plate voltage is low and therefore the output signal is represented by the lower level. In the state 1 the output plate voltage is high and this state is represented by the higher level.

Before the application of the first input pulse all binaries are in the state 0. The first external pulse applied to the first binary B_0 causes this binary to make a transition from state 0 to state 1. Referring to Fig. 11-1, we see that as a result of this transition a *positive* step is applied symmetrically through a capacitor to the second binary B_1. It will be recalled (Sec. 5-9) that the present method of triggering makes the binary relatively insensitive to a positive step. The second binary will therefore not respond to the positive step produced by the first binary. The over-all result is that binary B_0 has changed to state 1, while the other binaries remain in state 0, as indicated in Fig. 11-2.

The second externally applied pulse causes binary B_0 to return from state 1 to state 0. Binary B_1 now receives a negative step voltage to which the binary is sensitive and responds by making a transition from state 0 to 1. The binary B_2 does not respond to the transition in binary

B_1 because binary B_2 receives a positive step. The over-all result of the application of two input pulses is that binary B_1 is in state 1 while all other binaries are in state 0. We may similarly verify that the remainder of the *waveform chart* of Fig. 11-2 is correct by applying the following principles:

1. Binary B_0 makes a transition at each externally applied pulse.
2. Each of the other binaries makes a transition when and **only when** the preceding binary makes a transition from state 1 to state 0.

If we should differentiate each of the waveforms of Fig. 11-2, a positive pulse would appear at each transition from 0 to 1 and a negative pulse at each transition from 1 to 0. If now we count only the negative pulses (the positive pulses may be eliminated by the use of a nonlinear device such as a diode), then it appears that each binary divides by 2 the number of negative pulses which are applied to it. The four binaries together accomplish a division by a factor of $2^4 = 16$. A single negative pulse will appear at the output for each 16 pulses applied at the input. It should be clear that if n binaries are used, division by the factor 2^n will be achieved.

11-2. The Binary Chain as a Counter. The binary chain of Fig. 11-1 also constitutes a *scale-of*-16 *counter*. The circuit has 16 possible different states and at the occasion of each input pulse the circuit will make a transition progressively from state to state. After 16 pulses the circuit will reset itself into its original state. These features are easily recognized from the waveform chart of Fig. 11-2. The counting mechanism of the chain is intimately associated with the *binary system* of representing numbers, and we shall therefore discuss briefly this method of representation.

In the more familiar *decimal system* the base is 10, and ten numerals, 0, 1, 2, 3, . . . , 9, are required to express an arbitrary number. To write numbers larger than 9, we assign a meaning to the *position* of a numeral in an array of numerals. For example, the number 1,264 (one-thousand, two-hundred sixty-four) has the meaning

$$1{,}264 = 1 \times 10^3 + 2 \times 10^2 + 6 \times 10^1 + 4 \times 10^0 \tag{11-1}$$

Thus the individual digits in a number represent the coefficients in an expansion of the number in powers of ten. The digit which is furthest to the right is the coefficient of the zeroth power, the next is the coefficient of the first power, and so on.

In the *binary system* of representation the base is 2 and only the two numerals 0 and 1 are required to represent a number. In the binary system the numerals 0 and 1 have the same meaning as in the decimal system but a different interpretation is placed on the position occupied by a digit. In the binary system the individual digits represent the coefficients of powers of *two* rather than *ten* as in the decimal system. For example, the number *thirteen* is written in the binary representation as 1101 since

$$1101 = 1 \times 2^3 + 1 \times 2^2 + 0 \times 2^1 + 1 \times 2^0$$
$$= 8 \qquad + 4 \qquad + 0 \qquad + 1 \qquad = 13 \qquad (11\text{-}2)$$

A short list of equivalent numbers in decimal and binary notation is given in Table 11-1.

Now let us return to a consideration of the binary chain in connection with which we have prepared Table 11-2, which lists the states of all the binaries of our chain of four as a function of the number of externally applied input pulses. Table 11-2 may be verified directly by comparison with the waveform chart of Fig. 11-2. Note that in Table 11-2 the binaries have been ordered in the reverse direction from their order in Fig. 11-1.

TABLE 11-1. EQUIVALENT NUMBERS IN DECIMAL AND BINARY NOTATION

Decimal notation	Binary notation
0	00000
1	00001
2	00010
3	00011
4	00100
5	00101
6	00110
7	00111
8	01000
9	01001
10	01010
11	01011
12	01100
13	01101
14	01110
15	01111
16	10000
17	10001

TABLE 11-2. STATES OF THE BINARIES

No. of input pulses	State of binary			
	B_3	B_2	B_1	B_0
0	0	0	0	0
1	0	0	0	1
2	0	0	1	0
3	0	0	1	1
4	0	1	0	0
5	0	1	0	1
6	0	1	1	0
7	0	1	1	1
8	1	0	0	0
9	1	0	0	1
10	1	0	1	0
11	1	0	1	1
12	1	1	0	0
13	1	1	0	1
14	1	1	1	0
15	1	1	1	1
16	0	0	0	0
17	0	0	0	1

Comparing now Tables 11-2 and 11-1, we observe that the ordered array of the numerals 0 and 1 which represent the binary states gives precisely the binary representation of the number of applied input pulses. The state of the binary B_k is the coefficient of 2^k in the binary representation of the number of input pulses. This, then, is the sense in which the binary chain is said to count in the binary system. This feature gives added appropriateness to the designation *binary* which is used to refer to the bistable multivibrator. It is clear that the scale of a binary chain may be extended indefinitely by adding more binaries. A chain of n binaries will form a scale-of-2^n counter.

To read the count of a binary chain, it is necessary to determine the state of each individual binary in the chain. A very rudimentary voltmeter may be used for this purpose since we require to know only whether the output plate voltage is low (state 0) or high (state 1). A simple arrangement for this purpose uses a small neon bulb ($\frac{1}{25}$ watt) connected in series with a resistor between the output plate and some point of fixed potential, say ground. When the output plate is low, the voltage across the neon tube is not enough to cause a glow, but the neon tube will light up when the output plate is high. The neon bulbs connected to binaries B_0, B_1, B_2, and B_3 are labeled 1, 2, 4, and 8, respectively. To determine the count, it is then only necessary to add the numbers associated with those neon bulbs which are lit.

11-3. Counting to a Base Other than 2. An individual binary counts to the base two because it has two stable states. A device with r stable state will obviously be suitable for use in a counting system with a base r. We may, if we please, consider as a single unit a chain of two binaries. Such a two-binary chain has four stable states and may therefore serve as a system which counts to the base 4. It is similarly a trivial matter to construct a counting system with any base which is a power of 2. However, the requirement often arises for a counter whose base is not a power of 2. For example, we may prefer to count in the decimal system since this is the system with which we are most familiar. The scale of a binary chain counter may be changed in a variety of ways. The most common of these involves feedback of pulses from succeeding stages to preceding states of the chain. We shall now consider this method of scale changing.

In Fig. 11-3 the pairs of tubes T_1 through T_4 are the tubes of a chain of four binaries. In this schematic the cross-coupling connections from plates to grids as well as the cathode bypass capacitors have been omitted for simplicity. The signal at the output plate P_{4b} of the last binary is differentiated by the coupling network composed of R and C. The negative pulses which result when the last binary goes from state 1 to 0 are ineffective because the coupling triodes T_5 and T_6 are held below cutoff by the bias $-E_{cc}$. The positive pulses are inverted and fed back to P_{2a} and P_{3a}. It will be recognized that the triodes T_5 and T_6 are here being used in precisely the manner indicated in Fig. 5-12 for unsymmetrical triggering.

To see the effect of the feedback on the count, we examine now the waveform chart of Fig. 11-4.   We must remember that a binary does not respond instantaneously to an input pulse and that there is some additional delay before the binary output reaches full amplitude.   This feature has been taken into account in Fig. 11-4 by drawing the binary transitions with a finite slope and by starting the transition in a succeed-

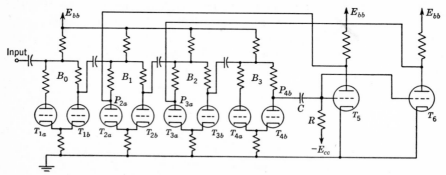

FIG. 11-3. A scale-of-16 binary chain modified by feedback to make a scale-of-10.

ing binary only at the completion of the transition in a preceding binary. The counting proceeds in the customary fashion through the seventh pulse.   At the eighth pulse, binary B_3 responds and negative pulses are fed back to P_{2a} and P_{3a}.   Since B_1 and B_2 are in state 0 after the eighth pulse, the right-hand tube of these binaries is conducting.   Hence, negative pulses at P_{2a} and P_{3a} (which are coupled to G_{2b} and G_{3b}) will cause

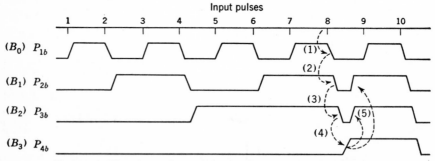

FIG. 11-4. Waveform chart of the feedback counter of Fig. 11-3.

transitions in B_1 and B_2, respectively.   Hence B_1 and B_2 are forced back to state 1 by this fed-back pulse.   Thereafter the count progresses normally and at the tenth pulse all binaries are again in state 0 so that the count is complete.

Observe that after the eighth pulse and before the feedback has had a chance to be effective the chain of binaries is in the state 1000 (8).   The feedback to binary B_1 reverses this binary and advances the count by

$2^1 = 2$.   The feedback to binary B_2 advances the count by $2^2 = 4$.   The two feedback paths advance the count by $2 + 4 = 6$, so that the counter recycles at pulse 10 instead of 16.

This discussion suggests the manner in which the general scheme of Fig. 11-3 may be used to build a counter with an arbitrary scale since feedback to binary B_n advances the count by 2^n.   (Remember that the first binary is B_0.)   Suppose, for example, we require a binary with a scale of 41.   We start with a binary chain which will count beyond 41. In this case, six binaries are called for since $2^6 > 41$, while $2^5 < 41$. Since $2^6 = 64$, we must advance the count by $64 - 41 = 23$.   This advance may be achieved by feedback to B_4, B_2, B_1, and B_0 since $2^4 + 2^2 + 2^1 + 2^0 = 23$.

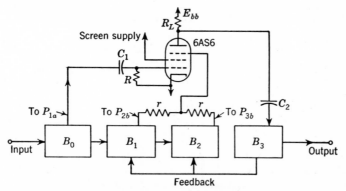

FIG. 11-5. Use of gating tube in high-speed decade counter.

11-4. Improvement of Resolution in a Binary Chain with Feedback.[1]

In a binary chain without feedback the delay between the transition of one binary and the next following is of no importance.   The resolution of the binary chain depends only on the resolution of the first binary and not on the total number of binaries in the chain.   Observe, however, that in Fig. 11-4 there are five separate consecutive delays between the time of occurrence of the eighth pulse and the time when binaries B_1 and B_2 have been completely reset.   These five delays are indicated by the dotted lines which are numbered consecutively from 1 to 5.   If the time interval between input pulses is not sufficient to allow binaries B_1 and B_2 to be reset before the occurrence of the tenth pulse, the counter will not operate correctly.   (The ninth pulse has only to reset binary B_0 so that the eighth and ninth pulses have only to be separated by the resolution time of a binary.)

One method which has been employed successfully to improve the resolution of a feedback counter is illustrated, in principle, in Fig. 11-5. This scheme is used in connection with the basic binary circuit of Fig. 5-9 as a 10-Mc counter in the Hewlett-Packard model 524A frequency counter. The coupling of the first three binaries and the feedback from B_3 to B_2 and B_1 are all in principle identical to the arrangement of Fig. 11-3. The last binary, however, receives its triggering signal through the 6AS6 gating tube.

The suppressor grid of the 6AS6 gating tube is at a potential which is equal to the mean potential at the plates P_{2b} and P_{3b}. The cathode voltage of the 6AS6 may therefore be adjusted so that the gating tube is open for transmission when and only when binaries B_1 and B_2 are both in state 1. Observe now from Fig. 11-4 that before the eighth input pulse occurs the binaries B_1 and B_2 are indeed in state 1, as is required to permit transmission through the gate. At the eighth pulse, binary B_0 makes

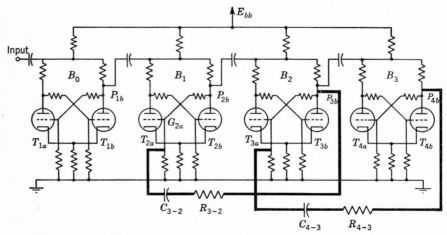

FIG. 11-6. Feedback used to reduce a scale-of-16 counter to a scale of 10.

a transition from state 1 to state 0. The corresponding signal at P_{1a} is a positive-going step which is differentiated by R and C_1 to produce a positive pulse at the control grid of the 6AS6. A negative pulse then appears at the 6AS6 output and is applied symmetrically through C_2 to binary B_3. The eighth input pulse, then, induces a transition in binary B_3 and the delays associated with binaries B_1 and B_2 have been avoided.

At the tenth input pulse, binary B_3 is returned to state 0 again through the mechanism of the gating tube. Observe, from Fig. 11-4, that binary B_3 can respond to a transition in binary B_0 only at the occurrence of the eighth and tenth pulse.

11-5. Additional Types of Decade Counters.[2] We shall now consider some alternative means by which decade scalers may be constructed. A commonly employed scheme is illustrated in Fig. 11-6. It has the advantage that it requires no additional trigger or gating tubes and is used in counters with a counting rate of 10^5 counts per second or slower. There are two feedback paths.   These are indicated by the heavy lines in the schematic.

The operation of the counter will be clear from an examination of the waveform chart of Fig. 11-7.   In this chart, for simplicity, we have neglected the time delay of each binary.   It should be kept in mind, however, that this delay is essential to the operation of a feedback counter.

Referring now to Fig. 11-7, observe that through the third input pulse the counting proceeds in the normal fashion.   At the fourth pulse, the transition 1 to 0 in B_0 causes a transition 1 to 0 in B_1, which in turn produces a transition 0 to 1 in B_2.   The positive step at the plate P_{3b} is applied to G_{2a} through the series RC combination and immediately causes a reverse transition 0 to 1 in binary B_1.   The heavy vertical line in the

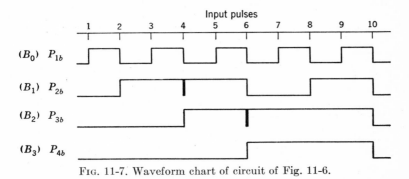

FIG. 11-7. Waveform chart of circuit of Fig. 11-6.

waveform P_{2b} at the time of the fourth pulse represents a transition 1 to 0 followed immediately by the reverse transition 0 to 1.   After the fourth pulse, the chain of binaries reads 0110 = 6 rather than 4 so that the count has been advanced by two steps by the feedback.   In a similar manner the feedback from binary B_3 to B_2 at the time of the sixth input pulse causes a reverse transition in B_2 and advances the count by four. The entire unit resets to its original state at the 10th pulse.

It is of interest to see if the feedback connections have any influences on the circuit other than those already indicated.   Consider, for example, the situation at the time of the second input pulse.   The transition in binary B_1 results in a positive step at P_{2b} and G_{2a} which is transmitted to P_{3b} through C_{3-2}, R_{3-2}.   This positive step has no influence on binary B_2 for the reason that it is applied through a high impedance, R_{3-2}, to a low impedance point, the impedance at the plate P_{3b} being low because T_{3b} is conducting.   Similarly, the positive step at P_{3b} at the fourth pulse and the positive step at P_{2b} at the eighth pulse are both ineffective. Again, the negative steps at both P_{3b} and P_{4b} at the tenth pulse are fed back to grids which are below cutoff.   Finally, in waveform P_{3b}, at the sixth input pulse, there appears a transition 1 to 0 followed immediately by the reverse transition 0 to 1. These two transitions constitute a negative pulse which is fed back to binary B_1 at grid G_{2a} which is below cutoff. Altogether, then, it is clear that the only influences of the connections involving R_{3-2}, C_{3-2}, and R_{4-3}, C_{4-3} are those already indicated in the waveform chart of Fig. 11-7.

It would be possible to read the count of the circuit of Fig. 11-6 by the use of four neon bulbs, one in each binary circuit, connected in the manner described in connection with the straight scale-of-16 counter. It would be necessary, however, to interpret the neon-tube indications in accordance with the waveform chart of Fig. 11-7. A more convenient count-indicating scheme uses 10 neon bulbs labeled 0, 1, 2, 3 . . . , 9 and these neon bulbs are wired into the counter circuit in such a manner as to indicate the count directly.[2] (See Prob. 11-7.)

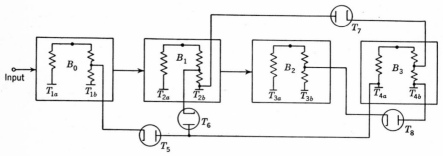

FIG. 11-8. A counter that uses diode clamps.

A final feature which is usually incorporated into counters, decade or other, is provision for *resetting* the count to zero. To include a reset feature, say in the circuit of Fig. 11-6, it is only necessary to add a single switch to the circuit. The lower end of the grid-leak resistors of the right-hand tube of each binary is connected to one side of the switch, the other side of the switch being connected to ground. When the switch is closed, the circuit is identically as represented in Fig. 11-6. When, however, the switch is opened, each of the right-hand tubes, T_{1b}, etc., must be conducting. Each individual binary is therefore in the state zero and the entire counter is at zero count. To reset the counter to zero therefore requires only a momentary opening of this reset switch.

We shall now examine a circuit which does not involve feedback for transforming a scale-of-16 to a scale-of-10 counter. The arrangement is represented in its essential details in Fig. 11-8, while the waveform chart appears in Fig. 11-9. This circuit is used in the Berkeley model 707A counter which is used to count at speeds of 1 Mc. The coupling of binary B_2 to B_1, B_1 to B_0, and B_0 to the external-drive signal is through the two-diode coupling arrangement of Fig. 5-14. These diodes are not indicated in the figure. The last binary, B_3, is driven unsymmetrically.

A signal transmitted through diode T_5 drives this binary from state 0 to state 1, while the reverse transition occurs in response to a signal transmitted through diode T_8. The two remaining diodes T_6 and T_7 are *clamping* diodes.

Let us now trace the operation of the device through its counting range. The voltage levels in the circuit have been adjusted so that when the counter is at zero count (all right-hand tubes conducting) diodes T_7 and T_8 are not conducting, while diodes T_5 and T_6 are conducting. At the first input pulse, binary B_0 reverses, the plate of T_{1b} rises and diode T_5 stops conducting. At the second input pulse, the plate T_{1b} drops, and were it not for the presence of diode T_6, a negative step would be transmitted through T_5 to binary B_3 in which a transition would result. However, diode T_6 is conducting and the signal voltage that would ordinarily

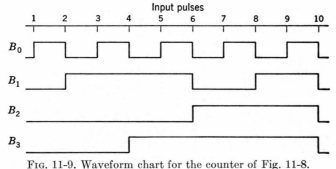

FIG. 11-9. Waveform chart for the counter of Fig. 11-8.

be transmitted to binary B_3 is instead shorted out through T_6. The second input pulse does, however, cause a reversal in binary B_1, diode T_6 stops conducting, and hence the clamp on binary B_3 is removed. But now diode T_7 is conducting. The third input pulse reverses binary B_0. The fourth input pulse would normally reverse both binaries B_0 and B_1. However, the negative step transmitted from binary B_0 to the plate of T_{2b} at the fourth input pulse is shorted out through diode T_7. Since diode T_6 is not conducting at the time of occurrence of the fourth pulse, this fourth pulse will also cause a signal to be transmitted through T_5, which signal will reverse binary T_3.

To recapitulate, we may say the following. In the zero count position, diode clamp T_6 restrains binary B_3 from being driven from binary B_0. At the count of 2, binary B_1 is reversed, the clamp on binary B_3 is released, but binary B_1 is now clamped by diode T_7. At the count of 4 the clamp on binary B_1 is released. Thereafter, as may be verified, the counting proceeds in a normal fashion and the counter resets at the tenth input pulse. Since feedback is not involved in the present scheme, we avoid the difficulties which ordinarily result from the cumulative delay in a chain of binaries.

The various methods which have now been described for altering the count of a binary chain do not by any means exhaust all possibilities. Other schemes[3] are possible and have been employed.

Counters generally, and decade counters particularly, find at present so many applications that a number of manufacturers have made these *decade counting units* or *DCU's* commercially available.   A typical DCU

Fig. 11-10. The Berkeley model 705A decimal counting unit.   (*Courtesy of Berkeley Division, Beckman Instruments, Inc.*)

is shown in Fig. 11-10.   The entire unit, including tubes and neon-bulb count indicators, is assembled on a small chassis, which in turn is mounted on a tube base.   Heater and supply voltages are connected to the tube socket into which the unit plugs.   Certain tube socket pins are used to provide input and derive output.   Provision is made to permit external connection of a reset switch.   Units of a given manufacturer are designed to have an adequate output signal to drive a succeeding DCU.   A number n of these units may be connected in cascade to provide a counter with a range 10^n.   Models are available with counting speeds which vary from about 20 kc to 1 Mc.

11-6. Reversible Binary Counter.[4]   A counter which can be made to decrease its reading by unity with each input pulse is called a *reversible counter* or a *forward-backward counter*.   Addition is performed with a binary counter if the coupling connection is from the right-hand side of the preceding binary as in Fig. 11-1.   Subtraction is obtained by changing this coupling connection to the left-hand plate, as we shall now verify.

If a binary makes a transition from state 0 to state 1, then the right-hand plate voltage changes in the positive direction.   Under these circumstances the left-hand plate falls in potential.   This negative pulse will cause a transition in the binary to which it is connected.   Hence, for the reversible connection the following rules are valid.

1. Binary B_0 makes a transition at each externally applied pulse.

2. Each of the other binaries makes a transition when and only when the preceding binary goes from the state 0 to the state 1.

If the rules are applied to any of the numbers in Table 11-1, the next smaller number in the table is obtained.   For example, consider the number 12, which is 1100 in binary form.   At the next pulse, the right-most 0 (corresponding to B_0) becomes 1.   This change of state from 0 to 1 causes B_1 to change state from 0 to 1, which in turn causes B_2 to change state from 1 to 0.   This last transition is in the direction such as not to affect the following binary, and hence B_3 remains in state 1.   The net result is that the counter reads 1011, which represents the number eleven.   Since we started with twelve and ended with eleven, a subtraction has taken place.

The output from either plate of a binary may be selected by means of a relay if the counting is at a slow rate.   For higher speeds, transmission gates must be used.   A detailed circuit is given in Prob. 14-5.

11-7. A Special Gas-filled Counter Tube.[5]   The basic decade counter, as we have seen, requires a minimum of four double triodes.   The wide range of applicability of counters has naturally prompted investigations into the design of special tubes which would permit the construction of counters with a greater economy.   In the present section we shall describe the *Dekatron*, a gas-filled

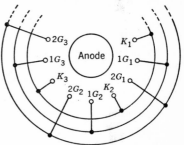

FIG. 11-11. Mechanical structure of the GC10B gas-filled counter tube.

counter tube which has many advantages, if counting speed is not an important consideration.

The mechanical structure of the gas-filled counter tube is shown in Fig. 11-11, while the electric circuit is indicated in Fig. 11-12.   The component values indicated in Fig. 11-12 are appropriate for the type GC10B which has a maximum counting speed of about 4 kc.

The central anode in Fig. 11-11 is surrounded by 30 identical electrodes. Of these, ten are cathodes, nine of which, K_1, K_2, . . . , K_9, are brought out to a common tube terminal, while the tenth, K_0, is brought out separately. Ten electrodes are referred to as *guide No. 1* electrodes and are labeled $1G_1$, $1G_2$, etc. The remaining ten electrodes are *guide No. 2* electrodes and are labeled $2G_1$, $2G_2$, etc. The $1G$ electrodes are brought out to a single tube pin and the $2G$ electrodes are connected to another terminal.

The tube operates as a cold-cathode glow-discharge tube. Let us assume initially that a glow discharge is taking place between the anode and the cathode K_1. Since the maintaining voltage of a glow discharge is smaller than the breakdown voltage, there is no likelihood that the

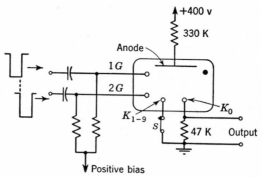

FIG. 11-12. The method of driving and obtaining output from the GC10B counter tube. The switch S is a normally closed reset switch.

discharge will of its own accord transfer to some other one of the cathodes. Since, furthermore, the guide electrodes are biased positively, there is similarly no possibility of a transfer of the glow to a guide electrode. Now suppose that a negative pulse is applied to the $1G$ electrodes of sufficient amplitude so that the voltage difference between anode and the $1G$ electrodes exceeds the breakdown voltage. Of the ten $1G$ electrodes, the $1G_1$ electrode closest to K_1 will have the lowest breakdown voltage since it is closest to the region of the discharge where the gas is most heavily ionized. The discharge will therefore transfer preferentially to the $1G_1$ electrode. The increased current which now flows through the plate-circuit resistor will lower the voltage between anode and K_1 to a value below the maintaining voltage so that the discharge to K_1 will be extinguished. The net result is that the glow has been transferred from K_1 to $1G_1$.

Now suppose that before the pulse applied to $1G$ has decayed, a negative pulse is applied to $2G$ which persists after the termination of the first pulse. Then the discharge will transfer to electrode $2G_1$. When finally this second pulse decays, the discharge will transfer to the nearest cathode, which in the present case is K_2. In a similar way the discharge may be transferred to K_3, K_4, etc.

The single triggering pulse which is to be used to drive the counter must first be transformed before application to the counter tube into two pulses which bear the time relationship indicated in Fig. 11-12. Actually, except where maximum counting speed is required the shapes of the driving pulses for the tube are not critical and a very simple circuit will suffice. One such elementary circuit is shown in Fig. 11-13. The pulse to be counted is used to trigger some type of pulse generator such as a monostable multi. The output from the multi is passed through an RC integrating circuit to obtain the required delayed-pulse-type waveform. The delayed pulse is applied to $2G$, while the undelayed pulse is applied

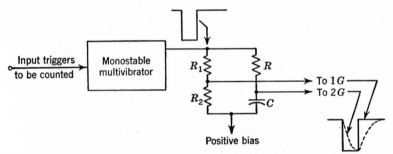

FIG. 11-13. One method of driving a multicathode counter tube.

to $1G$. The attenuator (R_1, R_2) for the undelayed pulse is used to make the two pulses comparable in amplitude. The duration of the multivibrator output pulse must be long enough to allow adequate time for deionization of the gas in the counter tube along the previous discharge path. Since there are three operations involved in a transfer, i.e., transfer from K_1 to $1G_1$, $1G_1$ to $2G_1$, and $2G_1$ to K_2, the multivibrator pulse duration should be roughly one-third the time interval between input triggering pulses at the maximum counting speed. The deionization time is the principal factor which limits counting speed. The fastest multicathode counter tube available in the year 1956 was the GC10D with a counting speed of 20 kc.

Each trigger input pulse advances the glow from one cathode to the next so that every 10th pulse results in an output signal across the cathode load resistor in Fig. 11-12. This output signal may be used, if desired, to drive a succeeding counter. The current drain of the tube is comparatively small, a tube drawing typically only 0.6 ma from the supply voltage. The tube drop is of the order of 160 volts, and the pulses required at $1G$ and $2G$ are of the order of magnitude of 100 volts. The count of the tube is easily read since the glow at the cathode is visible

through the top of the tube. A ring bearing numbers is mounted external to the tube and the position of the glow indicates the count. Special-purpose tubes are also available in which all 10 cathodes are brought
out individually. Such a tube makes available across 10 cathode resis-

Fig. 11-14. A gas-tube duodecade counter. (*Courtesy of Atomic Instrument Company.*)

tors 10 sequential gating-type waveforms. Under these circumstances
the tube behaves as a *stepping switch*. Tubes are also available with 12
separate cathodes. Such a tube, shown in Fig. 11-14, could be used,
depending on the external cathode connections, to divide by 2, 3, 4, 6,

or 12. Lastly, it is worth noting that if the connections to $1G$ and $2G$ are reversed, the tube will count backward, that is, it will subtract instead of add.

11-8. A Vacuum-type Counter Tube.[6] We wish to discuss now a vacuum-type counter tube which is designated generally as a *trochotron* or a *beam switching tube*. It will be necessary, first, to make a short digression to review the nature of the motion of an electron in perpendicular electric and magnetic fields.[7]

The motion of an electron in uniform perpendicular electric and magnetic fields is illustrated in Fig. 11-15. The path is termed a *trochoid*. The solid-line path a of Fig. 11-15 corresponds to the circumstances in which the electron is introduced into the fields with zero initial velocity. In this case the path is a common cycloid and has sharp cusps. In the

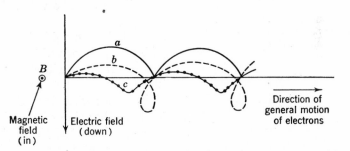

FIG. 11-15. The trochoidal paths of electrons in perpendicular electric and magnetic fields.

more general case of nonzero initial velocity the path may have subsidiary loops as in curve b or blunted cusps as indicated in curve c.

It is to be noted particularly that the motion of the electron in the direction of the electric field (see Fig. 11-15) is oscillatory and of *restricted amplitude*. The general motion of the electron upon which the oscillatory motion is superimposed is in the direction perpendicular to the electric field, that is, in the direction of the electric equipotential surfaces. Assume that a cathode serves as a source of electrons in perpendicular fields, the electrons being emitted with a distribution of initial velocities. Then individual electrons will follow trochoidal paths, but the electrons generally will form a broad beam which follows an equipotential.

An electrode placed in a vacuum tube which has a trochoidal electron beam has two important properties. The first of these is its ability to guide the direction of the beam; the second is referred to as the *self-locking* feature. We examine first the guiding property. Consider the simple configuration indicated in Fig. 11-16. Here two parallel plates maintained at 0 and 100 volts, respectively, provide an electric field, while a magnetic field exists perpendicular to the figure. A cathode K maintained at 50 volts and situated midway between the plates emits electrons. These electrons leave the cathode and individually follow a trochoidal path. The beam, however, is guided by the 50-volt equi-

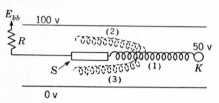

FIG. 11-16. The guiding effect on an electrode near a trochoidal beam. (*Courtesy of Tele-Tech.*)

potential. Suppose now that the electrode S is also maintained at 50 volts; then the 50-volt equipotential intersects the electrode S and the beam follows path 1 and will be collected. If, however, the electrode S is maintained at less than 50 volts, the 50-volt equipotential passes above the electrode and the beam follows path 2. Similarly, if the electrode is maintained at a voltage higher than 50 volts, the beam follows path 3.

The *self-locking* feature may be appreciated by considering the volt-ampere characteristic of the electrode S in the presence of the trochoidal beam. A plot of current, i vs. e, for the electrode S will clearly have a maximum at $e = 50$ volts, since at this voltage the beam goes directly toward the electrode. As e is varied in either direction, the current decreases as the beam moves to one or the other side of the electrode. The general appearance of the volt-ampere characteristic is shown in Fig. 11-17. If the electrode voltage e results from the application of a voltage E_{bb} through a resistor R, the resultant electrode current may be determined by superimposing the load line on the volt-ampere characteristic. There are three equilibrium points given by A, B, and C in Fig. 11-17. Of these, point B is unstable, since here a change in electrode current in either direction changes the electrode voltage in such a direction as to cause an additional current change in the same direction. In other words, to the right of the maximum the volt-ampere characteristic exhibits a negative resistance. We are left then with two stable points A and C. Suppose, then, that the initial operating point is at A. If the electrode voltage is lowered temporarily, the beam may then be directed toward the electrode. The current collected by this electrode

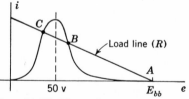

FIG. 11-17. The volt-ampere characteristic of an electrode near a trochoidal beam.

may now maintain the electrode at reduced voltage and the operating point will be shifted permanently, i.e., locked at point C. The current at operating point C is less than the total beam current and may, as a matter of fact, be made a very small part of the total current if R is large. The beam then barely skims along the surface of the electrode S and the rest of the beam current may be collected, if desired, by an auxiliary collector plate, not indicated in Fig. 11-16. Observe that the beam is in a stable position when it skims along one side of the electrode S but not when it skims along the other side.

The mechanical arrangement which is characteristic of trochoidal counter tubes is indicated in Fig. 11-18. The tube has cylindrical structure. A central cathode is surrounded by 10 electrodes which, because of their shape, are referred to as *spades*. This entire structure is surrounded by a cylindrical plate electrode. The spades shield the electrons from the field of the plate except when the electrons are very close to the plate. The formation of the trochoidal beam is therefore determined entirely by the spade voltages. A small permanent magnet maintains a magnetic field along the tube axis. If all spades are maintained at a positive potential, say, 100 volts, the beam simply circles around the cathode as in a static magnetron and no tube current flows. The static field potential lines and the beam formation which results when one of the spade voltages, S, is reduced to zero is shown in Fig. 11-18. The boundaries of the beam are indicated by the dotted lines. An individual electron whose trajec-

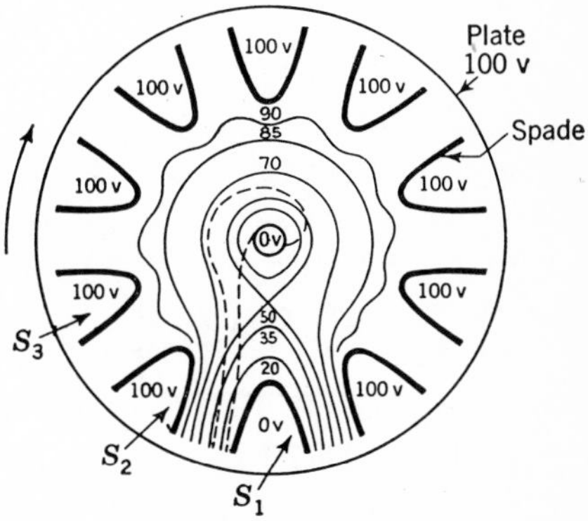

Fig. 11-18. Static field plot and beam formation in a trochoidal tube. (*Courtesy of IRE.*)

tory lies within these boundaries executes many trochoidal revolutions before reaching the plate. It is difficult to account with precision for the path taken by the beam, but we may note that the beam follows the general contour of the equipotential. The beam eventually skims along that side of the zero-voltage spade which corresponds to the stable operating point. That part of the beam which misses the spade is collected by the plate. If all the spades are initially at the same potential but are connected through resistors to a common supply voltage, then the beam may be formed by applying a short negative pulse to, say, S_1. The self-locking action described previously will maintain the beam.

Suppose now that the plate voltage should drop. Then the beam will be rejected by the plate and will be forced to strike spade S_2 on the side adjacent to S_1. This side of spade S_2 is the unstable side, and the beam will move across spade S_2 to the stable side. If the plate voltage continues low, the beam will continue to move in the clockwise direction from spade to spade at a rate determined by tube characteristics and loading capacitances present in the circuit. If, however, the plate voltage is lowered by the application of a pulse whose duration is comparable to the time required for the beam to move from one spade to the next, then such a pulse will advance the beam by only one spade.

The duration of the pulse which is applied to the plate to cause the beam to be forwarded by one step depends critically upon the spade time constants. If the pulse is too narrow, then the spade to which the beam is locked may not be able to rise sufficiently in potential and the adjacent spade may not be able to fall sufficiently to cause a switch from one spade to the next. On the other hand, if the pulse width is too great, it is possible for the beam to move forward more than one spade per pulse. This latter difficulty is avoided with the addition of a wire (called

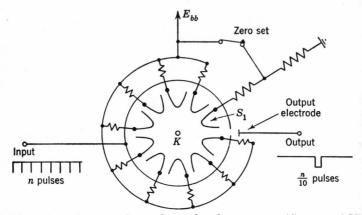

FIG. 11-19. A trochotron tube used as a decade counter. (*Courtesy of IRE.*)

a switching grid or byspade) between each spade. These grids are arranged in two groups, every other grid being interconnected. A push-pull voltage of rectangular waveform is applied to the two grid groups. For example, the output from one plate of a binary is used to excite one group and the output from the other plate of the multi goes to the second grid group. When a grid is pulsed negatively, the beam progresses to the next spade, and here it finds itself in the region of a positive grid. Hence, no matter how slowly the grids are pulsed the beam can never proceed by more than one step with each input pulse.

A trochotron used as a decade counter is illustrated in Fig. 11-19. The zero-set switch is normally closed. A hole is placed in the plate at one point between the spades so that the beam current can be collected by the output electrode. Negative pulses are applied to the plate, and each tenth pulse restores the beam to its original position, giving an output signal. Where it is required that an indication be made available of the count of the tube, additional plate holes and output electrodes may be included. A typical trochotron has about the same dimension as a standard receiving-type tube. It requires a magnetic field of about 350 gauss. The supply voltage is of the order of 100 volts and the tube current of the order of 10 ma. Typical input-pulse requirements are a negative pulse of about 100 volts amplitude and 0.3 μsec duration. Counting rates as high as 5 Mc are attainable.

11-9. Ring Counters.[8] The basic binary circuit may be generalized to a scale of n by arranging n tubes in a ring, as indicated in Fig. 11-20. One tube in the ring is in a state, say 1, which is different from the states of all the other tubes. The input pulse is applied simultaneously to all tubes and causes state 1 to progress one step around the ring. In such a ring counter it

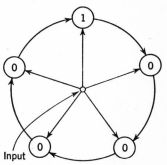

FIG. 11-20. A ring counter.

is required that every plate be coupled to every grid and as a result the circuit becomes unmanageably complicated for large n. Additionally the shunt capacitance to ground soon becomes prohibitively large so that such an arrangement is seldom used if n exceeds 5.

The above difficulty is overcome by using $2n$ tubes to count by the factor n. Each pair of tubes is essentially a scale-of-2 and these are

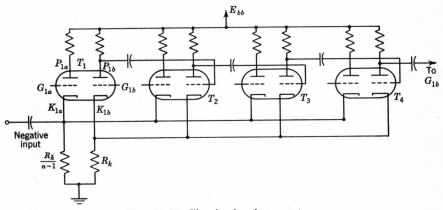

FIG. 11-21. Circuit of a ring counter.

again arranged in a ring, as in Fig. 11-20. A somewhat more detailed diagram is shown in Fig. 11-21. For the sake of simplicity, the coupling resistors and the commutating capacitors of the individual binaries have been omitted. Note that in addition to the usual coupling within each binary there is coupling from each right-hand plate to the right-hand grid of the succeeding binary. Initially the right-hand (b) section of T_1

is conducting, while in every other tube the a section is conducting and the b section is off. If the tube current is I, the drop across R_k is IR_k. The total current from the a sections is $(n-1)I$. The second cathode resistor has been selected to be $R_k/(n-1)$ to make the cathode-to-ground voltage the same for both sets of cathodes.

The operation of this counter is as follows. The negative input trigger turns *on* T_{1a}, and hence T_{1b} goes *off*. The plate P_{1b} rises and the positive step applied through the capacitor to G_{2b} turns *on* T_{2b} and T_{2a} goes *off*. There is a tendency for the input trigger applied at K_{2a} to turn T_{2a} *on* again unless the pulse shape and amplitude have been properly chosen. (The ENIAC computer in which this ring counter is employed uses a very special pulse-forming circuit in order to effect this "pulse dodging.") When T_{2b} goes *on*, P_{2b} drops and the consequent negative step applied to G_{3b} has no effect since T_{3b} is *off*. The net effect of the input pulse has been to switch the *on* state from T_{1b} to T_{2b}, all other tubes remaining unaffected.

A decade ring counter of the type just described requires 10 double triodes, while a binary decimal counter requires only 4 double triodes. Economy, therefore, usually favors the decade counter or one of the special counting tubes discussed in Secs. 11-7 and 11-8.

The ring arrangement is analogous to a *stepping switch* where each pulse causes an advance of one step. Hence, this circuit is used as a *distributor* or *sequencer*.

11-10. Application of Counters. We shall describe here briefly some of the many situations in which counters find application.

Direct Counting.[9] One of the earlier applications for counters arose in connection with research into the properties of the nucleus of an atom. In order to determine the radioactivity of a source, it is necessary to *count individually* the emitted particles for a given time interval. The emission of a radioactive particle may be converted into an electrical pulse through the use of a device known as a *geiger tube*. With a weak radioactive source, a mechanical register may, in many instances, act with sufficient speed, but more usually an electrical counter may have to be interposed between source and mechanical counter. For example, a scale-of-64 counter followed by a mechanical register will be able to respond to geiger pulses which occur at a rate 64 times greater than the maximum rate at which the mechanical register will respond. The net count in such a case will be 64 times the reading of the mechanical register plus the count left in the scale-of-64 counter.

Direct counting also finds application in many industrial processes. Counters will operate with reliability where human counters fail because of fatigue or limitations of speed. It is required, of course, that the phenomenon which is to be counted first be converted into an electrical signal, but this requirement usually imposes no important limitation. For example, objects may be counted by passing them single file on a conveyor belt between a photoelectric cell and a light source.

A *preset* feature may be incorporated into a counter to allow control of industrial processes. A *preset counter* is one which has been modified (at the expense of additional tubes and components) so that it will deliver an output pulse when the count reaches a predetermined number. Such a counter may be used, for example, to count the number of pills dropped into a bottle. When the preset count is attained, the output pulse is used to divert the pills to the next container and at the same time to reset the counter for counting the next batch. Decade preset counters which may be preset by push buttons at any count from 1 to 10 are commercially available.

Measurement of Frequency. The basic principle by which counters are used for the precise determination of frequency is illustrated in Fig. 11-22. The input signal whose frequency is to be measured is converted into pulses and applied through a gate to an electronic counter. To determine the frequency, it is now only required to keep the gate open for transmission for a known time interval. If, say, the gating time is 1 sec, then the counter will yield the frequency directly in cycles per second. The *clock* for timing the gate interval is an accurate crystal oscillator whose frequency is, say, 1 Mc. The crystal frequency drives a chain of dividers (discussed in Chap. 12) which divide the crys-

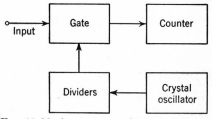

FIG. 11-22. A counter used in a frequency meter.

tal frequency by a factor of 1 million. The divider output consists of a 1-cps signal whose period is as accurately maintained as the crystal frequency. This divider output signal controls the gating time. The system is susceptible to only slight errors. One source of error results from the fact that a variation of ± one count may be encountered, depending on the instant when the first and last pulses occur in relation to the sampling time. A second source of error arises from *jitter* in the dividers (Chap. 12), which may produce an uncertainty of the order of 0.1 μsec in the sampling period. Beyond these, of course, the accuracy depends on the accuracy of the crystal.

Measurement of Time. The time interval between two pulses may also be measured with the circuit of Fig. 11-22. The first pulse is used to open the gate and the second pulse to close the gate. The crystal oscillator signal (or some lower frequency from the divider chain) is converted into pulses, and these are passed through the gate into the counter. The number of counts recorded is proportional to the length of time the gate is open and hence gives the desired time interval.

Measurement of Speed. A speed determination may be converted into a time measurement. For example, if two photocell-light-source combinations are set a fixed distance apart, the average speed of an object passing between these points is proportional to the time interval between the generated pulses. Projectile velocities have been measured in this manner.

Digital Computer. Counters constitute a basic building block in digital computers and are used to perform many functions. One of these functions is that of *storage*. Information is coded in digital computers in the form of binary numbers, and it is often required that the number be stored for future use. It will be immediately appreciated that a number may be stored in a *binary register* for an indefinite period of time.

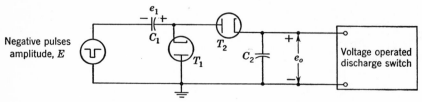

FIG. 11-23. A two-diode counting circuit.

Waveform Generation. The waveforms which occur at the plates or grids of binary counters may be combined either directly or in connection with other circuits (see Chap. 17) to generate complex pulse-type waveforms.

11-11. Storage Counters.[10] We consider now a circuit, known as a *storage counter*, which operates on a principle which is basically different from the counters previously described. A two-diode storage counter circuit is shown in Fig. 11-23. Let us neglect, for the present, the voltage-operated discharge switch and consider the output waveform e_o which results from the application to the circuit of a train of negative pulses of amplitude E.

Consider that initially there is no charge on either of the capacitors C_1 or C_2. The first input pulse will cause the capacitor C_1 to charge through the diode T_1. The time constant with which C_1 charges is the product of C_1 times the sum of the diode and generator resistances. If this time constant is very small in comparison with the duration of the pulse, then C_1 will charge fully to the value $e_1 = E$, with the polarity indicated. During the charging time of C_1, the diode T_2 does not conduct and the voltage across C_2 remains at zero. At the termination of the input pulse, the capacitor C_1 is left with the voltage $e_1 = E$, which now appears across

T_1 and across the series combination of T_2 and C_2. The polarity of this voltage is such that T_1 will not conduct. The capacitor C_1 will, however, discharge through T_2 into C_2 until the voltages across the two capacitors are equal. The time constant with which this transfer of charge takes place must be quite small in comparison with the interval between pulses in order to allow equilibrium to be established between the capacitor voltages. The capacitor C_2 is ordinarily quite large in comparison with C_1. As a consequence the voltage change across C_2 is small in comparison with the voltage $e_1 = E$ across C_1. The next input pulse restores the voltage on C_1 to E and at the termination of the pulse C_1 discharges

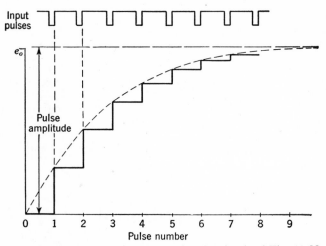

Fig. 11-24. The output voltage e_o for the circuit of Fig. 11-23.

again into C_2. Since now, however, C_2 has some initial charge, the amount of charge transferred from C_1 to C_2 will be smaller than before. Hence the second increment of voltage across C_2 will be smaller than the first. Each successive input pulse will cause a progressively smaller step in voltage at the output, the output approaching asymptotically the voltage $e_o = E$, as in Fig. 11-24. In this figure the voltage is plotted as a function of pulse number, and not time. If, however, the pulses are regularly spaced in time, the plot of Fig. 11-24 also gives the output waveform. Note, too, as indicated, that the voltage steps occur at the trailing edge rather than the leading edge of the pulse.

The counter is completed by the addition of a tube circuit which operates as a switch shunted across C_2. This switch is normally open, but it closes when e_o attains some preestablished reference value. One such switch circuit is shown in Fig. 11-25. The cathode of the blocking-oscillator tube is maintained at some positive voltage so that the tube is initially below cutoff. The blocking oscillator responds when the voltage across C_2 becomes high enough to bring the tube out of cutoff. At this point the capacitor C_2 discharges rapidly because of the large grid current during the pulse formation and at the same time an output pulse is furnished. In the present application the blocking oscillator serves in the capacity of a *comparator*. A comparator (Chap. 15) is a circuit which

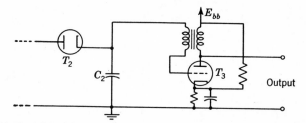

Fig. 11-25. A blocking-oscillator switch used with a storage counter.

responds when an input signal passes through some previously established voltage level. Quite generally, then, when some type of comparator-operated switch is included in the circuit, a counter results and the waveform across C_2 has the typical appearance shown in Fig. 11-26. Here the waveform has been drawn taking into account the possibility that the discharge switch may not discharge the capacitor C_2 to zero. The count

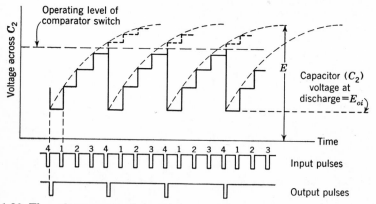

Fig. 11-26. The voltage across C_2 in a 4:1 counter, showing the time relationships to the input and output pulses.

down ratio shown is 4:1, since the comparator response voltage has been set between the voltage levels corresponding to the fourth and fifth pulse.

The counting ratio may be increased by raising the voltage at which the comparator responds. As the counting ratio is increased, however, the counter operation becomes progressively less reliable since the size of the steps decreases. This lack of reliability results from uncertainties in the level to which the voltage across C_2 drops at discharge and uncertainties in the operating voltage of the comparator. An expression showing how the step size decreases with pulse number may be derived as follows. Suppose that after the nth pulse has produced the nth step the net voltage across C_2 is e_n. Now let the $(n+1)$st pulse be applied. After the trailing edge of this pulse, diode T_1 is open, T_2 is closed, and the voltage across C_1 is E. An equivalent circuit for computing the jump in voltage across C_2 when T_2 conducts is shown in Fig. 11-27, in which S represents the diode T_2. From elementary electrostatics we find that the jump in voltage across C_2 after the $(n+1)$st pulse is

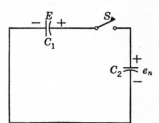

Fig. 11-27. Equivalent circuit for computing step size at C_2.

$$\Delta e_n \equiv e_{n+1} - e_n = (E - e_n) \frac{C_1}{C_1 + C_2} \qquad (11\text{-}3)$$

If we introduce y_n, defined by

$$y_n \equiv e_n - E \qquad (11\text{-}4)$$

then Eq. (11-3) reduces to the homogeneous equation

$$y_{n+1} - y_n = - \frac{C_1}{C_1 + C_2} y_n \qquad (11\text{-}5)$$

or

$$y_{n+1} = xy_n \qquad (11\text{-}6)$$

where

$$x \equiv \frac{C_2}{C_1 + C_2} \qquad (11\text{-}7)$$

Since the change in y_n is proportional to y_n, we may anticipate that y_n will vary exponentially with n. Hence, we shall seek a solution of the form

$$y_n = A\epsilon^{\alpha n} \qquad (11\text{-}8)$$

where A and α are to be determined so as to satisfy (Eq. 11-6) and the proper initial condition. Substituting Eq. (11-8) into Eq. (11-6), we find

$$A\epsilon^{\alpha(n+1)} = xA\epsilon^{\alpha n} \qquad \text{or} \qquad \epsilon^{\alpha} = x \qquad (11\text{-}9)$$

Hence $y_n = Ax^n$ and, from Eq. (11-4),

$$e_n = E + Ax^n \qquad (11\text{-}10)$$

The initial condition is that the capacitor voltage e_n equals E_{oi} for $n = 0$, and hence $A = E_{oi} - E$. Finally, the complete solution is

$$e_n = E - (E - E_{oi})x^n \qquad (11\text{-}11)$$

The difference between the $(n + 1)$st voltage level and the nth level is

$$e_{n+1} - e_n = (E - E_{oi})(1 - x)x^n \qquad (11\text{-}12)$$

If, for example, $E - E_{oi} = 100$ volts and $C_2 = 9C_1$, then $x = \frac{9}{10}$ and the first step has an amplitude of $(100)(1 - \frac{9}{10}) = 10$ volts. The eleventh step, on the other hand, is $100(1 - \frac{9}{10})(\frac{9}{10})^{10} = 3.5$ volts.

Since step size decreases with increasing pulse number and because of the instability in the value of E_{oi}, the comparator response voltage, and amplitude of input pulse, storage counters are normally not used for counting ratios larger than about 10. Storage counters, of course, may be cascaded to secure large counting ratios in the same manner that binary counters are cascaded. An important limitation of storage counters is that they may be used ordinarily only to count pulses which occur fairly regularly. This feature results from the fact that the count is determined by the charge on a capacitor and this charge will leak off slowly because of capacitor leakage or through the resistance of any device which is used to read the count. Even in Fig. 11-25, for example, where no grid-leak resistor is indicated for T_3, some leakage may result from the small grid current that may result from traces of gas in the tube. The leakage problem is complicated by the fact that the capacitors must be able to charge rapidly and must therefore be quite small. Still, where storage counters are applicable, they often effect a worthwhile economy of components over comparable binary counters. In comparing the binary and storage counters for economy, one must keep in mind that the storage counter must be driven from a pulse source of large and constant amplitude and of low impedance. The pulses must be of reasonably rectangular shape.

The counter of Fig. 11-23 may be operated with a positive input pulse. In this case C_1 charges first through T_2 and thereafter discharges through T_1. The step at C_2 then occurs at the leading edge of the input pulse. Similarly, with either polarity of input pulse, the counter may be operated with both diodes reversed. In this latter case the steps in voltage across C_2 are in the negative direction.

11-12. Linearization of Storage Counters. It is possible to extend somewhat the counting ratio of a storage counter by linearizing the envelope of the step waveform of Fig. 11-24 to yield steps of more nearly equal amplitude. The methods used to achieve this end are essentially the same as those used to linearize time-base waveforms, that is, bootstrapping and Miller integration (Chap. 7). Consider the circuit of Fig. 11-23 modified so that the plate T_1 is returned to a positive voltage e_R rather than to ground. Under these circumstances, immediately after the input pulse the voltage across C_1 is $E + e_R$ rather than E. Hence Eq. (11-3) may be rewritten

$$\Delta e_n = (E + e_R - e_n) \frac{C_1}{C_1 + C_2} \qquad (11\text{-}13)$$

where Δe_n gives again the size of the nth step. If then we arrange to make e_R equal to e_n, the step size will be independent of n. A cathode follower with nominally unity gain, as in Fig. 11-28, will achieve the desired end. It is not necessary that e_R be instantaneously equal to e_n, since it is sufficient that e_R follow the general rise of the output voltage e_n. A capacitor C may therefore be shunted across the output of the cathode follower to assist the rapid charging of C_1.

Although the circuit of Fig. 11-28 illustrates the bootstrapping principle, it is not a practical circuit. Let us consider the quiescent condition when no pulses are present and the supply voltages are first applied to the cathode follower. Since the grid-to-ground voltage e_n is initially

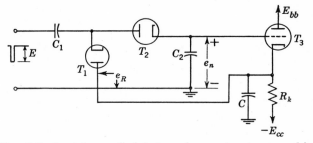

FIG. 11-28. Use of the bootstrap principle to make counter steps equal in amplitude. (See text for modifications necessary to convert this into a practical circuit.)

zero, the cathode-to-ground voltage e_R of T_3 will be a few volts positive. This positive voltage causes both T_1 and T_2 to conduct and the voltage e_n increases. This rise in grid voltage causes e_R to increase, which, in turn, raises e_n still further. This action continues until e_n equals e_R, so that the grid-to-cathode voltage is zero. If a pulse were now applied, this would tend to drive the grid positive and the circuit would not operate properly.

The above difficulty can be avoided by returning the plate of T_1 to a tap on the cathode resistor R_k such that the voltage e_R is less than zero when the voltage $e_n = 0$. This connection will reduce the gain of the cathode follower and cause the output to be somewhat less linear with the number of input pulses. However, if E_{cc} is large, the tap will be close to the cathode and the reduction in linearity will not be great.

A second method for avoiding the d-c instability of the circuit of Fig. 11-28 mentioned above is to reverse both diodes T_1 and T_2. With no input pulses and the voltage across C_2 equal to zero, the voltage e_R will be a few volts positive, say E_o. Hence, diodes T_1 and T_2 cannot conduct, and the action described above does not take place. The amplitude of the input pulse must exceed E_o or T_1 will never conduct. It should be mentioned that in the two circuits just discussed the voltage across C_2 will become negative in the quiescent condition because some small grid current flows even for negative grid voltages.

The use of the Miller integration principle to improve linearity is illustrated in Fig. 11-29. Here the voltage e_n between the cathode of T_2 and ground remains nominally zero. If the voltage across C_2 increases, then the bottom side of C_2 falls by this same amount in order to keep e_n constant. The virtual ground at the input terminals of the operational amplifier takes no current (see Sec. 1-12). Hence, all the charge C_1E

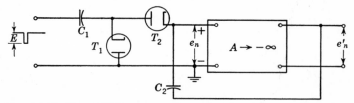

FIG. 11-29. Use of Miller integrating principle with storage counter.

which leaves capacitor C_1 must go to capacitor C_2. The increase in voltage across C_2 is, therefore,

$$\Delta e_{C_2} = -\Delta e_n' = \frac{C_1E}{C_2} \tag{11-14}$$

This equation verifies the fact that the output decreases by a constant amount for each input pulse.

11-13. Applications of Storage Counters. Among the most important uses of storage counters are the following:

A Divider. For every n pulses into the counter, one appears at the output. The waveform in such an application is illustrated in Fig. 11-26 for $n = 4$. The pulses must be fairly regularly spaced, although an exactly constant interval between pulses is not required. A storage counter is more economical as a divider than is a binary counter. Frequency division is considered in more detail in Chap. 12

Staircase Voltage Generator. The staircase waveshape of Fig. 11-26 is sometimes useful. One such application is to use the storage counter as a generator source to vary some voltage in a step fashion. A family of tube (or transistor) volt-ampere characteristics may be traced out on a CRO in this manner.

Frequency or Counting-rate Meter. If the capacitor C_2 in Fig. 11-23 is shunted by a resistor R, then the counter may be used as a frequency meter. Let E be the pulse amplitude and f be the pulse-repetition frequency. If $C_1Rf \ll 1$ and $C_2 \gg C_1$, then (see Prob. 11-17) the average output voltage is

$$E_{\text{d-c}} = EC_1Rf \tag{11-15}$$

Thus, for given values of C_1, R, and E a vacuum-tube voltmeter placed across the output may be calibrated in *frequency* or in pulses per unit time. Such a meter has found extensive application in nuclear radiation measurements[11] and in frequency-modulation radar systems.[12]

Capacitance Meter. If a known frequency is applied to a storage counter which has been modified so that Eq. (11-15) is valid, then the output voltage is proportional to the capacitance of C_1. Hence, this device may be used as a capacitance meter.

REFERENCES

1. Instruction Manual, Type 524A Frequency Counter, Hewlett-Packard Company, Palo Alto, Calif.
2. Instruction Manual, Types 700A, 705A, and 707A Decimal Counting Unit, Berkeley Division, Beckman Instrument Company, Richmond, Calif.
   Grosdoff, I. E.: Electronic Counter, *RCA Rev.*, vol. 7, pp. 438–447, September, 1946.
3. Kemp, E. L.: Gated Decade Counter Requires No Feedback, *Electronics*, vol. 26, pp. 145–147, February, 1953.
   Potter, J. T.: A Four-tube Counter Decade, *Electronics*, vol. 17, pp. 110–113, June, 1944.
4. Barney, K. H.: The Binary Quantizer, *Elec. Eng.*, vol. 68, pp. 962–967, November, 1949.
5. Bacon, R. C., and J. R. Pollard: The Dekatron—A New Cold Cathode Counting Tube, *Electronic Eng.*, vol. 22, pp. 173–177, May, 1950.
   McAsalan, J. H. L., and K. J. Brimley: Polycathode Counter Tube Applications, *Electronics*, vol. 26, pp. 138–141, November, 1953.
6. Kuchinsky, S.: Multi-output Beam-switching Tubes for Computers and General Purpose Use, *IRE Convention Record*, pt. 6, *Electron Devices*, pp. 43–45, 1953.
   Fitzpatrick, A. G.: PCM Coding System Uses Special Tubes, *Electronics*, vol. 26, pp. 173–175, November, 1953.
   Romanus, H., and H. Alfren: Trochotrons—A New Family of Switching Tubes, *Tele-Tech*, vol. 13, p. 94, June, 1954.
   Björkman, J., and L. Lindberg: Development of Trochotrons, *Trans. Roy. Inst. Technol., Stockholm, No.* 80, 1954.
   Kandiah, K.: Decimal Counting Tubes, *Electronic Eng.*, vol. 26, pp. 56–63, February, 1954.
7. Millman, J., and S. Seely: "Electronics," 2d ed., chap. 2, McGraw-Hill Book Company, Inc., New York, 1951.
8. Sharpless, T. K.: High-speed N-Scale Counters, *Electronics*, vol. 21, pp. 122–125, March, 1948.
   Beckwith, H.: Flip-flop Counter Has Extended Range, *Electronics*, vol. 28, pp. 149–151, January, 1955.
   Seren, L.: Decade Ring Scaling Circuit, *Rev. Sci. Instr.*, vol. 18, pp. 654–659, September, 1947.
   Regener, V. H.: Decade Counting Circuits, *Rev. Sci. Instr.*, vol. 17, pp. 185–189, May, 1946.
   Burks, A. W.: Electronic Computing Circuits of the ENIAC, *Proc. IRE*, vol. 35, pp. 756–767, August, 1947.
9. Thomason, T. H.: A Preset Counter for Time and Quantity Measurements, *Tele-Tech*, vol. 12, p. 82, August, 1953.

Wild, J. J.: Predetermined Counters, *Electronics*, vol. 20, pp. 120–123, March, 1947.

Blume, R. J.: Predetermined Counter for Process Control, *Electronics*, vol. 21, pp. 88–93, February, 1948.

10. Easton, A., and P. H. Odessy: Design of Counter Circuits for Television, *Electronics*, vol. 21, pp. 120–123, May, 1948.

Wintle, M. F.: Precision Calibrator for Low-frequency Phase-Meters, *Wireless Eng.*, vol. 28, pp. 197–208, July, 1951.

Bedford, A. V., and J. P. Smith: Precision Television Synchronizing Signal Generator, *RCA Rev.*, vol. 5, pp. 51–68, July, 1940.

11. Elmore, W. C., and M. Sands: "Electronics—Experimental Techniques," pp. 249–256, McGraw-Hill Book Company, Inc., New York, 1949.

12. Luck, D. G. C.: "Frequency Modulation Radar," chap. IV, McGraw-Hill Book Company, Inc., New York, 1949.

CHAPTER 12

SYNCHRONIZATION AND FREQUENCY DIVISION

A pulse or digital system may involve several different basic waveform generators. Such a system may require that these generators run synchronously, that is, in step with one another, so that each generator arrives at some reference point in its cycle at the same time. The frequency stability of waveform generators is never adequate to ensure synchronism. Even a very small frequency difference between generators will eventually cause the accumulation of a large error. In many pulse systems it is required that the individual generators be synchronized but be permitted to operate at different frequencies. We may require, say, that one generator complete exactly some integral number of cycles while a second generator executes only one cycle. Such a situation is described as synchronization with frequency division.

This chapter will discuss the mechanism of synchronization on a one-to-one basis and also synchronization with frequency division. The two processes are basically so nearly alike that no clean-cut distinction will be drawn between them.

The counting circuits of Chap. 11 may, of course, be used for frequency division. These counting circuits, with the exception of the storage counters, do not depend for their operation on the regularity of recurrence of the input waveform. If, say, the input signal consists of pulses, the counters will divide correctly, independently of whether the pulses occur regularly or in a random fashion. In the present chapter, however, we contemplate only the case of an input waveform of a nominally fixed recurrence rate. This feature, as we shall see, permits considerable economy in the circuits which may be used to achieve division.

12-1. Pulse Synchronization of Relaxation Devices. The term "relaxation circuit" is applied to any circuit in which a timing interval is established through the gradual charging of a capacitor, the timing interval being terminated by a relatively abrupt discharge (relaxation) of the capacitor. The relaxation circuits which have been described in earlier chapters include the thyratron sweep generator, the blocking oscillator, the multivibrator, and the phantastron circuit. Each of these circuits has in common a timing period and a relaxation (or recovery) period and each exists in an astable or monostable form.* The mechanism of synchronization and frequency division is basically the same for all of these relaxation devices.

In the monostable form, the matter of synchronization (1:1 division) to a pulse-type waveform is a trivial one. The circuit normally remains in a quiescent condition and awaits the arrival of a triggering pulse to initiate a single cycle of operation. It is only necessary that the interval between triggers be larger than the timing interval and recovery period combined.

The important features of pulse synchronization of an astable relaxation device may be exposed by examining the mechanism in connection with any of the circuits mentioned above. Let us select the thyratron sweep generator for examination since it is a slightly simpler circuit than the others. A thyratron sweep generator (see Sec. 7-2) is shown in Fig. 12-1a. In the absence of synchronizing pulses at the thyratron grid a complete cycle terminates when the thyratron plate voltage e_c reaches the breakdown voltage. Thereafter the capacitor C discharges abruptly through the tube, and the tube extinguishes at the extinction voltage. Then the capacitor starts to recharge and the cycle is again terminated when e_c reaches the breakdown voltage.

The situation which results when positive synchronizing pulses are applied to the thyratron grid is illustrated in Fig. 12-1b. The effect of the positive pulse is to lower, for the duration of the pulse, the thyratron breakdown voltage as indicated. A pulse train of regularly spaced pulses is shown starting at an arbitrary time $t = 0$. The first several pulses have no influence on the thyratron sweep generator, which continues to run unsynchronized. Eventually, however, the exact moment at which the thyratron fires is determined by the instant of occurrence of a pulse (at time T in Fig. 12-1b), as is also each succeeding firing of the thyratron. From this point on, the sweep generator runs synchronously with the pulses.

In order that synchronization may result, it is necessary that each pulse shall occur at a time when it may serve to terminate the cycle *prematurely*. This requirement means that the interval between pulses, T_p, must be *less* than the natural period, T_o, of the sweep generator. Additionally, even if the requirement $T_p < T_o$ is met, synchronization cannot result unless the pulse amplitude is at least large enough to bridge the

---

* The so-called "monostable multi" can be rendered astable, as has been described in Sec. 6-11. Similarly the so-called "astable multi" may be rendered monostable by applying an appropriate fixed negative bias to one tube. The essential distinction between these circuits is that the monostable multi has a single timing period and a single recovery interval, while the astable circuit has two timing periods and two recovery intervals per complete cycle.

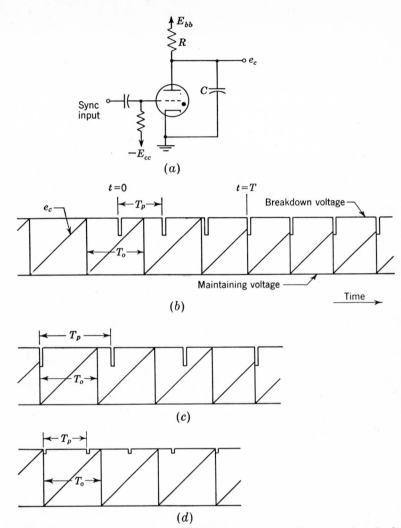

FIG. 12-1. (a) A thyratron sweep generator.   (b) An initially unsynchronized generator falls into synchronization shortly after the application of synchronizing pulses. (c) Illustrating that for synchronization to result T_p must be less than T_o.   (d) Illustrating failure of synchronization due to inadequate amplitude of sync pulses.

gap between the quiescent breakdown voltage and the sweep voltage e_c. In Fig. 12-1c the case is shown in which $T_p > T_o$.   Here synchronization of each cycle does not occur.   The pulses do serve to establish that four sweep cycles shall occur during the course of three pulse periods, but synchronization of this type is normally of no value.   In Fig. 12-1d we have the case where T_p is less than T_o as required, but the pulse amplitude is too small and again synchronization does not result.

12-2. Frequency Division in the Thyratron Sweep. In Fig. 12-2 we have a case in which $T_p < T_o$ but in which the pulse amplitude is too small to permit each pulse to terminate a cycle. The sweep cycles are therefore terminated only by the alternate pulse marked "2" in the figure. The pulses marked "1" would be required to have an amplitude at least equal to E_1 if they were to be effective. The pulses marked "2" are effective because they occur closer to the time when the cycle would terminate of its own accord. The sweep generator now acts as a divider, the division factor being 2, since exactly one sweep cycle occurs for each two synchronizing pulses. If T_s is the sweep generator period after synchronization, we have $T_s/T_p = 2$. Note that the amplitude E_s' of the sweep after synchronization is less than the unsynchronized amplitude E_s.

Suppose, referring again to Fig. 12-2, that T_p is progressively decreased. Eventually a point would be reached where even the alternate pulses

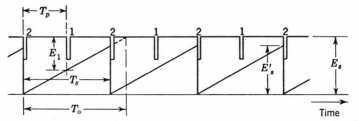

Fig. 12-2. Frequency division by a factor of 2 in a thyratron sweep generator.

would be too small in amplitude to fire the thyratron. At this point it might be that $T_o > 3T_p$, in which case division by a factor of 3 would result. If the condition $T_o > 3T_p$ is not met, then again we should have no synchronization. If, on the other hand, we make the pulse amplitude large enough, we may make sure that every $(n + 1)$st pulse is in a position to ensure synchronization before the nth pulse loses control.

The general behavior of the circuit for regularly spaced pulses of varying pulse period and pulse amplitude is illustrated in Fig. 12-3a. This diagram may be verified by making sketches such as that in Fig. 12-2. The amplitude scale extends from 0 to E_s, where E_s is the total sweep amplitude. (Any pulse amplitude E_p in Fig. 12-3 corresponds, of course, to a pulse amplitude E_p/μ at the thyratron grid, μ being the thyratron grid-control ratio.) The shaded areas of the diagram represent the regions of synchronization, unshaded areas regions of lack of synchronization. The diagram is to be interpreted in the following way. Suppose that the pulse amplitude is fixed at E_1. Then as the ratio T_p/T_o decreases from 1, there will be a range during which 1:1 synchronization will hold, followed by a range of no synchronization, followed by a range of synchronization in which 2:1 division will result, followed again by a range of no synchronization, and so on. If, on the other hand, the pulse amplitude is large, say E_2, then with decreasing T_p/T_o synchronization will always hold, the division changing abruptly from 1:1 to 2:1 to 3:1, and so on.

Next suppose that we maintain a fixed value of T_p/T_o, say $\frac{1}{5} <$ $T_p/T_o < \frac{1}{4}$. Then as the pulse amplitude is increased from zero, we

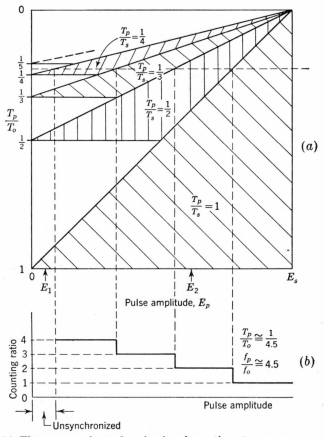

Fig. 12-3. (a) The ranges of synchronization for a thyratron sweep generator as a function of pulse amplitude or frequency. The sweep waveform is assumed to be linear. (b) The counting ratio as a function of pulse amplitude for $f_p/f_o \cong 4.5$.

shall initially have no synchronization, followed by ranges of synchronization where the counting ratio is first 4:1, then 3:1, then 2:1, and finally 1:1. The transitions in counting ratio are abrupt. This last-described characteristic is of much interest and is often represented in the form shown in Fig. 12-3b. Here the counting ratio is plotted as a function of pulse amplitude for the case where $T_p/T_o \cong 1/4.5$, the ratio of pulse frequency to natural frequency being $f_p/f_o \cong 4.5$. We should emphasize that as the pulse amplitude increases, the counting ratio decreases and the sweep amplitude also decreases.

12-3. Other Astable Relaxation Circuits. The synchronization and use for counting purposes of other types of relaxation oscillators differ only in detail and not in basic principle from the synchronization of the thyratron sweep generator.

Blocking Oscillator. The use of a blocking oscillator to accomplish pulse recurrence frequency (PRF) division by a factor of 4 is illustrated in Fig. 12-4. In Fig. 12-4a parallel triggering is indicated but, of course, any of the methods of trigger injection indicated in Sec. 9-17 may be employed. In Fig. 12-4b is shown the waveform at the blocking-oscil-

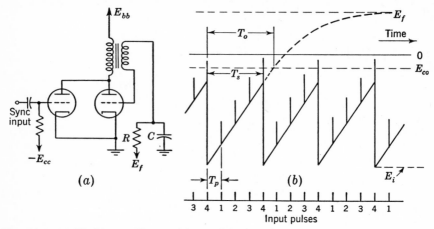

(a)   (b)

FIG. 12-4. (a) Blocking oscillator with parallel triggering. (b) Grid waveform (except for oscillator pulse) showing PRF division by 4.

lator grid. For simplicity, the pulse generated by the blocking oscillator itself is not shown. When the blocking oscillator fires, grid current charges the capacitor C, which is then left at an initial voltage E_i. The oscillator will fire again when the grid reaches the cutoff voltage E_{co}. The injected pulses are now shown superimposed on the rising grid voltage rather than on the critical firing voltage. The important point is that a pulse (No. 4) occurs at a time and has a sufficient amplitude to cause a premature firing of the oscillator. The oscillator therefore fires at a moment dictated by the occurrence of a pulse and is not permitted to terminate its cycle naturally. The synchronizing characteristics given in Fig. 12-3 for the thyratron sweep generator may be applied directly to the blocking oscillator, provided only that the sweep amplitude E_s is replaced by the corresponding amplitude $E_{co} - E_i$ for the blocking oscillator.

Astable Multi.[1] The astable multi in Fig. 12-5a may be synchronized or used as a divider by applying positive or negative triggering pulses to

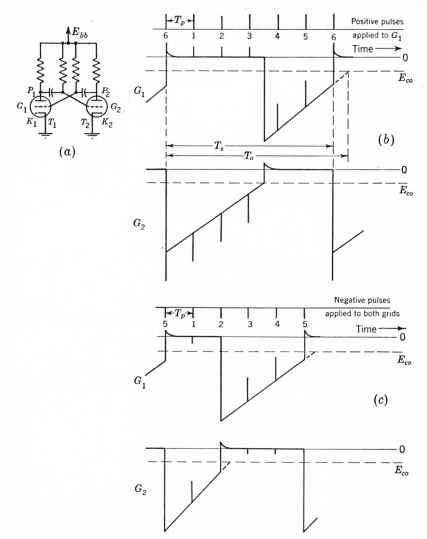

FIG. 12-5. (a) An astable multi. (b) Grid waveform for division by 6 through application of positive pulses to one grid. (c) Grid waveforms for division by 5 through application of negative pulses to both grids.

either tube or to both tubes simultaneously. These pulses may be applied either to the plate, grid, or cathode. If, for example, positive pulses are applied to G_1 or to P_2, or negative pulses applied to K_1, these pulses may produce synchronization by establishing the exact instant at which T_1 comes out of cutoff. If negative pulses are applied to G_2 or to P_1, or positive pulses are applied to K_2, then when T_2 conducts, *these pulses will be amplified and inverted and appear as positive pulses at G_1.*

Hence, again the pulses may establish the instant when T_1 comes out of cutoff.

In Fig. 12-5b are shown the grid waveforms for the case where positive pulses are applied effectively to one grid, say G_1. The division ratio is 6. The grid waveforms which would result if negative pulses were applied to one grid, say G_2, are the same with the following exceptions. The positive pulses which appear on G_1 when T_1 is conducting will be absent and instead negative pulses will appear superimposed on the G_2 waveform during the time T_2 is conducting. Observe that while the complete multi period has been synchronized, the individual portions are not synchronized. The waveforms have been simplified somewhat by neglecting the negative undershoot that occurs during the recovery periods which follow each timing interval. (See Fig. 6-17.)

The situation illustrated by the grid waveforms of Fig. 12-5c corresponds to the case of the application of negative pulses to both multi grids simultaneously. Here the division ratio is 5. Both timing portions of the multi waveform are synchronized and are necessarily of unequal duration since the division ratio is an odd number. The positive pulses superimposed on the exponential portions of the waveforms result from the combination of the negative pulses applied directly and the inverted and amplified (hence larger and positive) pulses received from the other tube.

A special situation of interest is illustrated in Fig. 12-6. Here positive pulses are being applied to G_1 through a small capacitor from a low impedance source. During the time when T_1 is conducting the grid draws current at each input pulse. At the end of the pulse the input capacitor discharges, giving rise to a negative overshoot. Alternatively, we may say that during the conduction period of T_1 the pulse input time constant is small and the input pulse is quasi-differentiated. The negative overshoot is amplified and inverted by T_1 and appears at G_2 as a positive overshoot, which may then serve to mark the end of the cutoff period of T_2. Hence, the net result is that both portions of the multi cycle have been synchronized without the need for applying pulses to both tubes simultaneously.

The diagram of Fig. 12-3a does not apply directly to the astable multi. However, for any particular method of synchronizing and degree of symmetry of the multi a similar diagram may be drawn. The general results deduced from Fig. 12-3a do, however, apply equally to the multi. That is, for large pulse amplitude the counting ratio makes abrupt changes as the ratio T_p/T_o is increased. For smaller amplitudes, regions of synchronization are separated by intervals of no synchronization. Similarly, for a fixed ratio T_p/T_o, a plot of counting ratio vs. pulse amplitude has the same general appearance as in Fig. 12-3b.

12-4. Monostable Relaxation Circuits as Dividers. Frequency division through the use of a monostable relaxation device, in this case a monostable multi, is illustrated in Fig. 12-7. Input pulses may be applied at G_1 or P_1, depending on the polarity. A coupling diode may be used (Fig. 6-14) to minimize the reaction of the multi on the pulse source. The waveform of Fig. 12-7b shows the voltage at G_2 with the

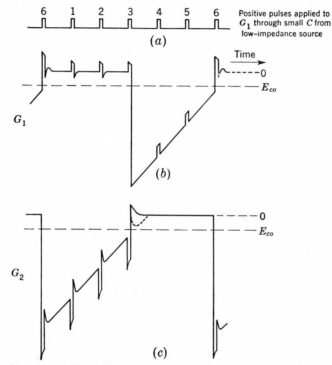

6   1   2   3   4   5   6   Positive pulses applied to
G_1 through small C from
low-impedance source

(*a*)

Time

0

E_{co}

G_1

(*b*)

0

E_{co}

G_2

(*c*)

Fig. 12-6. Synchronization of both portions of astable multi waveform by applying positive pulses to one grid through small capacitor from a low impedance source. Illustrating synchronization resulting from pulse overshoot at G_2.

superimposed input pulses. Each fourth pulse causes a transition of the multi, the remaining pulses occurring at times when they are ineffective. Observe that while the total multi cycle, consisting of timing portion and recovery period, is synchronized, the separate portions are not synchronized.

If positive pulses are applied, say, directly at G_1 through a small capacitor from a low impedance source, a situation may arise similar to the one illustrated in Fig. 12-6 for the astable multi. Here the overshoot due to differentiation of the input pulse may serve to terminate the timing cycle prematurely, as shown in Fig. 12-7c. In this case the two portions of the multi waveform will be synchronized. More importantly, in this latter case the counting ratio will change with increasing amplitude of pulse input. If the overshoot is large enough, the timing cycle will be terminated by the overshoot at pulse 2 or pulse 1, in which case the counting ratio will become, respectively, 3 or 2. Finally, with a large enough overshoot, the timing portion will terminate at pulse 4 and the circuit will not operate as a multi at all.

A second example of a monostable divider is shown in Fig. 12-8a. Here a monostable phantastron has negative pulses applied at the plate through a diode. The diode is not essential but makes the operation

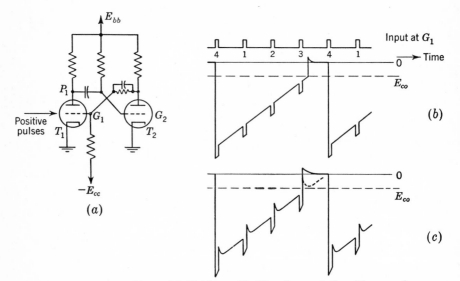

FIG. 12-7. (a) Monostable multi divider. (b) Waveform at G_2 with no pulse overshoot. (c) Waveform at G_2 with pulse overshoot.

more clean-cut. The plate waveform and timing with respect to the input pulses are shown in Fig. 12-8b for the case of division by a factor of 4. With the circuit in its stable state, the phantastron tube is at plate-current cutoff and the plate of T_2 is at E_{bb}. The plate and cathode of diode T_1 are therefore at the same potential and a negative pulse will be transmitted through the diode to initiate the timing cycle. Thereafter, until the timing cycle and recovery period are completed, the diode is open-circuited and the circuit is insensitive to pulses.

12-5. Stability of Relaxation Dividers. There will normally be some small delay between an input pulse to a divider and the output pulse. This delay is referred to as a *phase delay* and results from the finite rise time of the input trigger pulse and the finite response time of the relaxation device. The phase delay itself is subject to variation with time due to variations in tube characteristics, supply voltages, etc. Occasionally some extraneous signal may be coupled unintentionally into the divider. Such a signal may have an influence on the exact moment at which a grid waveform, say, reaches cutoff. In this case the phase delay may be subject to periodic variations. All these factors which affect the phase delay give rise to what is termed *phase jitter*. Even in the absence of an extraneous signal it is found experimentally that in the divider circuits described above, phase jitter is of the order of 0.1 μsec. In a large-scale counter consisting of many stages, the phase jitter is, of course, compounded. In many applications phase jitter is of no particular consequence, while sometimes, particularly in connection with milli-microsecond pulses, it constitutes an important difficulty.

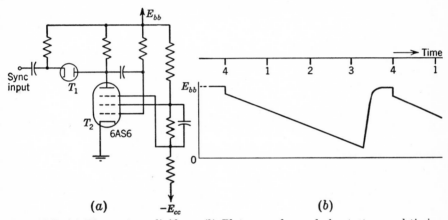

FIG. 12-8. (*a*) Phantastron divider. (*b*) Plate waveform of phantastron and timing with respect to input triggers.

A method for achieving division without phase jitter is illustrated schematically in Fig. 12-9 together with the waveforms depicting the operation. The train of regularly spaced input pulses (I) is applied to the divider input. The output of the divider consists of the pulses shown in waveform (D). These latter pulses trigger a gating waveform generator (say, a monostable multi) which provides a gate of duration T_g adequate to encompass each pulse labeled "1." This waveform is applied to a gating or coincidence circuit (see Chaps. 13 and 14) which is opened for transmission for the duration T_g. The input pulse train is applied to the gating circuit, and its output, waveform O, then consists of each pulse labeled "1." We may take advantage of the phase delay between waveform I and D (not shown in the figure) together with the finite rise time of the gating waveform to ensure that pulse n does not pass through the gating circuit. The duration of the gate is not critical, since it is only required that the duration be longer than the interval between pulses and shorter than the interval between alternate pulses $(T_p < T_g < 2T_p)$. Of course, the coincidence circuit must introduce no phase delay.

A much more commonly encountered jitter in dividers and synchronized relaxation oscillators results from the instability of the natural timing period of the oscillator. This instability of period is caused principally by the variability of tube characteristics and may result either in a loss of synchronism or an incorrect division ratio in a divider. For example, in an $n:1$ divider a change in natural timing period can cause the relaxation oscillator to fire at the $(n-1)$st or the $(n+1)$st pulse rather than at the nth pulse. Similarly, in a $1:1$ synchronized device, if the

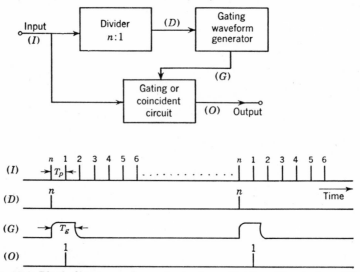

Fig. 12-9. Block diagram and waveforms for a divider without phase jitter.

natural period T_o should drift and become smaller than the interval between pulses, then synchronization of each cycle will be lost.

The factors which influence the stability of the natural period may be seen from Fig. 12-10. The timing waveform starts from an initial voltage E_i. The timing waveform increases exponentially and asymptotically toward the final voltage E_f, but the natural cycle is terminated when the waveform approaches some critical voltage E_c. This voltage E_c may be a cutoff voltage of a tube, as in a multi or blocking oscillator, or it may be the breakdown voltage of a thyratron. The period T_o is easily computed, but for the present we merely note that T_o depends on E_i, E_c, E_f, and the time constant of the exponential rise. The voltage E_f is easily derived from a regulated source and no difficulty need be encountered in reducing the instability of the time constant to a negligible amount. The voltages E_i and E_c, however, depend on tube characteristics. These voltages are stabilized only with the greatest difficulty and constitute the major source of timing instability.

In Chap. 6 it was pointed out (see Fig. 6-4) that it is customary to make E_f large enough so that the portion of the timing waveform between E_i and E_c is approximately linear. In this way the change in T_o with a variation in E_c is reduced somewhat. It is worthy of note, however, that in some cases the variability of E_i exceeds by far the variability of E_c and in such a case it may well be that a large value of E_f will add to the instability. For suppose that E_f is large enough so that the timing waveform is essentially linear between E_i and E_c. In this case a given percentage change in the voltage $E_c - E_i$ will clearly produce an equal percentage change in T_o. On the other hand, it can be shown (see Prob. 12-13) that if E_f is reduced so that the timing interval T_o is not linear, then a

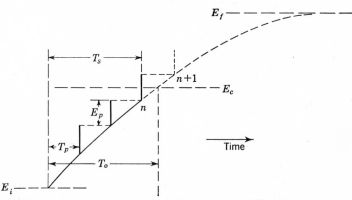

FIG. 12-10. Illustrating the factors which influence the stability of a relaxation divider.

given percentage change in $E_c - E_i$ *due to a variation in E_i* will produce less than an equal percentage change in T_o.

All relaxation oscillators have this instability in E_i, but the worst offender in this regard is the blocking oscillator. The value E_i depends on the charge accumulated on the grid capacitor during the interval when the tube draws grid current, and the grid-current characteristics are usually not well-defined features of a vacuum tube. In any event, with regard to the selection of E_f, an attempt should be made to adjust this voltage so as to reduce the uncertainty in T_o due to the variability of E_i or E_c, whichever variability is the larger.

The factors which determine the selection of the natural period T_o and the amplitude of the synchronizing pulses may be seen from Fig. 12-10. If the timing waveform is nominally linear over the interval T_o, then the natural period should be chosen so that $T_o = (n + \frac{1}{2})T_p$ and the pulse amplitude E_p should be equal to the voltage change of the timing waveform between pulses. Such an adjustment in a divider will yield a fixed counting ratio over the maximum range of variation of E_i or E_c. And for such an adjustment the combined allowable variation in E_i and E_c is $\Delta E_i + \Delta E_c = \pm \frac{1}{2} E_p$. If noise pulses of nominal amplitude E_n are present, then this last equation should read $E_n + \Delta E_i + \Delta E_c = \pm \frac{1}{2} E_p$. The most straightforward method of ensuring reliability of synchronization at a fixed division ratio is to keep the counting ratio low. In dividers which must operate without readjustment for long periods, a division ratio of 10 or less is customary.

12-6. Stabilization of Frequency Dividers by Resonant Circuits.[2] It is possible to use a resonant circuit to modify the grid-cathode waveform of a relaxation divider during its timing cycle in such a way as to improve the stability of operation. We shall illustrate the use of resonant stabilization in connection with a blocking oscillator.

A blocking oscillator with a parallel resonant circuit in the cathode is shown in Fig. 12-11a. Positive synchronizing pulses are indicated as being introduced across a small resistor r in series with the grid capacitor. The grid-to-ground waveform with the superimposed pulses is shown in Fig. 12-11b. The negative of the cathode waveform, $-e_{kn}$, is shown in Fig. 12-11c. At the time the blocking oscillator fires, a pulse of current flows into the cathode capacitor C_k, leaving the capacitor charged to a voltage E_o. Immediately after the blocking-oscillator pulse the tube is cut off and the resonant circuit in the cathode oscillates freely. The cathode waveform is sinusoidal with a period $T_k = 2\pi \sqrt{L_k C_k}$. The case illustrated is one for which $T_s = (1 + \frac{1}{2}) T_k = 6 T_p$; that is, one and a half complete cycles of the cathode waveform and six cycles of the sync waveform occur during the synchronized period T_s of the blocking oscillator. The resultant grid-to-cathode waveform with the superimposed synchronizing pulses is shown in Fig. 12-11d. Actually, the cutoff voltage E_{co} in Fig. 12-11d is not exactly constant, since the cutoff voltage is a function of the plate-to-cathode voltage which varies because of the signal at the cathode. A change Δe_{kn} in the cathode voltage produces a change of essentially $\Delta e_{kn}/\mu$ (μ = amplification factor) in the cutoff voltage. The signal e_{kn} has, therefore, a relatively small effect on E_{co}. In any event, since the amplitude of oscillation of the resonant circuit is not easily calculated with precision and since the effect of the variability of E_{co} is a second-order effect, we may, as in Fig. 12-11, neglect the matter entirely. The important feature to note is that the change in the grid-cathode waveform between the fifth and sixth pulse is appreciably larger than it would be if the resonant cathode circuit were not present. As a result, a larger synchronizing pulse may be used and the stability of synchronization is improved.

Before proceeding further with the discussion of resonant stabilization, we shall now verify that the cathode waveform of Fig. 12-11c is correctly

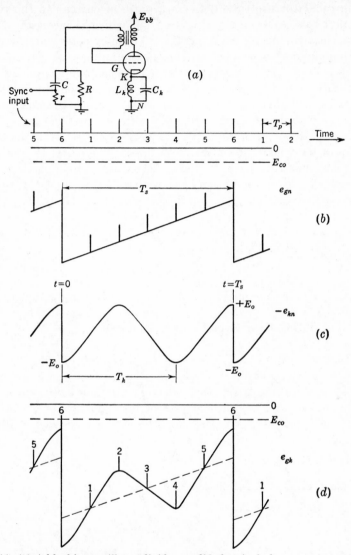

FIG. 12-11. (a) A blocking-oscillator divider modified to include a resonant stabilizing circuit. (b) The grid-to-ground waveform. (c) The negative of the cathode-to-ground voltage. (d) The grid-to-cathode voltage.

drawn.   We shall also examine the situation which results if the resonant period T_k is not exactly equal to $1\frac{1}{2}$ free oscillations in the synchronized period T_s.   Thus, let us assume that $T_s = (n + \beta)T_k$, where n is an integer and $0 < \beta < 1$.   We assume further that the damping of the resonant circuit is small enough so that no appreciable amplitude decrement occurs during the time T_s.   Lastly, we consider that at each firing of the blocking oscillator the tube delivers a pulse of current to the resonant circuit and that this pulse has a duration which is negligibly small in comparison with the resonant period. This impulsive current changes the voltage across C_k, but the current in the inductor L_k cannot change abruptly. When the blocking oscillator has been operating long enough for equilibrium to have been established, the total energy in the resonant circuit will thereafter remain constant. Since the coil current I is the same before as after the tube fires, the magnetic energy $\frac{1}{2}L_k I^2$ is unchanged. Hence, the capacitive energy $\frac{1}{2}C_k E_o^2$ after the impulse must equal its value before the tube fires. Therefore, the magnitude of E_o must remain unchanged at the discontinuity in capacitor voltage. This argument leads to the conclusion that if the capacitor voltage is $-E_o$ before the tube fires, it will jump to $+E_o$ immediately after the tube ceases conducting.

We shall now find the phase θ of the free oscillation. The cathode voltage, for $0 < t < T_s$, is given by

$$e_{kn} = E_m \cos (\omega_k t + \theta) \tag{12-1}$$

where E_m is the peak voltage and $E_o = E_m \cos \theta$ is the voltage after the discontinuity (at $t = 0+$). The inductor current i_L is equal to the capacitor current during the free oscillations, and hence

$$i_L = C \frac{de_{kn}}{dt} = -\omega_k C E_m \sin (\omega_k t + \theta) \tag{12-2}$$

From the physical concepts described above, it follows that at $t = T_s-$ the voltage e_{kn} must be the negative of its value at $t = 0+$ and i_L at $t = T_s-$ must equal its value at $t = 0+$. Since $T_s = (n + \beta)T_k$ and since $\omega_k T_k = 2\pi$, the above conditions are equivalent to

$$\cos \theta = -\cos (2\pi\beta + \theta) \qquad \text{and} \qquad \sin \theta = \sin (2\pi\beta + \theta) \tag{12-3}$$

The solution of Eqs. (12-3) is $2\pi\beta + \theta = \pi - \theta$, or

$$\theta = (1 - 2\beta) \frac{\pi}{2} \tag{12-4}$$

For $T_s = (1 + \frac{1}{2})T_k$, $n = 1$ and $\beta = \frac{1}{2}$. From Eq. (12-4) we find $\theta = 0$. Hence, $e_{kn} = E_m \cos \omega_k t$, which verifies the situation pictured in Fig. 12-11c.

Although it is not necessary that we adjust the resonant frequency so that T_s is exactly equal to $(n + \frac{1}{2})T_k$ (with $\beta = \frac{1}{2}$), we see, from Fig. 12-11d, that it is advantageous to satisfy this condition approximately. Under these circumstances the difference between the fifth and sixth pulse is accentuated by the sinusoidal cathode waveform, which is the desired effect. We note, however, that the second pulse has been lifted

closer to the cutoff level.   If, say, the amplitude of the cathode waveform were somewhat larger, it is possible that, as a result of the circuit
instability, firing might take place at the second pulse.   This situation
may be remedied by including in the cathode two resonant circuits as in

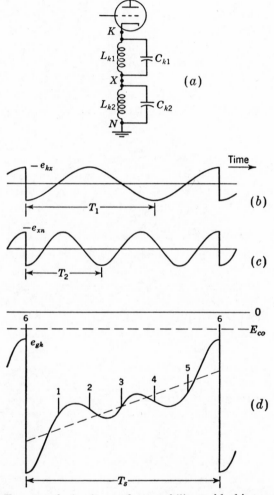

FIG. 12-12. (a) Two tuned circuits used to stabilize a blocking-oscillator divider.
(b, c) The waveforms across the cathode-tuned circuits.   (d) The resultant grid-to-
cathode waveform.

Fig. 12-12a, one tuned to a period T_1 and the second to a period T_2,
where $(1 + \frac{1}{2})T_1 = 6T_p$ and $(2 + \frac{1}{2})T_2 = 6T_p = T_s$.   The waveforms
which appear across the tuned circuits are shown in Fig. 12-12b and c
and the combined grid-to-cathode waveform appears in Fig. 12-12d.

The amplitudes of the free oscillations here have each been adjusted to be one-half the amplitude of the free oscillation shown in Fig. 12-11c. Observe that now the difference in level between the fifth and sixth pulse has been accentuated without moving any of the earlier pulses materially closer to the cutoff level than they would be if the resonant circuits were not used.

It is difficult to set down any general rules concerning the design of the resonant circuits except to note that each cathode circuit should be tuned so that $n + \frac{1}{2}$ cycles occur during the synchronized period of the blocking oscillator. This period requirement for an individual tuned circuit establishes only the product $L_k C_k$. We are therefore still at liberty to select C_k to adjust the amplitude of the free oscillation. If, when the blocking oscillator fires, the total charge delivered by the tube is q, then the capacitor will be left charged to a voltage $q/2C_k$, which then gives the amplitude E_o of the oscillation. The amplitude depends, of course, on the pulse duration and pulse current. Therefore, the amplitude is affected by the tube used, the size of the grid capacitor, and the pulse transformer of the blocking oscillator. Ordinarily, there is no need to employ more than two resonant cathode circuits to achieve a good measure of stability.

The principle of resonant stabilization may be applied not only to a relaxation oscillator which is synchronized by an externally applied signal but also to a free-running oscillator. A free-running blocking oscillator, say, with a resonant circuit in the cathode or grid circuit will have an effective grid-to-cathode voltage waveform similar to that which appears in Fig. 12-11d, with the exception, of course, that sync pulses will be absent. The slope of the grid-to-cathode voltage at the time the E_{co} line is crossed may be increased by the use of a resonant circuit ($\beta \cong 0.25$) with a consequent reduction of the sensitivity of period to variations in E_i and E_f (Fig. 12-10).

12-7. Synchronization of a Thyratron Sweep with Sinusoidai Signals. Up to the present we have considered the phenomenon of synchronization only for the case of pulse-type synchronizing signals. We have assumed that the synchronizing signal consists of a train of waveforms with leading edges which rise abruptly. We shall now consider the case in which the voltage variation of the sync signal is gradual rather than abrupt. We shall discuss explicitly only the case of a sinusoidal sync signal, but the results will easily be seen to apply to any gradually varying waveform. Again, the mechanism of synchronization is so nearly identical for all types of relaxation oscillators that we may without loss of generality select any one of them, say, the thyratron sweep generator, for detailed consideration.

Let us start then by considering the case of a thyratron sweep generator as in Fig. 12-1a.   To the grid of this tube is applied a sinusoidal sync signal whose period T (corresponding to T_p in Fig. 12-1b) is exactly equal to the natural period T_o of the thyratron sweep.   For a positive value of the sync signal, the breakdown voltage is lowered, as indicated in Fig. 12-13.   Since the grid-control ratio of the thyratron (Sec. 7-2) is constant, the breakdown voltage will vary sinusoidally if the sync voltage is sinusoidal.   The general results to follow, however, depend no more on the constancy of the grid-control ratio than they do on the precise sinusoidal nature of the sync signal.

Suppose that we consider that synchronization has been established. Since the sync signal period T is equal to T_o, synchronization requires

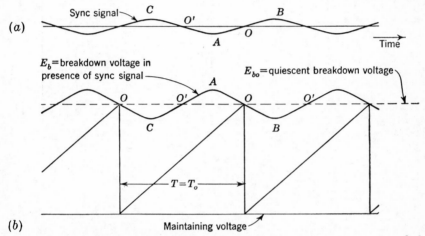

FIG. 12-13. Illustrating the timing relationship that must exist between E_b and the sweep voltage in a synchronized thyratron sweep when $T = T_o$.   (a) Sync signal at the grid.   (b) Synchronized output sweep.

that the period of the thyratron sweep shall not be changed by the sync signal.   Hence, the voltages which mark the limits of the excursion of the sweep voltage must remain unaltered.   The sweep cycle must therefore continue to terminate at E_{bo}.   This result, in turn, means that the intersection of the sweep voltage with the waveform E_b must occur, as shown in Fig. 12-13, at the time when E_b crosses E_{bo}, at the points labeled O in the figure.   The possibility that the sweep will terminate at the points marked O' will be considered shortly.

In the case of pulse synchronization we noted that synchronism could result only if the sync signal period was equal to or less than the natural period.   This feature resulted from the fact that a pulse could serve reliably only to terminate a timing cycle prematurely and not to lengthen it.   In the present case, however, synchronization is possible both when $T < T_o$ and when $T > T_o$.   The timing relationship between the sweep voltage and the breakdown voltage for both cases is shown in Fig. 12-14a. The sweep voltage drawn as a solid line has a natural period $T_o' > T$. The sweep voltage meets the E_b curve at a point below E_{bo} and is consequently prematurely terminated. The dashed sweep voltage has a natural period $T_o'' < T$. This sweep meets the E_b curve at a point above E_{bo} and is consequently lengthened. In each case the synchronized period T_s equals the period T. The general situation may be described by reference to Fig. 12-14b. When $T = T_o$, the sweep is terminated at

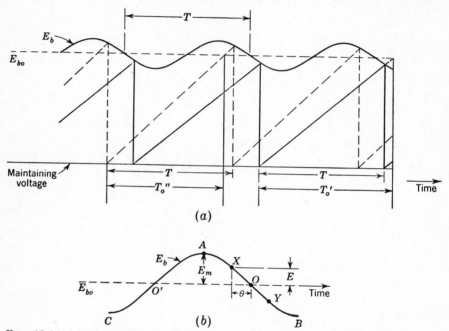

FIG. 12-14. (a) Illustrating the timing of the sweep voltage with respect to E_b for a case in which $T > T_o$ and in which $T < T_o$. (b) Pertaining to the general case when $T \neq T_o$.

point O, leaving the period unaltered. When $T > T_o$, the sweep terminates at a point such as X between O and the positive maximum A. When $T < T_o$, the sweep terminates at a point such as Y between O and the negative maximum B. When the period T is such that the sweep terminates either at the point A or B, the limits of synchronization have been reached, since at A the sweep period has been lengthened to the maximum extent possible, while at B the shortening is at maximum. The following illustrative example will show how one may calculate the range of synchronization.

EXAMPLE. An 884 thyratron sweep operates with a maintaining voltage of 16 volts and a breakdown voltage $E_{bo} = 40$ volts. A sinusoidal synchronizing voltage of peak-to-peak amplitude 0.5 volt is applied to the grid.   The grid-control ratio is 8. If the natural frequency of the sweep is 1,000 cps, over what range of sync signal frequency will the sweep circuit remain in 1:1 synchronism with the sync signal?

Solution.   The peak-to-peak amplitude of the a-c component of the breakdown voltage is $0.5 \times 8 = 4.0$ volts.   The sweep amplitude may therefore lie in the range $(40 - 16) - 2 = 22$ volts to $(40 - 16) + 2 = 26$ volts.   A sweep of $40 - 16 = 24$ volts is generated in 10^{-3} sec.   Hence, the times required to generate sweeps of 22 and 26 volts, respectively, are $^{22}\!/_{24} \times 10^{-3}$ and $^{26}\!/_{24} \times 10^{-3}$ sec.   The corresponding frequencies are $^{24}\!/_{22} \times 10^3 = 1{,}091$ and $^{24}\!/_{26} \times 10^3 = 923$ cps.   Thus the sweep generator will remain synchronized as the sync-signal frequency varies over the range from 923 to 1,091 cps.

We shall now look into the matter of the stability of a point of intersection of the sweep voltage with the E_b curve, as X in Fig. 12-14b. Suppose that as a result of some transient disturbance the intersection point during one cycle should occur at some point other than X.   Or suppose that when the sync voltage is first applied, the intersection point occurs initially at some arbitrary point.   We shall now show that intersection at X represents a stable situation and that with each successive cycle the intersection point will move closer and closer to point X.   This result is easily seen from the graphical construction of Fig. 12-16a.   Suppose that the intersection point required to make the sweep and sync periods equal is at point X.   Consider that during a particular cycle the intersection actually occurs at Y, that is, a time Δt too soon.   Then the timing of the sweep during the *next* cycle is as shown by the dotted line. The intersection is now at Z, *closer to X.*   We may now easily continue this graphical construction, which will show the intersection point moving closer to X at each cycle, eventually reaching X in the limit.

The sync voltage accomplishes its function by lengthening or shortening the sweep as required to make the sync and sweep periods identical. Referring to Fig. 12-14b, it will be clear that this end might be achieved if the sweep terminated at some point on the E_b curve between C and A as well as at some point between A and B.   Suppose then, as in Fig. 12-16b, the correct intersection point is at X' but that during a particular cycle the intersection occurs at Y', at time Δt too late.   Then the construction shows that during the *next* sweep cycle (dotted line) the intersection point moves to Z', *further away from X'.*   Hence X' is not a stable point.   Continuation of the graphical construction will show that the intersection point will move progressively with each succeeding cycle until it reaches the point X.   Here the sweep period is the same as at X', but at X the situation is stable, while at X' it is unstable.

In summary, we may conclude that a relaxation oscillator may be synchronized stably only on the *positive slope portion (AOB* of Figs. 12-13 or 12-14b) *of a sinusoidal input sync voltage.*   The particular phase θ of the input sine wave at which synchronization takes place is seen from Fig.

12-14*b* to be given by

$$\theta = \arcsin \frac{E}{E_m}$$

where E is the minimum voltage required for synchronization and E_m is the peak value of the sine-wave voltage.

12-8. Sine-wave Frequency Division with a Thyratron Sweep. The operation of a thyratron sweep as a divider is a natural extension of the process of synchronization. Figure 12-15 (solid lines) shows the sweep and synchronizing waveforms for division by a factor of 4. This case is one in which the natural period T_o is slightly smaller than $4T$. The sync

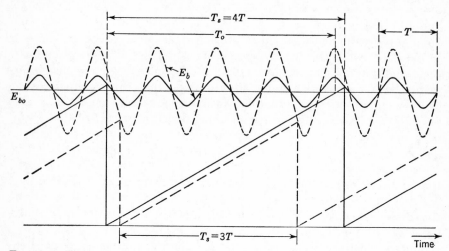

FIG. 12-15. The thyratron sweep used as a counter. Illustrating the change in counting ratio with sync-signal amplitude.

signal changes the sweep period from T_o to T_s, where $T_s = 4T$. The dotted waveforms in Fig. 12-15 show that for the situation illustrated an increase in amplitude of the sync signal can change the counting ratio from 4 to 3. Quite generally one may make the following observation with respect to a thyratron sweep as a counter. If the sweep terminates on the descending portion of the E_b curve and if as a consequence the period T_o is lengthened or shortened to T_s where $T_s = nT$, then the thyratron will operate stably as an $n:1$ counter.

It was tacitly assumed earlier that the range of synchronization (or counting) extends from the point where the sweep intersects the E_b curve at a maximum to the point where the intersection is at a minimum of the E_b curve. Such a result normally holds for small values of sync voltage, but may not necessarily apply when the sync amplitude is comparable to the sweep amplitude. Observe, for example, in Fig. 12-15 that the

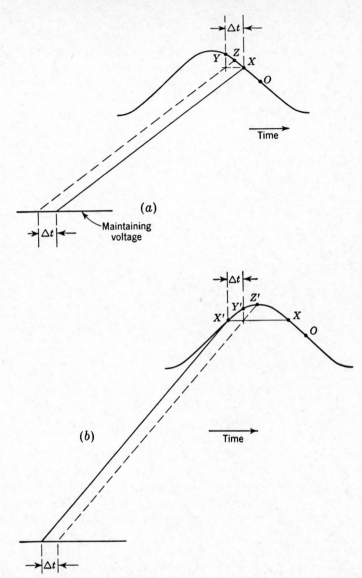

FIG. 12-16. (a) Showing that when the intersection point of the sweep with the E_b curve occurs on the descending portion of the E_b curve a stable situation results. (b) Showing that instability results if the intersection point occurs on the ascending portion of the E_b curve.

sweep will never be able to terminate at a maximum of E_b, since to do so would require that the sweep first cross the previous negative excursion of the E_b waveform. Figure 12-17 illustrates a case (dotted sweep) where the sync amplitude is in principle just large enough to cause 1:1 synchronization. The actual sweep waveform, however, as shown, consists of alternate long and short sweeps. Figure 12-17 suggests that when a thyratron sweep is used in connection with a cathode-ray oscillograph it is advisable always to use as small a sync signal as possible. A sweep waveform as in Fig. 12-17 will cause a piecewise display of each cycle of the signal being observed on a cathode-ray oscillograph.

We shall now compare the general results which hold for sine-wave synchronization with the characteristics associated with pulse synchronization. The features of pulse synchronization are effectively summarized in Fig. 12-3. As in Fig. 12-3, so in the case of sine-wave synchronization we find that, for small sync signals, synchronization holds over a

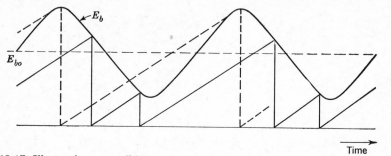

FIG. 12-17. Illustrating a possible result of excessive sync signal in a thyratron sweep.

small range in the neighborhood of integral relationships between T and T_o. With sine waves, however, unlike the situation that results with pulses, synchronization persists for variations of T_o/T in either direction. In both cases the range of synchronization increases with increasing sync-signal amplitude. Finally, with pulses, for large sync-signal amplitudes, synchronization holds for all values of $T_o/T_p > 1$, abrupt jumps in counting ratio occurring at critical values of T_o/T_p. With sine waves, however, while the range of synchronization may be large for large sync amplitudes, we cannot be sure that synchronization in a useful fashion will persist for all values of T_o/T. This last feature is in part brought out in Fig. 12-17.

12-9. Sine-wave Synchronization of Other Relaxation Devices. The mechanism of sine-wave synchronization of relaxation devices other than the thyratron sweep is similar in principle to that already discussed. Let us consider, as an additional and representative example, the sine-wave synchronization of an astable multivibrator.

To achieve synchronization, a sync signal must be applied in such a manner that it can influence the instant at which a timing cycle is terminated by a regenerative action. This regeneration occurs when a tube comes out of cutoff, and therefore the sync signal may be injected at a grid, a cathode, or a plate. In the latter case the sync signal is principally effective because it is coupled to a grid through a plate-to-grid coupling capacitor. The precise details of synchronization will depend on the manner of sync injection, on whether the sync is applied to one or both tubes, and also in each case on the impedance of the sync source.

Let us consider that a sinusoidal signal from a low-impedance source is applied to one grid, say G_1, in Fig. 12-5a. When T_1 is cut off, the sync voltage will appear superimposed on the exponential G_1 waveform. During the time T_2 is cut off, the amplified and inverted sync voltage will appear superimposed on the G_2 waveform. If, as is normally the case, the gain from G_1 to G_2 in the multi is large, then the sync voltage on G_2 will be large in comparison with the sync voltage on G_1. Hence, we shall not make a serious error by neglecting the sync voltage on G_1 and assuming that the instant G_1 comes out of cutoff is unaffected by the sync voltage. In other words, the first portion of the multi is unsynchronized. To determine graphically how the sync voltage on G_2 influences the instant at which the timing cycle of G_2 is terminated, we may either add the sine voltage to the exponential at G_2 or else we may invert the sine voltage at G_2 and add it to the cutoff voltage. A typical situation illustrating synchronization is indicated in Fig. 12-18. In Fig. 12-18a we show the sinusoidal sync voltage at G_1. In Fig. 12-18b this voltage has been amplified, inverted, and added to the exponential waveform at G_2. In Fig. 12-18c the sinusoidal sync voltage of Fig. 12-18b has been inverted and added to the cutoff level to give the effective cutoff-voltage curve shown. The waveform which would be observed on an oscilloscope whose input is at G_2 is that indicated in Fig. 12-18b. However, the construction in Fig. 12-18c is more useful from the point of view of analyzing the effect of the synchronizing voltage on the behavior of the multi. As previously discussed, stable synchronization requires that the multi exponential terminate on the effective cutoff voltage while the latter has a negative slope. And the general characteristics suggested by Fig. 12-3a and b apply to the astable multi as well.

To increase the range of synchronization of the multi, it is advantageous to synchronize both timing cycles of the multi by applying synchronizing signals to both grids simultaneously. Ordinarily in divider applications a multi is adjusted for nominally symmetrical operation, since no special advantage results from asymmetrical operation. For such a symmetrical multi, it is best to apply in-phase sync signals if the division ratio is to be an even number and to apply out-of-phase sync

signals if the division ratio is to be odd.   These results may be seen from
Fig. 12-19.   In Fig. 12-19a the division ratio (4:1) is even, the sync signals are in phase, and it appears that both timing exponentials meet the
effective cutoff voltage in a manner to ensure stability.   In Fig. 12-19b
the division ratio (3:1) is odd, the sync signals are again in phase, and
while the exponential of the G_1 waveform is synchronized in a stable fashion, the G_2 waveform is not.   Similarly, it is easy to show, by drawing
appropriate waveforms, that, when the sync signals are out of phase,

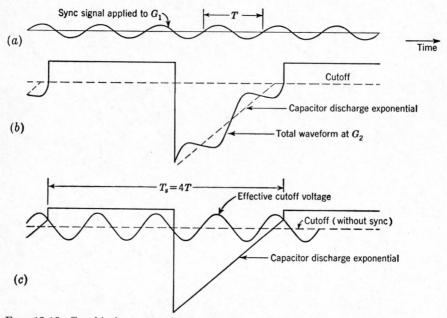

Fig. 12-18. Graphical construction to show synchronization of an astable multi to
sine waves.   (a) Sync waveform at G_1; (b) sync combined with exponential discharge
waveform at G_2; (c) sync combined with cutoff voltage at G_2.

both parts of the multi grid waveform will be synchronized in a stable
fashion only for odd division ratios.

A blocking oscillator may be made to provide its own sinusoidal synchronizing signal by using the principle of resonant stabilization.   Referring to Fig. 12-11, we note that, neglecting the sync pulses, the superimposed sinusoidal waveform may give the net grid-to-cathode waveform
a larger slope near the termination of the cycle than that of the exponential itself.   As a result, the usual sources of instability in a blocking
oscillator may give rise to much reduced frequency instability.

Before leaving the subject of sine-wave synchronization of relaxation
oscillators we wish to emphasize that such a divider does not deliver a
sinusoidal output.   In most cases the waveform is more nearly "square"

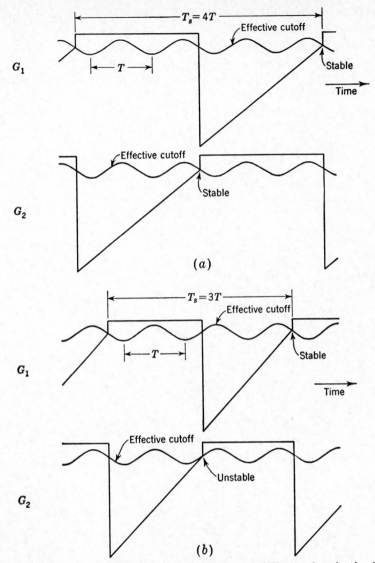

FIG. 12-19. Sync signal applied in phase to both grids. (*a*) The synchronization is stable for both portions of the multi waveform when the division ratio is even. (*b*) The division ratio is odd and the G_2 timing waveform is not locked in a stable fashion.

(from a multi) or "triangular" (from a gas-tube sweep or blocking oscillator). If a sinusoidal waveform is desired, then the output of the relaxation divider is applied to the input of an amplifier whose plate load is a tank circuit tuned to the desired frequency. Circuits for obtaining sinusoidal division without using a relaxation device are given in the next two sections.

12-10. A Sinusoidal Divider Using Regeneration and Modulation.[3]
The relaxation dividers do not normally operate reliably at frequencies
beyond about 1 Mc.   At these high frequencies the times of the regenerative transition between states and the recovery periods become comparable to the time of duration of a stable or quasi-stable state.   The
natural period of the divider becomes very unstable, being seriously
affected by small variations in stray capacitance, and stable frequency
division is achieved only with great difficulty.

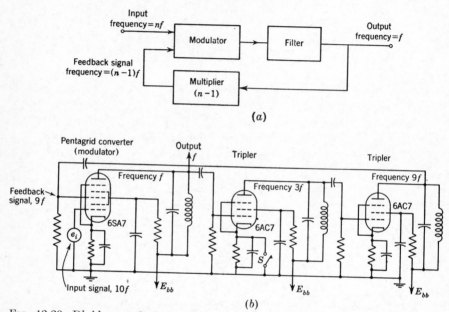

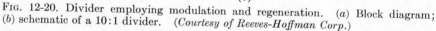

FIG. 12-20. Divider employing modulation and regeneration.   (a) Block diagram;
(b) schematic of a 10:1 divider.   (*Courtesy of Reeves-Hoffman Corp.*)

A divider for a sinusoidal signal which is capable of operating at very
much higher frequencies than relaxation dividers is shown in functional
form in Fig. 12-20a.   The signal of frequency nf, whose frequency is to
be divided by the factor n, is applied to an amplitude modulator.   Simultaneously a signal of frequency $(n - 1)f$, whose origin will appear shortly,
is also applied to the modulator.   In the modulator the signal nf is modulated by the signal $(n - 1)f$.   The modulator output contains many
frequencies, among which are the input frequencies $(n - 1)f$ and nf
as well as the sideband frequencies $nf + (n - 1)f = (2n - 1)f$ and
$nf - (n - 1)f = f$.   The filter selects the frequency f which then
appears as the output.   The output is applied to a frequency multiplier
which multiplies by the ratio $n - 1$ to produce the feedback signal of
frequency $(n - 1)f$ whose existence was postulated at the outset.   *The*

loop gain at the frequency f must exceed unity if the oscillations are to be sustained. This statement explains the use of the word *regeneration* in connection with this type of divider.

The modulator (refer to Fig. 12-20b) usually consists of a pentagrid converter tube such as is used in a radio receiver to heterodyne the incoming radio-frequency signal with the local oscillator signal to produce the intermediate-frequency signal. Such pentagrid converter tubes, of which the 6SA7 and the 6BA7 are examples, have two control grids. The signal component of the plate current of these tubes is essentially proportional to the *product* of the signals of the two control grids and for this reason the tube may be used as a modulator. The filter at the modulator output need consist of nothing more elaborate than a parallel-tuned LC circuit in the plate lead of the modulator tube. The frequency multiplier may be of the conventional type in which a pentode is driven by a large-amplitude grid signal, the plate load of the pentode being a resonant tank tuned to the $(n-1)$st harmonic of the input signal. If the input signal is large enough so that the plate current flows in pulses, this current will be rich in harmonics of the input signal. Assuming a high Q tank circuit, the output voltage will equal the product of the tank-circuit impedance at its resonant frequency times the component of plate current at this frequency. The upper frequency of operation of dividers of the type given in Fig. 12-20a is limited only by the frequency at which modulators, filters, and multipliers may be operated. A schematic of a 10:1 divider using two multipliers in cascade is shown in Fig. 12-20b.

We shall now show qualitatively that the only stable frequency at which the circuit can operate is precisely f. Assume, for example, that the output frequency momentarily drifts from f to some higher value $f + \delta$, where $\delta > 0$ and $\delta \ll f$. Then the output of the multiplier will be $(n-1)(f+\delta)$ and the modulator frequency will shift from f to $nf - (n-1)(f+\delta) = f - (n-1)\delta$, which frequency is less than f. Hence, if the frequency tends to increase, the circuit acts in such a direction as to counterbalance this tendency. Therefore, f may be a stable frequency.

If the multiplier were designed to deliver a frequency $(n+1)f$ instead of $(n-1)f$, then the output frequency would also be f. However, such a system is unstable. For example, if the output drifts from f to some higher value $f + \delta$ momentarily, then the modulator output will shift from f to $(n+1)(f+\delta) - nf = f + (n+1)\delta$. Since this frequency is further away from f than the assumed deviation δ, then the circuit causes the output frequency to drift away from the initial value f. When the frequency drifts far enough away from the central frequency of the tuned circuits (in the modulator and multiplier), the loop gain becomes less than unity and the output drops to zero. Therefore, we conclude that the multiplier must be designed for a frequency $(n - 1)f$ and not $(n + 1)f$.

The special case $n = 2$ is of some interest. Since $n - 1 = 1$ for $n = 2$, then the multiplication is by 1. Hence, division by 2 is accomplished without the use of a multiplier.

In the case of a relaxation oscillation we saw that increasing the size of the sync voltage might cause a change in division ratio. This result is not obtained with the circuit now under consideration. There exists a minimum voltage below which the circuit output is zero. However, if the sync voltage is increased beyond the minimum value, the frequency of the output remains unchanged, although the amplitude of the output increases.

The divider of Fig. 12-20 has two disadvantages. The first of these is its relative complexity. Second, it may turn out that the divider is not self-starting. The reason for this last feature is not difficult to see. The multipliers depend for their operation on having a large input signal so that the tubes will be vigorously overdriven. When the driving signal is small, the tubes may operate quite linearly and, hence, provide no appreciable harmonic components of plate current. Hence, the multipliers wait for the circuit to supply large driving signals, whereas the circuit cannot do so until the multipliers operate. To start the divider, it may be necessary to allow the tubes to warm up, to apply plate voltage, and then to introduce a large transient voltage into the circuit. The starting switch S in Fig. 12-20b is intended to introduce just such a large starting transient.

On the other hand, the divider in Fig. 12-20 has a number of worthwhile advantages. The first of these, of course, is its ability to operate at high frequencies. Second, the proper division ratio depends essentially only on the tuning of several passive filter circuits, which tuning is not critical, and not on the stability of tube characteristic. Lastly, if the tuning of the tank circuits should happen to drift out of range or if the input signal should be missing, the divider will furnish no output. The circuit, therefore, operates to give the correct output signal or it does not operate at all. These features are to be compared with, say, the astable multi which will divide incorrectly if the tube characteristics drift excessively and which will continue to give an output signal, necessarily incorrect, if the input signal should fail.

12-11. The Locked Oscillator as a Divider.[4] A *sinusoidal* oscillator can be used as a frequency divider. Assume that the natural frequency of the oscillator is f_o and that a nominally sinusoidal synchronizing signal of frequency f_s, nearly equal to nf_o (n = an integer), is injected into the oscillator. The oscillator frequency will change from f_o to f_s/n and thereafter will run synchronously with the injected signal. Under these conditions the oscillator is said to be *locked*.   The locked oscillator divider shares the advantage of the divider using modulation and regeneration in that it may be used at frequencies beyond the range of relaxation dividers. The locked oscillator has the further advantage of simplicity when compared with the divider using modulation and regeneration.   It suffers, however, from the relative disadvantage that it continues to yield an output even in the absence of a synchronizing signal.

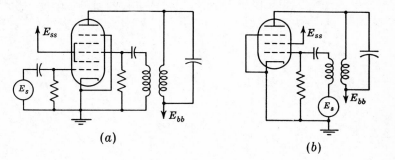

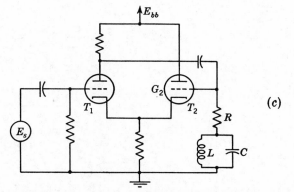

FIG. 12-21. Locked oscillator circuits.   (*a*) Using pentagrid converter for combining sync and oscillator signals.   (*b*) The sync and oscillator signals are applied to one grid. (*c*) A cathode-coupled circuit.

A careful analysis of the mechanism by which a sinusoidal oscillator locks to a synchronizing signal is difficult to achieve.   This difficulty does not arise because any basically new principle is involved.   The mechanism of locking in oscillators is similar to the mechanism involved in the divider using modulation and regeneration.   The complication arises in the present case because all the functions of modulation, regeneration, and harmonic generation are accomplished in a single tube.   The tube nonlinearity is essential to the locking mechanism.   Since a nonlinear characteristic is difficult to handle analytically, most locked oscillator *design* is carried out experimentally.

Several locked oscillator dividers are shown in Fig. 12-21.   In Fig.

12-21a the third grid of a pentagrid converter is used as the control grid for a tuned-plate oscillator, while the sync signal E_s is introduced on the first grid. In Fig. 12-21b the sync and oscillator signals are applied to the same grid. A cathode-coupled oscillator is shown in Fig. 12-21c in which the sync signal is introduced at the free grid.

12-12. Synchronization of a Sinusoidal Oscillator with Pulses.[5] Synchronization is basically a mechanism in which the phase of the sync signal is compared with the phase of the oscillator (relaxation or otherwise) and a continuous correction is applied to the oscillator to maintain

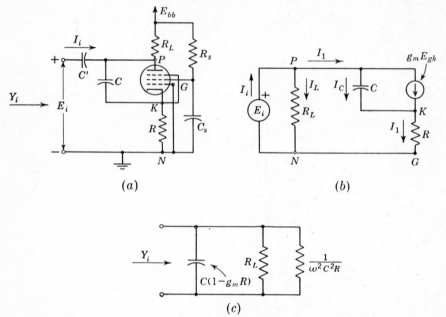

FIG. 12-22. (a) A cathode-coupled reactance tube. (b) The equivalent circuit for calculating the input admittance. (c) The effective input admittance.

some fixed phase relation. An extension of adaptability and certain other useful features may result if the operations of phase comparison and phase correction are carried out separately. We shall illustrate the process by discussing the one-to-one synchronization of a sinusoidal oscillator to a pulse-type sync signal.

The system to be described involves a *reactance tube* and a *phase comparison circuit* which we shall first describe very briefly. One of a number of possible methods of using a tube as a reactance tube is shown in Fig. 12-22a. The point of interest in connection with this circuit is the admittance Y_i presented at the input terminals. The capacitor C' is a d-c blocking capacitor of negligible reactance. The tube is a pentode so that its plate current is given by $g_m E_{gk}$. Hence, the equivalent circuit is as drawn in Fig. 12-22b. (Since the plate resistance r_p of the pentode is large compared with R_L or R, it has not been included in Fig. 12-22b.) The ratio $I_i/E_i \equiv Y_i$, and we find

$$Y_i = \frac{1}{R_L} + \frac{Y_c}{1 + g_m R + Y_c R} \tag{12-5}$$

where $Y_c = j\omega C$ is the admittance of the capacitor C. In the application under consideration (Fig. 12-25), $C = 0.015$ μf, $R = 10$ ohms, and $f = 15,750$ so that $|Y_c R| = (2\pi)(15,750)(10)(1.5)10^{-8} = 0.015$. Also, the largest value of g_m is 10^{-2} mho and hence $g_m R = 0.1$ maximum. Since this value and also the value of $|Y_c R|$ is much smaller than unity, we may divide the numerator of the second term in Eq. (12-5) by its denominator and neglect all but the first term in $g_m R + Y_c R$. Thus

$$Y_i \cong \frac{1}{R_L} + Y_c(1 - g_m R - Y_c R)$$

$$= j\omega C(1 - g_m R) + \frac{1}{R_L} + \omega^2 C^2 R \tag{12-6}$$

The input circuit is effectively a capacitance in parallel with two resistors, as indicated in Fig. 12-22c. We must emphasize that the reactive

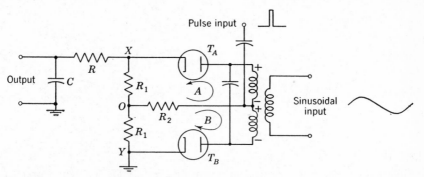

FIG. 12-23. A phase comparator or discriminator circuit for a pulse and sine wave.

component of the input admittance depends on g_m, which is a function of the quiescent tube current and which, in turn, depends on the bias voltage. If this reactance tube is now shunted across the tank of an oscillator, we shall then have a means for controlling the oscillator frequency by varying the d-c bias of the reactance tube. The voltage furnished by the RC phase-shifting network is introduced into the cathode of the reactance tube so that there will be a free grid for controlling the frequency.

A circuit suitable for comparing the phase of a sinusoidal signal and a pulse is shown in Fig. 12-23. The sinusoids are introduced into the meshes A and B in phase opposition with respect to the polarities of the diodes. The pulses are introduced in such a manner as to appear with the same polarity in both meshes. Let us neglect tentatively the effect of the pulses. Then, as a result of the sinusoidal input, unidirectional currents will flow in mesh A and mesh B on alternate half cycles of the sinusoidal voltage. The voltage drops e_{xo} and e_{oy} are as shown in Fig. 12-24a. The combined voltage e_{xy} is then a complete sinusoidal signal whose average value is zero. This signal is integrated by the RC integrating network which then provides zero output voltage. Now consider that positive pulses are applied which occur at such a time that the pulses exactly straddle the time when the sinusoidal signal passes

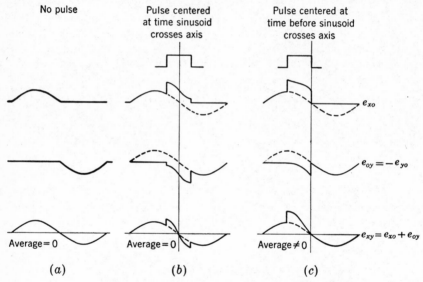

FIG. 12-24. The waveforms in the circuit of Fig. 12-23.

through zero. The waveforms are indicated in Fig. 12-24b. We see again that the average value of the voltage e_{xy} is zero and hence that the output voltage will again be zero. Finally, from Fig. 12-24c, it may be seen that if the pulse occurs earlier than the moment of zero phase of the sinusoids, the average value of e_{xy} is not zero and the integrating circuit in this case will provide essentially a positive d-c output voltage. Similarly, if the pulse is delayed, the output will be a negative d-c voltage.

The reactance-tube circuit and the phase-comparator circuit described above may be used to synchronize a sinusoidal oscillator to a pulse waveform. The pulse waveform and the oscillator signal are applied to the comparator whose output is used to control the bias of a reactance tube bridged across the oscillator tank. Suppose that the pulse frequency and the sinusoid frequency are identical and that an initial phasing adjustment has been made so that the circuit of Fig. 12-23 yields zero output. Now let the frequency of the sinusoidal signal decrease slightly. Then with each succeeding cycle the phase error will become progressively larger and an ever-increasing, positive, nominally d-c voltage will appear at the phase comparison circuit output. This output is applied to the reactance tube to increase its grid voltage and hence to increase the transconductance g_m. From Eq. (12-6) an increase

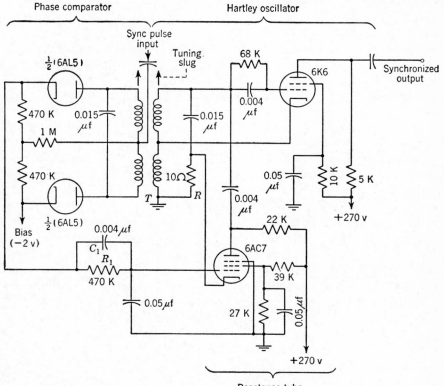

FIG. 12-25. A horizontal synchronizing system of a television receiver. Illustrating the use of a servo system for synchronization. (*Courtesy of Proceedings of the Institute of Radio Engineers.*)

in g_m will decrease the effective capacitance in the tank circuit, and hence the oscillator frequency will increase. Thus, an assumed decrease in frequency has resulted in a circuit reaction which has changed the frequency in the opposite direction. It is to be noted that the system here envisaged is basically a servo system in which the phase comparison circuit is the error-sensing device and the reactance tube is the agency through which the correction is applied.

A practical system employing this servo principle is shown in Fig. 12-25. This circuit is to be found in many television receivers where it is used to synchronize the horizontal-deflection generator (15,750 cps) to the horizontal synchronizing pulses received from the transmitter. The tuned transformer T serves both as the tank circuit for the Hartley oscillator and as the sine-wave input coupling system to the phase comparator. The effective tuning capacitance of the oscillator, as demonstrated above, is $C_i = C(1 - g_m R)$, where C is the fixed capacitance shunted across the oscillator tank. Since the 6AC7 has a g_m which varies by $\pm 5 \times 10^{-3}$ mhos and $R = 10$ ohms, then C_i varies by ± 5 per cent. Since the oscillator frequency varies inversely as the square root of C_i, then the frequency range of control of the servo system is ∓ 2.5 per cent. If the oscillator drifts further than this amount, it must be retuned, say, by adjusting the slug in the transformer T. The capacitor C_1 shunting the resistor R_1 of the integrating network is found to be necessary to prevent the servo system from hunting.

In a television receiver the synchronized output of the circuit of Fig. 12-25 is used in turn to trigger the horizontal sweep generator of the receiver. In connection with television receivers this present system has the distinctive advantage of providing relative immunity from noise pulses which are received with the sync pulses. The noise pulses will occur at random times and hence at random phases with respect to the sinusoidal voltage. Any individual noise pulse will have a negligible effect on the comparator output voltage and the combined effect of a large number of noise pulses will average out to zero.

The servo system of synchronization is a system of quite general applicability, although it has the disadvantage of involving usually fairly complicated circuitry. If it is required to synchronize a waveform generator of any arbitrary waveshape to a sync signal again of arbitrary form, it is only necessary to devise an appropriate phase-comparator circuit and frequency controlling device. The phase comparator of Fig. 12-23 is an example of a *gating circuit*. Gating circuits will be discussed in detail in Chap. 14. And a frequency control mechanism is usually not difficult to find. If, for example, the oscillator to be synchronized is of the relaxation type, the frequency can usually be varied conveniently through the adjustment of a grid bias.

REFERENCES

1. Shenk, E. R.: Multivibrator-Applied Theory and Design, pt. I, *Electronics*, vol. 17, pp. 136–141, January, 1944; pt. II, *ibid.*, vol. 17, pp. 140–145; pt. III, *ibid.*, vol. 17, pp. 138–142, March, 1944.
2. Builder, G.: A Stabilized Frequency Divider, *Proc. IRE*, vol. 29, pp. 177–181, 1941.
   Chance, B., et al.: "Waveforms," Massachusetts Institute of Technology Radiation Series, vol. 19, pp. 595–599, McGraw-Hill Book Company, Inc., New York, 1949.

3. Miller, R. L.: Fractional Frequency Generators Utilizing Regenerative Modulation, *Proc. IRE*, vol. 27, pp. 446–457, July, 1939.

"Instruction Book for Frequency Calibrator Set AN/FRM-3," Reeves-Hoffman Corp., Carlisle, Pa.

4. Tucker, D. G.: The Synchronization of Oscillators, pt. I, *Electronic Eng.*, vol. 15, pp. 412–418, March, 1943; pt. II, *ibid.*, vol. 15, pp. 457–462, April, 1943; pt. III, *ibid.*, vol. 16, pp. 26–30, June, 1943.

Adler, R.: A Study of Locking Phenomena in Oscillators, *Proc. IRE*, vol. 34, pp. 351–357, June, 1946.

Sulzer, P. G.: Modified Locked-oscillator Frequency Dividers, *Proc. IRE*, vol. 39, pp. 1535–1537, December, 1951.

Norrman, E.: The Inductance-Capacitance Oscillator as a Frequency Divider, *Proc. IRE*, vol. 34, pp. 799–803, October, 1946.

Hughes, W. L.: Analysis and Performance of Locked-oscillator Frequency Dividers Employing Nonlinear Elements, *Proc. IRE*, vol. 41, pp. 241–245, February, 1953.

5. Clark, E. L.: Automatic Frequency Phase Control of Television Sweep Circuits, *Proc. IRE*, vol. 37, pp. 497–500, May, 1949.

Clark, E. G.: Stabilizing Color Carrier Reinsertion Oscillator, *Electronics*, vol. 27, pp. 142–146, July, 1954.

CHAPTER 13

DIGITAL COMPUTER CIRCUITS

A *gate* is a device having several inputs and one output. Some of the inputs may be called signal inputs and others may be designated as control or selector inputs, although often the inputs are indistinguishable from one another.

There are two general classes of gates. The first, called the *transmission* or *linear* gate, is defined as one in which the output is approximately a replica of one of the inputs, but the output occurs only during times selected by the control inputs. Thus, the gate transmits the signal from input to output in a linear manner (minimum distortion) during selected times. This type of gate is discussed in Chap. 14.

The second class of gate, called the *switching* or *logical* gate, is defined as one in which the output is a pulse which may have no resemblance to any of the inputs except that the pulse occurs during the interval selected by the control voltages. The term *logical* is applied to these gates because the input-output characteristic of these circuits is suggestive of logical operations.

These gates find wide applicability in all fields of pulse circuitry, but are used particularly extensively in digital computers. For this reason we shall take our illustrations of the applications of these switching gates principally from the field of computers.

13-1. Some Features of a Digital Computer.[1] An electronic digital computer is a machine which solves problems of numerical computation of such complexity that solution by human calculators is not feasible. We may get some sense of the basic processes involved by thinking of the computer as a device which is able to perform numerical computation and to follow instructions with extreme rapidity but which is not able to make any decisions for itself. The numbers and the instructions which form the *program* the computer is to follow are stored in a part of the computer which is referred to as the *memory* and which is the first essential part of the computer. A second essential part of the computer is the *central control*. The function of the *control* is to interpret orders. The control must convert the order into an appropriate set of voltages to operate switches, etc., and thereby carry out the instructions conveyed by the order. A third basic element of a computer is the *arithmetic unit* which is the device which actually performs the arithmetic computations: addition, division etc. Finally, a computer requires appropriate *input-output* devices for inserting numbers and orders into the memory and for reading the final result.

Suppose we consider that as part of a larger routine an order to perform an addition or division, etc., has been transmitted to *central control*. In response to this order the control must select the correct operands from the memory, it must transmit these operands to the correct arithmetic unit, and it must return to the *memory* in some previously designated place the result of this computation. The *memory* serves, then, not only to store the original input data but also the partial results which

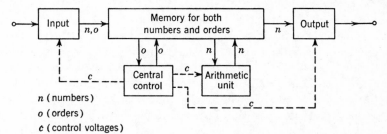

n (numbers)
o (orders)
c (control voltages)

FIG. 13-1. Showing interrelationship of basic elements of a digital computer. (*From C. H. Page, Digital Computer Switching Circuits, Electronics, vol. 21, pp. 110–118, September, 1948.*)

will have to be used again as the computation proceeds. Lastly, if the computation is not to cease with the execution of this order and the storage of the partial result, the order must convey to the *control* instructions with respect to where in the memory the control is to find its next order.

In terms of this crude representation of the functioning of a digital computer the interrelationship of the various components is as indicated in Fig. 13-1. The connection of the control unit back to the input is to permit insertion of more data when room becomes available in the memory.

In a computer a number is represented by a train of pulses. The individual pulses (or absence of pulses) represent, respectively, the 1 or 0 digits in the binary representation of the number. For example, the pulse train of Fig. 13-2 represents the binary number 11010111, which in decimal notation is 215 (conversion from the binary to the decimal system is explained in Sec. 11-2). In a similar way, the instructions which must be conveyed from place to place are also transmitted in the form of a train of pulses. Actually, then, a waveform representing a number is indistinguishable from a waveform representing an instruction. Since, however, numbers are dispatched only to the arithmetic unit and orders only to the control unit, no difficulty arises from this situation. In a pulse train, as in Fig. 13-2, the individual pulses are referred to as *bits* or *characters*, while the entire pulse train is referred to as a *word*. Thus, the pulse train of Fig. 13-2 represents an eight-bit word.

We shall be concerned in this chapter with the matter of transmitting, combining, modifying, etc., the pulses or pulse trains which compose the

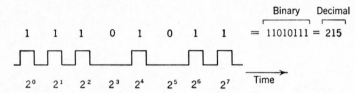

$$1 \quad 1 \quad 1 \quad 0 \quad 1 \quad 0 \quad 1 \quad 1 \quad = \quad 11010111 = 215$$

$$2^0 \quad 2^1 \quad 2^2 \quad 2^3 \quad 2^4 \quad 2^5 \quad 2^6 \quad 2^7 \quad \text{Time}$$

FIG. 13-2. A pulse train representing an order or a number in a digital computer.

language of digital computers. Two points are to be kept in mind, however. First, it is to be noted that the circuits to be described are of very wide applicability and are by no means restricted to computers. Second, the student should not expect to be left with an understanding of the detailed operation of a digital computer—any more than he would expect to understand the operation of a telephone exchange on the basis of an understanding of the operation of a telephone receiver, transmitter, and of a relay.

13-2. The *OR* Circuit.[2]   The *OR* circuit is basically a *buffer* or *mixing* circuit which permits a number of pulse sources of common pulse polarity to be connected to a common load.   The *OR* circuit minimizes the inter-

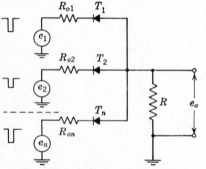

FIG. 13-3. A diode *OR* circuit.

action of the pulse sources on each other. The circuit has two or more inputs and a single output. If a pulse is applied to any one or more of the inputs, a pulse appears at the output. The circuit derives its name from the fact that an output pulse appears when a pulse is applied at input 1 *or* input 2 *or* any other input.

A diode *OR* circuit is shown in Fig. 13-3. The diode symbol is used to represent either thermionic or semiconductor diodes (usually germanium). In the present application, as in others, the germanium diodes have advantages with respect to space, power, and capacitance and disadvantages with respect to operation at high temperatures and low diode back resistance.

If a negative pulse is applied at input 1, diode T_1 will conduct and a negative pulse will appear at the output. If the load R is much larger than the generator output impedance, then, neglecting the small diode forward resistance, the output pulse amplitude will be nominally equal to the input pulse.   As the pulse forms at the output, all the other diodes are biased in their high impedance direction and the presence of the other generators does not result in an additional load on the generator e_1. If two or more pulses all of equal amplitude are applied simultaneously at the input, an output pulse will appear whose amplitude is equal to the input-pulse amplitude.   If the input pulses are of unequal amplitude, the output will be of an amplitude equal to the amplitude of the *largest* input pulse.   The circuit of Fig. 13-3 is appropriate for negative pulse inputs.   For positive pulses, the diodes must be reversed in polarity.

The influence of the shunt output capacitance and the diode capacitance on the output pulse is easily seen.   Assume, for simplicity, that

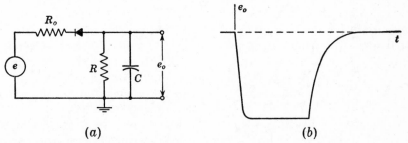

(a)   *(b)*

Fig. 13-4. (a) Equivalent circuit for an *OR* circuit with one input excited.   (b) Output waveform in response to input pulse.

only one generator is furnishing an input pulse.   Since, therefore, all diodes but one are back-biased during the input pulse, the capacitance shunted across the output is $C = C_o + (n - 1)C_d$, in which C_o is the capacitance across R and C_d is the diode capacitance.   We neglect here the impedances of all generators connected to the back-biased diodes and also assume that $R \gg R_o$, where R_o is the output impedance of the generator supplying the pulse.   This input pulse will appear at the output with a rounded leading edge whose time constant is R_oC. The equivalent circuit and waveform are shown in Fig. 13-4a and b. When the input voltage rises at the end of the pulse, the output capacitor will sustain the output voltage and every diode will be back-biased. The capacitor C (whose capacitance is now equal to $C_o + nC_d$) must discharge through R.   The trailing-edge decay time will therefore be very much longer than the leading-edge rise time.   The number of input circuits which may be used is determined by the required transient response of the network.   There will also be a small amount of coupling between generators because of the diode capacitances, but this effect need not be serious.

When capacitive coupling is employed, as in Fig. 13-5, additional shunt diodes are required for d-c restoration. The diode polarities shown are

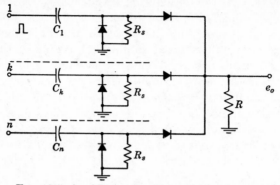

FIG. 13-5. An *OR* circuit with capacitive inputs.

appropriate for positive input pulses. The resistors R_s are large compared with R and may even be omitted altogether. When an input is

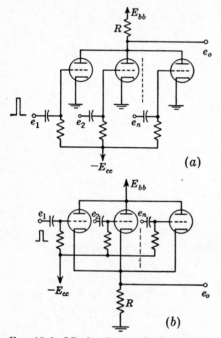

FIG. 13-6. *OR* circuits employing triodes. (a) Load in plate; (b) load in cathode.

excited by a pulse, the corresponding input capacitor will acquire a charge due to the current which flows through the series diode. At the termination of the pulse the capacitor will discharge through the shunt diode. Capacitive and direct inputs may be used simultaneously if required.

OR circuits using triodes are shown in Fig. 13-6a and b. In both cases the tubes are initially biased beyond cutoff. And in both cases the application of a positive pulse to one or more grids will result in an output pulse, negative if the load is in the plate circuit and positive if the load is in the cathode circuit. These circuits have the advantage over the diode circuit of providing a higher input impedance and somewhat better isolation of the input sources. These advantages must, however, be balanced against the extra expense, space, and supply drain.

If, in Fig. 13-6a, two inputs are excited simultaneously, the output pulse will be larger than if one input is excited. If, however, the load R is very large in comparison with the plate resistance of the tube, the output pulse will not be a very sensitive function of the number of inputs excited. The reason for this feature is that if R is very large, then, in response to a positive signal on any one grid, the plate voltage will bottom (see Sec. 4-3). If, then, additional inputs are excited, no appreciable increase in current through R will result. A similar result applies to the cathode-loaded circuit of Fig. 13-6b. In this case, when one input has been excited, the corresponding tube presents at its cathode a very low impedance. The additional current furnished now by any other tube which is caused to conduct will not cause any large change in output voltage.

The general appearance of an output pulse from either of the circuits of Fig. 13-6 will be as shown in Fig. 13-4. That is, the leading edge will have a faster rise time than the trailing edge. The reason is again that the total shunt capacitance across the output will charge through an impedance which is relatively low when the tubes are conducting. At the termination of the pulse, however, the capacitance must discharge through R alone.

Still another OR circuit is shown in Fig. 13-7. Here we make use of a tube which has two grids, either of which may be used to effect the

plate-current cutoff. Among tubes of this type are the 6AS6, the 5915, 6CS6, 7AK7, and 6BN6. Pentagrid converters such as the 6SA7 and the 6BA7 may also be used for the present purpose. In Fig. 13-7 the shading represents the fact that initially the biases on both grids have been adjusted so that the tube is conducting plate current. If now a sufficient negative pulse is applied either to grid 1 or grid 2 (or both), the plate current will cease and an output pulse will result. This circuit is restricted, of course, to only two inputs.

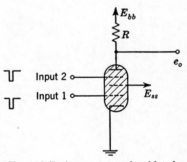

Fig. 13-7. A two-control-grid tube is used as an OR gate.

13-3. The AND Circuit.[2] The AND circuit (also called a *coincidence* circuit) has two or more inputs, to each of which is applied a pulse of common polarity. The circuit has a single output at which a pulse appears if and only if a pulse is applied simultaneously to *all* inputs. If the input pulses are not of the same time duration, the output pulse will appear during the time interval that the input pulses overlap.

The OR circuits of Figs. 13-3, 13-5, and 13-6 may be modified for use as AND circuits by the simple expedient of adjusting the circuits so that in the quiescent condition the tubes or crystals are *conducting* current rather than being in a *cutoff* condition. Negative input pulses must be used in the circuits of Fig. 13-6. Similarly, the *OR* circuit of Fig. 13-7 may serve as an *AND* circuit if the bias on *each* control grid is set below cutoff and if positive input pulses are used.

A diode *AND* circuit for positive input pulses is shown in Fig. 13-8. The diode T_o is not essential, but has nevertheless been included for a reason to appear shortly. To understand the operation of the circuit, assume initially that all the source impedances R_o are zero and that the diode T_o is not present. In this case, in the quiescent condition the output e_o will be clamped to ground since the diodes are conducting. If now positive pulses of amplitude E_{bb} or larger are applied simultaneously to all the inputs, the diodes will be back-biased and a pulse of amplitude E_{bb} will appear at the output. If, however, even one input fails to receive a pulse, the corresponding diode will continue to conduct, the output will remain clamped, and no output pulse will appear. If one or more of the input pulses has an amplitude less than E_{bb}, the

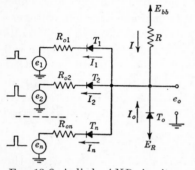

Fig. 13-8. A diode *AND* circuit.

output pulse will have an amplitude equal to the *smallest* input pulse, since when the output rises to the smallest input amplitude the corresponding diode will conduct.

Because of the finite value of the R_o's in a practical circuit, the initial clamping level will be somewhat positive, and even if there is no coincidence of pulses at all inputs the output e_o will respond slightly to the input pulses. If R is very much larger than the R_o's, the response at a coincidence will be very much larger than the response resulting even if all but one of the diodes is caused to stop conducting. In an *AND* circuit even this slight response to something less than a complete coincidence is often undesirable and to minimize this feature the diode T_o has been added. It is possible to achieve the same effect with a diode placed in series with the output (see Prob. 13-8).

In Fig. 13-8, E_R must be adjusted so that the individual diode currents $I_1, I_2, \ldots, I_n$ (which are nominally equal to one another) are each larger than the current I. In this case, even if all but one diode is back-biased by input pulses, the diode T_o will be required to continue to conduct, and the output will remain clamped to E_R. If, however, all the input diodes stop conducting, the diode T_o must also stop and an output signal will form. A limitation on the number of input circuits which may be employed is the current-carrying capacity of the diode T_o. The diode T_o keeps the output close to E_R for anything less than a complete coincidence but, of course, will not act as a perfect clamp because of the finite forward resistance R_f of T_o. If, say, some number $m < n$ diodes are cut off, the current in T_o must change by an amount ΔI_o and the output will change by $(\Delta I_o)R_f$. The magnitude of this change is easily calculated and may be made quite small in comparison to the output which results at a coincidence.

The waveform of the AND circuit output pulse will now be discussed. If we neglect the capacitance across the diodes, we may easily compute the form of the output pulse. When the output pulse is formed, all diodes are back-biased and the output capacitance C_o must charge through R. The output will therefore rise from E_R toward E_{bb} with a time constant RC_o. At the termination of the input pulses, the diodes $T_1, \ldots, T_n$ conduct and the output capacitance discharges at a rate determined by C_o and the parallel combination of R and n resistors. Each of these n resistors consists of the diode resistance in series with the output impedance of the generators. The output pulse will therefore decay much more rapidly than it rises.

The waveform is indicated in Fig. 13-9a for input amplitudes E greater than E_{bb}. This result is to be compared with the corresponding result for the OR circuit. The rise time may be improved at the expense of amplitude by making the input-pulse amplitude E smaller than E_{bb}. Under these circumstances the

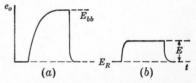

FIG. 13-9. Effect of capacitance on waveform of output of an AND circuit. (a) $E > E_{bb}$; (b) $E < E_{bb}$.

output rises toward E_{bb} but is clamped at the voltage E by the diode connected to the generator supplying this pulse E. This waveform is indicated in Fig. 13-9b. If the diode capacitances are taken into account, the output waveforms are modified only slightly from those indicated in Fig. 13-9.

An adaptation of the diode AND circuit to capacitive coupling is shown in Fig. 13-10. The source impedances of the driving pulse generators have been omitted for simplicity. The input sides of the diodes have here been returned to a negative source so that the quiescent level of the output may be at ground. The resistors R_k are required to provide a continuous path for the quiescent diode current. Each input capacitor may charge rapidly through its own diode and through T_o so that the negative excursion of the pulse at the input side of $T_1, \ldots, T_n$ may be rapidly restored to zero. In this way the peak positive excursion of the input side of $T_1, \ldots, T_n$ is always maintained equal to the peak-to-peak input-pulse amplitude independently of the duty cycle of the input pulses.

A triode AND circuit with a series diode is shown in Fig. 13-11. The input pulses are negative and drive the individual tubes beyond cutoff.

If less than a complete coincidence occurs, the small rise in the common plate voltage does not appear at the output because of the diode. At a complete coincidence, the plates rise to E_{bb} and an output pulse appears. The leading edge of the output pulse will be slower than the trailing edge for the reason already discussed in connection with the diode AND circuit. AND circuits corresponding to the OR circuits of Figs. 13-6b and 13-7 may readily be drawn.

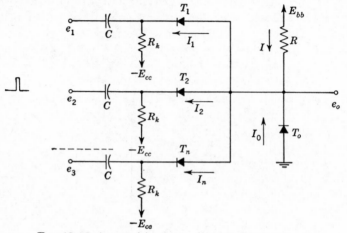

FIG. 13-10. A capacitive input diode AND circuit.

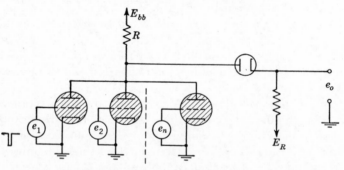

FIG. 13-11. A triode AND circuit.

13-4. The NOT Circuit. A circuit which inverts the polarity of a pulse is called an $INVERTER$ or NOT circuit. A plate-loaded triode, for example, therefore constitutes a NOT circuit. The discussion which follows will make clear the reason for this terminology.

Suppose that we have a variable voltage which is distinctive in that it can assume only one of two possible values. We might then designate these two voltages by the symbols A and B, 0 and 1, low and high, up and down, etc. A pulse or train of pulses constitutes just such a variable voltage, the pulse edges representing the (ideally) abrupt transition between the two possible states. A device which inverts a signal would then have the property that if the input were, say, in the state A, the output would be in the state B. Since, however, only two states are possible, rather than to say that the output is in state B we may say instead that the output is in the state *NOT A*. A *NOT* circuit is shown in Fig. 13-12a. The inverting pulse transformer constitutes basically the *NOT* circuit. The d-c restorer has been added to establish the absolute levels of the two states at the output. A *NOT* circuit is frequently used to advantage in conjunction with other switching gates, as will be illustrated in the next section.

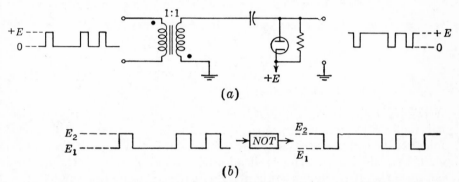

FIG. 13-12. (a) A *NOT* circuit. (b) Defining the operation of a *NOT* circuit.

A *NOT* circuit actually does somewhat more than simply invert a pulse. We may note that the reason a computer may work digitally, even though vacuum tubes are employed, is that each tube is either conducting heavily or nonconducting and never in an intermediate condition. Hence, within any particular digital circuit there are only two voltage levels which are recognized. If a *NOT* circuit simply inverted a pulse, we would have three levels to deal with, i.e., a positive pulse, a negative pulse, and no pulse. Hence, strictly, a *NOT* circuit is defined by the operation indicated in Fig. 13-12b, that is, it inverts the waveform but keeps the variable operating between the same two limits, E_1 and E_2, as shown. For example, in the NORC computer (International Business Machines Corporation Computer designed for the Naval Ordnance) the levels E_1 and E_2 are -25 volts and $+10$ volts, respectively. The *INVERTER* or *NOT* circuit used is a d-c amplifier in cascade with a cathode follower, as shown in Fig. 13-13. If the input changes from -25 volts to $+10$ volts, the output goes from 10 volts to -25 volts.

13-5. The *INHIBITOR* Circuit.[2] Let us describe a pulse train by saying that the waveform is in state A when the waveform is at its lower voltage level and in state B when the waveform is at its higher voltage level. In terms of the *NOT* terminology we may describe a diode *AND* circuit as follows. When *one* or more inputs is at *A*, the output is at *A*; when *all* inputs are at *B*, the output is at *B*. Suppose now that we have an *AND* circuit with $n + 1$ inputs and that the $(n + 1)$st input is preceded by a *NOT* circuit, as in Fig. 13-14*a*. Such a circuit is called a

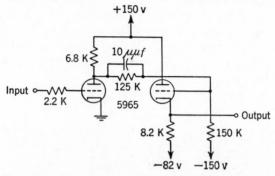

Fig. 13-13. The NORC *NOT* or *INVERTER* circuit.

NOT-AND circuit, an *INHIBITOR* circuit, or an *anticoincidence* circuit and has the following properties. If the input at the $(n + 1)$st terminal of the composite circuit is *A*, then the input to the $(n + 1)$st *AND* circuit terminal is *B*. Hence, if all other inputs become *B*, the output becomes *B*. If the input to the *NOT* circuit is *B*, then the input to the corresponding *AND* terminal is *A* and the output of the *AND* circuit

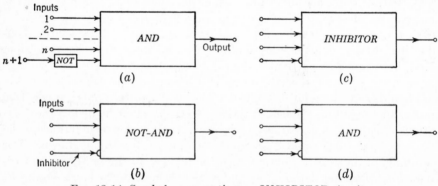

Fig. 13-14. Symbols representing an *INHIBITOR* circuit.

must remain at *A*, even if inputs 1, 2, . . . , *n* are at *B*. Stated otherwise, the circuit has the property that an output pulse will appear if and only if pulses are applied simultaneously to inputs 1 to *n* and no pulse is applied at the $(n + 1)$st input. The pulse applied to the $(n + 1)$st terminal is called the *inhibiting pulse* and the corresponding terminal is called the *inhibiting terminal*. When the *NOT-AND* circuit is represented by a single block, as in Fig. 13-14b, the inhibiting terminal is distinguished by the half circle, as indicated. Frequently no special recognition is taken of the *NOT* component of the *INHIBITOR* and the circuit is represented as in Fig. 13-14c or d.

An a-c coupled diode *INHIBITOR* circuit is shown in Fig. 13-15. The separate component parts have been included in dotted boxes. The resistors and capacitors not included in a box serve simply as a-c coupling inputs of the signal pulses. Initially, diode T_{n+1} is not conducting, while all other diodes are conducting. If inputs 1 to n go from the low level to the high level simultaneously, all diodes will be nonconducting

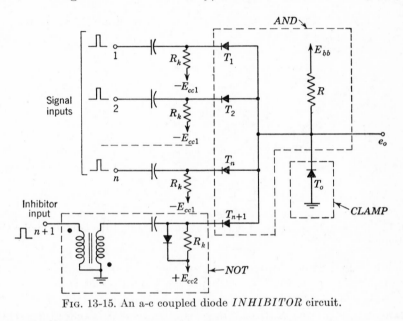

FIG. 13-15. An a-c coupled diode *INHIBITOR* circuit.

and the output will rise. If an inhibitor signal of amplitude large enough to overcome the back-biasing voltage $+E_{cc2}$ is applied, then T_{n+1} will conduct and keep the output clamped at the low level even if diodes $T_1, \ldots, T_n$ stop conducting. When an output signal does form, it will have an amplitude E_{bb}, E_{cc2}, or E (the signal input amplitude), whichever is the *smallest*.

If an inhibitor pulse is to allow none of the signal to be transmitted through the gate, it is necessary that the inhibitor pulse begin earlier and last longer than the signal pulses. In a system in which all pulses are nominally of the same duration some means is required effectively to *stretch out* the inhibitor pulse. Figure 13-16 represents schematically the use of delay lines to ensure that the inhibitor pulse completely overlaps the signal pulse. The signal pulse is delayed by the delay line D_s so that the inhibitor pulse arrives at the AND circuit before the signal pulse. The delay line D_i has a longer delay than D_s so that the inhibitor pulse also arrives after the signal pulse.

When a parallel set of triodes is used as an AND circuit (load either in common plate or cathode lead), the conversion of this circuit to an inhibitor requires again only that a NOT circuit be inserted in the path of one of the input signals. A similar modification will convert a multi-grid AND amplifier into an $INHIBITOR$ circuit.

13-6. An Example of a Switching Circuit.[3] A digital computer uses a very large number of switching gates. Hence, the fundamental circuits

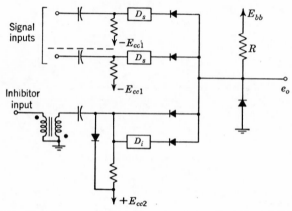

Fig. 13-16. Illustrating the use of delay lines to ensure that the inhibitor pulse shall overlap the signal pulses.

which are used over and over again are mounted into a minimum number of plug-in packages. The advantages with respect to manufacturing, replacement, and trouble shooting are apparent. One of the basic packages used in the National Bureau of Standards Computer, SEAC, which uses resistors, germanium diodes, and a single tube and pulse transformer, is shown in Fig. 13-17. The circuit has 15 input terminals and is able to drive simultaneously as many as 14 input terminals of a number of other similar packages. At the input we find 5 separate AND gates. Those input terminals which are in use are maintained at -8 volts, this voltage level being set usually as a result of being coupled to the output of a preceding package. The AND diode gates therefore conduct, as they should, and the voltage at the input side of the OR diodes is also about -8 volts. The output side of the OR gate diodes and the 6AN5 grid are clamped to -5 volts. The OR gate diodes are therefore back-biased to the extent of 3 volts. This 3-volt back bias prevents the OR gate diode from responding to anything less than a complete coincidence at any of the input AND gates.

When a coincidence occurs at one of the *AND* gates, the voltage at
the 6AN5 grid will be driven highly positive because it is connected
to the bleeder arrangement consisting of +62 volts, 10 K, 39 K, and
−65 volts.   The grid resistance of the 6AN5 is not low enough to limit

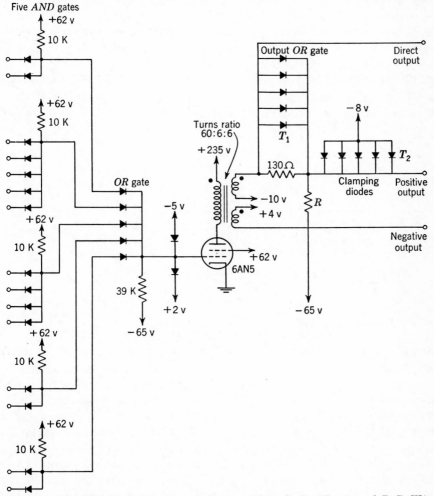

FIG. 13-17. The SEAC switching gate package.   (*From R. D. Elbourn and R. P. Witt,
Dynamic Circuit Techniques Used in SEAC and DYSEAC, Proc. IRE, vol. 41, pp.
1380–1387, October, 1953.*)

the grid voltage to a reasonable value and thus the additional clamping
diode is used to clamp the grid at +2 volts.   The 6AN5 grid, therefore,
swings between −5 and +2 volts in response to which the 6AN5 plate
current changes by about 42 ma.   This grid swing produces the maximum tube-current change consistent with the allowable grid dissipation.

The pulse which appears at the low impedance secondary windings of the transformer has an amplitude of about 20 volts.

We examine now the output circuit. The *positive* output circuit is designed so that the signal at the *positive* terminal may be used to drive the AND gates of a succeeding switching-gate package. The positive output circuit is redrawn in Fig. 13-18. Diode T_1 represents the parallel combination of the five OR gate diodes and T_2 the parallel combination of the five clamping diodes. We neglect temporarily the 130-ohm resistor which shunts the OR gate diodes.

To see the need for the output circuit arrangement of Fig. 13-18, consider that the indicated arrangement is replaced by one in which the transformer output winding is connected directly to the *positive* output

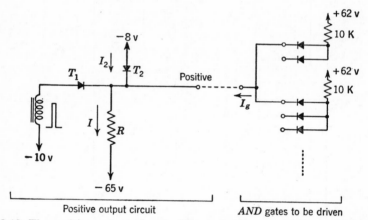

FIG. 13-18. The positive output circuit of the switching gate package of Fig. 13-17.

terminal. Assume also that this terminal is connected to one diode in each of a number of AND gates. Suppose that this output circuit is quiescent (no pulse) but that all the other diodes of the gates are pulsed. Then all the current which previously flowed in all other diodes must now flow back into the *positive* output terminal and through the transformer winding. The voltage at the *positive* output terminal must remain nominally constant in the presence of this pulse of current if the AND circuits are to be restrained from responding. It is therefore required that the transformer-winding output impedance be very low. In the SEAC computer the basic repetition rate of the pulses is 1 Mc, and even at this frequency the impedance of the transformer output winding is of the order of 300 ohms. Hence T_1 is used to prevent the current from flowing back into the transformer.

In the circuit of Fig. 13-18 note that before the connection of the *positive* terminal to the AND gates ($I_g = 0$) the diode T_2 conducts, clamping the output to -8 volts, as required. This current continues through R

$(I_2 = I)$, and diode T_1 is back-biased. When now connection is made to the AND gates, the current I_g will have no appreciable effect on the output until I_g exceeds nominally the current I. For when $I_g = I$, then I_2 will become zero. But for I_g less than I, the difference $I - I_g$ must be supplied by T_2 and the output will remain clamped at -8 volts. To avoid unnecessary drain of the supply voltages, the resistor R is made adjustable (between 0.53 K and 1.25 K) so that it can be tailored to the number of AND gates to be driven.

When a positive pulse does develop across the transformer winding due to a pulse at the 6AN5 grid, this pulse is coupled to the output terminal through the diode T_1. Under these circumstances the succeeding AND circuit diodes coupled to the output are driven to the back-biased direction and consequently do not load the output. If, however, a positive pulse is to appear at the output, the diode T_2 must stop conducting. Hence, the transformer output winding must now supply a current greater than I through the five-parallel-diode OR circuit.

The 130-ohm resistor in Fig. 13-17, heretofore neglected, is used as a transformer damping resistor. It will be recalled (Sec. 9-7) that the pulse derived from a transformer output winding is necessarily accompanied by an undershoot which may be oscillatory in nature. The damping is necessary to prevent the positive cycle of an oscillation from behaving as a false pulse. During the pulse itself the 130-ohm resistor is shunted across the conducting diode T_1 and hence has little effect. When the circuit is quiescent, the 130-ohm resistor permits about 15 ma to flow through the pulse transformer.

The negative output winding, because of its reversed polarity, constitutes essentially a NOT circuit and is used when a succeeding AND gate is to be used as an $INHIBITOR$. Observe that the quiescent $+4$-volt level of the negative terminal is appropriate to keep nonconducting the diodes of the AND gate to which it is connected.

The *direct* output is used for driving delay lines which present a nominally resistive load and to drive OR gates other than the output OR gate.

If it were desired to use the circuit of Fig. 13-17 simply as an OR gate, this result could be achieved by connecting a single input to all the diodes of one of the input AND circuits. This arrangement would then certainly seem uneconomical. However, the fact is that more generally the arrangement of a number of AND circuits followed by an OR circuit followed by a NOT circuit is one which fits nicely into the general switching requirements of a digital computer.

Throughout the remainder of this chapter we shall discuss a number of applications of the various switching gates.

13-7. The AND Circuit Used for Pulse Reshaping. In a digital computer the various mathematical manipulations required are performed by operations on pulses.   Pulses, or better, pulse trains, represent the numbers on which the computer performs operations.   Even the instructions which direct the computer are conveyed by means of pulse trains.   An individual pulse may be required to pass through several hundred transmission devices before it has completely served its purpose.   In the course of its successive transmissions a pulse may become appreciably deteriorated.   That is to say, its amplitude may have been attenuated and its rise and fall time increased to the point where the pulse is no longer usable.   The pulse must, therefore, be reshaped periodically.

Now there is available, in a digital computer, for exactly the purpose presently contemplated, a continuous sequence of *master clock* pulses. These are pulses of good waveshape whose recurrence rate is established usually by a crystal oscillator.   This stable oscillator determines the basic rate at which the computer operates and for this reason is

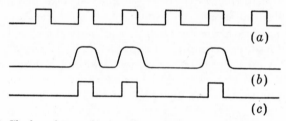

FIG. 13-19. (*a*) Clock pulses.   (*b*) A train of deteriorated pulses.   (*c*) The reshaped pulses produced by an *AND* gate.

referred to as the *clock*.   These clock pulses are distributed to all parts of the computer, where they are used to maintain the timing of the computer and to restore the pulse waveshapes.

One method of pulse reshaping is shown in Fig. 13-19.   In Fig. 13-19*a* is shown the continuous sequence of clock pulses, while in Fig. 13-19*b* we have a train of deteriorated pulses.   If these two signals are applied to a two-input *AND* gate, the output waveform will appear as in Fig. 13-19*c*. To see how the waveform of Fig. 13-19*c* comes about, it is only necessary to recall that the output of an *AND* gate is equal instantaneously to the smaller of the two inputs.   Figure 13-19 is drawn on the basis that the deteriorated pulse overlaps and is larger than the clock pulse.

In Fig. 13-20 is illustrated the situation in which the clock pulse is larger than the deteriorated pulse.   In this case the output of an *AND* gate still bears a vestige of the deterioration.   The pulse may, however, be restored in amplitude and shape by an amplifier which limits at the level indicated by the dotted horizontal line.

In Figs. 13-19 and 13-20 we have tacitly assumed that the clock pulse and information pulse are centered with respect to one another.   This assumption, however, is unrealistic since each transmission device in the computer will introduce some delay into the signal pulse so that even if the pulses were initially centered they would not long remain so. It is therefore necessary to make available in a computer a number of sources of clock pulses, each of different phase. Note that when a delay has accumulated in the signal pulse equal to the time interval between clock pulses, the original phase of the clock pulse may once again be used for reshaping since it does not matter with which clock pulse a particular signal pulse coincides. In the SEAC computer, for example, four crystal oscillator clock pulses are available, each one shifted in phase successively by 90°.

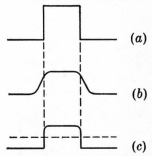

FIG. 13-20. A reshaped pulse produced by an *AND* circuit for the case where clock pulse (*a*) is larger than signal pulse (*b*). The reshaped pulse is shown in (*c*).

After reshaping, a signal pulse has the form of a clock pulse. As this reshaped pulse continues along its path, we shall want to reshape it again before its deterioration becomes particularly pronounced. Hence, the signal pulse will never be very much broader than the clock pulse, and even with a number of phases of clock pulses it will be difficult to achieve the ideal situation in which the signal pulse completely overlaps the clock pulse. The required overlap may be achieved by combining an *AND* circuit with regeneration to achieve reshaping by the principle of *regenerative broadening*. This method is described in Sec. 13-8. A completely different principle for pulse reshaping and retiming is explained in Sec. 13-13.

13-8. Regenerative Broadening.[2] Suppose that we have two pulses P_1 and P_2 which have a certain time interval of overlap. If these pulses are

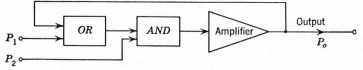

FIG. 13-21. A regenerative broadening circuit.

applied to an *AND* circuit, the output pulse will persist only for the time of the overlap. Hence, the output pulse will be terminated at the time of termination of either P_1 or P_2, whichever occurs first. If, however, we require that the output pulse terminate only at the termination of P_2 and not of P_1, we may achieve this end by the *regenerative broadening* circuit given in block form in Fig. 13-21. The blocks represent, respectively, an *OR* circuit, an *AND* circuit, and an amplifier. The operation of the circuit will be clear from Fig. 13-22. When P_1 and P_2 overlap, there will be an output from the *AND* circuit and, hence, an output from the amplifier.   This output is returned to the AND circuit through the OR circuit.   Even if P_1 drops to zero, the place of P_1 is taken by the feedback signal and the output P_o continues to persist.   When, however, P_2 is terminated, the AND circuit output falls and the pulse P_o is terminated. Observe that in this case, where P_2 terminates after P_1, the output P_o has been *stretched* or *broadened* to the time of termination of P_2.   Waveform

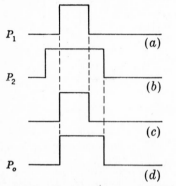

P_1 (a)

P_2 (b)

(c)

P_o (d)

Fig. 13-22. Illustrating regenerative broadening. (a) and (b) are input pulses to circuit of Fig. 13-21.   Output is shown at (d).   Waveform (c) would result if P_1 and P_2 were applied to a simple AND circuit.

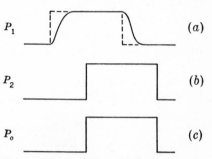
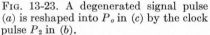

P_1 (a)

P_2 (b)

P_o (c)

Fig. 13-23. A degenerated signal pulse (a) is reshaped into P_o in (c) by the clock pulse P_2 in (b).

c of Fig. 13-22 represents the output that would be furnished by a simple AND circuit.

The circuit of Fig. 13-21 is called an *active element*.   The application of this circuit to pulse reshaping is shown in Fig. 13-23.   In Fig. 13-23a is shown the degenerated signal pulse P_1 which is derived from some previously reshaped pulse shown dotted.   The pulse P_2 in Fig. 13-23b is the

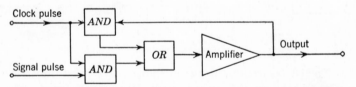

Fig. 13-24. Another form of regenerative broadening circuit.

clock pulse, while P_o in Fig. 13-23c is the output reshaped pulse.   Observe that, to secure a reshaped pulse, it is no longer required that P_1 completely overlap P_2.   It is only necessary that P_1 overlap the leading edge of P_2.

An alternative form of the regenerative broadening circuit is shown in Fig. 13-24.   Note that this arrangement of AND, OR, and amplifier circuits allows a direct adaptation of the SEAC package of Fig. 13-17.

13-9. The *EXCLUSIVELY-OR* Circuit. An *EXCLUSIVELY-OR* circuit is a gate with two inputs which performs the following logic. If a pulse appears at either input terminal, an output results; but if pulses appear simultaneously at both inputs, no output pulse results. The circuits of Fig. 13-25a and b will accomplish this gating function.

In Fig. 13-25a individual pulses at input A or B will pass through the *OR* circuit and the *INHIBITOR* circuit to the output. If pulses are present at both inputs, the output of the *AND* circuit will provide a signal at the inhibitor terminal of the *INHIBITOR* circuit which will prevent a pulse from reaching the output. Similarly, in Fig. 13-25b if pulses are present at both

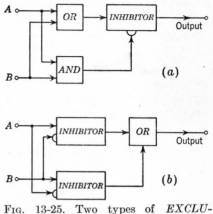

Fig. 13-25. Two types of *EXCLUSIVELY-OR* circuits.

inputs, both *INHIBITOR* circuits will prevent pulses from reaching the output.

We may note that there is no output from the *EXCLUSIVELY-OR* circuit if and only if $A = B$. Hence, this circuit may be used to test for the equality of two words. Advantage is taken of this property to check the operation of a computer. For example, a digital computer may consist actually of two identical machines which operate side by side on the same problem. Corresponding points in the two computers are coupled to the two inputs of an *EXCLUSIVELY-OR* circuit and if the words at these corresponding positions are not identical an output is obtained which provides a warning signal.

The *EXCLUSIVELY-OR* circuit is also known as the *AND-NOT* gate.

13-10. Registers. Suppose that it is required to perform an arithmetic operation, say addition, on two numbers which are stored in the main computer memory. Now, ordinarily, it will not be possible to abstract both numbers from the memory simultaneously. Since the unit which will actually perform the arithmetic may require that both numbers be applied simultaneously, it will generally be required that at least one of the numbers be stored, temporarily, in a one-word memory device. Similarly, it may not be feasible to return the arithmetic unit output immediately to the main memory. In this case, again, a one-word *memory*[4] or *storage device*, which is called a *register*, is needed.

A set of n binary circuits may clearly be used to store an n digit binary number since we have but to set the states of the binaries at 0 or 1, depending on the value of the digit which the binary is to represent. The binary number may appear in serial form as a train of pulses, and one method for inserting the number into the binary-circuit register is as shown in Fig. 13-26. The input pulse train is applied to a delay line which is tapped at intervals D equal to the basic pulse separation time. Hence, at the moment the last pulse of the train appears at the input of the delay line, the earlier pulses will appear at the delay-line taps. If, at this moment, the *register line* is pulsed, then the AND circuits will transmit to each binary the pulse (or lack of pulse) at the corresponding delay-line taps. The output of the AND circuit is coupled unsymmetrically to the binaries in such a fashion that the AND circuit pulse (if one is present) will leave the corresponding binary in state 1. The register may be cleared by a pulse on the *clear* line. This pulse is again applied unsymmetrically and in a manner which will cause each binary to remain in or return to state 0.

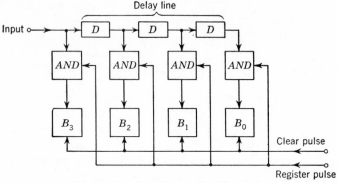

FIG. 13-26. A register using binaries.

Consider that the output plates of successive binaries are coupled through a second set of AND circuits to corresponding points of an additional delay line which is a duplicate of the input line. Then the clear pulse, which is also applied to the second set of AND circuits, will not only clear the register but also establish on this output line the initial temporal arrangement of the pulses. Hence, the clearing operation will also regenerate the original pulse train.

A second type of register, known as a *shift register*, may be constructed from binaries by using the scheme represented schematically in Fig. 13-27. The input consists again of the train of pulses which is to be stored in the register. The shift pulse line is excited now, not by a single pulse, but rather by a continuous train of pulses which are timed to occur nominally *midway* between the pulses of the input number. The delay sections have a delay much smaller than the time interval between pulses and are required to ensure that an individual binary shall not receive a triggering signal simultaneously from the shift line and from a preceding binary.

Both sets of pulses are applied unsymmetrically. The shift pulses always drive the binaries to state 0. The coupling between binaries is such that a succeeding binary will respond only if the preceding binary goes from state 1 to state 0. And the pulse which results from this transition will drive the succeeding binary to state 1.

Now suppose we want to register the number 1011. The pulse pattern is as indicated in Fig. 13-27. The first pulse (a) drives binary B_3 to state 1. The shift pulse now returns binary B_3 to 0 and a short time later (depending on the delay D) binary B_2 is driven to state 1 by the pulse received from the previous binary. The first digit (a) which was initially registered in binary B_3 has been shifted to B_2 and B_3 has been cleared (returned to 0) so that it may now register the next pulse (b). We may now easily follow the procedure from this point and see that, by

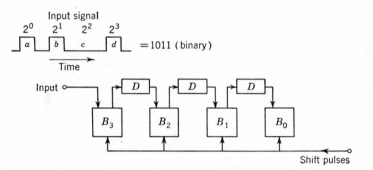

Fig. 13-27. A shift register using binaries.

this process of registering and shifting to make room for the next pulse, the input number will eventually become installed in the register. Of course, the shift pulses must cease at the moment the number has been registered.

To read this register, it will only be necessary to apply four shift pulses. In response to these shift pulses the original number will appear at the output of binary B_0.

13-11. Dynamic Registers.[5] The techniques used in constructing the registers of Sec. 13-10 are known as *static techniques*. The reason for this designation is that when a register is simply storing a number all voltage levels in the circuit are fixed. The basic mechanism of a *dynamic register* is the following. The word (pulse train) is introduced at one end of a delay line whose delay time is equal to the time duration of the word, and the output signal is returned to the delay-line input so that the word continues to circulate around a closed path. A dynamic register is shown in Fig. 13-28a; the portion of the circuit which is enclosed in the dotted box will be recognized as the regenerative broadening circuit of Fig. 13-21 which is used to reshape the pulses after each loop trip. The clock pulses in the present case are used not only for reshaping but also to maintain synchronism between the circulating pulse train and the pulses in other portions of the computer. This synchronization is required since the word may take many trips around the circuit and if the total loop delay is even slightly incorrect a large error may accumulate. The dynamic register has the following advantages over the static register: (1) Fewer tubes are required. (2) The output may be read without removing the information from the register. (3) The output of the active element may drive many auxiliary circuits. (4) The circuit is more stable.

The pulse train circulates and reappears continuously at the output. The register may be read by exciting the *read* lead of the output *AND* circuit by a number of pulses equal to the digits in one word. A sometimes useful feature of the circuit is that the register may be read without destroying the register content. The register may be cleared by exciting the *erase* lead of the inhibitor in the circulation path. Note that to erase

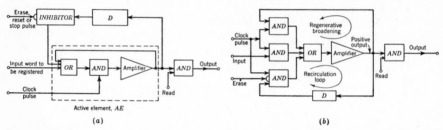

(a)   (b)

FIG. 13-28. Two recirculating storage circuits with regenerative pulse reshaping and retiming.

an *n*-digit word, *n* consecutive erase pulses are required, which pulses coincide with the clock pulses. Alternatively a single erase pulse may be used whose duration is sufficient to encompass the entire word.

Another form of dynamic register is indicated in Fig. 13-28*b*. This circuit can be constructed from the SEAC package of Fig. 13-17.

In order to represent a ten-digit number in the decimal system requires 34 binary bits. If the clock-pulse repetition rate is 2 Mc, then one word will require 17 μsec. If the total storage capacity of the computer is 1,000 words, then a single delay line 17 msec long could supply all the storage. However, a prohibitively long waiting time would then be required before a word is available. As a compromise between speed and equipment some 50 lines, each 20 words (or 340 μsec) long, might be used. The attenuation of electrical delay lines (about 6 db/μsec delay at a frequency of a few megacycles) is excessive for the present application. An improvement results if the block marked *D* in Fig. 13-28 is an acoustical delay line. The pulse train representing a word is used to modulate a carrier frequency of 30 Mc. These 30-Mc pulses in turn drive a quartz crystal transducer which generates waves in a mercury column.   A receiving crystal at the other end of the line detects the pulses after they have traveled down the column.

Many different memory systems,[4] besides the mercury line, are now in use or have been suggested for future computers.   These memory devices include solid acoustical lines, magnetic drums, a magnetic-core matrix, electrostatic storage on a CRT, and others.

13-12. The Dynamic Binary.   The dynamic register circuit of Fig. 13-28 suggests an interesting special case.   Suppose the input were to consist of a single pulse instead of a pulse train and that the total circuital delay were adjusted to be equal to the time interval between pulses.   In this case the circuit could exist in either of two possible states, i.e., a state 0 in which there is no circulating pulse or a state 1 in which there is a circulating pulse.   This one-digit (or one-bit) dynamic storage circuit

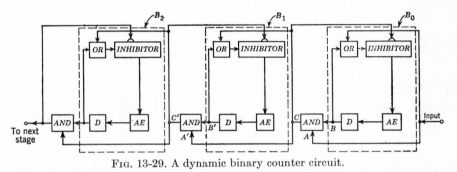

Fig. 13-29. A dynamic binary counter circuit.

then shares the basic digital property of a bistable multivibrator and may be used in similar applications.

A three-stage dynamic binary counter is drawn in Fig. 13-29.   This circuit consists essentially of a cascade of three one-digit storage cells of Fig. 13-28a.   The output of each binary is taken at the junction of the delay D and the OR circuit and is fed to an AND circuit, as shown.   The input to each stage is also fed to the AND circuit which couples this stage to the next.   Note that the input to the entire circuit is fed from the extreme right in Fig. 13-29.   This arrangement puts the least significant binary digit at the right, as is customary.

To study the operation of the counter, assume that each binary is initially in the 0 state, and consider what happens as each pulse arrives at the input.   The first pulse appears at the AND circuit at input A. There is no pulse at input B of this AND circuit because binary B_0 is in the zero state.   Hence, there is no output C from this AND circuit and no pulse is delivered to binary B_1 or any of the succeeding binaries. Therefore these binaries all remain in the 0 state.

The input pulse enters binary B_0 at the OR circuit.   Since there is no pulse at the $INHIBITOR$ input terminal, the $INHIBITOR$ circuit will deliver a pulse to the active element (AE) and this pulse will circulate around the loop of binary B_0. Hence, its state has been changed from the 0 to the 1 state. After the first pulse, the counter reads 001 in binary language, or 1 in decimal arithmetic.

Assume that a second pulse is now applied to the input. This appears at A and since the circulating pulse is at B there is an output at C. This pulse will change the state of binary B_1 from the 0 to the 1 condition but will leave binary B_2 in the 0 state. The second pulse is applied to the OR circuit of binary B_0, but the $INHIBITOR$ pulse from C prevents this pulse and the circulating pulse from reaching the active element (AE). Hence, binary B_0 is switched back to the 0 state, so that after the second pulse, the counter reads 010 in binary language, or 2 in decimal arithmetic. To summarize, *a pulse changes a 0 to a 1 state and delivers no carry pulse. A pulse changes a 1 to a 0 state and delivers a carry pulse.*

If these rules are followed, then the 010 reading after pulse 2 is changed to 011 after pulse 3 and 100 after pulse 4, etc. These are the correct binary representations of the decimal numbers 3, 4, etc., and hence the counter is operating properly.

It should be noted that the carry time in this type of dynamic counter is very small since the only delays are those in the coupling circuits between stages. A 12-stage counter has been constructed[5] with less than 0.3 μsec carry time.

Some simplifications have been made in the circuit of Fig. 13-29. Actually the coupling element between stages is not an AND circuit, but is rather an *active element* which permits the pulses to be reshaped and retimed between stages. Additionally, the clock pulses required for each *active element* have been omitted in Fig. 13-29.

13-13. The Havens Delay Circuit. A fundamental circuit used for pulse reshaping and retiming (and many other applications to be described below) was invented by B. L. Havens of the Watson Scientific Computing Laboratory of International Business Machine Corporation. It is used to a limited extent in the IBM 701 Electronic Data Processing Machine.[6] This circuit is the basic element of the NORC (Naval Ordnance Research Calculator), there being over 1,500 delay circuits in this machine.

The clock in NORC is a 1-Mc crystal-controlled oscillator. The computer operates between two levels, $+10$ volts (considered a 1) and -25 volts (considered a 0), and each of these levels is maintained for a full microsecond in synchronism with the clock. The delay circuit is an element which receives a deteriorated 1-μsec pulse during any microsecond interval and produces a reshaped 1-μsec pulse during the succeeding microsecond interval. The circuit diagram is drawn in Fig. 13-30 and the basic waveforms in Fig. 13-31. The *sync* and *clamp* pulses shown in the latter diagram are obtained from the master clock and are transmitted throughout the computer. In Fig. 13-30, T_1 is a critically damped tuned-plate amplifier in which the plate coil resonates with its stray capacitance. This tube has a diode AND circuit (T_3 and T_4) at its grid terminal. When there is a 0 at the input, the grid of T_1 is at -25 volts and this tube is cut off. The storage capacitor C_1 is connected to the plate of T_1 through C_2 and diode T_6. Point A is clamped to -30 volts by diode T_5. When there is no pulse at the input, C_1 is held at approximately -30 volts by the *clamp* signal of Fig. 13-31c through diode T_7 and the 1.2-K resistor. One input to the AND circuit is the *sync* signal of Fig. 13-31b which is above ground level only during the last one-third of any microsecond interval. If a pulse should appear at the input in coincidence with the *sync*, T_1 will conduct and cause a negative swing at

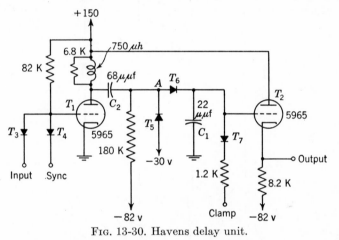

Fig. 13-30. Havens delay unit.

its plate, as shown in Fig. 13-31d. This fall in plate voltage is not transmitted to C_1 because it causes T_6 to be back-biased. When T_1 is again cut off at the end of the *sync*, there is a positive swing at the plate of T_1 which causes the capacitor C_1 to be charged to approximately $+10$ volts. Although the *clamp* is present during the positive overshoot, its effect is overridden because the overshoot is of longer duration. Capacitor C_1 will then stay charged until the next *clamp* pulse which will restore C_1 to -30 volts, provided there is no input during this 1-μsec interval. The output is taken from the cathode follower T_2, the grid of which is connected to C_1. The dotted lines in Fig. 13-31a show the minimum levels and time duration of the input which will give satisfactory operation. Therefore, a pulse which has passed through a series of logical elements which cause a deterioration of rise and fall times and a loss of d-c level will be restored and retimed by the delay unit, provided that the pulse exceeds zero voltage within the first 0.7 μsec. It is of interest to note that all power-supply voltages used are unregulated.

Among the many uses which are made of the delay unit in the NORC are the following: (1) The unit is used for the basic applications of reshaping and retiming pulses, as has already been described. (2) Sixteen of these units are cascaded to give accurate time delays in 1-μsec

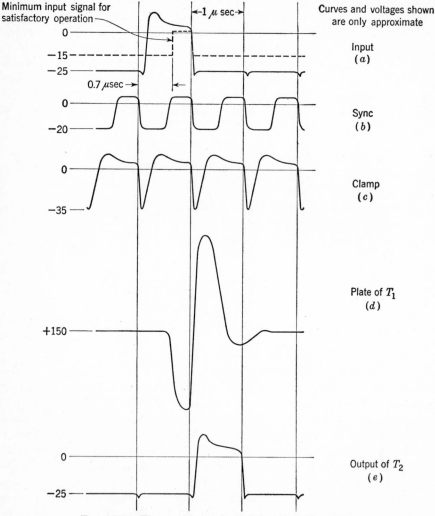

Fig. 13-31. The waveforms in the circuit of Fig. 13-30.

steps up to 16 μsec. (3) Eight delay circuits are cascaded in a ring (with the output of the eighth connected back to the first) to form an octal ring or commutator. (4) In Fig. 13-32a is shown the delay unit (the block marked μ) connected as a one-bit storage cell or register. This circuit should be compared with the one-bit memory of Fig. 13-28. The waveforms of the register are given in Fig. 13-32*b*. (5) Units of the type indicated in Fig. 13-32*a* may be interconnected to form a shift register. (6) A dynamic binary counter, analogous to that indicated in Fig. 13-29, may be formed from μ, OR, AND, and $INHIBITOR$ blocks (Prob. 13-20). (7) If the signal delay unit in Fig. 13-32*a* is replaced by 16 μ blocks in cascade, then a 16-bit dynamic memory results.

13-14. Binary Addition.[7] A digital computer must obviously contain circuits which will perform arithmetic operations, i.e., addition, subtraction, multiplication, and division. The basic operations are addition and subtraction, since multiplication is essentially repeated addition, while division is essentially repeated subtraction. It is entirely possible to

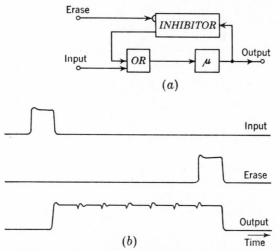

FIG. 13-32. (*a*) A one-bit storage circuit using the delay unit μ. (*b*) The waveforms.

build a computer in which an *adder-subtractor* is the only arithmetic unit present. Multiplication, for example, may then be performed by *programming;* that is, the computer may be given instructions telling it how to use the adder repeatedly to find the product of two numbers.

In Fig. 13-33*a* and *b* are shown typical pulse trains representing, respectively, the decimal numbers 13 and 10. Pulse trains representing the sum (23) and difference (3) are shown in Fig. 13-33*c* and *d*, respectively. A serial *adder* is a device with two inputs and a single output which will take as inputs the two waveforms of Fig. 13-33*a* and *b* and deliver the output waveform in Fig. 13-33*c*. Similarly, a *subtractor* will yield the output shown in Fig. 13-33*d*.

One form of an *adder-subtractor* is composed of two *half adder-subtractors*, a delay line, and an OR circuit. We shall first state how a *half adder-subtractor* is constructed from the basic gate circuits and finally we shall show how the complete *adder-subtractor* is assembled

A *half adder-subtractor* has two inputs and three outputs and is represented by the symbol in Fig. 13-34. The inputs A and B are synchronous pulse trains such as the waveforms of Fig. 13-33a and b. Three output pulse trains result: d (digits), c (carry), and b (borrow). In a *half adder*

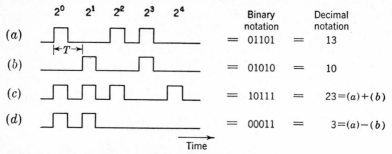

FIG. 13-33. (a) and (b) Pulse waveforms representing numbers. (c) Pulse waveform representing sum (a) + (b). (d) Pulse waveform representing difference (a) − (b).

d and c are used, while in a *half subtractor* d and b are used. Considering the pulse trains as consisting of periodic transitions between state 1 (pulse) and state 0 (no pulse), the operation of the *half adder-subtractor* is specified by Table 13-1, which gives the state at d, c, and b for all possible combinations of states at A and B. The relevance of Table 13-1 to arithmetic in the binary system may be seen from the following. The d column represents the sum of A and B so long as the sum can be represented by a single digit. When, however, the sum is larger than can be represented by a single digit, the d column gives the digit in the result which is of the same significance as the individual digits being added. Thus in the first three rows of Table 13-1, d gives $A + B$ directly. In the

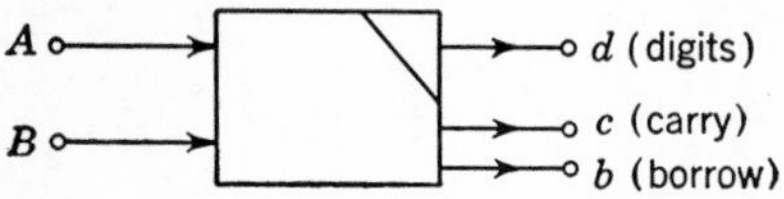

FIG. 13-34. Representation of a half adder-subtractor.

TABLE 13-1. STATES AT THE OUTPUT OF A HALF ADDER-SUBTRACTOR
FOR ALL POSSIBLE COMBINATIONS OF STATES AT THE INPUTS

A	B	d	c	b
0	0	0	0	0
0	1	1	0	1
1	0	1	0	0
1	1	0	1	0

last row, $d = 0$ because $01 + 01 = 10$ in binary notation. The c (carry) column gives the digit which must be carried to the place of next higher significance. Finally, where subtraction ($A - B$) is contemplated, the

b (borrow) column gives the digit which must be borrowed from the place of next higher significance when the subtraction may not be carried out directly, as when B is larger than A.

From Table 13-1 we see that d obeys the logic of an *EXCLUSIVELY-OR* circuit, c follows the logic of an *AND* circuit, and b obeys the logic "B but not A." Figure 13-35 shows a circuit which meets this logic, based upon the *EXCLUSIVELY-OR* circuit of Fig. 13-25b. Another

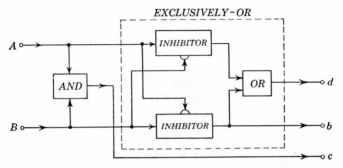

Fig. 13-35. Block diagram of a half adder-subtractor.

form of half adder-subtractor is possible using the configuration of Fig. 13-25a.

The sum of two multidigit numbers may be formed by adding to the sum of the digits of like significance the carry (if any) which may have resulted from the next lower place. With respect to the pulse trains of Fig. 13-33, the above statement is equivalent to saying that, at any instant of time, we must add (in binary form) to the pulses A and B the carry pulse

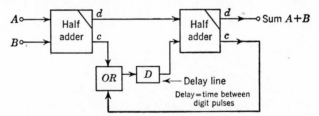

Fig. 13-36. Construction of a complete *adder* from two *half adders*.

(if any) which comes from the resultant formed one period T earlier. The carry pulse may be due to the direct sum of two digits (each 1) or to the addition of the digits 1 and 0 and a carry 1 from the preceding interval. The logic outlined above is performed by the *full adder* circuit of Fig. 13-36, which consists essentially of two *half adders* in cascade. The delay line D in series with the carry has a delay equal to the time T between pulses. Hence, the carry pulse (from either of the two sources mentioned above) is delayed T sec and added to the digit pulses in a and b, exactly as it should be.

The *adder* of Fig. 13-36 becomes a *subtractor* if the *c* outputs of the *half adders* are replaced by the *b* (borrow) outputs.

It is possible to construct a complete adder without the use of half adders. This circuit has three inputs: *A*, *B*, and the carry *c*. Two such circuits are indicated in Probs. 13-26 and 13-27.

13-15. Code-operated Multiposition Switch.[8] As noted earlier, in a digital computer, instructions as well as numbers are conveyed by means of pulse trains. If, say, 5 pulses of a word are set aside to convey instructions, then 32 different instructions are possible. These instructions are *coded* in binary form. There arises frequently in computers a need for a multiposition switch which may be operated in accordance with this code.

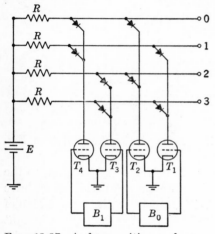

FIG. 13-37. A four-position code-operated switch.

A code-operated four-position switch is shown in Fig. 13-37. The triodes are connected to the output leads of the binaries. Assume that the voltage levels of the binary outputs have been adjusted so that when binary B_0 is in state 0, T_1 conducts heavily, while T_2 is well beyond cutoff. Similarly, consider that when binary B_1 is in state 0, T_3 conducts and T_4 is cutoff. Then when B_0 is in state 1, triode T_2 will conduct and T_1 will be cut off, and similarly when B_1 is in state 1, triode T_4 will conduct and T_3 will be cut off. Let us assume for the sake of simplicity that a conducting triode behaves essentially as a short circuit so that if, say, T_1 conducts then its plate is essentially at ground. And let us further assume that the diodes indicated are perfect.

Suppose now that the binaries are registering the number 2. In binary notation the state is 10, which means B_1 is in state 1 and B_0 is in state 0. We may easily verify from Fig. 13-37 that in this case the leads marked 0, 1, and 3 will be shorted to ground through one or more diodes so that the voltage at each of these leads is zero. On the other hand, lead 2 is not shorted, so that at output 2 the voltage is E. We may then say that the signal at leads 0, 1, and 3 is in state 0 while the state at lead 2 is 1. Hence, generally, it is seen, we may single out a particular lead and change its state, the particular lead selected depending on the instruction registered in the binaries. The change in state at some particular lead may be used to control a gate elsewhere in the computer. By changing the instruction registered in the binaries we may then change some operation in the computer. To get the instruction recorded in the binaries, we may connect the binaries as a *static register*, as in Fig. 13-26.

The network array of Fig. 13-37 is referred to as *rectangular* because of the rectangular array of wires between which the diodes are connected. The design of a rectangular array is not difficult to achieve. As an example, consider a 16-position switch, and let us consider how to connect diodes to some arbitrary output lead, say, to (decimal) lead 12. These connections are shown in Fig. 13-38. Here, for simplicity, the binaries and switching triodes of Fig. 13-37 have been replaced by single-pole double-throw switches, each position corresponding, as indicated, to the state 0 or 1. The binary code for decimal 12 is 1100. For this code, lead 12 should be unshorted. If any of the switches is connected in the complementary digit position (1 instead of 0 or 0 instead of 1), the lead should be shorted to ground. This result is achieved by connecting diodes from lead 12 to the vertical wires 0011 of binaries B_3 to B_0.

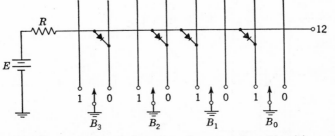

FIG. 13-38. Illustrating the design of a code-operated multiposition switch.

If n binaries are used, the number of switch combinations, instructions, or positions available will be 2^n, and in this case $(n)(2^n)$ diodes will be required in a rectangular array. For example, a 256-position switch will require 2,048 diodes. Because of the large number of diodes required, crystal diodes rather than thermionic diodes are employed. It turns out that where the number of switch positions is 16 or more, it is possible to rearrange the network into other than a rectangular array with an attendant saving in diodes. For example, the most economical 256-position switch requires only 598 diodes against 2,048 for the rectangular array. The effect of the finite back resistance of crystal diodes used in a multiposition switch is considered in Ref. 8.

Additional applications for the multiposition gate suggest themselves. In Fig. 13-39 the circuit has been used not to generate gating voltages but rather as the gating circuit itself. For any one configuration of the switches, only one of the inputs e_0, e_1, e_2, or e_3 will reach the output terminals. A diode *OR* circuit has been added so that all the signals may appear at a common-output terminal. The circuit is, of course, suitable only for positive pulse-type inputs.

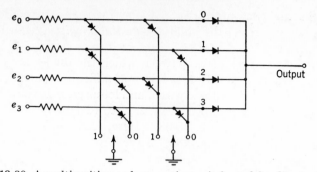

FIG. 13-39. A multiposition code-operation switch used for direct gating.

The circuit may also be used as an electronic distributor or commutator. Suppose that in Fig. 13-37 the binaries are coupled together and to an external pulse source to form a scale-of-4 counter. The circuit will then commutate from one channel to the next at the occurrence of each input pulse.

Finally, in Fig. 13-40 is shown a scheme for translating a decimal number into the binary code. The circuit is referred to as being *degenerate*, since only half the usual number of diodes are required. Suppose that initially all switches are open and that therefore the voltages at terminals A, B, and C are zero. Now let switch 5 close. Then the relay coils associated with terminal A and C will be excited and the corresponding armatures will lift, while the relay armature at B will remain down. The voltages at A and C will change abruptly from 0 to E, and this voltage change may be differentiated to give positive pulses. Of course when switch 5 opens, the relay armatures will fall and negative pulses will result, but one may easily arrange to eliminate the negative pulses. The relays employed here for simplicity may be replaced by vacuum-tube circuits which will accomplish the same function.

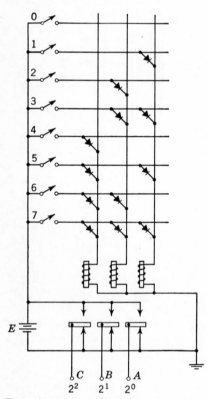

FIG. 13-40. A modification of a code-operated switch to transform decimal numbers into binary code.

13-16. Magnetic-core Binary Elements.[9] We have seen the importance, in pulse and digital circuitry, of binary elements, that is, elements which can remain in one of two stable states. A type of binary element, which offers advantages in reliability and economy in many applications that do not require very high speed, is a toroidal core of magnetic material. These cores consist either of a ceramic ferrite material or of an extremely thin ferromagnetic alloy tape wound on a nonferromagnetic spool. The essential features of these cores is that they exhibit a very nearly rectangular hysteresis loop, as indicated in Fig. 13-41. If a positive magnetizing force H is applied to the core and then removed, the core will be left with a residual magnetic flux ϕ_r. If the magnetizing force is

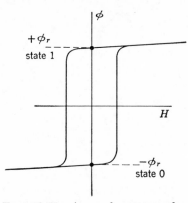

Fig. 13-41. A nearly rectangular hysteresis loop.

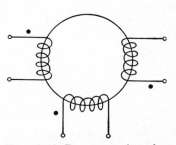

Fig. 13-42. Representation of a magnetic-core binary with three windings.

negative, the core will be left with a residual flux $-\phi_r$. These two conditions of residual flux $+\phi_r$ and $-\phi_r$ constitute the two states 1 and 0 of the magnetic binary element. An obvious advantage of a magnetic binary is that it will remain in either of its two states without the consumption of power. Depending on the application, the magnetic toroids vary in size from about $\frac{1}{10}$ in. to an inch or so in diameter.

A magnetic-core binary with three windings is represented schematically in Fig. 13-42. The dots indicate the winding directions and the convention is that a current into a dotted end sets the core in state 1.

13-17. Applications of Magnetic Binary Cores.[10] We shall illustrate the use of magnetic binary cores by considering their application in a shift register and in a counter.

A magnetic-core shift register is shown in Fig. 13-43. Digital information is "written" into the magnetic core when a current pulse (of the order of magnitude of 150 ma) is applied to its input winding. After "write-in," the information is shifted down the line by the simultaneous application of a shift pulse to all register stages.   At each application of a shift pulse, the stored data is advanced one stage.   The operation proceeds as follows.

When the shift pulse is applied to the shift windings, all the cores are reset to the state 0.   Any core that was initially in the state 1 will develop a voltage across its output winding as it resets to 0.   This voltage drives a current through the diodes into the temporary-storage capacitors C. After the decay of the shift pulse, any capacitor which has acquired a charge will now discharge into the input winding of the next core and thus set this core into state 1.   If a core is in state 0, it does not charge the capacitor, and hence the succeeding core will be left in the state 0 where it was set by the shift pulse.   It is therefore clear that after each shift

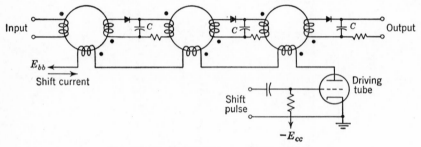

Fig. 13-43. Magnetic-core shift register.

pulse each magnetic core is left in the state of the previous core.   Magnetic registers are available (Raytheon SR-500) which will operate at repetition rates up to 500 kc.

A magnetic binary counter is shown in Fig. 13-44.   The magnetic cores require at least four windings.   A fifth winding may sometimes be included to allow for feedback to change the scale of the counter.   Only two windings of the input magnetic core need be used and M_i may be viewed as an ordinary pulse transformer.   The 2^0 digit is stored in M_0, the 2^1 digit is stored in M_1, etc.   The bias $-E_{cc}$ is enough to keep all tubes T_i, T_o, T_1, etc., below cutoff in the quiescent condition.   Let us consider that all cores are initially in state 0 and that a positive pulse is applied at the grid of T_i.

This first pulse sets core M_0 in state 1 because of the pulse of current in winding A_0.   As a result of the reversal in state of M_0 a pulse voltage is induced in B_0.   The polarity of the voltage in B_0 is such to make the point X go negative.   A voltage is also induced in D_i because of the current in C_i and this voltage is of a polarity to make point X more positive.   These two voltages are in opposite directions, and the net change in voltage at X is not enough to cause tube T_0 to enter its grid base.   Also, at this reversal in M_0, the voltage pulse induced in D_0 is negative so that T_1 also remains cut off. The net effect of the first pulse is that M_0 has reversed state, while all succeeding cores remain in state 0.

The second input pulse, initially at least, has no effect on M_0. Now, however, the positive voltage pulse which appears in winding D_i is no longer balanced by a negative pulse across B_0. The net positive pulse at X is integrated by the RC network. The purpose of this network is to stretch the pulse so that the grid of T_0 is within its grid base even after the current through A_0 has ceased. The consequent current through winding C_0 resets core M_0 to the state 0. The same current which resets M_0 to state zero, in flowing through winding A_1, sets M_1 into state 1. One may

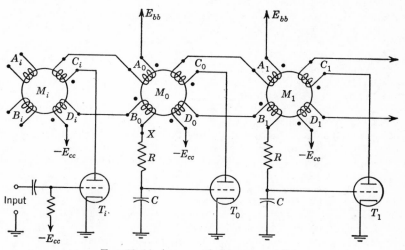

Fig. 13-44. A magnetic binary counter.

now easily follow the operation on succeeding pulses. The third pulse will set M_0 to state 1 and leave M_1 in state 1. The fourth pulse will set M_0 and M_1 to 0 and will set M_2 to 1, etc.

Magnetic-core binaries may be used as the basic building blocks in many of the digital circuits discussed in this chapter, such as the AND, OR, etc., circuits.[11]

REFERENCES

1. Walker, T. H.: Fundamentals of Digital Computer Programming, *Proc. IRE*, vol. 41, pp. 1245–1249, October, 1953.
   Page, C. H.: Digital Computer Switching Circuits, *Electronics*, vol. 21, pp. 110–118, September, 1948.
2. Felker, J. H.: Typical Block Diagrams for a Transistor Digital Computer, *Trans. AIEE*, vol. 71, pt. 1, *Communication and Electronics*, pp. 175–182, July, 1952.
   Chen, T. C.: Digital Computer Coincidence and Mixing Circuits, *Proc. IRE*, vol. 38, pp. 511–514, May, 1950.
   Hussey, L. W.: Semiconductor Diode Gates, *Bell System Tech. J.*, vol. 32, pp. 1137–1154, September, 1953.

Booth, A. D., and A. D. Holt: The Selenium Rectifier in Digital Computer Circuits, *Electronic Eng.*, vol. 26, pp. 348–355, August, 1954.

Booth, A. D.: The Physical Realization of an Electronic Digital Computer, *Electronic Eng.*, vol. 24, pp. 442–445, 1952.

3. Elbourn, R. D., and R. P. Witt: Dynamic Circuit Techniques Used in SEAC and DYSEAC, *Proc. IRE*, vol. 41, pp. 1380–1387, October, 1953.

Greenwald, S., R. C. Hauter, and S. N. Alexander: SEAC, *Proc. IRE*, vol. 41, pp. 1300–1313, October, 1953.

Gluck, S. E., H. J. Gray, C. T. Leondes, and M. Rubinoff: The Design of Logical OR-AND-OR Pyramids for Digital Computers, *Proc. IRE*, vol. 41, pp. 1388–1392, October, 1953.

4. Eckert, J. P.: A Survey of Digital Computer Memory Systems, *Proc. IRE*, vol. 41, pp. 1393–1406, October, 1953.

Chance, B., et al.: "Waveforms," Massachusetts Institute of Technology Radiation Laboratory Series, vol. 19, chaps. 21 and 23, McGraw-Hill Book Company, Inc., New York, 1949.

5. Packer, L.: Dynamic Binary Counter with Analog Read-out, *IRE Convention Record*, pt. 7, pp. 13–19, March, 1953.

6. Ross, H. D.: The Arithmetic Element of the IBM Type 701 Computer, *Proc. IRE*, vol. 41, pp. 1287–1294, October, 1953.

7. Gray, H. J.: Logical Description of Some Digital-computer Adders and Counters, *Proc. IRE*, vol. 40, pp. 29–33, January, 1952.

8. Brown, D. R., and N. Rochester: Rectifier Networks for Multiposition Switching, *Proc. IRE*, vol. 37, pp. 139–147, February, 1949.

9. Brown, D. R., and E. Albers-Schoenberg: Ferrites Speed Digital Computers, *Electronics*, vol. 26, pp. 146–149, April, 1953.

Sands, E. A.: Behavior of Rectangular Hysteresis Loop Magnetic Materials under Current Pulse Conditions, *Proc. IRE*, vol. 40, pp. 1246–1250, October, 1952.

Wang, A., and W. D. Woo: Static Magnetic Storage and Delay Line, *J. Appl. Phys.*, vol. 21, pp. 49–54, January, 1950.

10. Karnaugh, M.: Pulse-switching Circuits Using Magnetic Cores, *Proc. IRE*, vol. 43, pp. 570–583, May, 1955.

Guterman, S., R. D. Kodis, and S. Ruhman: Logical and Control Functions Performed with Magnetic Cores, *Proc. IRE*, vol. 43, pp. 291–298, March, 1955.

11. Loev, D., W. Miehle, J. Paivinen, and J. Wylen: Magnetic Core Circuits for Digital Data-processing Systems, *Proc. IRE*, vol. 44, pp. 154–162, February, 1956.

CHAPTER 14

TRANSMISSION GATES

An ideal *transmission gate* is a circuit in which the output is an exact reproduction of an input waveform during a selected time interval and is zero otherwise. The time interval for transmission is selected by an externally impressed signal which is called the *gating signal* and is usually rectangular in waveshape. These gates are also referred to as *time-selection circuits*. In many applications, a less than ideal gate is entirely acceptable. It may be, for example, that the input signal consists essentially of a unidirectional pulse. In such a case a gate will be required to respond to an input signal of only one polarity. Furthermore, it is frequently required only that an output pulse appear in response to an input pulse, and the preservation of the input waveshape is not critical. Under such circumstances it is not even required that the gate operate linearly during its transmission interval. It will be recognized that the AND circuit of Chap. 13 is just such a unidirectional gate. In other applications, on the other hand, a gate is required which will not only handle signal input excursions of both polarities, but additionally, linearity of transmission is of prime importance. In the present chapter we shall discuss gate circuits of both these latter types.

14-1. Basic Operating Principle of Gates. The basic principle of a linear gate is illustrated in Fig. 14-1a and b. In Fig. 14-1a, switch S is normally open and is closed during the desired transmission interval. In Fig. 14-1b, switch S is normally closed and is opened during the desired transmission interval. In practice, the switches will be replaced by diodes (thermionic or semiconductor), triodes, or multigrid tubes which will be biased in the conducting or nonconducting direction as required. Ideally, the switches should have zero resistance when closed and infinite resistance when open, but, of course, in practice such will not be the case. When thermionic devices are used as the switches, the circuit of Fig. 14-1a is usually favored over the circuit of Fig. 14-1b. The reason for this preference is that in the nonconducting direction a thermionic device may be counted on to have a nominally infinite resistance. Hence in Fig. 14-1a when S is open, the output will be zero as required. In Fig. 14-1b the output should be zero when S is closed. Since, however, the con-

429

ducting or forward resistance R_f will range from several hundred to several thousand ohms, it will be necessary that R be quite large; that is, it is required that $R \gg R_f$ in order for the shunting effect of the switch to be effective.   In this latter case, some small residual output will continue to persist.   Also, during the transmission interval, the input and output will be separated by the large resistance R.   If then there is some stray capacitance shunting the output, it will not be possible to transmit fast waveforms without deterioration of the waveform.

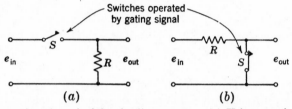

(a)   (b)

FIG. 14-1. Illustrating the principle of a linear gate.   (a) Using a series switch.   (b) Using a shunt switch.

The advantage of the circuit of Fig. 14-1a over the circuit of Fig. 14-1b is, however, by no means clean-cut.   In Fig. 14-1a we shall have to take into account the inevitable stray capacitance across S, which will permit some signal transmission when S is opened.   Additionally, in Fig. 14-1a the signal is transmitted through S, and hence there will be attenuation and distortion introduced by the nonlinearity of the tubes used for this switch.   In Fig. 14-1b the nonlinearity of the switch in its closed position has no effect on the transmission of the signal.

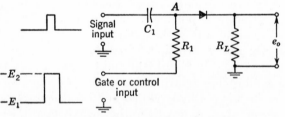

FIG. 14-2. Unidirectional diode gate.

Semiconductor diodes do not have infinite back resistance and their forward resistance may lie in the range of only several ohms.   When such diodes are employed, there is no generally apparent advantage in either circuit and the decision with respect to the circuit of choice must depend on the particular application.

14-2. Unidirectional Diode Gate.   The gate of Fig. 14-2 is suitable for a positive-going input signal.   The gate signal (also called a *control* pulse, a *selector* pulse, or an *enabling* pulse) is a rectangular waveform which makes abrupt transitions between the negative levels $-E_1$ and $-E_2$.

When the gate voltage is $-E_1$, the diode is heavily back-biased and there will be no response at the output to an input signal unless the peak amplitude of the input signal is larger than the magnitude of the back-biasing voltage. (Actually, because of the capacitative coupling, the signal input voltage will appear at point A with an average value of zero. Hence the peak positive excursion of the signal at A, with respect to zero voltage will be smaller than the peak-to-peak voltage of the input signal. For simplicity, we shall neglect this feature and consider simply that the input signal consists, say, of a very low duty-cycle pulse train, in which case this effect would be negligible.) When the gate rises to its higher level $-E_2$, a time-coincident signal input pulse may be transmitted to the output. The effect on the output of the level $(-E_2)$ attained by the gate waveform is illustrated in Fig. 14-3. In Fig. 14-3a, $-E_2 = -5$ volts and for a 10-volt input pulse a 5-volt output pulse appears. Operation

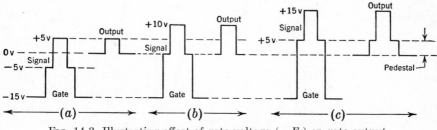

Fig. 14-3. Illustrating effect of gate voltage $(-E_2)$ on gate output.

in this manner is often advantageous when the base line of the input signal has some noise signal superimposed. The level $-E_2$ may be adjusted so that only that part of the signal above the noise threshhold appears at the output. When used in this manner, the circuit is referred to as a *threshhold gate*. In Fig. 14-3b, $-E_2 = 0$ and the entire input pulse is transmitted to the output, while in Fig. 14-3c, $-E_2$ is positive and the signal appears superimposed on a *pedestal*.

The waveforms of Fig. 14-3 are unrealistic in that they have neglected the fact that the $R_1 - C_1$ network constitutes an integrating network for the gate waveform. Hence, the gate voltage will not appear abruptly at A as required, but rather will rise exponentially with a time constant R_1C_1 and fall at a similar rate. Hence, this type of gate is not particularly suitable for selecting a portion of a continuous waveform. If, however, the signal is a pulse whose duration is reasonably smaller than the gate width, the result may be entirely satisfactory, as shown in Fig. 14-4.

The advantages of this gate are the following: (1) It is extremely simple. (2) There is very little time delay through the gate since the input is coupled directly to the output through C_1 and the diode. (3)

The gate draws no current in its quiescent condition (i.e., no "stand-by" current). This feature becomes very important in a system requiring many gates. In this respect also, the present gate should be compared with the *AND* gate which will accomplish the same general result as the present gate but which does draw stand-by current. (4) As is shown in Sec. 14-4, this gate is easily extended into a multi-input *OR* circuit with an *INHIBITOR* terminal.

The disadvantages of the gate are the following: (1) There will be interactions between the signal source and control-voltage source. (2) The gate is of limited use because of the slow rise of this control voltage at the diode. The rise time of the control voltage at A may be improved by reducing R_1 but only at the expense of increasing the coupling between signal and gate. If an attempt is made to improve the rise time by reducing C_1, other complications ensue. For example, suppose a gate time constant of 0.2 μsec is required and that values of R_1 less than 10 K permit too much of the control signal to couple back to the signal input. Then for $R_1 = 10$ K, $C_1 = 20$ $\mu\mu$f. Now suppose that the output capacitance C_o shunted across the output terminals is $C_o = 10$ $\mu\mu$f. Then the gate will attenuate the signal, allowing only two-thirds of the signal to pass through.

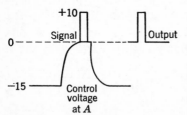

Fig. 14-4. Illustrating the distortion of the effective gate waveform at A in Fig. 14-2.

The rise-time difficulties of the control pulse may be eliminated by replacing the capacitor C_1 by a resistor R_2. A first disadvantage of such an arrangement is that now the signal will be attenuated. For example, if $R_2 = R_1$, the attenuation will be $\frac{1}{2}$. Additionally, in such a case, d-c coupling of the signal will be required, and such coupling may not be feasible.

14-3. An Application of the Unidirectional Diode Gate. One application of the gate of Fig. 14-2 is as a coupling circuit between stages of a binary counter in order to reduce the *carry time*. The carry time of a binary chain is the time required for the chain to complete its response to an input pulse. The carry time is longest when all binaries in the chain are in state 1. For, in this situation, the next input must cause all binaries to change state. Any particular binary will not respond until the previous binary has nominally completed its transition. Hence, the carry time will be of the order of the sum of the transition times of all the binaries. If the binary chain is long, then the carry time may well be longer than the interval between input pulses. And, in such a case, it will not be possible to read a counter between pulses.

The carry time of a long binary chain may be reduced appreciably by interposing gates between the binaries in the manner indicated in **Fig. 14-5.** The control input terminal of the gate is connected to a point in the binary which is at a high voltage when the binary is in state 1 and consequently at a low voltage when the binary is in state 0. Hence the gate is open for transmission when the preceding binary is in state 1 and closed against transmission when the binary is in state 0. Consider then that all the binaries are in state 1. When the next input pulse occurs, each of the binaries will make the required transition in response to this input pulse which is transmitted down the chain through the gates. And the delay before the last binary responds is the sum of the very small delays in the gates rather than the sum of the transition times of all the binaries. To compensate for the attenuation through the gates, it may be necessary to interpose amplifiers between stages. However, even with the additional delay of these amplifiers, the carry time is quite small.

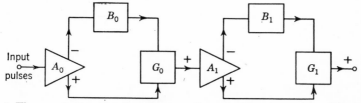

Fig. 14-5. The use of gates to reduce the carry time of a binary counter. The amplifier output is transformer coupled, and pulses of either polarity are available.

For example, a 5-stage 2-Mc counter has been built,[*] using gates between stages, in which the carry time is only 0.16 μsec. For this counter the minimum interval between input pulses is 0.5 μsec, and hence there is time to read and reset the counter between pulses.

Note, that in the above application, it has been assumed that the control voltage remains essentially constant over the signal pulse time. For example, when a pulse changes binary B_0 from a 1 to a 0 state, then G_0 must remain enabled long enough for the signal pulse to pass through. In this respect, observe, then, that the relatively long transition time of the binary is of advantage. We may assist further in satisfying this requirement by making the time constant R_1C_1 large enough to allow the voltage at point A (Fig. 14-2) to fall relatively slowly.

14-4. Other Forms of the Unidirectional Diode Gate. The unidirectional diode gate may be adapted to accept more than one signal input, as in Fig. 14-6. Here two signal inputs e_{s1} and e_{s2} are indicated but, of course, more than two may be used. When the control signal is at its higher level (say zero voltage), the circuit is recognized as a capacitive *OR* circuit (see Sec. 13-2). When the control voltage is at its lower level, the gate is closed against all inputs. Hence, the negative of the control

---

[*] At the Electronics Research Laboratories, Department of Electrical Engineering, Columbia University

pulse may be considered an inhibitor signal.   Here then is a multi-input *OR* circuit with an *INHIBITOR* terminal.

A difficulty associated with the arrangement of Fig. 14-6 is that the loading on the control input becomes increasingly heavy as the number of inputs increases.   This difficulty may be corrected through the use of one additional diode, as indicated in Fig. 14-7.   In this latter circuit the control input voltage does not feed into the signal sources.   In neither case, however, is there any stand-by current.

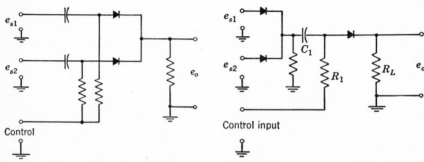

FIG. 14-6. The unidirectional diode gate adapted for more than one signal input.

FIG. 14-7. A two-input gate in which the signal sources do not load the control signal.

It is possible to arrange the diode gate so that it will be open for transmission only as the result of the simultaneous occurrence of a number of gate voltages.   Such a circuit is shown in Fig. 14-8.   Suppose that the control signal levels are zero and $-E$.   Then when *any one* of the control signals e_c is at $-E$, point A is negative with respect to ground by an amount, say, E', and the gate is closed unless the input signal is larger than E'.   When *all* control voltages are at zero, the back bias on diode T_o is removed, and the gate will be open.   It will be recognized that this circuit, except for the signal input connection and capacitor, is an *AND* circuit (Sec. 13-3).   This circuit differs from the gates previously described in that it draws a quiescent current from the E_{bb} supply, although this current may be kept low.

A threshhold gate which may be opened by any one of a number of control signals (an *OR* circuit) is given in Prob. 14-4.

All the forms of the unidirectional diode gate considered up to the present have a common feature which may, on some occasions, constitute a disadvantage.   This feature may be noted in Fig. 14-2 where it appears that unless the upper level of the gating waveform is exactly zero, then either a portion of the input signal will not get through the gate or else the transmitted signal will be superimposed on a pedestal.   This situation may be corrected as in Fig. 14-9 by the use of an additional diode.

Initially, in the absence of an enabling signal at the control terminals, diode T_1 conducts and the consequent current through R keeps diode T_o back-biased. A positive-going gate signal causes T_1 to cease conduction and the gate is thereby opened for transmission. The signal must be d-c coupled but the gate may be either a-c coupled as indicated or d-c coupled. If a-c coupling is employed, then, of course, the time constant R_1C must be large in comparison with the gate duration.

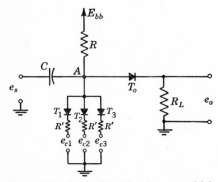

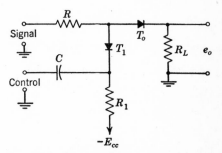

FIG. 14-8. A unidirectional gate which opens only at a coincidence of a number of gate voltages.

FIG. 14-9. A gate whose response is not sensitive to the upper level of the gating voltage.

14-5. Bidirectional Gates Using Multielement Tubes. All the above gates have the limitation that they pass only unidirectional signals. We shall defer consideration of diode bidirectional gates until we have examined first some simpler bidirectional gates which employ multi-element tubes.

Several examples of linear gates using multielement tubes are shown in Fig. 14-10. In Fig. 14-10a the signal voltage e_s and the control voltage e_c are applied through a resistor matrix R_1 and R_2 to the grid of a triode (or pentode). The gating voltage is again a pulse waveform between the levels $-E_1$ and $-E_2$ with a duration t_p equal to the required transmission-interval duration. When the control voltage is at its lower level $-E_1$, the tube is biased well below cutoff. However, when the selector voltage is at its upper level $-E_2$, this bias brings the grid up out of cutoff and into the grid base. So long as the gate persists, the amplifier will amplify the signal voltage, which will then appear at the output.

In the gating circuit of Fig. 14-10b separate grids are available for the signal and gating voltage. This arrangement lowers the loading on the gating and signal sources and eliminates the coupling between the two sources. When the control voltage e_c is at its upper (positive) level $+E_2$, the bias on T_1 is of such a magnitude that tube T_2 is cut off because of the large drop across the cathode resistor. When the selector is at its lower (negative) level $-E_1$, tube T_1 is driven below cutoff and T_2 then operates as an amplifier.

In Fig. 14-10c is illustrated the use of a multigrid tube as a gate. The tube employed has, in addition to the usual control grid, a second control grid which may be used for plate-current cutoff. Initially, the second control grid is biased for plate-current cutoff. The application of the gate voltage e_c to this grid permits the tube to operate as an amplifier. This circuit is similar to the *OR* circuit of Fig. 13-7.

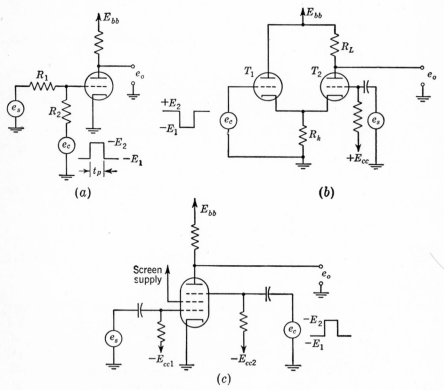

(a)

(b)

(c)

Fig. 14-10. Examples of linear gates.

14-6. Reduction of Pedestal in a Gate Circuit. The gate circuits of Fig. 14-10 share a common feature which may on occasion constitute a disadvantage. Initially, the voltage level at the output is E_{bb}. When the gating signal is applied, the amplifier tube draws current and the output therefore establishes itself at a new lower quiescent level. When, now, the signal is applied, the output signal is superimposed on this new quiescent level. The appearance, typically, of the output during a gating interval is as shown in Fig. 14-11, where it appears that the gated portion of the signal is superimposed on a *pedestal*.

The appearance of the pedestal can be largely suppressed by the symmetrical arrangement shown in Fig. 14-12. Here the gating circuit employed is essentially that indicated in Fig. 14-10a or b, except that, for simplicity, the gating and signal voltages have been placed directly in series. The gating tube is T_1, while T_2 is used to minimize the pedestal. Gating voltages of opposite polarity are applied to the tube grids. During the nongating time, T_2 draws current, while T_1 does not. During the gating interval, T_1 draws current, and T_2 does not. The bias voltages $-E_{cc1}$ and $-E_{cc2}$ and the gate signal amplitude have been adjusted so that the two tube currents are identical and as a result the quiescent output voltage level will remain constant.

If, as is usually the case, the gate waveform has a finite rise time, then the arrangement of Fig. 14-12 does not solve completely the problem of

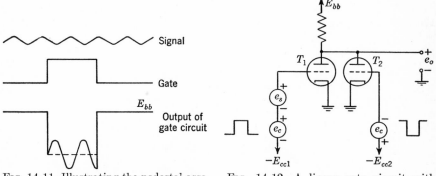

FIG. 14-11. Illustrating the pedestal associated with the linear gates of Fig. 14-10.

FIG. 14-12. A linear gate circuit with provision to cancel the pedestal.

the pedestal, as may be seen from the following considerations. Let us assume, for example, that the gate signal is large in comparison with the grid base so that each tube, when it is not conducting, is biased far below cutoff. Then when the gate voltage appears, T_2 will be driven to cutoff before T_1 starts to conduct, while at the end of the gate T_1 will be cut off before T_2 starts to conduct. Hence, as a result of the gate signals themselves, the output will appear as in Fig. 14-13. The gated signal voltage will appear superimposed on this waveform. If the gate waveform rise time is small in comparison with the gate duration, these spikes may not be seriously objectionable.

For unidirectional (positive) signals, the circuit of Fig. 14-10b may be used without generating a pedestal if tube T_2 is operated at cutoff. However, in order to be certain not to lose small signals, it may be necessary to adjust the bias so that a slight quiescent current exists. Such a bias will result in a small pedestal which may be acceptable. Even though the tube is operated near cutoff, the circuit will be quite linear because of the degeneration introduced by the large cathode resistor.

Gain is sacrificed for linearity. This circuit has been used successfully to gate the video signals from a radar system.

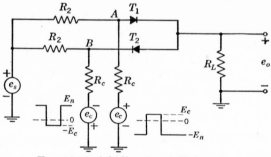

FIG. 14-13. Illustrating the spikes which may occur in the gate circuit of Fig. 14-12.

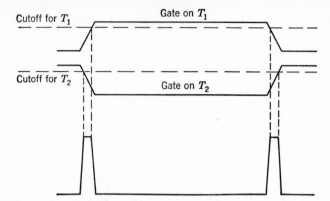

FIG. 14-14. A bidirectional diode gate.

14-7. A Bidirectional Diode Gate.[1] A bidirectional gate may be constructed, using diodes instead of multielement tubes. Such diode gates have advantages of linearity of operation and ease of adjustment to ensure zero pedestal. Such a bidirectional gate is shown in Fig. 14-14. We may observe that the gate consists essentially of two gates of the type shown in Fig. 14-2 with the modification that C_1 is replaced by a resistor. The circuit is redrawn in the form of a bridge is Fig. 14-15. Two sym-

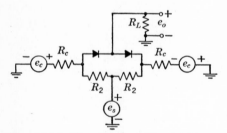

FIG. 14-15. The circuit of Fig. 14-14 redrawn in the form of a bridge network.

metrical gating voltages $+e_c$ and $-e_c$ are now required. When the gating or control voltages are at the levels E_n and $-E_n$, respectively, the diodes are nonconducting and the gate is closed against transmission of the signal e_s. When the control signals are at the levels E_c and $-E_c$, the gate is open for transmission. Provided that the diodes are identical in characteristics (the diodes need not be perfect), it follows from the complete symmetry of the circuit that no pedestal can appear at the output in response to the gating voltages. In the following discussion we shall compute some of the properties of this gating circuit. For simplicity, we shall neglect the impedance of the signal source. The formulas given below are modified in Ref. 1 to take into account this signal source impedance R_s.

Gain. The *gain* of the gate is defined as the ratio e_o/e_s during the transmission interval. The gain is easily calculated from the equivalent circuit of Fig. 14-16. This circuit is derived from the circuit of Fig. 14-14 through the application of Thévenin's theorem. The control voltages cancel at the output. Let R_f equal the diode forward resistance, R_1 equal the parallel resistance of R_c and R_2, and $R_3 \equiv R_1 + R_f$. The impedance to

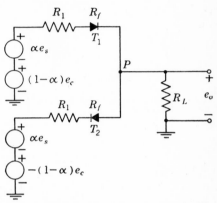

FIG. 14-16. An equivalent circuit for the bidirectional diode gate.

$$\alpha = \frac{R_c}{R_2 + R_c} \qquad R_1 = \frac{R_2 R_c}{R_2 + R_c}$$
$$R_3 = R_1 + R_f$$

the left of point P in Fig. 14-16 is $R_3/2$ and the open-circuit voltage from P to ground is αe_s. Hence, the gain is given by

$$A = \alpha \frac{R_L}{R_L + R_3/2} = \frac{R_c}{R_c + R_2} \frac{R_L}{R_L + R_3/2} \qquad (14\text{-}1)$$

The Control Voltage E_c. Suppose that the signal voltage attains a maximum voltage E_s. Then there is a minimum control voltage E_c that is required to ensure that *both* diodes will continue to conduct. That there is such a minimum required value for E_c may be seen from the following considerations. Initially, in the presence only of the gate voltages the diodes T_1 and T_2 conduct equal currents. The load current is zero and the pedestal is zero. Now assume, say, that e_s is a positive-going signal. Then the current in T_1 increases and the current in T_2 decreases, the difference current flowing through R_L. Eventually the current in T_2 will become zero.

To compute the required minimum E_c, assume that diode T_2 has just stopped conducting. Then the voltage across R_3 associated with T_2 is zero. Hence, the voltage $\alpha E_s - (1 - \alpha)E_c$ must equal the output voltage, or

$$\frac{R_L}{R_3 + R_L} [\alpha E_s + (1 - \alpha)E_c] = \alpha E_s - (1 - \alpha)E_c \qquad (14\text{-}2)$$

from which we find

$$E_c = \frac{R_c}{R_2} \frac{R_3}{R_3 + 2R_L} E_s \equiv (E_c)_{\min} \qquad (14\text{-}3)$$

We note from Eq. (14-3) that $(E_c)_{\min}$ decreases with increasing R_L. There is, however, an important consideration which limits the size of R_L. Suppose we consider that a total stray capacitance C shunts the output terminals in Figs. 14-14 or 14-16. Suppose also that at the end of the gating interval the output is at some finite voltage level due to the signal e_s. Then, when the gate closes and the diodes cut off, the output voltage must decay to zero with a time constant $R_L C$. This difficulty is of the same type described in Sec. 4-3 in connection with diode selectors and in Sec. 13-2 in connection with logical gates.

The Control Voltage E_n. Just as there is a minimum control voltage $(E_c)_{\min}$ required to keep both diodes conducting over the full range of the input signal so there is also a minimum control voltage $(E_n)_{\min}$ required to ensure that *both* diodes are back-biased when the gate is required to be closed. The voltage $(E_n)_{\min}$ is the voltage necessary so that current will flow in the inverse direction in both diodes. Hence, the expression for $(E_n)_{\min}$ may be obtained from Eq. (14-3) by replacing R_3 by

$$R_3' = R_1 + R_b$$

in which R_b is the diode back resistance. When thermionic diodes are employed, values of R_b of the order of 100 Meg may be obtained with some care. Hence, normally, we shall have that $R_3' \gg R_L$ and therefore

$$(E_n)_{\min} \cong \frac{R_c}{R_2} E_s \qquad (14\text{-}4)$$

In practice, the control voltage E_c and E_n should be somewhat larger, say 25 per cent larger, than the minimum values given in Eqs. (14-3) and (14-4). In the case of E_n this additional voltage is essentially a safety factor. In the case of E_c the additional voltage is not only a safety factor but also serves to improve the gate linearity. The larger E_c, the greater is the ratio of control current to signal current in the diodes. Hence, the more nearly constant will be the diode forward resistance R_f over the range of the signal current.

14-8. Balance Conditions in a Bidirectional Diode Gate. The gate circuit of Fig. 14-14 has been redrawn in Fig. 14-17a to make the symmetry of the circuit more evident. Here the signal source impedance R_s (not previously shown) has been included in the circuit. We may note now, that as a result of this symmetry, not only is the output free of pedestal but also that no current flows through the signal-source imped-ance R_s in response to the control voltage. The inverse is, of course, not true. The signal source does cause a current to flow through the control signal generators.

If the two control voltages are equal in amplitude, the points A and B in Fig. 14-17a are at voltages which are equal but opposite in polarity. Hence, the junction point of the diode resistors R_f and the junction point of the resistors R_2 are both at zero potential and balance is ensured at both output and input. If it is not convenient to establish precisely equal control signal amplitudes or if the circuit components are not pre-cisely matched, balance may be restored by either of the potentiometers r_f or r_2 indicated in Fig. 14-17b.

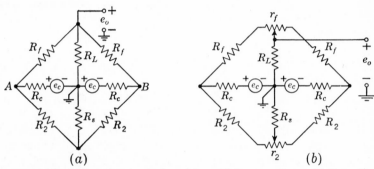

(a) (b)

FIG. 14-17. (a) The bidirectional gate drawn to exhibit symmetry. (b) Potentiometers used for balance of the gate.

An initial adjustment to make the control voltages equal or a slight adjustment of the gating circuit to correct for small unbalance is usually not difficult. We have considered that the gating waveform is rectangu-lar in shape. However, unless it is important that the gate open and close rapidly, there is no need for the gating waveform to make an abrupt transition between levels. Similarly, if the control voltage levels are able to keep the diodes either definitely conducting or definitely non-conducting, there is no need for the control voltage to remain absolutely constant between transitions. What is important, with respect to balance, is that whatever the shape of the control voltages, these voltages must be *identical in waveshape*, except, of course, for polarity. If, for example, the two control voltages have different rise times, voltage spikes will appear at the output at the times of opening and closing of the gate.

When the gate signal duration is long in comparison with the gate signal rise time, the spikes which appear may not be objectionable. However, when gates of the order of, say, a microsecond duration are required, it may well be difficult to reduce the gate rise times sufficiently. In such cases it may be necessary to resort to extreme measures to ensure identical waveforms. One method which often proves effective is to derive the control signals from identical and bifilar-wound windings of a pulse transformer.

In Sec. 4-4 we found that the effect of the finite emission velocity of electrons from a thermionic diode is equivalent to a voltage source E_H in the cathode lead. It may be seen that these voltage sources added to Fig. 14-17 balance to give no resultant current either through the load R_L or the impedance R_s, provided the sources are equal in voltage.

14-9. Signal Input Impedance and Connections. The current drawn from the input signal source does not depend on the control voltage except in so far as it depends on whether or not the diodes are conducting. This result follows from the fact that, as we have seen, no current flows through R_s in response to the control voltages. Assuming that the diode resistances R_f and R_b are zero and infinity, respectively, we may write the input impedances by inspection from Fig. 14-14 or Fig 14-15 as

$$Z_{\text{in}} \cong \frac{R_c + R_2}{2} \qquad \text{diodes open} \qquad (14\text{-}5)$$

and
$$Z_{\text{in}} \cong \frac{R_L R_c}{2R_L + R_c} + \frac{R_2}{2} \qquad \text{diodes conducting} \qquad (14\text{-}6)$$

An equivalent circuit which gives the correct gain and input impedance and which takes into account the absence of pedestal and reaction of control signals on input is shown in Fig. 14-18. Switch S is closed or open, depending on whether or not the diodes are conducting.

So far we have considered only d-c coupling of the signal input. We may, however, also use a-c signal input coupling. In the case of the

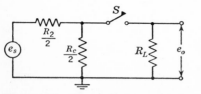

unidirectional gate of Fig. 14-2, the use of the input coupling capacitor C_1 had the markedly disadvantageous effect that the capacitor prevented the gate voltage at the diode from rising abruptly. In the present case, however, no such difficulty exists and the gate will operate basically in the same manner, independently of whether or not an input capacitor is employed. This

FIG. 14-18. An equivalent circuit of the bidirectional gate which gives correctly the gain and input impedance.

feature results from the fact that no current flows through the input capacitor due to the control signals.

14-10. Effect of Circuit Capacitances. Example. The capacitances which have a principal effect on the operation of the gate circuit are the following: (1) the capacitance C_o across the gate output terminals, (2) the capacitance C_d across each diode, and (3) the shunt capacitances C_s to ground from each of the junctions of the resistors R_2 and R_c. The capacitance C_o has an adverse effect on the ability of the gate to transmit fast waveforms. The capacitance C_s not only accentuates this inability to transmit fast waveforms but also limits the speed with which the gate can be opened and closed. Finally, the diode capacitances C_d provide a transmission path across the gate even when the diodes are not conducting.

When the diodes are conducting, the shunt capacitances effect the high-frequency response. From the equivalent circuit of Fig. 14-19 (derived from Fig. 14-18 through the use of Thévenin's theorem), we see that the gate behaves as a low-pass resistance-capacitance circuit

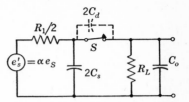

FIG. 14-19. Illustration of the capacitances which influence transmission in a bidirectional diode gate.

whose time constant is $C_o + 2C_s$ times a resistance equal to the parallel combination of R_L, $R_c/2$, and $R_2/2$.

The residual transmission which results owing to the capacitance which shunts the diodes may be calculated from Fig. 14-19 by opening switch S and shunting across the switch a capacitance equal to the sum of the diode capacitances.

EXAMPLE. In the circuit of Fig. 14-14 consider that $R_L = R_c = 100$ K, $R_2 = 50$ K, and that the signal e_s has a peak value of 20 volts. Find A, $(E_c)_{min}$, $(E_n)_{min}$, and Z_{in}. Also, calculate the upper 3-db frequency of the gate.

Solution. In view of the order of magnitude of the impedances involved, we may assume that the diodes are perfect (that is, $R_f = 0$ and $R_b = \infty$).

$$R_1 = \frac{R_2 R_c}{R_2 + R_c} = 33.3 \text{ K} = R_3$$

From Eqs. (14-1), (14-3), and (14-4), we find

$$A = 0.57 \qquad (E_c)_{min} = 5.7 \text{ volts} \qquad (E_n)_{min} = 40 \text{ volts} \qquad (14\text{-}7)$$

the impedance seen by the signal source is given by Eqs. (14-5) and (14-6) as

$$Z_{in} = 75 \text{ K (diodes open)} \qquad Z_{in} = 58 \text{ K (diodes conducting)} \qquad (14\text{-}8)$$

Now $R_1/2$ $(= 16.7$ K$)$ in parallel with R_L $(= 100$ K$)$ is equivalent to 14.3 K. If we assume a total shunting capacitance $C_o + 2C_s$ of 20 $\mu\mu$f, then the time constant is $\tau = (20 \times 10^{-12})(14.3 \times 10^3) = 0.29$ μsec and the upper 3-db frequency f_2 is given by $f_2 = 1/2\pi\tau = 0.55$ Mc.

14-11. Four-diode Gate.[1] Among the disadvantages of the two-diode gate of Fig. 14-14 are its low gain, its sensitivity to control-voltage unbalance, the possibility that the voltage $(E_n)_{min}$ may be excessive, and the fact that there may be appreciable leakage through the diode capacitances. These features may be improved by the use of two additional diodes, as in Fig. 14-20. Two additional balanced voltages $+E$ and $-E$

are required, but since these are fixed d-c voltages they need occasion no difficulty.

Qualitatively, the operation is as follows. When the control voltages are E_c and $-E_c$, respectively, the diodes T_3 and T_4 are back-biased. The diodes T_1 and T_2 are conducting because of the voltages $+E$ and $-E$ and the signal source is coupled to the load through the resistors R_2 and the conducting diodes. Since, under these circumstances, the control voltages are disconnected from the gate by the back-biased diodes, an unbalance in control signals cannot result in a pedestal at the output.

When the control voltages are E_n and $-E_n$, respectively, the points P_1 and P_2 are clamped to these voltages and the diodes T_1 and T_2 are back-biased. Under these circumstances, the gate will not transmit.

The gain of the gate of Fig. 14-20 is the same as that of the gate of Fig. 14-14 and is given by Eq. (14-1). In connection with the circuit of Fig.

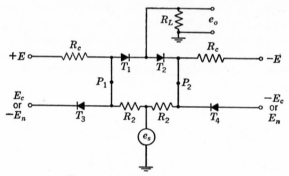

FIG. 14-20. A four-diode gate.

14-14 we found earlier that a gain close to unity is not conveniently attained. The reason for this feature is that to achieve such a gain it is necessary to make $R_c \gg R_2$ and $R_L \gg R_3$. However, as is apparent from Eq. (14-4), under such circumstances the required value of $(E_n)_{\min}$ becomes prohibitively high. In the gate of Fig. 14-20 the principal requirement on R_2 is that it be large in comparison with the diode-conducting resistance, so that the diodes may be effective as clamps. The minimum value of R_2 is also limited by the fact that when the diodes T_3 and T_4 conduct, the control source must furnish a current E_n/R_2, and the signal source, a current $2E_s/R_2$, approximately. Hence, R_2 must not be so low as to draw excessive control or signal current.

We compute now the required minimum values of E, E_c, and E_n. When diodes T_3 and T_4 are not conducting, the gates of Fig. 14-15 and 14-20 are identical with the voltages $+E$ and $-E$, replacing the voltages E_c and $-E_c$. Hence, $E_{\min}$ is given by Eq. (14-3).

The voltage $(E_c)_{\min}$ is computed as follows. We shall assume that $R_f \ll R_L$. Then for a positive-going signal of amplitude E_s the voltage at point P_1 becomes AE_s, A being the circuit gain. If the diode T_3 is to continue to be back-biased, the voltage E_c must be at least

$$(E_c)_{min} = AE_s \qquad (14\text{-}9)$$

The voltage E_n must be selected not only to keep the transmission diodes back-biased but also to keep the clamp diodes conducting in the presence of a signal E_s. The voltage at P_2 for a positive signal E_s, and hence the minimum value of E_n, is

$$(E_n)_{min} = E_s \frac{R_c}{R_c + R_2} - E \frac{R_2}{R_2 + R_c} \qquad (14\text{-}10)$$

EXAMPLE. In the circuit of Fig. 14-20 consider that $R_L = R_c = 100$ K and that $R_2 = 10$ K. (Assume thermionic diodes with $R_f = 250$ ohms, in which case the value selected for R_2 should give adequate clamping.) For $E_s = 20$ volts, compute A, E_{min}, and $(E_c)_{min}$. Compute $(E_n)_{min}$ for $E = E_{min}$.

Solution. From Eqs. (14-1), (14-3), (14-9), and (14-10), we have

$$A = 0.87 \qquad E_{min} = 8.8 \text{ volts} \qquad (E_c)_{min} = 17.4 \text{ volts} \qquad (E_n)_{min} = 17.4 \text{ volts}$$

The two auxiliary diodes not only improve the gate circuit in the manner described previously, but, as is seen from the example above, an improvement results also in the gain and the value of $(E_n)_{min}$.

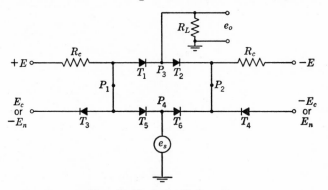

FIG. 14-21. A six-diode gate.

14-12. Six-diode Gate.[1] The four-diode gate of Sec. 14-11 has a higher gain than the two-diode gate, but the gain still falls appreciably short of the maximum gain of unity. This feature results from the need to use resistors R_2 of appreciable size in order to permit diodes T_3 and T_4 to operate as clamps. This situation may be corrected by replacing resistors R_2 by diodes T_5 and T_6 as in Fig. 14-21.

When the gate is open for transmission, the control voltages are at E_c and $-E_c$, respectively, and the diodes T_3 and T_4 are back-biased. The required voltage E depends upon the amplitude E_s of the signal and is determined by the condition that the current be in the forward direction in each of the diodes T_1, T_2, T_5, and T_6. The current in each diode consists of two components, one due to E (as indicated in Fig. 14-22a) and the other due to E_s (as indicated in Fig. 14-22b). The current due to E is $E/2R_c$ and is in the forward direction in each diode, but the current due to E_s is in the reverse direction in T_5 (between P_1 and P_4) and in T_2 (between P_3 and P_2). The larger reverse current is in T_5 and equals

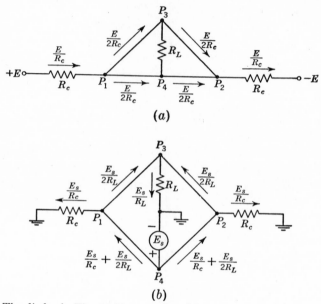

Fig. 14-22. The diodes in Fig. 14-21 are replaced by short circuits. (a) The currents due to E; (b) the currents due to E_s.

$E_s/R_c + E_s/2R_L$, and hence this quantity must be less than $E/2R_c$. The minimum value of E is therefore given by

$$E_{\min} = E_s \left(2 + \frac{R_c}{R_L} \right) \tag{14-11}$$

The above derivation assumes that R_f is much less than R_c or R_L. A balancing potentiometer may be inserted between T_5 and T_6 so as to give zero output for zero input. If the potentiometer is assumed to be set at its mid-point, if the total resistance of the potentiometer is R, and if R and R_f are both much less than R_c or R_L, then, proceeding as in Fig. 14-22, we find (Prob. 14-12) that

$$E_{\min} = E_s \left(2 + \frac{R_c}{R_L} \right) \left(1 + \frac{R}{4R_f} \right) \tag{14-12}$$

The voltage $E_{\min}$ may become excessive if the potentiometer resistance R is too large relative to R_f. When a balancing potentiometer is used, the value of E_{min} in Eq. (14-12) should be used rather than the approximate equation (14-11), which may easily be incorrect by quite a large factor.

If R_c and R_L are large compared with R_f and R, we see, from Fig. 14-22b, that the gain will be very close to unity.

$$A \cong 1 \qquad\qquad (14\text{-}13)$$

The exact expression for A is given in Prob. 14-13.

From Fig. 14-21 we see that if the clamping diodes T_3 and T_4 are to remain back-biased for a signal amplitude E_s, then E_c must be at least equal to $(E_c)_{min} = E_s$. On the other hand, it is also apparent that if the points P_1 and P_2 are clamped at a voltage E_n, then none of the transmission diodes will conduct until E_s exceeds E_n. Hence, the minimum required value of E_n is $(E_n)_{min} = E_s$. To summarize, we have

$$(E_c)_{min} = (E_n)_{min} = E_s \qquad\qquad (14\text{-}14)$$

Using the same parameters as above, namely, $E_s = 20$, $R_f = 0.25$ K, $R_L = R_c = 100$ K, and with $R = 1$ K, we find

$$A \cong 1 \qquad (E_c)_{min} = (E_n)_{min} = 20 \qquad \text{and} \qquad E_{min} = 120 \text{ volts}$$

The deviation from linearity of such a gate may be less than 0.1 per cent.

Another advantage of this six-diode gate is that the control- and signal-source currents may be very low if R_c and R_L are high (see Probs. 14-15 and 14-16).

An approximate equivalent circuit for estimating the leakage through the gate due to the diode shunt capacitances is indicated in Fig. 14-23. The leakage is small, particularly be-

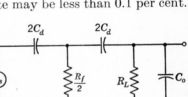

FIG. 14-23. Equivalent circuit for estimating six-diode gate leakage due to diode shunt capacitance.

cause of the low value of the shunting resistance $R_f/2$. In a typical case it can be calculated for the circuit of Fig. 14-23 that less than 1 per cent leakage will result at signal frequencies below 1 Mc.

Series, parallel, and series-parallel combinations of diode gates are discussed in Ref. 1.

14-13. Synchronous Clamp.[2] In Sec. 4-6 we described the function of a synchronous clamp and indicated very briefly the manner of its operation. The synchronous clamp is a gate-type circuit of the form indicated in Fig. 14-1b, in which the resistor R is replaced by a capacitor. It is to be recalled that the function of this clamp is not so much to prevent signal transmission during a selected interval as it is to restore the quiescent level of the output signal to some reference voltage (see Fig. 4-26).

The bidirectional diode gates of the preceding sections may be used as synchronous clamps. A two-diode clamp, with capacitively coupled control voltages, is shown in Fig. 14-24 and will now be discussed in detail. Initially, for the sake of orientation, we shall indicate the order of magnitude of the components employed. The resistor R_i is used to isolate the signal lead from the capacitance of the clamp circuit during the interval when the diodes are not conducting. This resistor is not essential, but when it is used will ordinarily be of the order of several thousand ohms. The resistor R_g is a grid-leak resistor for T_3 and serves to provide a d-c return during the interval when the grid would otherwise be isolated

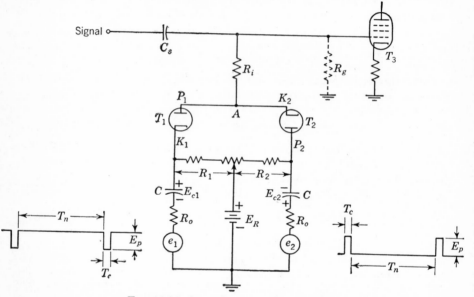

Fig. 14-24. A synchronous clamp circuit.

direct-current-wise because the diodes are back-biased. Actually, unless very long time intervals elapse between clamping pulses, the resistor R_g may be omitted. However, even if an actual grid leak is not included in the circuit, it may be necessary to consider that an effective grid leak is present because of gas current or grid emission in T_3. We may reasonably consider R_g to be of the order of 10 Meg.

The time constant $R_g C_s$ must be large enough to transmit the signal without distortion over a time interval equal to the time between clamping pulses. Hence, it is required that $R_g C_s \gg T_n$, where T_n is the interval between clamping pulses. As an example, consider the situation which arises in color television systems. Here synchronous clamping is required to perform the function which is achieved by d-c restorer circuits in monochrome television. The interval T_n in television systems is about

53.5 μsec. A capacitor $C_s = 1,000$ $\mu\mu$f gives a time constant (for the assumed value $R_g = 10$ Meg) of $R_g C_s = 10^4$ μsec, which is more than adequate. The resistor R_o represents the control-generator output impedance. If the clamp pulses are derived from low impedance windings of a pulse transformer, these impedances may be as low as several ohms. If a phase inverter as in Fig. 1-14 is used instead, these impedances will be of the order of thousands of ohms. In this connection it is of interest to note that common practice is to apply a negative clamp pulse to the phase-inverter grid. In this case the output pulses form as the tube cuts off and the waveform, impedance, and amplitude of the two required clamp pulses are more easily adjusted to equality.

We shall see that the principal requirement, with respect to capacitor C, is that its capacitance be large in comparison with C_s. In the example given above, where $C_s = 0.001$ μf, a value of $C = 0.1$ μf is certainly adequate, while a capacitance value of 0.01 μf may well be sufficient. The resistors R_1 and R_2 (nominally equal) must be large enough so that $R_1 C$ or $R_2 C$ shall be very large in comparison with T_n. For the values indicated above, resistors of the order of 0.5 Meg should be adequate.

14-14. Operation of Synchronous Clamp. To understand the operation of the clamp circuit of Fig. 14-24, let us initially disconnect the clamp portion of the circuit from the signal lead. Specifically, let us consider that the connection of resistor R_i to point A has been opened. The circuit which remains should now be compared with the d-c restorer circuit of Fig. 4-16. The present circuit (with R_i disconnected) is essentially a symmetrical form of the d-c restorer circuit, as the following description will indicate.

During the interval T_c, when e_1 is negative and e_2 is positive, current will flow through the diodes, charging the capacitors. If the resistors R_1 and R_2 were not present, then there would be no means for the charge so acquired to leak off. Hence, after a number of clamping pulses, the capacitors would charge fully and the diodes T_1 and T_2 would no longer conduct. Conduction will stop when

$$2E_p = E_{c1} + E_{c2} \qquad (14\text{-}15)$$

since under these circumstances the voltage drop from the plate of T_2 to the cathode of T_1 will never be positive. It should now be clear that a process of *d-c restoration* has taken place. The waveform at P_2 will be identical in form to the waveform e_2, while the waveform at K_1 will be identical to the waveform e_1. However, independently of the d-c levels of the signals e_1 and e_2, the peak positive level of the waveform at P_2 will coincide with the peak negative level of the waveform at K_1. We shall show later [Eq. (14-18)] that the common peak voltage level attained by the two waveforms is E_R volts with respect to ground.

These results are modified slightly by the presence of the resistors R_1 and R_2. Because of these resistors the capacitors will discharge slightly during the interval T_n. Hence the diodes must conduct somewhat during the interval T_c to supply the capacitor charge which is lost.

We shall now compute the absolute voltage levels of the waveforms which appear at K_1 and P_2. We shall assume, simply as a matter of convenience, that the clamping signal e_1 goes from zero volts to $-E_p$, while e_2 goes from zero to $+E_p$. Since these signals are isolated from the remainder of the circuit by capacitors, the operation of the circuit cannot depend on the d-c levels of these signals. Hence, there is no loss of generality in this assumption. We shall also assume, for simplicity, that the capacitors C are large enough so that the rectangularity of the clamping signals are preserved at K_1 and P_2. During the interval T_c the capacitors charge through the diodes and each capacitor acquires an equal amount of charge. We may neglect the charge acquired due to current flow in R_1 and R_2 during this interval because the resistors R_1 and R_2 are very large in comparison with the total resistance in the diode-charging path, that is, $2R_o + 2R_f$, where R_f is the diode forward resistance. During the interval T_n the capacitors discharge through R_1 and R_2, respectively. Since each capacitor acquires equal charge during the interval T_c, then, in an equilibrium situation, each capacitor must lose equal charge during the interval T_n. Since the times of discharge are the same, the discharge currents must be the same. Hence, if we neglect R_o in comparison with R_1 and R_2, we may write

$$\frac{E_{c2} + E_R}{R_2} = \frac{E_{c1} - E_R}{R_1} \tag{14-16}$$

Combining Eqs. (14-15) and (14-16), we have, for the special case $R_1 = R_2$,

$$E_{c1} = E_p + E_R \tag{14-17}$$
$$E_{c2} = E_p - E_R$$

During the interval T_c the voltages E_{k1} and E_{p2} at K_1 and P_2, respectively, are

$$E_{k1} = -E_p + E_{c1} = E_R \tag{14-18}$$
$$E_{p2} = E_p - E_{c2} = E_R$$

Hence, also, during this interval T_c, the point A in Fig. 14-24 is at the voltage E_R.

Now let us reconnect the point A to the signal lead in order to see how the circuit operates to restore the voltage level of the signal lead to E_R during the interval T_c when the input signal is quiescent. Suppose that at the end of the interval T_n the signal lead is left at a voltage

$E_R + \Delta E$.   Then there is an excess of charge $C_s \, \Delta E$ on the signal capacitor C_s.   During the clamping interval T_c, since K_1 and P_1 attain the level E_R, then diode T_1 alone will conduct and the excess charge will leave C_s and flow into the capacitor C, which is in series with generator e_1.   An equivalent circuit for computing the discharge of capacitor C_s into capacitor C is given in Fig. 14-25.   The resistor R_s represents the impedance of the signal source while R_f is the diode forward resistance of T_1.   We have considered that the quiescent level of the signal source is E_R, in order that we shall have to deal only with the *excess* charge on capacitor C_s.   If the capacitor C is very much larger than C_s, the excess charge on C_s can flow into C without changing the voltage across C appreciably.   This excess charge transfers with a time constant $C_s(R_s + R_i + R_f + R_o)$. This time constant should be small in

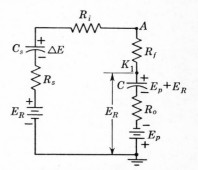

FIG. 14-25. Equivalent circuit for computing discharge of capacitor C_s.

comparison with T_c.   If necessary, the resistor R_i may be omitted and R_o made small by deriving the clamping signals from a low impedance winding of a pulse transformer.

During the interval T_n the excess charge which has been transferred to C may leak off C through the resistor R_1.   In order that time be available for all this charge to leak off, we require that

$$\frac{E_{c1} - E_R}{R_1} \, T_n = \frac{E_p}{R_1} \, T_n \geq C_s \, \Delta E \qquad (14\text{-}19)$$

This last equation may be used to determine the maximum allowable value of R_1 after E_p has been determined and after some estimate has been made for ΔE.   We shall return to these matters shortly.

If at the end of an interval T_c the signal lead is at a voltage $E_R - \Delta E$, then there is a deficiency of charge on C_s.   In this case, during the interval T_c, C_s will acquire charge through diode T_2 from the capacitor C which is in series with e_2.   The charge lost by C is replaced again through R_2.

The required minimum size of the clamping pulses is determined by the consideration that neither diode shall conduct during the interval T_n. Suppose that the signal has a peak value $\pm E_s$ with respect to its quiescent level.   Then, since during the interval T_n the voltages at K_1 and P_2 are, respectively, E_{c1} and E_{c2} as given by Eq. (14-17), we require that

$$E_p > E_s \qquad (14\text{-}20)$$

We return now to Eq. (14-19) to consider how to compute a reasonable value for R_1. Suppose that we are dealing with a television signal for which $T_n = 53.5$ μsec and suppose that the peak signal amplitude is 2.0 volts. Let $C_s = 1,000$ $\mu\mu$f and $E_R = +1.0$ volt. From Eq. (14-20), E_p must be greater than 2 volts. Let us take $E_p = 5$ volts. The type of signal which will give the largest ΔE is one which has the largest average value. Such a signal is shown in Fig. 14-26a. For an effective grid leak $R_g = 10$ Meg, the voltage ΔE in Fig. 14-26b which accumulates after one interval T_n is $E_s T_n / C_s R_g \cong 10$ mv. For $\Delta E \cong 10$ mv, Eq. (14-19) gives $R_1 < 27$ Meg. Hence we see that the required size of R_1 constitutes no problem. Actually, we would make R_1 of the order of $\frac{1}{2}$ to 1 Meg, since R_1 serves effectively as the d-c return path from grid to ground.

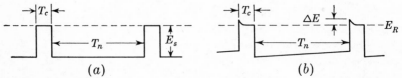

FIG. 14-26. Pertaining to the computation of the voltage ΔE. (a) A signal which is constant during the interval T_n. The signal amplitude is E_s. (b) The voltage at the grid of T_3 in Fig. 14-24.

14-15. Balance Conditions in Synchronous Clamp. Unlike the bidirectional gates, the synchronous clamp circuit does not require, for proper operation, that the clamping signals be equal in amplitude. The reason for the difference lies in the fact that in the clamp circuit the clamping signal is a-c coupled. The nominally fixed voltages E_{c1} and E_{c2} across the capacitors will always adjust so that during the interval T_c both K_1 and P_2 will be at the same voltage. Suppose, however, that the positive and negative clamp pulses have different amplitudes E_p^+ and E_p^-, respectively. Then it may be demonstrated that the effective reference voltage will be

$$E_R' = E_R + \frac{E_p^+ - E_p^-}{2} \tag{14-21}$$

If the pulse amplitudes are equal but the resistors R_1 and R_2 are unequal, it may be shown that the effective reference voltage becomes

$$E_R' = E_R + E_p \frac{R_1 - R_2}{R_1 + R_2} \tag{14-22}$$

Hence, the balancing potentiometer in Fig. 14-24 may be used to make a small adjustment of the effective reference voltage or to compensate for a small unbalance in the pulse amplitudes.

Up to the present we have neglected the effect of the finite resistance of the charging path of the capacitors C during the interval T_c. This resistance is $2R_a = 2R_o + 2R_f$. If the circuit is entirely symmetrical, this resistance R_a has no effect on the effective reference voltage. If however, say, $R_1 \neq R_2$, then the effective reference voltage becomes

$$E'_R = E_R + E_p \frac{R_1 - R_2}{R_1 + R_2 + 2\tau R_a} \qquad (14\text{-}23)$$

where $\tau = T_n/T_c$.

14-16. Other Forms of Gating and Clamping Circuits.[3] We now consider qualitatively a number of other forms of gate circuits. These circuits do not attain the precision of the multidiode gates considered above and do not have the general applicability of the multigrid tube gates, but they are quite useful nevertheless.

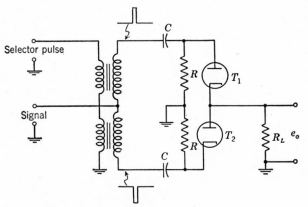

Fig. 14-27. Series-diode bidirectional gate.

Series-diode Bidirectional Gate. This gate circuit, shown in Fig. 14-27, is intended to be used with a regularly recurring selector pulse. The circuit has much in common with the synchronous clamp circuit. The repeated application of the selector pulses charges the capacitors C to such a voltage that the diodes are back-biased except during the peak of the selector pulses. At the selector pulse peaks, the diodes have nominally zero plate-to-cathode voltage and are delivering the currents necessary to replace the capacitor charge lost through resistors R. During the selector pulse interval, a positive-going input signal will be transmitted to the output through diode T_1, while a negative-going input will be transmitted through T_2. It is to be noted that, even if we assume that the impedance of the selector pulse generator is zero, the signal, in going from input to output, must still pass through the leakage inductance of the transformer. This factor must be taken into account in considering the waveform distortion which will be produced by the gate. A second source of distortion is the ringing which may be induced in the transformer at the leading and trailing edges of the control pulses.

An alternative form of the circuit which uses two additional diodes, but does not require a center-tapped transformer, and uses only a single capacitor and resistor is shown in Fig. 14-28. Here again the capacitor charges so that the diodes are conducting only at the peak of the control

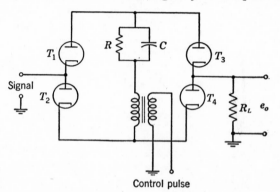

FIG. 14-28. Alternative form of the gate of Fig. 14-27.

signal. A positive-going input signal, for example, is transmitted to the output through T_2, through the leakage inductance of the transformer, through C, and through T_3.

Shunt-diode Bidirectional Gate. A shunt-diode bidirectional gate is shown in Fig. 14-29. In the absence of a selector pulse the signal output point is clamped to ground, against signal excursions in either direction,

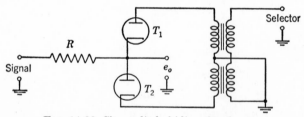

FIG. 14-29. Shunt-diode bidirectional gate.

through the diodes and leakage inductance of the transformer windings. The selector pulse is of a polarity to back bias the diodes so that the signal output is free to follow the input signal.

A shunt-diode bidirectional gate in which the control signals are applied through capacitors is shown in Fig. 14-30. The resistors R_1 have been returned to voltages $+E$ and $-E$ to keep a reasonable current flowing in the diodes in the absence of the gate pulses. In this way the diode resistances are kept low. Clamping of the signal output point is achieved through the diodes, through the capacitors, and through the output impedances of the gate generators. Hence, the gate-generator output impedances must be kept low compared with R.

The gate of Fig. 14-30 has the following disadvantages. First, the quiescent level of the output signal point depends on the balance between the voltages $+E$ and $-E$ and on the balance between the two resistors

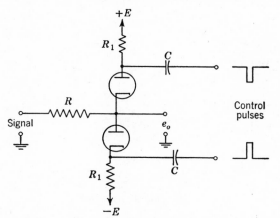

FIG. 14-30. Shunt-diode bidirectional gate with the control signal capacitatively coupled.

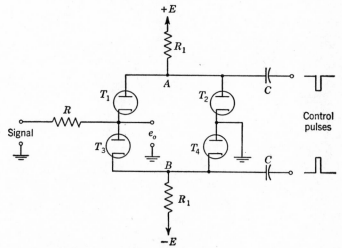

FIG. 14-31. A four-diode shunt bidirectional gate with capacitive coupling of the control signals.

R_1. (Since R_1 is normally large in comparison with the diode forward resistance, unbalance in the diodes has a negligible effect.) Second, the gate requires low impedance control signal generators. Both these disadvantages are corrected by the use of two more diodes in the circuit of Fig. 14-31. To see these results most simply, consider that the diode forward resistances are zero. Then, independently of any unbalance in the resistors R_1 or the voltages $+E$ and $-E$, the quiescent level of the output will be ground. Hence, so long as the diodes T_2 and T_4 continue to conduct, the points A and B will be at ground potential and the diodes T_1 and T_3 will serve as effective clamps against signal appearing at the

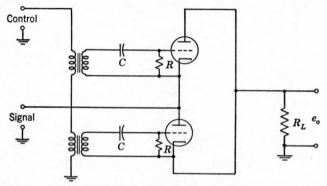

Fig. 14-32. A double-triode series gate.

output of the gate. The presence of control pulses, however, back-biases the diodes and allows the output to follow the input signal.

Double-triode Gates. A series triode gate is shown in Fig. 14-32. The repeated control pulse charges the capacitors C, through grid current, so that the triodes are cut off except at the occurrence of the gating signal.

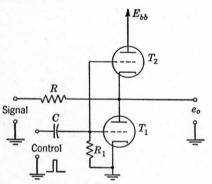

Fig. 14-33. A double-triode shunt gate.

An advantage of this circuit over the two-diode circuit of Fig. 14-27 is that in the present case the signal does not have to pass through the transformer winding. The circuit has the advantage over the single triode gate (Fig. 14-10a) in that the output is free of pedestal. Since, however, the signal source provides all the tube current, the tube current is normally small, and the triodes do not operate particularly linearly at low input signal levels.

A shunt triode gate is shown in Fig. 14-33. Here again the triodes are cut off except during the interval of the control pulse. The positive limit of this pulse is restored to ground by the grid circuit of T_1. When tubes and supply voltage are specified, the clamp level can be calculated.

Synchronous Clamps. We noted earlier that a synchronous clamp was essentially a circuit of the type of Fig. 14-1b in which the resistor R was replaced by a capacitor. Hence, actually, any of the shunt gating circuits of Figs. 14-29, 14-30, 14-31, and 14-33 may be used as synchronous clamps by simply replacing the input resistor by a capacitor. Similarly, a synchronous clamp may be constructed with a coupling capacitor and any of the series gating circuits. It is only necessary to connect the series gating circuits so that the input and output terminals become the two terminals of the switch in Fig. 14-1b. In this case, of course, the series gates will now be operating as shunt gates.

REFERENCES

1. Millman, J., and T. H. Puckett: Accurate Linear Bidirectional Diode Gates, *Proc. IRE*, vol. 43, pp. 27–37, January, 1955.
2. Wendt, K. R.: Television DC Components, *RCA Rev.*, vol. 9, pp. 85–111, March, 1948.
   Rhodes, R. N.: Factors in the Design of Keyed Clamping Circuits, *RCA Rev.*, vol. 15, pp. 362–371, September, 1954.
3. Chance, B., et al.: "Waveforms," Massachusetts Institute of Technology Radiation Laboratory Series, vol. 19, chap. 10, McGraw-Hill Book Company, Inc., New York, 1949.

CHAPTER 15

VOLTAGE COMPARATORS

Earlier we considered a class of circuits which were used to transmit a signal only after the signal had attained a fixed reference level. These *clipping circuits* (also known as *voltage-selection* circuits) reject the signal until the reference voltage is attained, and thereafter, ideally, transmit the signal without distortion. The essential element required in these circuits is one which exhibits a sharp discontinuity in its transmission characteristics, i.e., diodes, triodes at cutoff, etc. We consider now a type of nonlinear circuit which is used to mark distinctly the exact time at which an arbitrary waveform attains a reference level. The distinction between the presently considered *comparator circuits* and the voltage-selection or clipping circuits is that in a comparator circuit there is no interest in reproducing any part of the signal waveform. Frequently, the comparator output is a large-amplitude short-duration pulse which occurs at the instant the signal attains the reference voltage but is otherwise independent of the signal.

15-1. Applications of Voltage Comparators. *Accurate Time Delays.* Suppose that there is available a precisely linear saw-tooth voltage whose slope is known. If this sweep voltage is applied to a comparator which responds when the sweep voltage attains some fixed d-c reference voltage, a pulse is obtained which is separated in time from the beginning of the saw tooth by a precisely known interval. If the sweep voltage is being used for a CRO display, the comparator output may be employed as an accurate time marker. Comparators are used extensively in this manner for timing purposes in radar systems. This same technique is also used extensively for converting analogue information to digital form (see Sec. 16-3).

Pulse-time Modulation. In the above application, if the reference voltage is modulated by some information, a succession of timed pulses is generated which results in a *time-modulation* system of communication.

Timing Markers Generated from a Sine Wave. If a comparator is used to detect the instant of equality of the instantaneous value of a sine wave with a d-c reference voltage, pulses will be obtained which are synchronized to the sine wave. Thus, a sine wave is converted into a

458

series of pulses (one or two per cycle). There are many important applications of this sort.

Phasemeter. When a comparator is used with sinusoidal signals, as above, then it is advantageous that the reference voltage be zero. Under these circumstances the pulses are locked in phase with the zero of the sine wave, and, ideally, are independent of the amplitude of the sinusoidal voltage. The phase angle between two voltages can be measured by a method based upon this principle. Both voltages are converted into pulses and the time interval between the pulse of one wave and that obtained from the second sine wave is measured. This time interval is proportional to the phase difference. Such a phase meter can measure angles from zero to 360°.

Amplitude-distribution Analyzer. It is possible to design a comparator circuit so that its output is not a pulse but rather its output has one magnitude if the input voltage e_i exceeds the reference voltage E_R and has another value if e_i falls below E_R. In other words, the comparator acts as a switch which closes if $e_i > E_R$ and opens if $e_i < E_R$. This circuit may be used as an amplitude-distribution analyzer and is important in connection with studies of noise generated in a vacuum tube, the voltage spectrum of pulses developed by a nuclear-radiation detector,[1] etc.

To be specific, suppose that the output of the comparator is 100 volts if $e_i > E_R$ and zero if $e_i < E_R$. Let the input to the comparator be tube noise. A d-c meter is used to measure the average value of the output square wave. For example, if E_R is set at zero, the meter will read 100 volts, which is interpreted to mean that the probability that the amplitude is greater than zero is 100 per cent. If E_R is set at some value E_R' and the meter reads 70 volts, this is interpreted to mean that the probability that the amplitude of the noise is greater than E_R' is 70 per cent, etc. In this way the cumulative amplitude probability distribution of the noise is obtained by recording meter readings as a function of E_R.

Square Waves from a Sine Wave. If the comparator output is a signal which assumes either one of two levels, as discussed above, then a sine-wave input will result in a square-wave output. If the reference voltage E_R is set to zero, then a symmetrical square wave results.

Voltage-operated Switch. An example of a comparator used with a storage counter as a voltage-sensing switch is given in Sec. 11-11.

15-2. Classification of Comparator Circuits. Existing comparator circuits fall into one of the following classes:

1. A diode and a nonregenerative amplifier
2. A triode or pentode operating at cutoff
3. A regenerative amplifier with a diode in the regenerative loop
4. Regenerative circuits (without a diode switch)
5. Gas-tube switches

These circuits will now be discussed in turn.

15-3. A Diode in Cascade with a Nonregenerative Amplifier. In the present section we shall discuss the diode-amplifier comparator not only for the purpose of understanding this particular circuit but also in order to develop some general ideas about comparators.

An elemental diode comparator circuit is shown in Fig. 15-1. The reference voltage is E_R, and for the sake of illustration a ramp input voltage is indicated. The form of the circuit is identical with the diode voltage-selector circuit or clipping circuit of Sec. 4-3. It is referred to as a comparator, however, in the present instance, because of its intended application. Let us assume, tentatively, that the diode is perfect in the sense that the transition in the diode from the nonconducting to the conducting condition is arbitrarily abrupt. Then the output waveform is as shown, i.e., a ramp voltage starting at the level E_R.

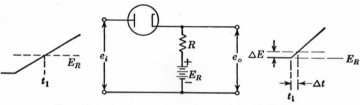

FIG. 15-1. A comparator using a pick-off diode.

Suppose that the ramp-voltage input is being used as a sweep voltage for a cathode-ray oscilloscope. The purpose of the comparator is to mark the *time* when the sweep voltage attains the level E_R. Toward this end we shall apply the comparator output to the cathode of the cathode-ray tube. Beginning at the instant the ramp starts to rise at the comparator output the intensity of the CRO trace will begin to diminish, and we may then say that the input ramp has reached E_R at that time on the sweep where the beginning of this diminution of intensity is observed.

Because of the limited ability on the part of the human observer to perceive small changes in CRO trace intensity, there will be some small range of uncertainty, ΔE in Fig. 15-1, corresponding to a time uncertainty Δt in the determination of the exact instant at which the comparator reference level is reached. This situation may be improved by amplifying the diode-circuit output voltage before application to the cathode of the cathode-ray tube. The voltage uncertainty ΔE remains unaltered; but the slope of the signal is increased, and the signal passes through the range ΔE in a correspondingly shorter time. The uncertainty Δt may be reduced without limit by continuing to increase the amplification. Now, generally, a high-gain amplifier will not normally have a very stable gain, but this feature need cause no difficulty in this application since we need but to make the amplifier gain initially substantially larger than is necessary to reduce Δt to the required interval.

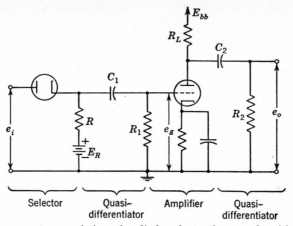

FIG. 15-2. A comparator consisting of a diode selector in cascade with a rate-of-rise amplifier.

The comparator arrangement of Fig. 15-1 has an important disadvantage. The output waveform indicated serves the purpose required but also has the feature that it will blank out the entire CRO trace after the comparator point is reached. This situation may be remedied by including in the circuit two RC differentiating circuits as in the circuit of Fig. 15-2. This circuit, aside from the diode, will be recognized as the rate-of-rise amplifier discussed in Sec. 2-3. In Fig. 15-3 waveform a is the ramp input, b is the grid signal e_g, while c gives the resultant output e_o. The general expression for e_o is given by Eq. (2-22) and is plotted in Fig. 2-9. The output waveform plotted in Fig. 15-3c corresponds to the special case $R_1C_1 = R_2C_2 = \tau$. For this case, and if the amplifier gain has a magnitude A, the output is

$$e_o = -A\alpha\tau x\epsilon^{-x} \qquad (15\text{-}1)$$

where $x = (t - t_1)/\tau$. The over-all result is that the ramp has been con-

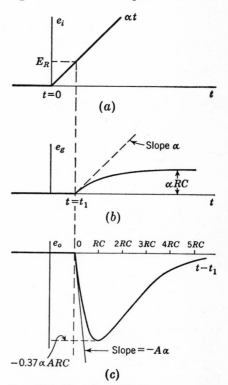

FIG. 15-3. Waveforms in the comparator of Fig. 15-2. (a) Input; (b) grid voltage; (c) output.

verted into a pulse so that the portion of the CRO trace after the comparator point may still be visible. The pulse amplitude is found from Eq. (15-1) to be

$$e_{max} = 0.37\alpha A\tau = 0.37\alpha ARC \tag{15-2}$$

while the pulse width, measured at half amplitude, is found to be

$$t_p = 2.4\tau = 2.4RC \tag{15-3}$$

We note from Eqs. (15-2) and (15-3) that both pulse amplitude and width are proportional to RC. A narrow pulse may therefore be obtained only at the expense of a loss in amplitude. But usually neither the amplitude nor the duration is of any great consequence. Before we used the double differentiation to generate the pulse, we depended for comparator operation on the abrupt rise of the comparator output voltage. Similarly, when the comparator output is a pulse, we shall depend again on the abrupt rise since the pulse nature of the comparator output is advantageous only with respect to preventing the comparator signal from masking that part of the waveform under examination which follows the comparator signal. Hence, it is important to note that the rate of rise of the pulse, at least initially, is nominally the same as the rate of rise of the comparator waveform without differentiation. This result may be verified from Eq. (15-1) by computing

$$\frac{de_o}{dt} = -A\alpha(1 - x)e^{-x} \cong -A\alpha(1 - 2x) \tag{15-4}$$

The approximation is valid for $x \ll 1$. At $x = 0$, $de_o/dt = -A\alpha$, which equals the input slope multiplied by the amplifier gain.

A reasonable value for the time constant RC of the differentiating circuits may be arrived at in the following way. Suppose that we decide that as the leading edge of the pulse passes through the range ΔE in Fig. 15-1, the slope shall never become less than the slope of the undifferentiated waveform by more than 10 per cent. Then, from Eq. (15-4), $x = 0.05$ and, from Eq. (15-1), we have, approximately,

$$\tau \cong 20 \frac{\Delta E}{A\alpha} \tag{15-5}$$

Under these circumstances, we may also note, from Eq. (15-2), that the pulse will have an amplitude $e_{max} \cong 7.4\Delta E$.

If, in a particular application, the output indication desired is a step instead of a pulse, then the second differentiating circuit can be omitted. The output will then be that indicated in Fig. 15-3b multiplied by the gain of the amplifier. Or, if a pulse output is desired, an alternative method of obtaining this waveform is to use a pulse transformer in the plate circuit of the amplifier instead of the second RC circuit. In this case the gain of the amplifier will be μ (the amplification factor of the tube) which is larger than the gain obtained with a resistor in the plate circuit. Other advantages of the transformer are that it allows for changing the output amplitude or impedance level and that it makes either polarity of signal available. Of course, if μ times the input slope is very large, then the shunt capacitance and leakage inductance of the transformer must be taken into account.

Before leaving the subject of the simple comparator circuit of Fig. 15-1, we may note that if the output is taken across the diode rather than across the resistor, the circuit will continue to operate as a comparator. A comparator of this type with typical input and output waveforms is shown in Fig. 15-4. The diode in Fig. 15-1 is often referred to as a *pick-off* diode, while the diode in Fig. 15-4 is called a *breakaway* diode.

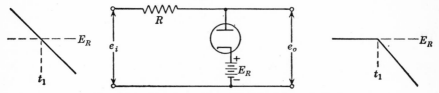

FIG. 15-4. A comparator using a breakaway diode.

It is clear that the stray capacitance shunting the output will limit the abruptness of the change in output waveform more seriously in the circuit of Fig. 15-4 than in the circuit of Fig. 15-1. For this reason the former circuit is not frequently used where fast waveforms are encountered. On the other hand, in the series diode circuit of Fig. 15-1 some of the input voltage, for fast waveforms, will appear at the output even for voltages less than E_R because of the diode shunt capacitance.

15-4. Factors Affecting Comparator Operation. Up to the present we have assumed that the break in the diode characteristic from the region of nonconduction to the region of conduction has been arbitrarily abrupt. In an actual diode such is, of course, not the case. The appearance of the transfer curves of a diode-resistor comparator is as shown in Fig. 15-5. These curves agree well with the theoretical results to be expected if the current varies exponentially with the diode voltage, $e_i - e_o$, in the form (see Sec. 4-1)

$$i = i_0\epsilon^{(e_i - e_o)/E_T} \tag{15-6}$$

Note that as the resistor R increases, the shape of the curve does not change appreciably, but the curve is essentially displaced to the left. Hence, the input voltage corresponding to some fixed output voltage is a function of R. The fact that the diode break is gradual rather than abrupt affects adversely the precision of the comparator. The quantitative effect on the precision depends very largely on the characteristics of the device which is used to respond to the comparator output signal.

A linear amplifier *following* a comparator device does not improve the sharpness of the comparator break characteristic. However, a method of reducing the effect of the uncertainty due to the lack of abruptness of the diode break is to use an amplifier *before* the comparator. Thus, suppose that the input signal to a diode comparator must go through a range Δe_i in order to carry the diode through its break region. Then, if the

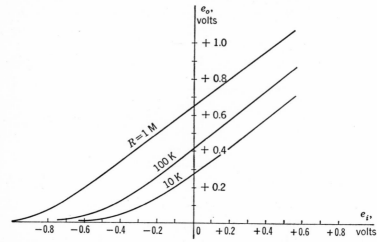

Fig. 15-5. The transfer curves for the circuit of Fig. 15-1 (with $E_R = 0$) for $R = 10$ K, 100 K, and 1 Meg. The diode is a 6AL5.

amplifier has a gain A, the input signal to the amplifier need only go through the range $\Delta e_i/A$ to carry the diode through its break region. A simple example of a comparator using this principle is shown in Fig. 15-6a. Replacing the vacuum-tube amplifier by its equivalent circuit, we have the circuit shown in Fig. 15-6b, in which A is the gain and R_o is the output impedance of the amplifier. The battery E represents the quiescent plate voltage. This circuit is recognized as the basic comparator circuit of Fig. 15-4 in which the output is taken across the diode rather than across the resistor. A plot of output against input exhibits the sharp break indicated in Fig. 15-6c. The use of an amplifier preceding a comparator is discussed further in Sec. 15-13.

In addition to the lack of sharpness in the comparator-element break region, there is a second source of difficulty in comparators. This difficulty results from the instability of the components constituting the comparator circuit. For example, as was pointed out in Sec. 4-1, a 10 per cent change in filament voltage will shift the volt-ampere curve of a thermionic diode about 0.1 volt. Such a shift will have a corresponding effect on the effective reference point of a diode comparator. To minimize instability of this type, it may be required to use some one of the compensating schemes described in Sec. 4-4, or it may be necessary to regulate heater voltages. The use of an amplifier preceding the comparator element will not ordinarily assist to reduce the effect of comparator drift. The reason for this feature is that the amplifier will have to be d-c coupled to the comparator, as in Fig. 15-6. And it may easily be that the drift in the quiescent operating point of the amplifier will be larger than the drift in the diode.

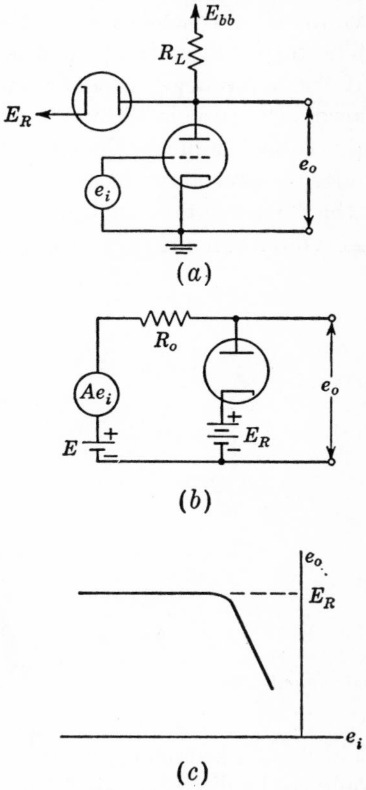

For some types of input waveforms it is possible to use an a-c coupled linear amplifier before the comparator and to maintain the d-c level by means of a restorer circuit. For example, this arrangement would be feasible if the input were a sweep voltage followed by a *dead time*. However, the accuracy of the comparator would then depend on the stability of the diode of the restorer circuit and no net advantage may result.

Finally, there is a type of error encountered in comparators which results from the presence of reactive elements in the circuit. Such reactive elements are energy-storing elements and therefore the effective reference point of a comparator may depend somewhat on the past history of the circuit. The reference point will then be a function of the nature of the input signal, i.e., its amplitude, repetition rate, etc.

FIG. 15-6. An amplifier used before a comparator element to improve precision. (a) Circuit; (b) equivalent circuit; (c) typical transfer curve.

15-5. A Tube Operating at Cutoff. A comparator using the cutoff characteristics of a multielement tube is shown in Fig. 15-7. In Fig. 15-7a the referencing voltage E'_R is connected in series with the input signal. The voltage E'_R is selected to be equal to the sum of the desired reference voltage E_R plus the magnitude of the tube cutoff voltage. Alternatively, a referencing voltage may be applied to the cathode as in Fig. 15-7b.

The arrangement in Fig. 15-7b is often more convenient than the arrangement in Fig. 15-7a. However, in such a case in which one voltage is applied to the grid while the other voltage is applied to the cathode, a small difficulty arises. For example, consider the use of a 6SN7 with a plate voltage of 200 volts and the cathode initially at zero. The cutoff voltage is $^{200}\!/_{20} = 10$ volts (assume, for simplicity, that $\mu = 20$ at cutoff). The tube will start to conduct when the grid signal rises to -10 volts. If the referencing cathode voltage is now raised to $+20$, the voltage across the tube is 180 volts, and the cutoff voltage is -9 volts. Hence, the tube conducts when the grid signal rises to $+11$ volts. The true referencing voltage has changed by 20 volts, while the effective reference (the input voltage required to bring the tube to cutoff) has changed by 21 volts. In an ideal comparator a change in reference voltage ΔE_R

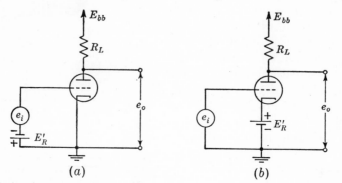

(a)   (b)

Fig. 15-7. A tube operating at cutoff is used as a comparator. (a) The referencing voltage is connected in series with the signal. (b) The referencing voltage is applied to the cathode.

should result in exactly the same change ΔE_R in the comparison voltage. This would be true in the case of a triode if the tube current corresponded only to the difference signal between grid and cathode. As demonstrated above, however, there is also a small current change due to a simultaneous change in both cathode and grid voltage which leaves the difference unaltered. A simultaneous variation of both electrode voltages is known as a *common-mode signal*. The error in comparator operation resulting from a common-mode signal is called the *common-mode effect*.

The common-mode effect is illustrated further with reference to Fig. 15-8a, which shows a triode having a signal voltage e_i applied to its grid and a reference voltage E'_R to its cathode. If the reference voltage is changed by an amount $\Delta E'_R$, what change in signal voltage Δe_i will keep the current constant? The equivalent circuit is given in Fig. 15-8b. For $\Delta I = 0$, it is seen that

$$\frac{\Delta e_i}{\Delta E'_R} = \frac{\mu + 1}{\mu} \tag{15-7}$$

If the equivalent circuit is considered valid near cutoff, and if $\mu = 20$, the result, $\Delta e_i/\Delta E'_R = {}^{21}\!/_{20}$, agrees with the numerical calculation given above.

The common-mode effect may be greatly reduced by using a cathode follower to apply the reference voltage to the cathode of the amplifier tube. This modification leads to the circuit shown in Fig. 15-9a. In

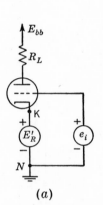

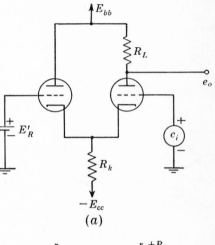

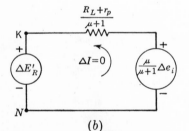

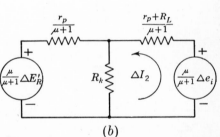

FIG. 15-8. (a) Illustration of the common-mode effect in an amplifier. (b) The equivalent circuit (under the condition given in the text).

FIG. 15-9. (a) A difference amplifier arrangement is used to reduce common-mode error in a cutoff comparator. (b) The equivalent circuit.

Fig. 15-9b we have the equivalent circuit from which the current change ΔI_2 in T_2 may be calculated. We see that if $R_k \gg r_p/(\mu + 1)$, ΔI_2 will remain zero if $\Delta e_i = \Delta E'_R$. It will be recognized that the present circuit is the *difference amplifier* discussed in Sec. 1-10, where it was shown that the difference amplifier discriminates against the common-mode effect.

Comparators using cutoff in triodes and pentodes have the advantage that they may be arranged to produce negligible loading on both signal and reference sources. Since cutoff is, however, neither as sharp nor as stable as the break in a diode[2] (with the possible exception of the gated beam tube[3]), diode comparators are often favored when precision is at a premium.

15-6. Regenerative Comparators. An excellent comparator character-istic can be realized through the use of a regenerative circuit arranged in such a way as to be triggered when an input voltage attains a reference voltage. Thus, this difference between input and reference is made to control the transfer properties of a switching component in the regenera-tive feedback loop. The control element should have a sharp break char-acteristic and usually consists of a thermionic diode, a triode near cutoff or in clamp, etc. If the controlled component operates in the low slope region which keeps the loop gain less than unity, the circuit is in one of its

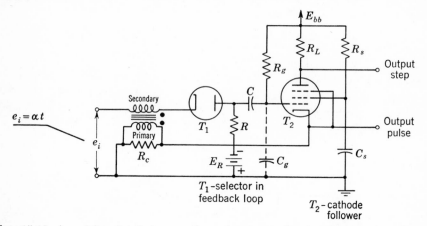

FIG. 15-10. A multiar circuit for negative-going input signals. The total shunting capacitance at the grid is C_g. Tube T_2 may be a triode.

quiescent conditions. If the changing input signal causes the controlled component to shift its operation to the high slope region so that now a loop gain greater than unity results, regeneration will occur. A regenera-tive circuit often uses a single component which assumes both the function of input-controlled switching and amplification.

In the next four sections we shall discuss in turn the following regenera-tive comparators: the multiar, the blocking oscillator, the a-c coupled multi, and the d-c coupled multi comparator.

15-7. The Multiar.[4] If a diode is used as a series switching element in the feedback loop of a regenerative circuit, the resulting circuit makes an excellent comparator. A circuit of this type, known as a *multiar*, is indicated in Fig. 15-10. The feedback loop consists of a diode-resistor network (T_1 and R), a cathode follower T_2, and a pulse transformer in cascade. The difference between the input waveform and the reference voltage E_R controls the gain of the switching network $T_1 - R$. The main function of the tube T_2 is to provide cathode-follower transmission from the output of the switching network to the transformer. The plate-load resistor R_L is not essential but is convenient if an output gate-type waveform is required. The pulse transformer windings must be connected into the circuit with the polarities as shown in order to have regeneration similar to that in a blocking oscillator. Since the combined maximum gain of the switching network and the cathode follower is always less than unity, then there must be a voltage step-up in the transformer in completing the loop from the cathode of T_2 back to the diode. Hence, the number of turns in the secondary winding must exceed the number in the primary winding—a ratio of 1.5 or 2 is usually sufficient.

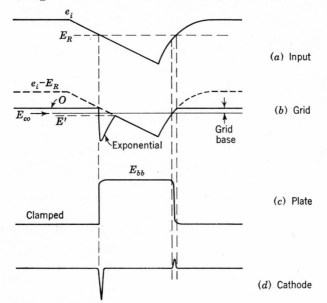

FIG. 15-11. Waveforms in the circuit of Fig. 15-10 at (a) input, (b) grid, (c) plate, and (d) cathode of T_2.

We shall assume that the input is a negative-going sweep voltage. Initially, the grid of T_2 is clamped to the cathode and the tube is conducting heavily. The switching network $T_1 - R$ has zero transmission until the input waveform drops sufficiently to bring the diode T_1 into its break region. At some point of this region the gain of the switching circuit becomes sufficiently high to cause an over-all loop gain of unity. The grid of T_2 will then drop and regeneration will take place. The waveforms in the circuit are indicated in Fig. 15-11, where we see that a negative pulse is generated at the cathode (or in a tertiary transformer winding, not indicated) and a gate waveform at the plate. We shall now give a detailed explanation of the waveshapes.

Initially the rapid fall of cathode and grid voltages results from regenerative action. When tube T_2 reaches cutoff, regeneration ceases. As a result, however, of the abrupt turnoff of tube current, the circuit in the cathode of T_2 rings (see Sec. 2-8). If the primary inductor is critically damped by the resistor R_c, then the cathode voltage of T_2 executes a single oscillation without a backswing. In this manner the pulse waveform indicated in Fig. 15-11d is formed. During the rapid drop of cathode voltage the polarity of voltage induced in the secondary winding is in a direction to cause diode T_1 to conduct. Hence the charging current for the capacitor C_g is supplied by the secondary winding of the transformer, and the grid voltage drops abruptly. During the time of the trailing edge of the pulse in Fig. 15-11d the cathode of T_1 is driven in the positive direction, and the diode becomes back-biased. The grid of T_2 is therefore isolated from the transformer secondary winding, and hence the grid voltage must change slowly.

After the diode becomes back-biased, the equivalent circuit for computing the rise of the grid voltage of T_2 is as indicated in Fig. 15-12. If

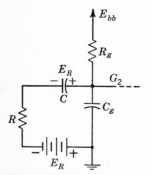

FIG. 15-12. Equivalent circuit at G_2 of the multiar shortly after regeneration begins.

$C \gg C_g$, we may assume that the voltage across C remains constant at E_R during the interval under consideration. Hence, the voltage at G_2 rises toward $(E_{bb}R)/(R + R_g)$ with a time constant $C_g RR_g/(R + R_g)$. When the voltage at G_2 rises to a value E' (see Fig. 15-11b) at which the rising grid voltage meets the falling input voltage, then the diode T_1 conducts again. Once the diode begins to conduct, we may neglect the presence of the small capacitance C_g. We shall assume tentatively that E' is below the cutoff voltage E_{co} of T_2. Hence the grid continues to follow the incoming negative voltage approximately to the end of the sweep, as indicated in Fig. 15-11b.

The requirement that the grid voltage should remain below cutoff to the end of the ramp places a restriction on the time constant R_gC. Thus, if we neglect the cutoff voltage E_{co} compared with E_{bb}, the current in R_g must be at least E_{bb}/R_g. This current passes through C and hence $C|de_i/dt| > E_{bb}/R_g$ or, to keep the grid below cutoff, we require that

$$CR_g > \frac{E_{bb}}{\alpha} \qquad (15\text{-}8)$$

where α is the absolute value of the slope of the sweep voltage. For slow sweeps, it may be desirable to return R_g to a voltage lower than the plate-supply voltage E_{bb}. If Eq. (15-8) is satisfied, then the regeneration point is determined by the $T_1 - R$ network and not by the grid-current characteristic of T_2.

When T_2 comes out of cutoff at the end of the sweep, the cathode of T_2 rises with the grid voltage. Since the transformer step-up ratio is larger than unity, the voltage at the cathode of the diode rises more rapidly than the grid voltage. As a result the diode is driven to the back-biased condition. Therefore, the feedback loop is opened and there is no regeneration as the pentode is brought into conduction. The plate voltage of T_2 falls to its clamped value relatively slowly. The duration of this fall equals the time it takes the grid voltage to pass through the grid base of the amplifier, as indicated in Fig. 15-11c. A positive pulse of this same duration is formed at the cathode because the transformer voltage is proportional to the rate of change of current. Since there is no regeneration at the end of the sweep, and since the tube T_2 passes slowly through its grid base, the positive pulse has a smaller amplitude and a longer duration than the negative pulse.

The negative pulse (formed during the falling portion of the input voltage) is timed with a stability which depends primarily on the $T_1 - R$ switching combination. The stability of this network is affected principally by changes in the filament supply if T_1 is a thermionic diode or by changes in temperature if T_1 is a crystal diode. Changes in the gain of the cathode follower T_2 affect the stability of the negative pulse only slightly if the break region of the $T_1 - R$ network is steep.

The voltage at the plate of T_1 must return to its steady-state value before each comparison. This condition places a restriction upon the product RC, because after the grid of T_2 has returned to zero the plate of T_1 will approach E_R with this time constant RC. Hence, the value of RC must be small compared with the interval between the instant the cathode follower cuts in and the comparison point in the next cycle.

In the above discussion, we made the assumption that after the first negative grid pulse, the grid voltage rises to meet the input voltage e_i at a value E' which is more negative than the cutoff value E_{co} (see Fig. 15-11b). If this restriction is not satisfied, then the circuit may execute several oscillations before the tube is finally driven below cutoff. This situation is pictured in Fig. 15-13. For times smaller than t_1, the waveforms are identical with those in Fig. 15-11. Between times t_1 and t_2 the grid of T_2 is above cutoff and the amplifier current increases from zero. Hence, the plate voltage falls as in Fig. 15-13c and the cathode voltage increases with the rate of change of current as shown in Fig. 15-13d. At time t_2, the input voltage equals the grid voltage E', the diode T_1 conducts, and regeneration again takes place. Since at this instant of time the current in T_2 is less than the clamped current, the resultant drop in the plate, cathode, and grid voltages are less than the corresponding values at t_o. The grid voltage now rises again, reaching cutoff at t_3 and becoming equal to the input voltage E'' at t_4. Between t_3 and t_4 there is a dip in plate voltage and another oscillation takes place at the cathode as shown in Fig. 15-13d. It is possible for a large number of oscillations to be generated in this manner (with successively smaller amplitudes) until finally the grid voltage rises to the input voltage E''' which is below the cutoff voltage E_{co} in Fig. 15-13b.

In order to minimize the possibility of generating several oscillations of the type discussed above, one or more of the following conditions should

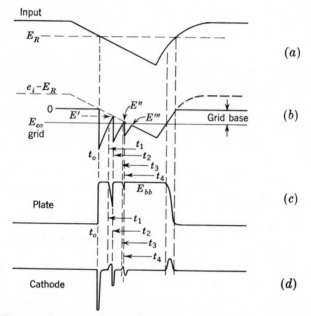

FIG. 15-13. The waveforms in the multiar circuit under the conditions where multiar oscillations take place.

be satisfied: a tube T_2 with a small grid base should be used; the top of R_g should be tied to a smaller voltage than E_{bb}; also, the value of C_g should be increased by adding external capacitance between the grid of T_2 and ground. However, this additional capacitance will result in a smaller output pulse and a slower rise time of plate waveform.

In the above discussion we have assumed that the transformer was critically damped. If the resistor R_c which shunts the transformer in Fig. 15-10 is removed so that ringing occurs, then multiple oscillations may also result. Instead of putting a shunting resistor across the transformer, a damper diode (see Sec. 4-7) may be used to prevent the undesired oscillations.

If it is desired that the input signal wavefore be capacitively coupled to the multiar, then a d-c restorer may be used at the input terminals. The restorer diode uncertainties must now be taken into consideration in a precision circuit.

If a gate voltage is not desired, the transformer primary can be moved to the plate circuit. The circuit then closely resembles a blocking oscillator except that the grid cannot be driven highly positive because of the diode.

We may use the same input sweep voltage for several multiar comparator circuits since there is small loading of the input by this comparator if R is large. In radar ranging the multiar is used to obtain many ranges from a single master sweep circuit and hence the name *multi-r* (*r* for range).

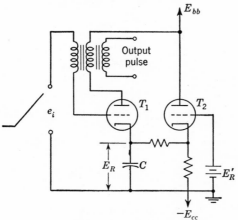

FIG. 15-14. A blocking-oscillator comparator.

The multiar is not useful for positive-going voltages. The application of this circuit to obtain square waves from sine waves is explained in Sec. 15-12.

15-8. Blocking-oscillator Comparator. An example of a blocking-oscillator comparator is shown in Fig. 15-14. The feedback loop consists of the triode amplifier T_1 and the pulse transformer. The reference voltage is applied to the cathode of the oscillator tube T_1 through the cathode follower T_2. The difference between the positive-going input waveform e_i and the reference voltage E_R controls the switching operation of T_1 through the grid characteristics near cutoff. The capacitor C is used to bypass the large-current short-duration pulse.

Shortly after the rising input brings T_1 out of cutoff, the loop gain exceeds unity, regeneration takes place, and an output pulse is delivered. Since the blocking oscillator draws a large grid current, this circuit reacts back on the input waveform and this feature may be objectionable.

On the other hand, in some applications this reaction may be essential for the proper operation of the circuit. For example, in the storage counter circuit of Fig. 11-25, the blocking-oscillator comparator is used as a voltage-operated switch to reset the counter capacitor to its initial value when the selected reference voltage is reached by the counter output.

The instability of the blocking-oscillator comparator is governed by the grid characteristics of T_1 near cutoff. The instability of these characteristics which are affected by factors such as variations in supply voltages, tube aging, and tube replacement may be excessive for many applications. Also, stable operation requires that the capacitor C reach its quiescent state before each regeneration.

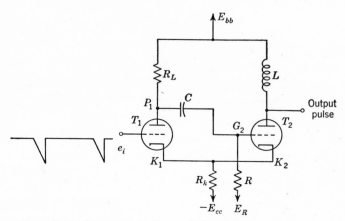

Fig. 15-15. The a-c cathode-coupled multi as a comparator.

15-9. The A-C Coupled Multivibrator Comparator. The cathode-coupled multi used as a comparator is indicated in Fig. 15-15. When this circuit is used as a *delay multi* (Sec. 6-6), T_1 is *off* and T_2 is *on* in the quiescent state. As a *comparator* the circuit is usually adjusted in the reverse manner so that T_1 is *on* and T_2 is *off* in the quiescent condition. The feedback loop consists of a plate-to-grid connection between two tubes T_1 and T_2 which have in turn a transmission between their cathodes through the resistor R_k. The input signal is a negative-going voltage. There are two possible modes of operation for this circuit.

Consider first the case where R_k is so large that $(\mu + 1)R_k \gg R_L + r_p$ and also $R_k \gg R_L$. Then with T_2 below cutoff, T_1 acts as a cathode follower. Hence, as the input voltage e_i falls, the cathode K_2 falls by the same amount. The grid G_2 remains essentially at E_R because the gain from grid to plate of T_1 is very small. The switching function is determined by the grid characteristic of T_2 operating in the cutoff region. When e_i falls to the point where the grid-cathode voltage of T_2 equals the cutoff value, then T_2 starts to conduct. Soon thereafter the loop gain exceeds unity and regeneration takes place. The output is a negative pulse obtained from the peaking coil L (see Sec. 2-6). We note that this circuit (with the capacitor missing) is essentially the difference amplifier of Fig. 15-9. Hence, if a large dynamic cathode resistor is used, the common-mode difficulty is minimized. Also the effect of heater voltage variations and slow drifts in the supply voltages E_{bb} and E_{cc} are small (see Probs. 15-14 and 15-15). However, if changes in E_{bb} and E_{cc} are of high enough frequency so that changes in voltage at P_1 are transmitted through C to G_2, much greater errors are introduced.

If the input signal were first amplified by an amount A and if this amplified voltage were used to bring T_2 out of cutoff, then the time uncertainty in the output indication would be divided by A. This mode of operation is obtained with the circuit of Fig. 15-15 by reducing R_k so that, with T_2 off, the gain A of T_1 from grid to plate is much greater than unity. The lower limit on the value of R_k is determined by the fact that when T_2 is conducting the loop gain of the circuit must exceed unity.

15-10. The D-C Cathode-coupled Multivibrator Comparator. This circuit is indicated in Fig. 15-16 and is essentially the Schmitt circuit of Sec. 5-10. If T_2 is cut off and the input is a negative-going voltage, then this circuit can be operated in the modes discussed in connection with the a-c coupled circuit. It should be noted, however, that the loop gain is less here because of the attenuation in the $R_1 - R_2$ combination. The effect of positive and negative power supply drifts may be serious because even slow changes at P_1 are transmitted to G_2 through the resistive connection.

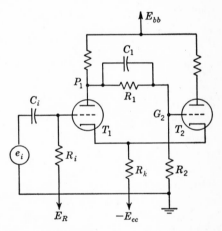

FIG. 15-16. The d-c cathode-coupled multi as a comparator.

There are two other modes of operation of the circuit of Fig. 15-16: T_2 *within its grid base* or T_2 *in clamp*. The input waveform is now more appropriately a positive-going voltage. With T_2 within its grid base, regeneration occurs when T_1 comes out of cutoff far enough so that the loop gain exceeds unity. The instability is now governed mainly by the cutoff characteristics of T_1. If T_2 is in clamp, then regeneration will take place when the input signal amplified by T_1 causes T_2 to come out of clamp. The instability of the grid-current characteristics of T_2 at clamp is divided by the gain A of T_1. Hence, this mode should result in more stable operation than the one just discussed where T_2 is within its grid base and T_1 is operated near cutoff.

The cathode-coupled multi comparator has been used very successfully for obtaining the amplitude distribution of nuclear pulses[1] and of random noise.[5] The input pulses are a-c coupled to the input by the $R_i - C_i$ combination shown in Fig. 15-16. If the pulses are positive, there is an advantage in using a large value of R_k, since it is then difficult to drive the input grid positive with respect to its cathode. If grid current were drawn by this input grid, it would charge C_i and hence change the effective level of the input voltage. This situation must, of course, be avoided.

Often a preamplifier is used preceding the comparators discussed in this or the preceding section. An excellent circuit for this purpose is a difference amplifier (see Sec. 15-13) which is d-c coupled to the Schmitt circuit.

The circuits of Figs. 15-15 and 15-16 exhibit hysteresis, as explained in Sec. 5-10. If the difference in input levels at which the circuit regenerates for a positive-going waveform and for a negative-going voltage is E_h volts, then the minimum amplitude of pulse which can be detected is E_h volts. If the input size is smaller than this value E_h, the circuit will flip in one direction at the leading edge of the pulse, but it will not return to its original state at the termination of the pulse. If a preamplifier of gain A is used, the effective hysteresis is E_h/A volts, which is another advantage of using a preamplifier. The use of a resistor in series with the cathode of T_2 to eliminate hysteresis is explained in Sec. 5-11.

15-11. A Gas-tube Comparator Used as a Switch. In Sec. 11-11, in connection with the discussion of storage counters (see Fig. 11-25), we saw the need for a comparator which would accomplish two functions. When the voltage across capacitor C_2 reaches the reference level, it is not only necessary that the comparator respond with a pulse but also the comparator must discharge the capacitor C_2. A thyratron comparator used for this purpose is shown in Fig. 15-17.

The combination $C_1T_1T_2C_2$ is a storage counter arranged so as to accept negative pulses. The diodes T_1 and T_2 will clamp the cathode voltage of the thyratron T_3 to the positive voltage E at the instant after T_3 fires. If the tube drop is neglected, the tube current is $(E_{bb} - E)/R$. If this current is less than that necessary to maintain the arc, the tube will extinguish itself. The quiescent conditions for T_3 are now a plate voltage of E_{bb}, a cathode voltage of E, and a grid voltage of zero. Each negative input pulse now lowers the cathode potential E_k of T_3. When $E_k = E'$ such that $-E'$ is the critical grid breakdown voltage corresponding to the plate voltage $E_{bb} - E'$, the tube fires. The time constant RC is chosen small compared with the interval between pulses. A negative output spike is obtained from the plate of T_3 and the circuit returns to its quiescent state before the next input pulse arrives. The stability of the circuit is determined principally by the constancy of the critical grid starting characteristic of the thyratron.

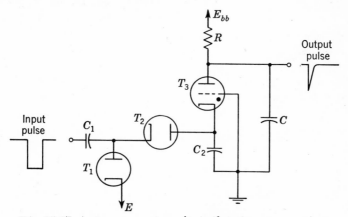

FIG. 15-17. A storage counter using a thyratron comparator.

15-12. Comparators for Sinusoidal Voltages. For some applications it is necessary to generate a series of pulses in exact synchronism with a sinusoidal waveform. It is often required that these pulses shall occur at some fixed phase of the sinusoid, as explained in some of the applications of Sec. 15-1. In this case the zero of the wave is selected as the level of comparison because the slope is greatest here and because the comparator operation will then be independent of the amplitude of the sine wave. This problem of obtaining pulses locked to the zero phase of a sinusoid of variable amplitude will now be discussed.

Consider a sine wave of amplitude which is large compared with the grid base of a tube. The simple circuit of Fig. 15-18 gives an output which approximates a square wave since the tube limits on the one side

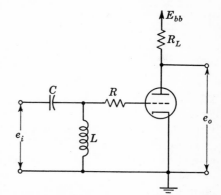

FIG. 15-18. A simple squaring circuit for an input sine wave. The tube may be a triode or a pentode.

due to cutoff and on the other side due to grid clamping or to bottoming (see Sec. 4-3). Pulses are obtained, if required, by differentiating the square wave. An inductor L rather than a resistor is employed as a grid return to prevent d-c restoration in the grid circuit. If the inductor L

has negligible resistance, then the d-c voltage across it is zero and the grid voltage must swing above and below ground. In other words, the capacitor C acquires no d-c voltage. This method of avoiding d-c restoration is practical only for frequencies much higher than the audio range where the inductor will not become an excessive load on the signal source. It should be remembered that iron core chokes may not be used if accurate phase lock is desired, because of the distortion introduced by the non-linearity of the iron.

If RC coupling is used, then d-c restoration may be suppressed by an input circuit such as illustrated in Fig. 15-19. If the diodes are perfect, then either T_1 or T_2, but not both, conduct at a given instant. Also T_2 prevents the grid of T_3 from being driven positive. We shall assume that no grid current flows for negative grid voltages. Under these circumstances the capacitor C sees a constant impedance, namely, R_g, at all times and hence there can be no shift in d-c level. Other possible input circuits are given in Prob. 15-18.

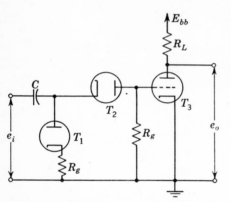

FIG. 15-19. The two diodes T_1 and T_2 prevent a shift in d-c level at the input.

The pulses which result from the differentiation of the output of the circuits of Figs. 15-18 and 15-19 are of alternating polarity corresponding to a phase of zero and 180°. The precision of the phase lock (i.e., the precision with which the pulses occur at the instant the sinusoid crosses zero) depends on the availability of an adequately large input signal. The large input is required in order that the signal shall pass through the region of the comparator break in the shortest possible time. If the signal is not initially large enough, some amplification must be provided.

The problem of amplification to obtain stability of phase lock is not a simple one, because this amplification must be done without distortion, or at least with distortion which is symmetrical with respect to the zero of the sine wave. Any unsymmetrical change of waveshape means a shift in the d-c level and the new average voltage will appear across any coupling capacitors present.

This shift in average level is equivalent to a bias voltage and hence the comparator break will be traversed in a region other than the zero of the original sine wave. Under these circumstances the output pulse position will change in phase as the amplitude of the input sinusoid changes, or as the gain of the circuit changes. Usually a multistage amplifier is used in order to improve the precision and then there is the possibility of a shift in d-c level at the input to each stage.

The above difficulty can be avoided by eliminating the coupling capacitors. The result would be a d-c amplifier and there would be the usual problems of drift to contend with. Another solution is to use capacitor coupling but to clip the top and bottom of the input wave to every grid in a symmetrical fashion. The circuit is as indicated in Fig. 4-10, with E_1 equal to E_2 and with the addition of a series capacitor and shunt resistor. The amplifiers are operated not at cutoff but in the center of their linear range. The clipping is done between narrow limits, say ± 0.5 volt and this ensures that the amplification is done without

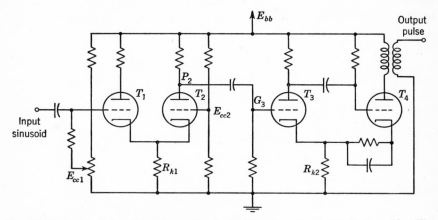

FIG. 15-20. A circuit for obtaining pulses locked in phase to an input sinusoid. The input stage $T_1 - T_2$ is a cathode-coupled clipper. The output stage $T_3 - T_4$ is a multi comparator.

distortion. Thus, there is no shift in d-c level. The stability of phase lock depends upon using balanced diodes and balanced clipping voltages. If the amplitude of the input sinusoid is small, then several stages of amplification will be needed in order for the output to approach the ideal square wave which has vertical sides.

A clipping circuit which does not depend upon the use of balanced diodes and which has a high input impedance is the cathode-coupled clipper of Fig. 4-12 (see also Fig. 15-20). If R_{k1} is large, then peak input signals of 100 volts or more may be applied before grid current is drawn in the first tube. Hence, this circuit makes an excellent input stage because it does not load down the source, it gives amplification, and by proper adjustment of E_{cc1} it gives an output which is symmetrical about the zero of the input sine wave. Since there is no shift in d-c level, several stages may be a-c coupled. A phasemeter has been built[6] using such a circuit. A more economical design in which only one cathode-coupled clipper stage is followed by a cathode-coupled multi is shown in Fig. 15-20. If the circuit parameters are chosen so that the limited output at P_2 is small enough so as not to drive G_3 into the positive grid region, then a-c coupling may be used between P_2 and G_3. Experimentally, it has been found that such a circuit gives a phase lock within 1° for peak-to-peak voltages from about 0.1 volt to 100 volts at 400 cps. The multi comparator is operated with a small value of R_{k2} so that gain is obtained in T_3 and a pulse is obtained when T_4 is brought out of cutoff.

The multiar circuit used to obtain a square wave or pulses from a sine wave is indicated in Fig. 15-21. The method of avoiding d-c restoration is that given in Fig. 15-19. The cathode resistor R_k is used for self-bias so that the triode (or pentode) T_2 is not drawing grid current in the quiescent state. The behavior of the circuit is essentially that

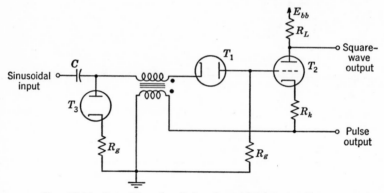

Fig. 15-21. A multiar circuit for sinusoidal input voltages.

given in Sec. 15-7. As explained in that section, the stability is determined primarily by $T_1 - R_g$ combination. Regeneration will take place when the loop gain reaches unity, and this may not be precisely at the zero of the input sine wave. If zero phase lock is important, then a small biasing voltage must be introduced effectively in series with the diode T_1. The pulse obtained when the sine wave passes through zero in the negative direction is sharp and is determined by regeneration. The pulse obtained when the sine wave approaches zero in the positive direction is smaller and broader and is obtained when T_1 comes out of cutoff as indicated in Fig. 15-11d. In this circuit there also exists the possibility of multiple oscillations as pictured in Fig. 15-13.

If a transformer is available whose impedance is high enough so as not to load down the source, this may be used to couple the sinusoid to the multiar in place of the CT_3R_g combination. Also, as explained in Sec. 4-4, another diode may be used to compensate for filament voltage drifts in the selector diode T_1.

15-13. Amplifiers for Comparators. It has been pointed out that the precision of a comparator may be improved by a factor A if the comparator is preceded by an amplifier of gain A. The amplifier must normally be d-c coupled to the comparator. Hence, the quiescent voltage output of the amplifier must be stable if the improvement in precision is not to be undone by a loss of accuracy. If the reference level of the comparator is adjustable, then a further requirement which must be imposed on the amplifier is that it operate with extreme linearity.

The requirement of extremely linear operation may be removed by using the amplifier not directly for the purpose of amplifying the signal but rather for the purpose of amplifying the difference between the input signal and the reference voltage. An amplifier-comparator combination which incorporates this principle is shown in Fig. 15-22. The reference voltage E_R is applied to one grid while the signal is applied to the other grid of the symmetrical amplifier employing a type 5755 (Western Electric) vacuum tube. The 12AX7 is used in the cathode circuit for the purpose of achieving an extremely large effective cathode resistor without at the same time requiring an excessively large voltage drop across this resistor. This application of the 12AX7 in the cathode circuit is discussed in Sec. 1-10. The advantage of a large effective cathode resistor in the circuit will be discussed below. The 5651 is a stable glow-tube regulator used here to establish a fixed voltage between the 12AX7 grid and the -300-volt supply. The 12AU7 is a comparator of the difference-amplifier type shown in Fig. 15-9.

The operation of the circuit is as follows. If the amplifier is completely symmetrical, then when the signal voltage e_i is equal to the reference voltage E_R, the voltages at the two plates of the 5755 will be identical. The resistor R may be adjusted so that under these conditions the currents through T_{2a} and T_{2b} are nominally equal. The difference amplifier can handle linearly only a limited range of input signal. Hence, as the voltage difference between the 5755 plates departs from zero, a break occurs in the difference-amplifier output as one or the other of the 12AU7 sections passes through cutoff. (Note that if T_{2a} cuts off, T_{2b} will be operating with a very large cathode resistor and the response of T_{2b} to a signal at its grid will be very small.) For a negative-going sweep input signal, as indicated in Fig. 15-22, the response at the plate of T_{2b} will be a positive-going step, as shown. (The output differentiating circuit will transform this step to a pulse.) The step will begin when the input signal e_i is different from the reference E_R by some fixed voltage. Alternatively, the resistor R may be adjusted so that the step forms at the moment $e_i = E_R$. We may now discuss some of the advantageous features of the circuit of Fig. 15-22.

The 5755 vacuum tube has parameters $\mu = 65$ and $r_p = 200$ K. The gain of the amplifier, defined as the ratio of the plate-to-plate output voltage to the signal input e_i, is therefore (see Sec. 1-10)

$$A = \frac{\mu R_L}{R_L + r_p} = \frac{65 \times 510}{510 + 200} = 46.6 \tag{15-9}$$

Hence, there is an improvement by a factor 46.6 in the precision of the comparator as compared to the precision which would result without the amplifier.

The amplifier is highly stable. This stability results not from any particular circuit features but rather from the nature of the tubes employed. The type 5755 tube was especially designed for balanced d-c amplifier service. The manufacturer guarantees that, for equality of tube current, the maximum difference in grid voltages is 0.3 volt. More importantly it is claimed that over a 7-hr period a change of no more than 5 mv need be made at most at one grid to keep the currents balanced. Similarly, the 5651 tube is a very stable reference voltage regulator. Over the normal operating range of 1.5 to 3.5 ma, its maintaining voltage under continuous operation will not drift with age by more than about 0.3 volt.

If the circuit is to be free of common-mode effect, the individual voltages at the plates of the 5755 must be the same whenever $e_i = E_R$ independently of the value of E_R. To see the extent to which the amplifier satisfies this condition, let us consider the common-mode rejection ratio ρ of the 5755 circuit. Proceeding as in Sec. 1-10, we have the result that if $(\mu + 1)R_k \gg R_L + r_p$ and $\mu \gg 1$, then approximately

$$A_d = \frac{\mu R_L}{2(R_L + r_p)} \quad \text{and} \quad A_c = -\frac{R_L}{2R_k} \tag{15-10}$$

In Eq. (15-10) A_d and A_c are, respectively, the gain for a difference signal and the gain for a common-mode signal. The results in Eq. (15-10) are slightly different from the results given in Eq. (1-21) since in the present circuit both tubes have plate resistors R_L. The *common-mode rejection ratio* ρ is

$$\rho \equiv \frac{A_d}{A_c} = \frac{-\mu R_k}{R_L + r_p} \tag{15-11}$$

If e_i and E_R both change by an amount ΔE, the voltage change at one amplifier plate will be the same as if only the signal voltage changed by an amount Δe_i given by

$$\Delta e_i = \frac{\Delta E}{\rho} \tag{15-12}$$

In the amplifier of Fig. 15-22 the resistor R_k to be used in Eq. (15-11) is the resistance seen looking into the plate of the 12AX7. This resistance

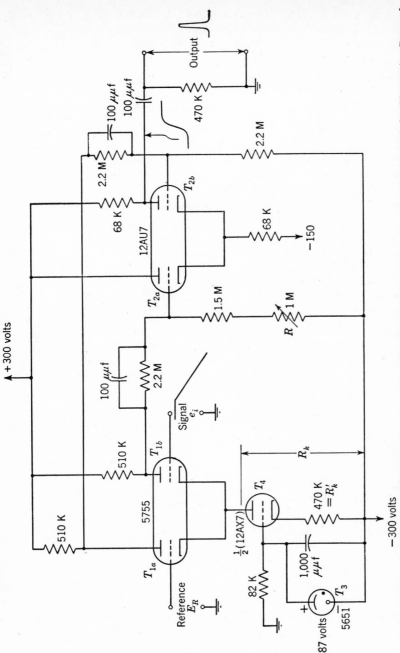

FIG. 15-22. A symmetrical amplifier followed by a difference-amplifier comparator. (Courtesy of the Electronics Research Laboratories, Electrical Engineering Department, Columbia University.)

483

is $R_k = r_p + (1 + \mu)R_k'$. For the 12AX7 ($r_p = 0.1$ Meg and $\mu = 100$) we have $R_k = 47$ Meg. From Eqs. (15-11) and (15-12) we compute that, for a 100-volt sweep, $\Delta e_i = -23$ mv. This small common-mode error is due to the large effective cathode impedance which results from the use of the 12AX7 in the cathode circuit. The over-all common-mode error of the entire circuit is reduced even further by the common-mode rejection of the difference-amplifier comparator.

Equal changes in the cathode temperature of the 5755 section constitute a common-mode signal against which the circuit will discriminate. A similar situation applies with respect to a change in the cathode temperature of the 12AX7 or a change in the 5651 maintaining voltage.

REFERENCES

1. Van Rennes, A. B.: Pulse-amplitude Analysis in Nuclear Research, *Nucleonics*, vol. 10, pp. 20–27, July, 1952, and pp. 50–56, October, 1952.
2. Chance, B., et al.: "Waveforms," Massachusetts Institute of Technology Radiation Laboratory Series, vol. 19, p. 73, McGraw-Hill Book Company, Inc., New York, 1949.
3. Adler, R.: A Gated Beam Tube, *Electronics*, vol. 23, pp. 82–85, February, 1950.
4. Williams, F. C., and N. F. Moody: Ranging Circuits, Linear Time-base Generators and Associated Circuits, *J. IEE*, pt. IIIA, vol. 93, no. 7, pp. 1188–1198, 1946.
5. Bernstein, R., H. Bickel, and E. Brookner: *Memorandum Rept. M-1/A-VIII*, March, 1954, Electronics Research Laboratories, Electrical Engineering Department, Columbia University.
6. Yu, Y. P.: Precision Phase-meter Design, *Electronic Equipment*, vol. 2, no. 11, pp. 14–15, November, 1954.

CHAPTER 16

TIME MODULATION AND MEASUREMENT

Time modulation is the term used to describe the process by which we may control the time interval occupied by some feature of interest in connection with a waveform. With pulse-type waveforms the principal features are pulse duration and time interval between pulses. One of the most important applications of time modulation occurs in connection with precise time measurements. For example, the distance of an aircraft from a radar set is measured by the time which elapses between the pulse radiated by the radar set (the reference pulse) and the pulse which returns as an echo. The most precise method of measuring this elapsed time is to generate locally a pulse whose time delay with respect to the reference pulse is known and controllable. Then this local (index) pulse is adjusted until a coincidence in time is observed between index and echo. Quite generally a method for determining the time duration of an entirely arbitrary waveform consists of generating a controllable index pulse which is then brought into coincidence with a position of interest on the arbitrary waveform. The coincidence may be observed either on a cathode-ray-tube display or through the use of coincidence circuits where feasible.

A second application of time modulation occurs in pulse communication systems. Here the information to be transmitted is frequently conveyed as a modulation of the duration of pulses, or alternatively as a modulation of the interval between a reference pulse and the modulated pulse. A third important application of time modulation is in the conversion of analogue to digital data and is discussed in Sec. 16-3.

Circuits for producing time modulation usually fall into one of the following three categories: (1) time-base systems, (2) phase-modulated systems, and (3) delay-line systems. These three systems will now be considered in turn.

16-1. Time-base Modulation Systems. A most important analogue method used for time modulation is achieved by means of a combination of a linear time-base generator and a comparator. A reference signal starts the generation of a time-base waveform and the index pulse occurs at the instant the waveform attains the reference level of the comparator.

485

Modulation is accomplished usually by varying the comparator reference level. An important advantage of this method is that the modulation may be accomplished electrically. If, as is very frequently the case, it is required that the timing interval vary linearly with the modulating signal, it will be required that the time-base waveform be linear and that the comparator reference voltage vary linearly with the modulating signal. If some relationship other than linearity is to exist between timing interval and modulating signal, an appropriate nonlinear timing waveform will be required, or else the comparator reference voltage will have to be related to the modulating signal in accordance with the required functional relationship.

An accuracy of 0.1 per cent is obtained with a time-base system only with great difficulty. The accuracy of the time modulator depends upon the following items:

1. The constancy of the voltage level from which the timing waveform starts (i.e., the zero level)

2. The constancy of the voltage level at which the comparator responds

3. The constancy, cycle after cycle, of the timing waveform

4. The accuracy with which the timing waveform fits the required functional relationship between modulating signal and required timing

Where linearity is required between timing and modulating signal, item (3) refers to the constancy of the slope from cycle to cycle, while item (4) refers to the linearity of any individual timing waveform. We shall consider only linear modulation. It is of some interest to tabulate the various features which may characterize a combination of linear time-base generator and comparator. Time modulators may differ in one or more of the following items:

1. *Type of comparator* (a classification into five categories was made in Sec. 15-2)
2. *Linearity*
   a. No feedback to improve linearity
   b. Bootstrapping
   c. Miller feedback
3. *Gating*
   a. External
   b. Internal
   Some circuits require that an external gating voltage be applied to generate the time base, while others require only a trigger pulse to start the time base, the gating voltage being generated internally.
4. *Synchronization*
   a. External
   b. Internal

An externally synchronized system is used for random pulses since it accepts an applied pulse to initiate the timing. An internally synchronized system determines its own instant of timing and delivers an index pulse delayed from the starting pulse in accordance with the modulating signal.

5. Lastly, in some circuits the function of the time-base generator and comparator are well separated and the portions of the circuits which accomplish each function are easily recognized. In other circuits the two functions are not easily separable.

This listing includes the almost unending variety of time-modulating circuits[1] available. Certain special circuits have found very wide application because of their simplicity. Notable among these is the cathode-coupled monostable multivibrator (Sec. 6-8) and the phantastron (Sec. 7-7). In these circuits feedback is used to improve linearity, the gating is internal, the synchronization is external, and no clear-cut separation exists between the time-base generator and the comparator.

16-2. Comparison of Bootstrap and Miller Time-base Generators.[2] We discuss now the items on which the time-modulator accuracy depends. The constancy of the voltage level at which the comparator responds is a matter with which we have already dealt in Chap. 15 and need not be repeated. Similarly, the methods which are available to improve linearity have already been considered in Chap. 7. It is, however, appropriate to note that with respect to *linearity* of time-base waveforms the Miller integrator circuit enjoys some advantage over the bootstrap circuit. The reason for this circumstance is not hard to find. It will be recalled that in the case of the bootstrap circuit the departure from linearity is measured by the extent to which the amplifier gain is different from unity. Now the only simple amplifier which is practical for use in the bootstrap generator is the cathode follower. Even with high g_m tubes, gains in excess of, say, 0.99 are difficult to attain. The gain required of the amplifier in a Miller circuit to achieve equivalent linearity is $1/(1 - 0.99) = 100$. It is, of course, not difficult to build an amplifier for use in a bootstrap circuit whose gain approaches arbitrarily close to unity. But such amplifiers are, in principle, of such nature that their gain may, due to various instabilities, become greater than unity. A gain larger than unity is as objectionable as a gain less than unity. Furthermore a decrease in gain of say 1 per cent from 0.99 to 0.98 reduces the linearity improvement by a factor of 2. On the other hand, no great difficulty is encountered in building a conventional amplifier with a gain far in excess of 100. And in this case a small drift in gain causes no difficulty.

The largest source of error by far usually results from the instability in zero level and slope because of the variability of operation of the tubes used for switching. Figure 16-1 represents a bootstrap time-base generator in which it is considered that $E' = E_{bb} + e_c$; that is, E' is the sum of some quiescent supply voltage E_{bb} and a voltage equal to that developed across the capacitor. We have for simplicity returned the cathode of the gating tube to a negative supply voltage so that initially the voltage $e_c = 0$. Because of the bootstrapping the slope of the time-base voltage is constant and is equal to its initial value E_{bb}/RC. Now suppose that because of heater voltage change, tube aging, or even tube replacement the initial value e_c is no longer zero but is ΔE. Then

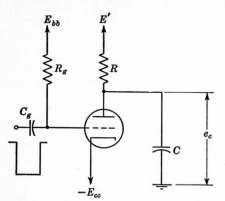

FIG. 16-1. A bootstrap circuit. The voltage E' is variable.

$$e_c = \Delta E + \frac{E_{bb} - \Delta E}{RC} t \tag{16-1}$$

If e_c is applied to a comparator whose reference level is E_c, the time interval established will be approximately

$$t = RC \frac{E_c}{E_{bb}} \left(1 - \frac{\Delta E}{E_c} + \frac{\Delta E}{E_{bb}} \right) \tag{16-2}$$

The first correction term represents the error due to the fact that the zero level has changed, while the second term results from the change in slope of the time base. In the limiting case where $E_c = E_{bb}$, the error is quite small, being given by the higher-order terms neglected in Eq. (16-1). More usually E_c is appreciably smaller than E_{bb} and the zero error is much larger than the slope error.

The triode clamp of Fig. 16-1 will provide an extremely unstable zero level. The tube current at fixed bias is highly variable. In addition, where a clamped grid is employed the precise level at which the grid clamps is a function of the grid-current characteristics. In many tubes manufacturers do not control grid-current characteristics. Consequently, even with large plate and grid resistors, the clamping voltage of the circuit of Fig. 16-1 may vary by an appreciable fraction of a volt. A diode is much more stable than the triode as a clamp, and hence the circuit of Fig. 16-2a offers some advantage. A further improvement results if the double-diode arrangement of Fig. 16-2b is employed. As described in Sec. 4-4, the second diode serves as a stabilizing influence against the effect of heater voltage variation.

An additional precaution to be observed with bootstrap sweeps is that the signal must not be taken from the cathode of the cathode follower since the d-c voltage difference between the grid and cathode is itself quite variable. One must therefore apply to the comparator the signal which appears across the sweep capacitor.

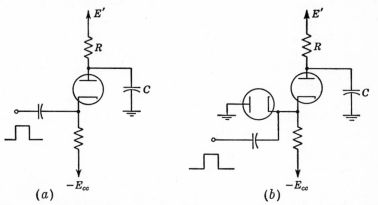

FIG. 16-2. (a) A diode clamp for a bootstrap circuit. (b) A second diode added to help compensate for cathode temperature changes.

Instead of trying to stabilize separately the clamping level of the sweep and the reference level of the comparator one may try to balance one error against the other. This situation is illustrated in Fig. 16-3. T_1 is the clamping diode and T_2 is the comparator diode. One may expect that a change in cathode emission will change the zero level and the

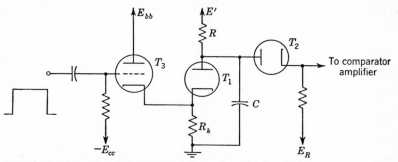

FIG. 16-3. A circuit used to balance the drift in clamping level of the sweep against the drift in reference level of the comparator.

comparator reference level by approximately the same amount. Of course, this arrangement will not correct the slope error which accompanies the zero shift.

A change in cathode emission is represented by the introduction of a voltage source E_H in series with the cathode lead. In Fig. 16-3 such a voltage E_H will cause an equal change in the clamping voltage only if the impedance in the cathode circuit of T_1 is small. Hence, a cathode follower T_3 is used to gate the diode T_1. The bias on T_3 is such as to cut the tube off except during the gating time; hence the d-c instability of the triode is unimportant.

Now consider a Miller sweep. The stability difficulties associated with the Miller time-base generator are more troublesome than in the case of the bootstrap circuit. The amplifier in the circuit (as in Fig. 16-4) must be a d-c amplifier. The zero level of the output suffers not only on account of the instability of d-c output voltage of the amplifier but also from the amplified instability of the clamp. Furthermore, the linear sweep starts after a step voltage (see Fig. 7-22) has formed and the variability of the step is in effect a zero error. Nothing much can be done about the variability of the step except to try to make it as small as

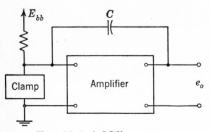

FIG. 16-4. A Miller sweep.

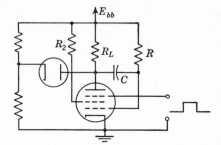

FIG. 16-5. A method for reducing the initial step in the output voltage of a Miller sweep.

possible. A means which is available for reducing the size of the step is shown in Fig. 16-5. The diode current (with zero pentode plate current) is adjusted to be somewhat less than the current which flows through R_L at the instant the circuit is gated on. The step which forms at plate and grid is then equal to the plate resistor R_L multiplied by the difference between diode current and pentode current. The step cannot be eliminated entirely since some negative step at the plate is required to cut off the diode during the sweep formation.

Fluctuations in cathode emission will cause a slope error. If, say, the emission increases, then the initial current through R (Fig. 16-5) will increase correspondingly. Two methods of minimizing slope error from this source are indicated in Fig. 16-6a and b. In Fig. 16-6a the variation of cathode emission is stabilized by an additional diode in exactly the same manner used in Fig. 16-2b. It is assumed here that the effective cathode potential of the pentode is affected by cathode emission in the same manner as for the diode. In the second method (Fig. 16-6b) the supply voltage E_{bb}'' to which R is returned changes nominally by the same amount and in the same direction as the initial grid level. The net initial voltage difference across R is more constant than before and consequently the initial slope of the timing waveform is less variable.

When zero error is the principal difficulty, it is advantageous to make the time-base amplitude (in either the bootstrap or the Miller sweep) as large as possible and to use the circuit in such a manner that the minimum comparator reference level is as large as possible. A reasonable estimate for zero error is about 0.3 volt. If the sweep amplitude is, say, 200 volts, then the resultant accuracy is $0.3 \times {}^{100}\!/_{200} = 0.15$ per cent. Much can also be accomplished in reducing uncertainty by selecting tubes and by preaging tubes, since it has been found experimentally that the rate of tube drift is usually largest when tubes are first put into service.

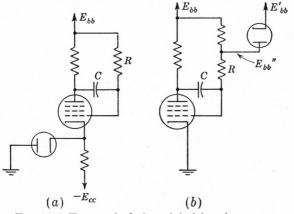

FIG. 16-6. Two methods for minimizing slope error.

If a system may be internally synchronized, then the zero-level difficulties may be eliminated by using two comparators instead of only one. The first comparator is set to respond at an arbitrary voltage level and this comparator signal is used to mark the reference time. The second comparator has its reference level set to respond at a later and variable time. The time interval marked off is therefore the time required for the time-base voltage to rise from one level to another. The accuracy of such an arrangement depends only on the linearity of the sweep and the accuracy of the two comparators, provided the slope error is negligible. A precaution which must be observed in such an arrangement is that the reference comparator must not affect the time-base linearity. A low impedance time-base waveform is to be preferred, and here, since the zero level does not matter, the cathode waveform of a bootstrap sweep circuit will be suitable.

16-3. An Analogue-to-Digital Converter. It is often required that data taken in a physical system be delivered directly to a digital computer for processing. Such data would normally appear in electrical analogue form. For example, a temperature difference would be represented by the output of a thermocouple, the strain of a mechanical member would be represented by the electrical unbalance of a strain-gauge bridge, etc. The need therefore arises for a device to convert analogue information into digital form. A very large number of such devices have been invented.[3] We shall consider below one such system which involves a time-modulation scheme of high precision.

In this system[4] a continuous sequence of equally spaced pulses is passed through a gate. The gate is normally closed and is opened at the instant of the beginning of a linear sweep. The gate remains open until the linear sweep voltage attains the reference level of a comparator, which comparator level is set equal to the analogue voltage to be converted. The number of pulses in the train which passes through the gate is therefore proportional to the analogue voltage. If the analogue voltage

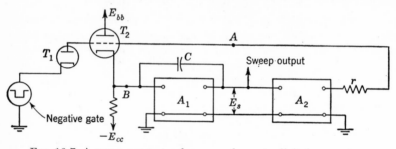

Fig. 16-7. A sweep generator for an analogue-to-digital converter.

varies with time, it will, of course, not be possible to convert the analogue data continuously, but it will be required that the analogue data be sampled at intervals. The maximum value of the analogue voltage will be represented by a number of pulses n. It is clear that n should be made as large as possible consistent with the requirement that the time interval between two successive pulses shall be larger than the timing error of the time modulator. The recurrence frequency of the pulses is equal, as a minimum, to the product of n and the sampling rate. Actually the recurrence rate will be larger in order to allow time for the circuit to recover between samplings.

The first basic requirement of the converter is a time base of precise linearity and negligible zero error and slope error. A system for achieving such a time base is shown in Fig. 16-7. To achieve linearity, the sweep is generated in the operational integrator consisting of R, C, and the high-gain amplifier of gain A_1. In a typical case the gain A_1 may be as large as 10^4 and linearity of the order 1 part in 10^4 over a sweep amplitude of 100 volts has been attained. The amplifier A_1 is a chopper-stabilized d-c amplifier[5] whose d-c drift is entirely negligible. The amplifier A_2 is similarly stabilized and the d-c level of the output of A_2 is adjusted so that in the absence of a gate the diode T_1 is nonconducting while the triode T_2 is operating within its grid base.

Suppose now that the circuit connection at A is broken and that the bias for T_2 were derived from some fixed voltage source. In this case the amplifier A_2 may be left out of consideration and the triode serves simply as a clamp on the voltage at point B to prevent the formation of a sweep.

The principal source of error will be the drift in the zero level of the sweep which results from the instability in the clamping level because of the drift in the triode T_2. To correct this difficulty, the chopper-stabilized amplifier A_2 is added, the gain A_2 being positive. We may represent the effect of the drift in the clamping level by the introduction of an error voltage E_e in series with the input lead to the amplifier A_1 at the point marked B. In the absence of the amplifier A_2 the drift in the zero level of the sweep would be $E_s{}^0 = A_1 E_e$. With A_2 present, and assuming that the gain from the grid of T_2 to its cathode is unity, the drift is calculated to be $(E_s{}^0)'$, where

$$(E_s{}^0)' = \frac{E_e A_1}{1 - A_1 A_2} = \frac{E_s{}^0}{1 - A_1 A_2} \qquad (16\text{-}3)$$

The denominator $1 - A_1 A_2$ is positive since A_1 is necessarily negative and A_2 positive. Since $A_1 A_2 \gg 1$, the effective drift of the sweep zero level has been reduced from $A_1 E_e$ to E_e / A_2. It is most interesting to note that the resultant drift of the zero level is now quite independent of the gain A_1. The reason for this result is that an increase in A_1 not only amplifies the drift E_e but at the same time increases the correcting feedback signal in the same proportion. If A_2 is taken to be 50 and if we allow E_e to be, say, 0.5 volt, the drift in sweep zero will be only 10 mv.

The effect of the drift in the amplifiers themselves may similarly be taken into account. In connection with d-c amplifiers it is customary to specify the drift in terms of the d-c input voltage required to cause the amplifier output signal to change by the amount of the drift. To allow for the drift in A_1, we need but add an additional voltage to E_e, while to allow for the drift in A_2, a voltage may be placed in series with the lead which couples A_1 to A_2. A drift $E_e{}^{(1)}$ in amplifier A_1 will appear as a drift $E_e{}^{(1)}/A_2$ in the sweep zero. A drift $E_e{}^{(2)}$ in amplifier A_2 will appear as a drift in the sweep zero of amount

$$\frac{A_1 A_2 E_e{}^{(2)}}{1 - A_1 A_2} \cong E_e{}^{(2)} \qquad (16\text{-}4)$$

It is, however, feasible to build a chopper-stabilized amplifier in which the drift may be represented by an input signal no larger than 50 μv. Hence, the amplifier drifts are negligible.

Referring again to Fig. 16-7, the sweep is formed when the negative gate appears. The diode T_1 conducts and draws the grid of T_2 below cutoff. The resistor r, which may be simply the output resistance of the amplifier, is necessary to permit the grid voltage to drop when the diode conducts. Since now T_2 is cut off, the point B is released from clamp and the feedback path through A_2 is open so that a sweep voltage may be formed. Clipping diodes are used to prevent overloading in amplifier A_2 and to make sure that the grid of T_2 is not brought above cutoff because of the signal from the amplifier A_2. At the end of the negative gate, T_2 conducts again and discharges the capacitor C.

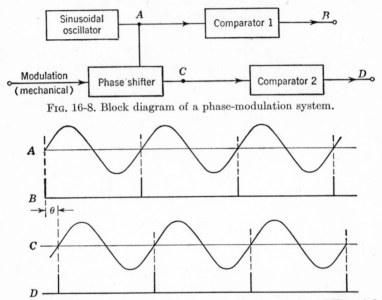

Fig. 16-8. Block diagram of a phase-modulation system.

Fig. 16-9. The waveforms in the phase-modulation system of Fig. 16-8.

Using the comparator of Fig. 16-7, an analogue-to-digital converter has been built which is capable of converting an analogue voltage in the range 0 to 100 volts with a full-scale digital output of 4,096 pulses (12 binary places).

16-4. Phase-modulation System. The basic principle involved in a time-modulation system using phase modulation is indicated in the block diagram of Fig. 16-8. The waveforms of such a system are given in Fig. 16-9. A sinusoidal signal A is delivered to comparator 1 whose output consists of a series of pulses B which are generated each time the sinusoid crosses the zero axis while going in the positive direction (or alternatively every time the sinusoid passes through zero in the negative-going direction.) The sinusoid is also applied to a phase-shifting device the output of which is shown in C. A second comparator produces the pulses shown in D. If the phase shifter provides a phase shift θ as shown in the diagram, the second set of pulses will be separated in time from the first set by an interval $t = \theta/\omega$, in which ω is the angular frequency of the sinusoidal signal.

It is, at present, not possible to build an accurate and reliable phase shifter whose phase angle is controllable by a simple electrical signal. For this reason the phase shifter employed is usually a mechanical device and the modulating "signal" is also mechanical, such as a shaft rotation. One prefers not to vary the timing interval by variation of the reference level of the comparators, since sine-wave amplitude comparison is most accurate when the selection takes place at zero phase where the slope is a maximum. Additionally, in such a case, the time interval would not vary linearly with the comparator reference voltage.

The error in a phase-modulation system arises principally in the phase-shifting circuits and devices. For a carefully designed system, an error of about $0.5°$ may be expected. Hence, the accuracy is

$$\frac{0.5}{360} \times 100 = 0.14 \text{ per cent}$$

provided that the comparator error can be neglected. The phase-modulation system is therefore somewhat less accurate than the time-base system. An advantage of phase modulation is the convenience with which it fits into multiple-scale time-modulation systems (Sec. 16-6).

16-5. Phase-shifting Devices and Circuits. The devices used for phase shifting are polyphase capacitors, resolvers, and sine-cosine potentiometers. These will now be described.

Phase-shifting Capacitors.[6] A polyphase capacitor consists of p capacitors which have one common plate and a rotatable dielectric slab whose angular position determines the individual capacitances between each of the segments and the common plate. It is possible to design[7] the geometry of the device in such a manner that the variation of capacitance C_n between the nth segment and the common plate is sinusoidal with the angular rotation θ of the shaft. Thus,

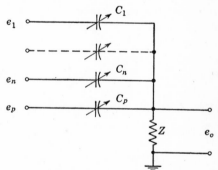

Fig. 16-10. Schematic representation of a p-phase capacitor circuit ($p = 3$ or 4).

$$C_n = C_o + C \cos\left[\theta + (n - 1)\frac{2\pi}{p}\right] \qquad n = 1, 2, \ldots, p \quad (16\text{-}5)$$

In practice p is either 3 (three-phase) or 4 (four-phase).

The circuit of Fig. 16-10 is excited with p-phase voltages so that

$$e_n = E \sin \left[\omega t + (n - 1) \frac{2\pi}{p} \right] \qquad n = 1, 2, \ldots, p \qquad (16\text{-}6)$$

The output voltage is given by the product of the short-circuit current times the impedance seen looking back from the output terminals. Thus,

$$E_o = \frac{\displaystyle\sum_{n=1}^{p} E_n j\omega C_n}{\displaystyle\sum_{n=1}^{p} j\omega C_n + 1/Z} \qquad (16\text{-}7)$$

where E_n is the sinor voltage corresponding to the instantaneous voltage e_n. After some trigonometric manipulation this expression reduces to

$$E_o = \frac{pEC e^{j\theta}}{2pC_o + 2/j\omega Z} \qquad (16\text{-}8)$$

This equation shows that the output voltage will have an amplitude which is independent of the angle θ and a phase which is a linear function of θ. Thus, we have converted a mechanical angle of rotation into an electrical phase angle. It is, of course, necessary that $C < C_o$, since C_n may not be negative. Even in the limiting case where $C = C_o$ and $\omega Z = \infty$, the ratio $E_o/E = \frac{1}{2}$ in the cases of both the four-phase and three-phase capacitors. More usually it turns out that the ratio C/C_o is such as to make the maximum possible value of $E_o/E \cong \frac{1}{15}$. A finite value of ωZ increases the attenuation further. Since large signal amplitude is required for comparator operation, the use of phase-shifting capacitors is restricted to frequencies usually higher than 20 kc.

Induction Resolvers. A *resolver* (sometimes also called a *synchro*)[8] as used for phase-shifting purposes is a device with two fixed stator windings and a single rotor winding located in the region of the magnetic fields produced by the stator windings. The stator windings are mechanically arranged to provide fields which are at right angles to one another in space. If these windings are excited by currents which are out of phase by 90° electrically, the rotor will find itself in a rotating magnetic field of constant amplitude. The voltage induced in the rotor will then be of constant amplitude and will have a phase which depends on its angular position.

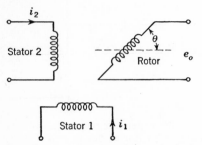

FIG. 16-11. A two-phase resolver which gives an output voltage whose phase angle equals the angle of the rotor.

the rotor will then be of constant amplitude and will have a phase which depends on its angular position.

The arrangement of windings in a resolver is illustrated schematically in Fig. 16-11.   The mutual inductances between stators and the rotor are $M_{1r} = M \cos \theta$ and $M_{2r} = M \sin \theta$, respectively.   If $i_1 = I_0 \sin \omega t$ and $i_2 = -I_0 \cos \omega t$, then

$$e_o = M_{1r} \frac{di_1}{dt} + M_{2r} \frac{di_2}{dt} = M\omega I_0 (\cos \theta \cos \omega t + \sin \theta \sin \omega t)$$

$$= M\omega I_0 \cos (\omega t - \theta) \tag{16-9}$$

This equation verifies the statement that the resolver converts a mechanical angle of rotation into an electrical phase angle.

An alternative method[9] of using a resolver which requires only a *single-phase applied voltage* is indicated in Fig. 16-12.   The output from the first stator is $e_1 = E \sin \omega t \cos \theta$ and is applied to the operational amplifier A, which (for a large value of gain) gives an output e_{o1} which is shifted

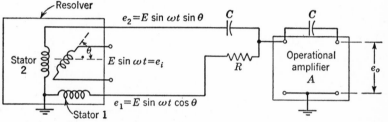

Fig. 16-12. A resolver–operational amplifier combination used to convert a mechanical angle into an electrical angle.

in phase by 90° or $e_{o1} = (E/\omega RC) \cos \omega t \cos \theta$.   The output from the second stator $e_2 = E \sin \omega t \sin \theta$ is also applied to the operational amplifier which inverts this voltage and delivers the output

$$e_{o2} = -E \sin \omega t \sin \theta$$

The net output e_o is

$$e_o = e_{o1} + e_{o2} = \frac{E}{\omega RC} \cos \omega t \cos \theta - E \sin \omega t \sin \theta \tag{16-10}$$

If ωRC is chosen equal to unity, then $e_o = E \cos (\omega t + \theta)$, thus confirming the fact that an electrical voltage is obtained whose phase angle equals the rotational angle of the resolver.   Note that the output voltage is of constant amplitude.

There are also available synchros having three stator windings which must be excited with three-phase voltages, and again the output from the rotor will have an electrical phase angle equal to the angle of rotation.

The accuracy of phase shift with a high-quality resolver is much better than that obtainable with phase-shifting capacitors.   Resolvers find application in the frequency range below about 20 kc.

Sine-Cosine Potentiometer.[10] This device consists of a *resistance card* wound with parallel wires, as shown in Fig. 16-13. Four brushes placed 90° apart in space move on a circle on this card (actually the card rotates

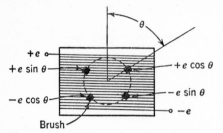

and the brushes are stationary in order that only two, instead of four, slip rings be required). A brush is broad enough to cover about two wires. A single-section RC filter is used in each lead to suppress potentiometer noise. The four outputs are proportional to $e \cos \theta$, $e \sin \theta$, $-e \cos \theta$, and $-e \sin \theta$, where $\pm e$ are the voltages applied

FIG. 16-13. A sine-cosine potentiometer.

at the ends of the card and θ is the angle of rotation.

The circuit for converting the space angle θ into an electrical angle is the same as that of Fig. 16-12 with the sine-cosine potentiometer replacing the resolver. The input to the potentiometer is $\pm E \sin \omega t$. The outputs $E \sin \omega t \cos \theta$ and $E \sin \omega t \sin \theta$ are applied to the operational amplifier which then delivers $E \cos (\omega t + \theta)$.

Phase-shifting Circuits.[11] A network suitable for use with a four-phase capacitor is shown in Fig. 16-14. The transformer is center-tapped. By

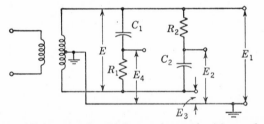

FIG. 16-14. A phase-shifting circuit which may be used with a polyphase capacitor.

drawing a sinor (phasor) diagram it may be verified[12] that the magnitude of the voltages E_1, E_2, E_3, and E_4 are all equal to $E/2$ and that if

$$\omega C_1 R_1 = \omega C_2 R_2 = 1$$

the phase of the voltages differs progressively by 90°.

If we use the voltages E_1, E_2, and E_4 of Fig. 16-14, three-phase voltages suitable for use with a three-phase capacitor will be provided. The signal amplitudes are again each equal to $E/2$. To provide the required 120° phase shifts, it is necessary to adjust

$$\omega C_1 R_1 = 1/\sqrt{3} \qquad \text{and} \qquad \omega C_2 R_2 = \sqrt{3}$$

The network of Fig. 16-14 behaves as indicated only if the signal terminals are not loaded. The small loading effect of the phase-shift capacitor may be minimized by using small values of R_1 and R_2 and large values for C_1 and C_2 so that the output impedance of the phase-shifting network will be low.

The circuit of Fig. 16-14 using only one RC network will produce the two-phase voltages required for the resolver circuit of Fig. 16-11. In this case buffer amplifiers might have to be used between the outputs and the resolver coils. A circuit which provides two-phase voltages without using a transformer is given in Prob. 16-8. An operational amplifier connected as a phase shifter may also be used for this purpose.

16-6. Multiple-scale Modulation.[13] The time-modulation systems already described are referred to as *single-scale* systems since only one timing cycle is involved. The accuracy of such systems is, as we have

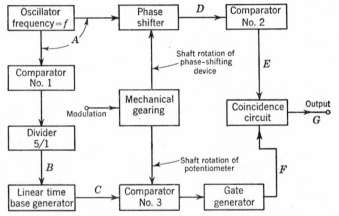

Fig. 16-15. A block diagram of a double-scale phase-modulation system.

seen, of the order of 0.1 to 0.2 per cent. The accuracy can be improved by orders of magnitude by the use of *multiple-scale* systems. A *double-scale* system is illustrated in functional form in Fig. 16-15. The associated waveforms are indicated in Fig. 16-16.

The sinusoidal output of the oscillator (waveform A) of frequency f is converted to a train of pulses by a comparator. This train of pulses (not indicated in the waveforms) is applied to a 5:1 divider (Chap. 12), the output of which appears in waveform B. These pulses, which are separated by a time interval $T_5 = 5/f$, are used to trigger a linear time-base generator whose waveform appears in C. The total time duration of the time-base voltage is made somewhat shorter than T_5 to allow the time-base generator to recover between pulses. The sweep generator may be self-gating or may require an external gate generator. In any event the gating function is assumed to be incorporated in the block of the time-base generator and is not shown separately.

The oscillator output is used simultaneously to excite a phase shifter of the types discussed in Sec. 16-5.   The phase-shifter output, shifted in phase with respect to the oscillator output by an arbitrary angle, is shown in D.   A second comparator provides the pulses shown in E at each positive-going crossing of the zero axis of the phase-shifter output.

The time-base waveform is applied to still a third comparator whose reference level is set at E_R, as shown in C.   This last comparator triggers a gating-waveform generator whose waveshape appears in F.   Finally,

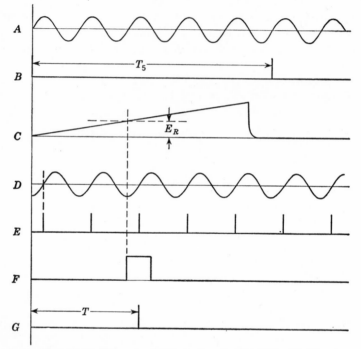

Fig. 16-16. The waveforms in the circuit of Fig. 16-15.

the gating waveform together with the pulse output of comparator 2 are applied to a coincidence circuit.   This gating circuit passes on to the output that one of the pulses of waveform E which occurs during the time of the gate at F so that the final output appears as in G and a timing interval T has been established.

Now suppose that one varies simultaneously the reference voltage E_R of comparator 3 and the phase shift produced by the phase shifter in such a way that the train of pulses at E and the gate at F are shifted on the time scale by the same amounts.   Then the time interval T may be varied continuously from nominal zero to $T = T_5$.

The important difference between the present time-modulation system and the single-scale system of Fig. 16-8 is that the *range* of time modulation has been extended from a range $1/f$ to the range $5/f$. The principal source of error is still the accuracy of the phase shifter. The absolute error of the phase shifter is unchanged, but since the range has been extended by a factor of 5, the *percentage accuracy* of full scale has been increased by a factor of 5. The linearity of the time-base voltage and the time of occurrence and duration of the gating waveform has no influence on accuracy. It is only required that the gating voltage be generated with enough precision to single out continuously one and only one pulse of the train.

In Fig. 16-15 the phase is shifted by rotation of the phase-shifting device, while the reference level of the comparator is adjusted by means of a potentiometer. The comparator reference level will go through its full range in one complete rotation of the potentiometer, while the phase shifter will require nominally five complete rotations. If the potentiometer is of conventional design (say 300° rotation), some mechanical gearing will be required between potentiometer and phase shifter. The necessity for the gearing (but not the coupling) between phase shifter and potentiometer may be eliminated if a multiturn potentiometer (a helipot) is used which requires five turns to cover its range.

If a divider which divides by n is used (in place of $5:1$ division), the accuracy will be improved n-fold. If n is equal, say, to 100, then the beginning of the gating waveform must be held to a precision of 1 per cent of full scale if one particular pulse is to be continuously selected. Otherwise a gross error will be made which makes the system entirely useless. Linear time-base comparator, single-scale timing circuits can be held to a precision appreciably better than 1 per cent, but to allow a comfortable safety factor a value of $n < 100$ is used.

16-7. Delay-line Modulation. A supersonic delay line[14] consists of a quartz crystal transmitter and a crystal receiver mounted in a tank of liquid (mercury, water, etc.). A pulse modulates a carrier frequency of, say, 30 Mc. This pulse-modulated carrier is then applied to a transmitting crystal which generates waves in the liquid column. A receiving crystal detects the pulse after it has traveled down the tank. Thus a delay of l/v sec is obtained, where l is the length of the column between input and output transducers and v is the velocity of propagation of the acoustical wave. This system has been used[15] to obtain delays variable over a range of 2 to 240 μsec with an extremely high degree of accuracy. The delay is varied by adjusting the spacing between the input and output crystals. The difficulties associated with this system are (1) the tank must be temperature-controlled since the velocity of propagation is a function of the temperature of the liquid, (2) the attenuation in the system is very high, (3) the device is difficult to maintain under field conditions, (4) the tank is heavy, and (5) an intricate mechanical arrangement is needed for moving the receiver relative to the transmitter within the liquid.

For short delays (about 10μsec or less), electrical lines may be used. The electrical delay line is ordinarily used to establish a fixed time interval. Such a line does not readily adapt itself to provide for a continuously variable, precisely determinable delay. However, a circulating-pulse technique, similar to that used in dynamic registers of a digital computer (Sec. 13-11), has been developed[16] for obtaining a highly stable variable time-delay system. In principle, this method consists of applying a pulse to the input of an electrical delay line, amplifying the output pulse in order to compensate for the attenuation of the line and then feeding the

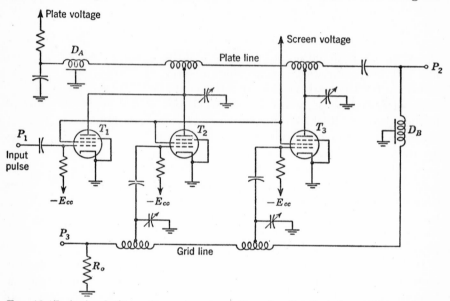

FIG. 16-17. A circulating-pulse system consisting of a distributed amplifier and two additional delay lines, D_A and D_B.

output of the amplifier back to the beginning of the line. The pulse then starts its second round trip over the loop consisting of delay line and amplifier. Thus the output is a train of pulses separated by a constant interval from one another. We shall see shortly how such a pulse circulating device is incorporated in a variable time-delay system. For the present, however, we may note that one possible application of this system might be in connection with high-speed oscillography. A sweep circuit may be triggered by the input pulse and the train of pulses from the delay line may be applied to the grid of the CRT to provide accurate and stable time markers.

If millimicrosecond pulses are to be transmitted in the circulating-pulse system, a distributed amplifier (Sec. 10-7) is required. Figure

16-17 shows the basic circuit, and the timing sequences of pulses are given in Fig. 16-18. Two additional delay lines D_A and D_B are required in addition to the delay lines of the distributed amplifier. For simplicity, we assume in the following description that the delays in the distributed amplifier are negligible in comparison with the delays of D_A and D_B. The operation of the circuit is as follows. A positive pulse applied at the input P_1, is amplified and inverted by tube T_1. The resulting negative pulse travels along the plate line of the amplifiers T_2 and T_3, then through the delay line B (having a delay D_B) and along the grid line, and is absorbed in the characteristic terminating resistance R_o. This negative pulse also travels through line A (having a delay D_A) and is reflected from the shorted end of this line as a positive pulse. This positive pulse travels down the plate line and appears at P_2 delayed by $2D_A$. This pulse also travels through line B and appears at P_3 an interval D_B later. Since T_2 and T_3 are biased beyond cut-off, negative pulses are not amplified. However, the positive pulse which appears at the grids of T_2 and T_3 is amplified and appears as a negative pulse in the plate line. This negative pulse travels along the paths indicated above for the first negative pulse which

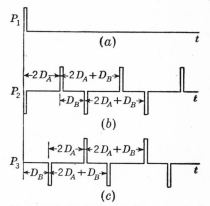

FIG. 16-18. The pulse trains generated in the circuit of Fig. 16-17.

appeared at the plate of T_1. The sequence of events then repeats itself and the result is equivalent to a having a pulse circulate around the loop continuously. The pulse trains which appear at P_2 and P_3 are shown in Fig. 16-18.

If, instead of a pulse train, a single pulse is desired whose delay may be modulated in accord with a d-c reference voltage E_R, the circuit[16] of Fig. 16-19 is added to that of Fig. 16-17. The pulses at P_3 (Fig. 16-18c) are applied to a blocking oscillator which is biased so that only the positive pulses are effective. These blocking-oscillator pulses enter a storage counter and generate a staircase voltage as in Fig. 11-26. When this voltage reaches a level determined by E_R, the comparator delivers a pulse which in turn generates a gating voltage. This gate is applied to a coincidence circuit which has as its second input the pulse train at P_2 (Fig. 16-8b). The gating voltage is wide enough to overlap one (but not more than one) of the positive pulses at P_2. Hence, a single pulse will be delivered from the coincidence circuit and delayed $2D_A$ plus an integral multiple of $2D_A + D_B$ from the input pulse to the system. The delay can be varied in steps of $2D_A + D_B$ by changing the reference voltage E_R of the comparator. The gating generator also activates a turnoff circuit which applies an additional negative bias to the grids of T_2 and T_3. This negative bias prevents further circulation of pulses around the distributed amplifier loop and the pulse train is terminated. The system is now quiescent until another external pulse is applied at P_1 of Fig. 16-17.

The high stability of the above system is due to the fact that the delay is determined by the number of reflections in lines A and B and is almost independent of variations in cutoff characteristics of tubes, noise, hum, temperature, and changes in supply voltages, provided that the levels of the pulses are high, say 50 volts.

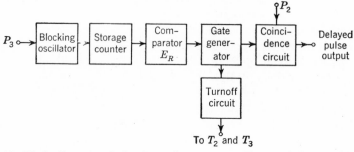

Fig. 16-19. Block diagram of circuit used to convert Fig. 16-17 into a single-pulse delay system.

16-8. Pulsed Oscillators.[17] The time-base and delay-line systems discussed in this chapter are externally synchronized. However, the phase-modulation system has the limitation that it must be internally synchronized. The versatility of this system would be improved appreciably if it were possible to synchronize the system to an external pulse which occurs at random. What is required for such a purpose is that the continuously running oscillator of Fig. 16-15 be replaced by a *pulsed oscillator*.

A pulsed oscillator is one which is normally quiescent but which can be turned on for the time duration of a gating waveform. Ideally such a pulsed oscillator should provide zero output voltage before and after the gate and a sinusoid of fixed amplitude, frequency, and phase during the gate. When the oscillator is gated on, there will be a switching transient associated with the gating, and as a result the first several cycles of the oscillator waveform may not be suitable for timing purposes. To minimize this transient, one tries to arrange, as far as possible, that the initial currents and voltages at the time of switching shall be the same as those that would occur if the oscillator were running continuously. For this purpose the most suitable oscillator is one with few components such as an LC oscillator.

Consider initially the *ringing* circuit of Fig. 16-20. The inductor L and capacitor C constitute the oscillating circuit and R represents the damping losses of L. The resistor R_L is adjusted so that with the tube in clamp the inductor current is I. A negative gate cuts off the tube and the cathode circuit is free to execute natural (unforced) oscillations. The transient behavior of a ringing circuit is discussed in detail in Sec. 2-8, where it is shown that the amplitude of oscillations decreases to $1/\epsilon$th its peak value in Q/π cycles. Since the Q of a coil in this application is of the order of 25, this decrement is too rapid to make the circuit of Fig. 16-20 very useful as a source of pulsed oscillations. The circuit does, however, find some application for calibration of the time axis of a cathode-ray oscillograph, since, in spite of the damping, the times at

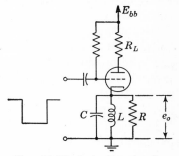

Fig. 16-20. A ringing circuit.

which the waveform crosses the zero axis are equally spaced. In this application the gating waveform which generates the cathode-ray oscillograph time base also triggers the ringing circuit. The ringing circuit output is displayed on the CRO screen and the sweep speed may be determined if the ringing frequency is known.

A pulsed oscillator which has been widely used[18] is shown in Fig. 16-21. The tube T_1 is the gating tube and is cut off during the oscillations. With R_3 zero, the remainder of the circuit is identical to the conventional Hartley oscillator. If the oscillator tube T_2 were omitted, the voltage across the tank circuit would have an initial amplitude $\omega L I$, I being the initial current in L. If the feedback due to the presence of T_2 is adjusted to approximately the value required to supply the tank-circuit losses, the initial amplitude will remain at $\omega L I$. We may actually expect that the amplitude will grow or decay very slowly, depending on whether the loop gain is slightly more or less than unity. This is a matter of small concern since the oscillator will be permitted to run for only a short time.

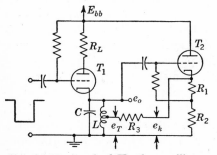

Fig. 16-21. A pulsed Hartley oscillator.

The resistor R_3 is used to adjust the loop gain to unity. R_3 is adjusted experimentally to the value which results in constant amplitude of sinusoidal signal. An approximate value of R_3 is easily calculated. For simplicity, let us assume that the gain of T_2 (cathode follower) is nominally unity. Let us further assume that the coil is tapped at its midpoint and that the coupling between the two halves of the coil is perfect. The impedance R_T seen looking into the terminals e_T is then one-fourth of the resonant impedance of the tank circuit, or $R_T = \frac{1}{4}\omega LQ$. Since the tank voltage e_o equals $2e_T$, then for the loop gain to be 1, the ratio e_k/e_T must equal 2. Hence $R_T/(R_3 + R_T) = \frac{1}{2}$, or $R_3 = R_T = \frac{1}{4}\omega LQ$.

The output signal is taken directly from the tank circuit and is exceptionally free of harmonic distortion. In a conventional LC oscillator, the tube operates class C, and we depend on this filtering action of the tank circuit to provide a sinusoidal waveform. In the pulsed oscillator of Fig. 16-21, the oscillator tube is self-biased through R_1 so that it operates very nearly linearly with a consequent improvement in waveform.

In Fig. 16-21 the cathode-to-heater capacitance of T_1 and the input capacitance of T_2 may well constitute a large fraction of the total timing capacitance, which capacitance is subject to change with tube replacement and variations in supply voltage. In order to minimize this effect T_2 is replaced by a pentode and a second cathode follower T_3 (not shown in Fig. 16-21) is added.[19] The input of T_3 is e_k and the output of T_3 is connected to the center tap of the filament transformer feeding T_1. The effective cathode-heater capacitance of T_1 is thereby multiplied by the factor $1 - A$, where A is the gain from the grid of T_2 to the cathode of T_3. When these precautions are taken, the stability of frequency may be maintained with an accuracy of several parts per million for reasonable changes in plate and filament voltages. Where necessary, it is not uncommon to find the tank circuit enclosed in a temperature-controlled oven to prevent frequency drift with temperature due to mechanical changes in L and C. The phase-shifting system which is used for continuous sine waves may also be used for pulsed sinusoids. In the pulsed case, however, some minor complications may occur as a result of the transient response which accompanies the abrupt turning on of the sine wave.[17]

16-9. Double-scale Time-modulation Systems, Externally Synchronized. The system of Fig. 16-15 may be modified in the following way to arrange for the timing operation to be initiated by an external pulse. Comparator 1 and the 5:1 divider are no longer needed. Instead the external initiating pulse is applied directly to the linear time-base generator and also to a gating generator (not shown) which provides a gate somewhat longer than the duration of the time base. This gate is used to gate *on* the normally quiescent sinusoidal oscillator. The operation of the rest of the system is the same as described earlier. After the end of the gate which turns on the oscillator, a short time interval must be allowed to pass to permit the oscillator to return to its quiescent condition before the system may be pulsed again.

The system of Fig. 16-15 uses a combination of time-base modulator and phase-shift modulator. A double-scale system employing two phase modulators is shown in Fig. 16-22. The operation is basically the same

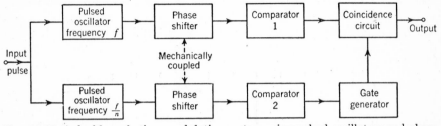

FIG. 16-22. A double-scale time-modulation system using pulsed oscillators and phase shifters.

as before, except here the timing previously accomplished by the time-base generator is done instead by a lower frequency oscillator and a phase shifter. The two phase shifters must be geared in the ratio n so that the rate of change of delay is the same in both the coarse and fine timing circuits. The details of waveforms are left to the student.

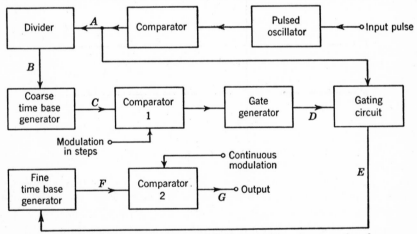

FIG. 16-23. A double-scale time-modulation system using two time bases.

In Fig. 16-23 is shown a system in which two time-base modulators are used. The waveforms are shown in Fig. 16-24. The *coarse time-base generator* together with its associated circuitry selects one of the train of pulses which appear at A. This selected pulse triggers the *fine time-base generator*, which is used to interpolate between a pair of the fixed pulses. The modulation of the reference level of comparator 1 is stepwise to select one or another of the pulses; the modulation of comparator 2 is continuous.   When the modulation control of comparator 2 (say a potentiometer) has been advanced to its maximum position, it must then be returned to zero and the modulation control of comparator 1 must be advanced by a step to select the next pulse.   In this respect the present system is not as convenient as a system which uses phase modulation, as in Figs. 16-22 and 16-15.   In these latter systems the fine and coarse controls may be ganged and a continuous variation in one direction will provide time modulation over the entire range.

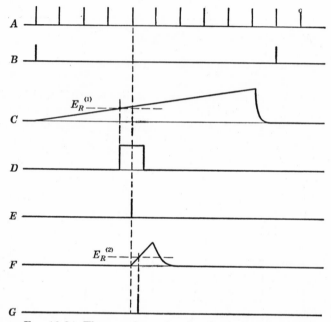

FIG. 16-24. The waveforms for the circuit of Fig. 16-23.

16-10. Time Measurements.   Consider that we wish to measure the time interval T between two pulses.   Or, alternatively, suppose we wish to determine the time span between two points on a waveform.   The simplest method of carrying out this measurement is to display both the waveform and a train of timing markers on a CRO.   The timing indices may be generated by the method outlined in Sec. 16-8.   These markers may be displayed as a deflection superimposed upon the waveform or, alternatively, the timing pulses may be used to intensity-modulate the CRO.   The desired time interval is found by counting the number of timing marks between the two pulses (or the two points on the wave-form).   If the interval does not contain an integral number of timing pulses, then we may interpolate between markers.

Another method of measurement is obtained by generating a single movable timing index (instead of a timing pulse train). The first pulse defining the interval in question is used to trigger a delay device such as a cathode-coupled monostable multi or a phantastron. The delayed pulse is next adjusted until it coincides with the second pulse of the interval in question. The spacing between pulses is then read directly from the calibrated delay device. Accuracies of about 1 per cent of full scale may be obtained in this manner. Higher accuracies may be obtained by using one of the more complex time-modulation methods discussed in this chapter to generate the movable index.

An alternative method of time measurement which may be carried out with a counter is indicated in block-diagram form in Fig. 16-25. The reference or *start pulse* opens the gate and the second or *stop pulse* closes it. The number of accurately timed pulses from the crystal oscillator or the divider which occurs in the desired interval is then read directly on the counter. The reading is correct to within ± 1 count. Decade-counter time-interval instruments are available

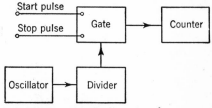

FIG. 16-25. A block diagram of a counter system for measuring the time interval between two pulses.

commercially from a number of manufacturers. Time intervals in the range from 10 μsec to 100,000 sec may be measured with these instruments.

The accuracy of counting instruments (± 1 count) can be increased by several orders of magnitude by using an *interpolation* or *vernier system*. Consider, for example, that a 1-Mc counter is available and that we wish to make measurements to an accuracy of 0.01 μsec (10 mμsec). The method* is illustrated in block-diagram form in Fig. 16-26. An internally synchronized system is assumed. Pulses, spaced 1 μsec apart, from a crystal-controlled clock generator are counted down to supply the start pulse P_1. The purpose of the apparatus is to measure the time interval between the reference (or start) pulse P_1 and a pulse P_2, called a *stop* pulse. A transmission gate (Sec. 14-2) is opened by P_1 and allows clock pulses to be recorded in the coarse counter. The *vernier count generator* is of the circulating-pulse type described in Sec. 16-7 (Fig. 16-17), and when the stop pulse P_2 arrives it generates a train of pulses with a spacing of 0.99 μsec. The vernier generator pulses are recorded in the *fine* or *vernier counter*. The outputs from both generators are applied to a *coincidence* or *AND* circuit which delivers a pulse when

* This vernier system was developed at the Electronics Research Laboratories, Electrical Engineering Department, Columbia University. The oscillograms reproduced in this section were taken at these laboratories.

a clock and a vernier pulse coincide in time. The output from the coincidence circuit inhibits the vernier-count generator so that it delivers no further pulses and it also closes the transmission gate so that no further clock pulses enter the coarse counter. If the coarse-count

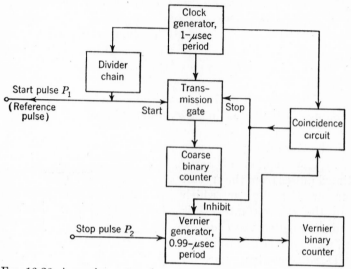

FIG. 16-26. A vernier system for very accurate time measurements.

reading is C and the vernier-count reading is V, then the time interval T between P_1 and P_2 is given by

$$T = (C - V) \times 1 \ \mu\text{sec} + V \times 0.01 \ \mu\text{sec} \tag{16-11}$$

as will now be demonstrated.

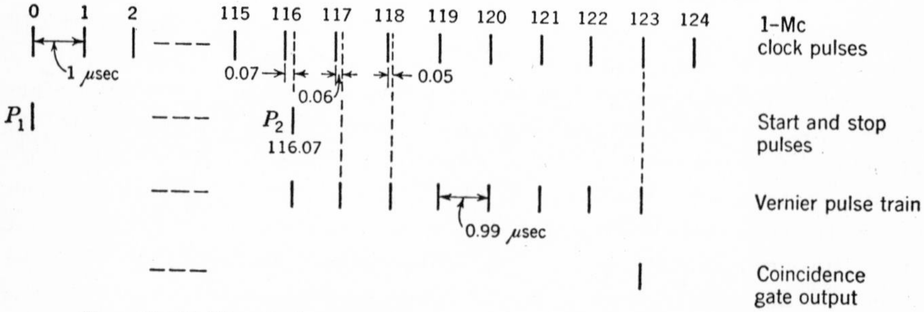

FIG. 16-27. The timing waveforms in the vernier system of Fig. 16-26.

The operation of the circuit may be understood by referring to the timing sequences in Fig. 16-27. For purposes of illustration a timing interval of 116.07 μsec has been assumed. The pulse P_2 occurs 0.07 μsec after the 116th clock pulse. The first pulse delivered by the vernier generator occurs 0.06 μsec after the 117th clock pulse, the second vernier pulses occurs 0.05 μsec after the 118th pulse, etc. In other words, because of the 0.01-μsec difference in the periods of the two generators, each succeeding vernier pulse slides back 0.01 μsec relative to the corresponding clock pulse. Therefore, after 7 vernier pulses are generated, there will be a coincidence between a clock pulse and a vernier pulse. This condition obtains at clock pulse 123. Hence, the number of integral multiples of the clock period in the interval between P_1 and P_2 is

$$C - V = 123 - 7 = 116$$

The remainder of the interval is given by $0.01V = 0.07$ μsec. This explanation justifies Eq. (16-11). A mechanical vernier ruler operates on precisely the above principle, and this is the reason this method is called a *vernier system*. Figure 16-28 is an oscillogram of the vernier pulses superimposed upon the clock pulses.

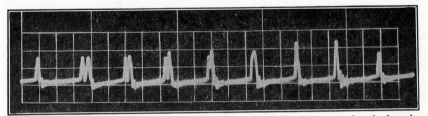

FIG. 16-28. An oscillogram of the vernier pulses superimposed upon the clock pulses.

It might appear that the system could be simplified by using the stop pulse directly to close the transmission gate and hence stop the coarse counter. However, if the pulse P_2 were used to stop the coarse count, it is possible that the counter may read too high by one count. This error will occur if a clock pulse follows immediately after P_2 so that the transmission gate does not close quickly enough to eliminate this unwanted clock pulse.

In this system the pulse generators must be extremely stable. Consider, for example, the vernier-pulse generator which may have to deliver as many as 99 pulses. If the total error is to be less than 0.01 μsec, then the delay of each pulse must be in error by less than $0.01/99 \cong 10^{-4}$ μsec over an interval $99 \times 0.99 = 98$ μsec. By increasing the frequency of the clock generator the accuracy requirement may be made less stringent and also the total time required for the vernier count may be decreased. For example, if a 2-Mc clock is used, the time between pulses is 0.5 μsec, the vernier interval is 0.49 μsec, and the maximum number of vernier counts is 49. Hence, the maximum time required for the vernier count is $49 \times 0.49 = 24$ μsec instead of 98 μsec for a 1-Mc clock. Also, now the delay of each pulse must be in error by less than $0.01/49 \cong 2 \times 10^{-4}$ μsec over an interval of 24 μsec. Since the delay in the circulating pulse generator is determined principally by a passive element (the delay line), it is possible to achieve this stability.[16]

The second critical element in the system is the AND gate which must be able to detect a coincidence to within 0.01 μsec. An oscillogram of the clock and vernier pulses is given in Fig. 16-29, and we see that the

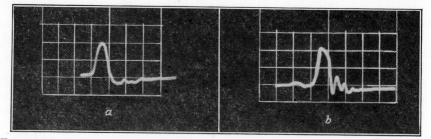

Fig. 16-29. (a) A clock pulse; (b) a vernier pulse. Scales: abscissa, -0.05 μsec per division; ordinate, -12 volts per division.

pulses are approximately 0.03 μsec wide at half amplitude. A multielement tube of the type discussed in Sec. 14-5 (Fig. 14-10c) has been used successfully for the AND circuit. Figure 16-30 gives the circuit consisting of the coincidence tube T_1 followed by an amplifier T_2. The bias voltage for T_1 is chosen so that only the tops of the pulses are effective in deter-

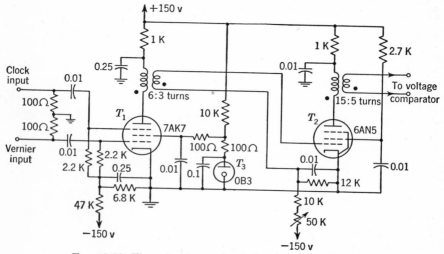

Fig. 16-30. The coincidence circuit for the vernier system.

mining a coincidence. The output at the plate of T_2 consists of several pulses, as indicated in Fig. 16-31a, because there is a partial overlap of several vernier and clock pulses. The amplifier is followed by a voltage comparator whose reference level is adjusted so that only the largest pulse in Fig. 16-31a is counted as a true coincidence. It is, however, possible (for some values of the interval between P_1 and P_2) to have the situation shown in Fig. 16-31b, where two output pulses have approximately the same amplitude. Under these circumstances the vernier counter may be in error by one count (0.01 μsec). The output from the amplitude comparator supplies a pulse to inhibit the counters, as indicated in Fig. 16-26.

It is possible, with added complexity, to use the vernier method in an externally synchronized system. Since the start pulse in such a system is randomly timed with respect to the clock pulses, an additional vernier

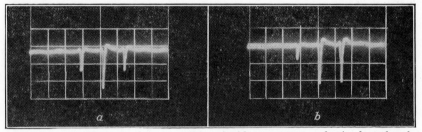

FIG. 16-31. An oscillogram of two possible coincidence patterns obtained at the plate of amplifier T_2 of Fig. 16-30.

measurement must be made. This measurement gives the interval between the start pulse and the preceding clock pulse.

REFERENCES

1. Chance, B., et al.: "Electronic Time Measurements," Massachusetts Institute of Technology Radiation Laboratory Series, vol. 20, chap. 5, McGraw-Hill Book Company, Inc., New York, 1949.
2. Chance, B., et al.: "Waveforms," Massachusetts Institute of Technology Radiation Laboratory Series, vol. 19, pp. 477–490, McGraw-Hill Book Company, Inc., New York, 1949.
3. Burke, H. E.: "A Survey of Analog-to-Digital Converters," *Proc. IRE*, vol. 41, no. 10, pp. 1455–1461, October, 1953.
4. Slaughter, D. W.: An Analog-to-Digital Converter with an Improved Linear-sweep Generator, *IRE Convention Record—Electronic Computers*, pp. 7–12, 1953
5. Korn, G. A., and T. M. Korn: "Electronic Analog Computers," sec. 5.6, McGraw-Hill Book Company, Inc., New York, 1952.
6. Ref. 1, pp. 492–499.
7. Blackburn, J. F.: "Components Handbook," Massachusetts Institute of Technology Radiation Laboratory Series, vol. 17, chap. 9, McGraw-Hill Book Company, Inc., New York, 1949.
8. Ref. 7, chap. 10.
9. Robinson, A. S.: An Electronic Analog Computing Technique for the Solution of Trigonometric Problems, *IRE Trans. Electronic Computers*, vol. EC-4, pp. 95–101, September, 1955.
10. Ref. 7, pp. 284–286.
11. Ref. 2, pp. 136–140.

12. Millman, J., and S. Seely: "Electronics," 2d ed., pp. 360–364, McGraw-Hill Book Company, Inc., New York, 1951.
13. Ref. 1, pp. 58–62.
14. Ref. 7, chap. 7.
15. Ref. 1, pp. 132–135.
16. Yu, Y. P.: "A Highly Stable Variable Time-delay System," *Proc. IRE*, vol. 41, pp. 228–235, February, 1953.
17. Ref. 2, pp. 140–158.
18. Elmore, W. C., and M. L. Sands: "Electronics: Experimental Techniques," pp. 66, 291, and 345, McGraw-Hill Book Company, Inc., New York, 1949.
19. Ref. 2, pp. 143–145.
20. Ref. 2, p. 158.

CHAPTER 17

PULSE AND DIGITAL SYSTEMS

The circuits and techniques which have been described in the preceding chapters are the basic building blocks and methods used in a large number of important types of systems. Among these systems are television, radar, pulse communications, pulse telemetering, a wide variety of instruments and digital computers—to mention just a few. In the present chapter we shall discuss certain aspects of a television system and of radar displays. The purpose of this discussion is twofold: first, to acquaint the student briefly with the principles of television and radar and, second, to illustrate how the various pulse-circuit building blocks are assembled into a complete system.

17-1. Fundamental Principles of Television Transmission. Of the many possible systems which may be used for the continuous transmission of pictures, the system which employs the principle of linear scanning has been found to be the most practical. The picture to be transmitted is explored by a sensing element of small area (called the *picture element*) which passes successively over all parts of the image area. An electrical signal is generated which is proportional to the brightness of the picture at the position of the sensing element. This brightness signal is transmitted to the place where the picture is to be reproduced. Here a small luminous area is moved across a screen along a path corresponding to that taken by the exploring area. The brightness of the luminous spot is controlled by the brightness signal and in this manner the original picture is reproduced. The scanning process is continuous, starting over again each time the scanning has covered the full picture area.

The geometry of the picture area and the method of scanning which are used in broadcast television are illustrated in Fig. 17-1. The picture area is rectangular, having a ratio of width w to height h (called the *aspect ratio*) of 4:3. The scanning is done by moving the picture element almost horizontally from left to right with a uniform speed along a straight line. When the extremity of the picture area to the right is reached, the picture element moves abruptly to the left of the screen to scan a second line below the first line and parallel to it. The spacing between scanning lines is approximately equal to the height of the picture element. When the bottom line has been scanned, the picture element returns abruptly to the upper left-hand corner and the entire process is repeated.   A complete scanning of the picture area is referred to as a *frame*.

It appears, then, that the picture is transmitted piecemeal, one picture element at a time.   The viewer, however, has the impression that all parts of the picture have been presented simultaneously, principally because of the persistence of vision of the eye.   Some of the detail of the original scene must necessarily be lost because of the finite size of the scanning element. The eye has, however, only a finite resolving power, that is, a finite ability to distinguish fine detail.   When the size of the scanning aperture has been reduced to the point where, at a normal viewing distance, the limit of resolution of the eye has been reached, no advantage results from a further decrease in the size of the scanning element.

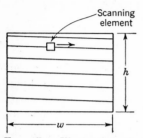

FIG. 17-1. Illustration of the principle of scanning.

The device which is used quite universally for picture reproduction is the cathode-ray tube known, in this application, as a *kinescope*.   The scanning is accomplished by appropriate deflection of the electron beam in the vertical and horizontal directions.   The intensity of the screen illumination is controlled by modulation of the beam current (Z axis modulation).   The persistence of phosphorescence of the screen coating serves to augment the persistence of vision of the eye.

Various devices (cameras) are available for translating the visual scene into an electrical signal in the manner described above.   Among these are a series of special vacuum tubes known as *iconoscopes*, or *orthicons*.   In each case the scanning is once again accomplished by an electron beam which explores a photosensitive surface, called a *mosaic*, on which the picture to be transmitted has been brought to focus.

17-2. Interlaced Scanning.   When the picture consists of a changing scene, it is necessary that the frame repetition rate be rapid enough so that no perceptible change in scene takes place from frame to frame.   It is found, however, that even when the frame rate is sufficient to give the impression of continuity of motion an objectionable feature may yet remain in the transmitted picture.   This difficulty arises from the fact that the luminous spot which forms the picture spends only a relatively small fraction of the time in the neighborhood of any particular region of the viewing screen.   Consequently, the observer is aware of a flicker in the illumination of any particular area and also of the entire picture. The flicker may be reduced by increasing the frame rate, but such an increase requires a corresponding increase in bandwidth of the communication channel.   When the frame repetition rate has been increased to the point which yields continuity of motion, it is possible to increase the frame rate, *so far as flicker is concerned,* by a method which requires no extension of bandwidth. This saving is accomplished by a method known as 2:1 *interlaced scanning.*

The principle of 2:1 interlaced scanning is illustrated in Fig. 17-2. The scanning, now, does not progress uniformly from one line to the next. Instead the lines are scanned in the order 1, 3, 5, 7, etc., until half the lines have been scanned. Then the scanning begins again at line 2 and proceeds in the order 2, 4, 6, etc., until the entire frame has been scanned. The scanning of a frame is thus divided into two parts, each part being referred to as a *field.* The field composed of the odd-numbered lines (solid lines in Fig. 17-2) is called the *odd field.* The remaining lines (dashed)

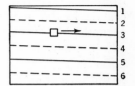

Fig. 17-2. Illustration of the principle of interlaced scanning.

compose the *even field.* The effect of such interleaving is to increase the large area rate of flicker by a factor of 2 to the point where the flicker is no longer perceptible to the eye.

We consider next how the horizontal and vertical saw-tooth deflecting signals must be related in order to generate the 2:1 interlaced scanning

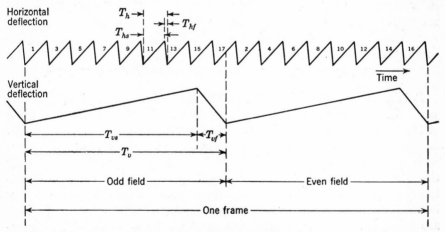

Fig. 17-3. Horizontal and vertical deflections for a 17-line interlaced frame.

pattern described above. The principle of interlacing may be understood by reference to Fig. 17-3 in which are plotted, as functions of time, the horizontal and vertical beam deflections required for a 17-line scanning pattern. For vertical deflection, T_{vs} and T_{vf} are, respectively, the scanning and flyback time intervals, while $T_v = T_{vs} + T_{vf}$. Similarly, the total horizontal-line time interval is $T_h = T_{hs} + T_{hf}$. Each of the above time intervals is entirely arbitrary except for the condition that

$2T_v = 17T_h$ so that a complete scanning pattern will have been generated in a time $2T_v$.

It may now be seen from Fig. 17-3 that the vertical position occupied by a line numbered $2m$ (m is an integer and hence $2m$ is even) in the even field falls exactly midway between the positions occupied by the lines numbered $2m - 1$ and $2m + 1$ in the odd field. This situation results from the fact that the odd-field vertical-deflection interval T_v ends exactly in the middle of a horizontal-deflection interval T_h. Thus, for example, line 2 begins at a time $\frac{1}{2}T_h$ after the beginning of the vertical sweep, while lines 1 and 3 begin, respectively, at the beginning of the horizontal sweep and at a time T_h afterward. Similarly, say, line 8 begins at a time $3\frac{1}{2}T_h$, while lines 7 and 9 begin at times $3T_h$ and $4T_h$, respectively.

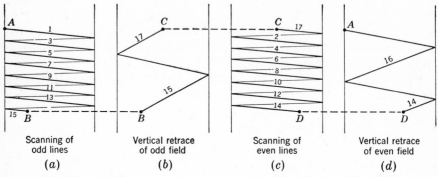

FIG. 17-4. Motion of scanning beam for deflection signals of Fig. 17-3.

It is assumed, for simplicity, in Fig. 17-3 that the beginning of the vertical sweep in the odd field is exactly coincident with the beginning of the horizontal sweep of line 1. This feature, however, is not essential to achieve interlaced scanning. Rather, the results stated above with respect to the interlacing hold quite generally, provided only that the total number of line intervals T_h per frame is *odd*. The advantage of using an odd number of line intervals is that interlacing may be achieved with a vertical deflecting signal, alternate cycles of which are identical. On the other hand, if the total number of line intervals per frame were *even*, a vertical deflecting signal would be required in which alternate cycles would be different.

The motion of the scanning beam corresponding to the deflecting signals of Fig. 17-3 is shown in Fig. 17-4. At the beginning of the frame the beam is at the position A. (We consider that the sweep progresses horizontally to the right and vertically downward.) The useful scan of the odd field (a) ends at B during the 15th line interval. The vertical retrace (b) occupies part of the 15th and 17th intervals and ends at C. The useful scanning lines of the even field (c) begin during the 17th line interval and end at D during the 14th line.   Finally, in (d) is shown the vertical retrace which ends the frame and returns the beam to the starting point at A.   If Fig. 17-4c were superimposed on Fig. 17-4a it would, of course, be found that the even and odd lines are exactly interlaced.   Similarly, it would be found that the two vertical retraces would be interlaced, but this last feature is not important.   Neither is it important that the retraces be linear, this feature having been assumed in Figs. 17-3 and 17-4 for simplicity of construction.

Observe that actually there are only approximately 15 useful scanning lines.   The system described above is nevertheless referred to as a 17-line system.   Since no useful picture information may be presented during the horizontal and vertical flyback time, it will be desirable to blank out the beam during these intervals.   To allow a margin of safety, the blanking intervals may well be longer than the flyback times.

17-3. Composite Television Signal.   We may now consider what signals must be sent from a television transmitter to a receiver in order to permit a picture to be reproduced.   These are:

1. A *synchronizing signal* to ensure that the scanning generators at the receiver are precisely synchronous with the scanning generators at the transmitter.   The synchronizing signal is made up of two parts, a horizontal sync signal and a vertical sync signal.   The sync signal will ordinarily be generated at the transmitter and will be used locally as well as at the receiver.

2. A *blanking signal*, again composed of two parts.   One signal is to be used to turn off the beam for an interval somewhat longer than the horizontal flyback time and a second signal serves the same function in connection with the vertical retrace.   These signals may also be generated locally at the transmitter and used to advantage to blank out the camera scanning beam except when picture information is to be transmitted.

3. The *picture* (*video*) *signal* derived directly from the camera and to be used at the receiver for intensity modulation during the time intervals of the scanning lines.

For the purposes of transmission over long distances it is necessary to superimpose the sync and video information on a radio-frequency carrier. Since only a single communications channel is normally available between transmitter and receiver, all the required information must be assembled into a *single composite* signal.   The signal must be of a form which permits its individual component parts to be separated from one another relatively easily.   A not inconsiderable portion of a commercial television transmitter and receiver is devoted to generation, modulation, selection, and amplification of this radio-frequency signal and eventually to the detection of the radio-frequency envelope. The principles involved in the radio-frequency circuitry of both transmitter and receiver are not unlike the principles used in radio broadcasting. One difference of importance results, however, from the relatively large bandwidth required for good-quality picture transmission. As a consequence the *radio-frequency* and *intermediate-frequency* bandwidths must be much greater for television than for radio broadcasts, and hence higher-frequency radio-frequency carriers are employed. And to conserve space in the radio-frequency spectrum, semi-single-sideband transmission is used. We shall not further concern ourselves with the communication link, but in the remaining discussion we shall concentrate on the television signal itself.

17-4. The Synchronizing Signal. The standards of commercial television broadcasting in the United States as established by the Federal Communications Commission (FCC) require a system with 525 line intervals per frame and a frame repetition rate of 30 frames per second. Interlacing of 2:1 is called for so that the field repetition rate is 60 fields per second. The synchronizing signal consists of a sequence of pulses, and those pulses which are intended for horizontal synchronization are distinguished from those intended for vertical synchronization by their time duration. The principle by which pulses of appreciably different duration may be separated is illustrated in Fig. 17-5. In Fig. 17-5a a short-duration pulse is applied to a differentiating circuit and the output consists of alternate positive and negative spikes. We may easily arrange a scanning generator to be sensitive only to, say, the positive spike so that it may be synchronized by the leading edge of the original pulse and be insensitive to the trailing edge. In Fig. 17-5b and c a short- and long-duration pulse is applied to an integrating circuit and the output is connected to a comparator. The integrating time constant and comparator reference level may easily be adjusted so that the long-duration pulse causes the comparator to respond, while the short-duration pulse is ineffective. Hence, if the train of long and short pulses are applied simultaneously to a differentiator and to an integrator-comparator combination, one circuit will give an indication at the time of occurrence of the leading edge of short pulses, while the second circuit will give an indication somewhat after the time of occurrence of a long pulse. The short pulse may then be used, say, for horizontal synchronization and the long pulse for vertical synchronization. Of course the long-duration pulse will also give an output spike when applied to the differentiator. For this reason we shall have to arrange that the leading edge of the long pulse occurs either at a time when a horizontal-scanning generator is insensitive to it or else at a time when the generator would normally require a synchronizing pulse.

We shall lead up to the complete sync signal by considering initially the sync-signal waveform of Fig. 17-6a.   The portion of the signal shown is that which marks the ending of the even field and the beginning of the odd field.   For simplicity, a number of essential features have been left out of the waveform of Fig. 17-6a, and these will be added later.   The narrow pulses are the horizontal sync pulses and the broad pulse is the vertical sync pulse.   The time interval between horizontal sync pulses is $H = 1/(525 \times 30)$ sec $= 63.5$ μsec.   The duration of the H

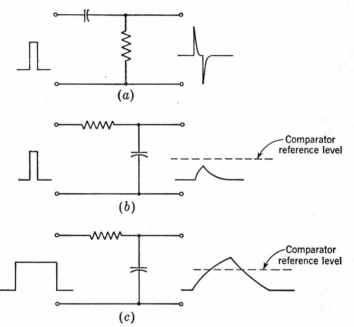

(a)

(b)

(c)

Fig. 17-5. Illustration of a method by which pulses may be distinguished according to their duration.

pulses is set by FCC standards at nominally $0.08H = 5.1$ μsec.   The vertical sync pulse V is somewhat longer than $3H$.   The leading edge of the V sync pulse coincides with the position that would otherwise be occupied by the leading edge of H pulse 524.   The pulses which are derived by differentiating the rising edges of the waveform of Fig. 17-6a are shown in Fig. 17-6b.   These are the pulses which will be used to synchronize the horizontal scanning generator.   Observe that pulse 524 used for horizontal sync is actually derived from the leading edge of that pulse in Fig. 17-6a which has been termed the vertical sync pulse.   The result of integrating the waveform (Fig. 17-6a) is shown in Fig. 17-6c.   And the vertical sync pulse which is derived from a comparator is shown in Fig. 17-6d.   The H sync pulses 1, 3, and 5 are missing.

We may now easily deduce the required location of the V sync pulse which will terminate the odd field and give the required interlacing. The time interval between V pulses must, of course, be exactly equal to one-half the time interval $525H$. The vertical sweep occurs at some arbitrary but fixed time after the beginning of the V sync pulse. Hence, the beginning of succeeding V pulses must be separated by exactly $525\frac{1}{2}$ line intervals H or $262\frac{1}{2}H$. Counting off $262\frac{1}{2}$ line intervals from pulse 524 brings us to a point exactly midway between H pulses 523 and 525. The sync waveform showing the V pulse which ends the odd field is

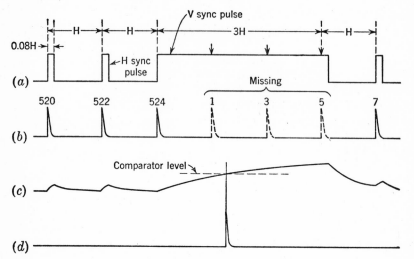

Fig. 17-6. (a) Sync signal (incomplete) at end of even field. (b) Horizontal sync pulse derived through differentiation from positive-going edges of sync signal. (c) Response of an integrating network to sync signal. (d) The comparator response to the waveform in (c) provides the vertical sync pulse.

accordingly as shown in Fig. 17-7a. The differentiation of the rising edge of the vertical sync pulse will yield an undesired H sync pulse. Because of its timing, however, it need cause no difficulty. The unsynchronized period of the scanning generator is slightly greater than the interval H. The H pulses thus terminate the sweep period slightly prematurely and in this way $1:1$ synchronization is achieved. In order for this extra pulse to be effective, it must change the sweep period by a factor of 2. The synchronizing pulse amplitude may be adjusted so that reliable synchronization $1:1$ is achieved, leaving this extra pulse ineffective.

A more serious source of difficulty is the absence of pulses 1, 3, and 5 in Fig. 17-6 and pulses 525, 2, and 4 in Fig. 17-7a. The scanning generator runs continuously, and if left without synchronization for several periods, it may drift appreciably. When sync pulses reappear, some difficulty may well be encountered in restoring synchronization. This feature is remedied by *serrating* the vertical sync pulses as in Fig. 17-7*b*. The serrations are negative pulses which occur within the vertical sync pulse. Since it is the rising edge of the pulses which are used for horizontal synchronization, these serrating pulses must be timed correspondingly. Hence observe in Fig. 17-7*a* that it is the *trailing* edge of the serrating pulses rather than the leading edge which is separated from the preceding and succeeding horizontal sync pulses by the interval *H*. In the vertical sync pulse which terminates the even field, three serrations are also required, and these will occur in Fig. 17-6*a* at the positions indicated by the arrows.

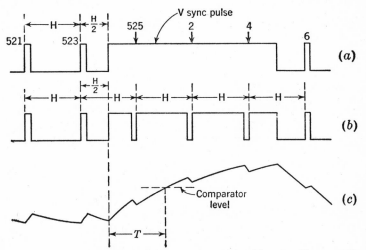

Fig. 17-7. (*a*) Sync signal (incomplete) at end of odd field. (*b*) The serration of the vertical sync pulse. (*c*) Response of an integrating network to the waveform in (*b*).

In Fig. 17-7*c* the result of integration of the waveform in Fig. 17-7*b* is indicated and the time interval between the beginning of the vertical sync pulse and the attainment of the comparator reference level is given by T. It will be recalled that for proper interlacing the time T must be the same for both fields. Now there are two reasons why the interval T may differ from field to field. In the first place, it may well be that the time interval between successive horizontal sync pulses may not be long enough to allow the integrating capacitor to discharge completely. At the end of the even field a full interval H separates the last horizontal sync pulse from the beginning of the vertical pulse, while at the end of the odd field only a half-line interval intervenes. Hence, the initial capacitor charge may well be different at the beginning of the vertical sync pulses which terminate the two fields. Second, the serrations of the vertical sync pulse have an effect on the net integrating capacitor charge at any given time after the beginning of the vertical sync pulse. And again the timing of the serrations is different in the two cases.

The second of these difficulties may be remedied by serrating *each* of the vertical sync pulses six times rather than three times. At the required line intervals, then, in each case, horizontal sync pulsess will be available. Of course, additional undesired horizontal sync pulse will occur midway between the required sync pulses. As we have seen, one may easily arrange the scanning generators so that they do not respond to these half-line interval pulses.

In the same way the initial charge on the integrating capacitor may be equalized by adding to each field several additional pulses at half-line intervals. These additional pulses are known as equalizing pulses. The number of equalizing pulses required is dictated by the consideration that in each field the integrating circuit shall see identical waveforms for

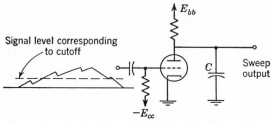

Fig. 17-8. A simple synchronized sweep whose operation depends on both the charge and the discharge of the vertical-sync-signal integrating capacitor.

a reasonable time interval before the beginning of the vertical sync pulse. In practice, it is found that three additional pulses leaves a comfortable margin of safety.

Ordinarily the voltage across the vertical sync-circuit integrating capacitor is applied to a comparator such as a blocking oscillator. The blocking oscillator may then be used to discharge the capacitor in the vertical sweep circuit. In such a case the manner in which the sync-circuit integrating capacitor discharges is of no consequence.

The possibility exists, however, that, depending on the method used for synchronizing the vertical scanning generator, it may be important that the discharge of the sync-circuit integrating capacitor be identical for the two fields. Consider the simple sweep generator of Fig. 17-8. Here the capacitor C charges linearly with time while the tube is cut off. The capacitor discharges through the tube when the integrated vertical sync pulse brings the grid out of cutoff. The total time available for C to discharge then depends on the manner in which the sync-circuit integrating capacitor both charges and discharges. If, in alternate fields, the sweep capacitor discharges to different voltage levels, the sweep will be different in amplitude from cycle to cycle. To avoid this difficulty, equalizing pulses are inserted after the vertical sync signal as well as before. The sync signal at the end of the even field is shown in Fig. 17-9. The vertical sync signal is serrated six times and thus is broken up into six pulses. The vertical sync signal is preceded and followed by six pulses, three of which are used for horizontal synchronization, while the other three are used for equalization. It is customary, nevertheless, to refer to the entire group of six as *equalizing pulses*. During the equalizing interval where the pulses occur at twice the normal rate, the pulse widths are reduced by a factor of 2. In this way the integrated area under the pulses is kept constant and the integrating capacitor in the vertical sync circuit will not begin to build up its voltage until the beginning of the vertical sync pulse.

The signal at the end of the odd field is identical in waveshape to the signal shown in Fig. 17-9 over the interval from the first equalizing pulse

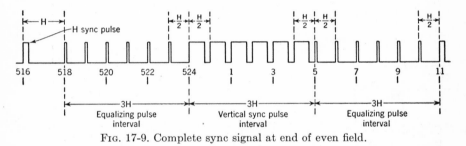

FIG. 17-9. Complete sync signal at end of even field.

preceding the serrated vertical pulse to the last equalizing pulse following it. At the end of the odd field, however, the last sync pulse (pulse 517) would occur at a time $H/2$ before the first equalizing pulse and the first sync pulse (pulse 12) after the second equalizing interval would occur at a time H after the last equalizing pulse.

According to the standards for commercial television the vertical blanking interval starts just slightly before the first equalizing pulse and lasts for a period not less than $0.05V$ nor more than $0.08V$, in which V is the time between successive fields. The blanking interval therefore extends over about 13 line intervals at minimum and about 21 lines at most. During this interval no picture information need be transmitted and the signal of Fig. 17-9 is all that is required.

The picture information which conveys the required variation of beam intensity during the active portion of a scanning line is superimposed on the sync signal, as indicated in Fig. 17-10. Of the total peak-to-peak amplitude of the signal the synchronizing portion occupies approximately 25 per cent, while the picture information occupies 75 per cent. The *black level* is intended to correspond to the circumstance where the kinescope beam is cut off so that the screen is dark. The synchronizing pulses then lie in the *blacker-than-black* region.   The signal is kept at the black level for a short time both before and after the sync pulse.   This blanking level persists for a time nominally twice as long as the sync pulse.   The portion of the blanking interval after the sync pulse is longer than the portion before the sync pulse to allow adequate time for the decay of any transient which might be associated with the scanning-generator flyback.

17-5. Signal Separation at the Receiver.   At the television receiver, the input carrier, amplitude-modulated by the composite video signal, will be converted to an intermediate-frequency signal and then detected to yield the carrier envelope.   At the point at which detection takes place, the video signal level is customarily of the order of only several volts so that additional video amplification must take place.   Usually

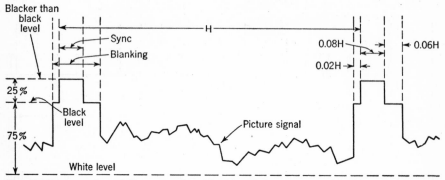

Fig. 17-10. A portion of the composite video signal showing sync, blanking, and picture components.

one or two stages of video amplification are sufficient to raise the signal level to the order of 20 to 50 volts.

The entire video signal, sync pulses and all, may be applied directly to the kinescope grid.   The polarity of the video signal at the kinescope grid is opposite to the polarity indicated in Fig. 17-10, so that the sync pulses extend in the negative direction.   If the kinescope is correctly biased, the sync pulses will lie below cutoff and therefore have no influence on the picture.   The kinescope bias should be adjusted so that the blanking level (i.e., *black level* in Fig. 17-10) should correspond to cutoff.   Ordinarily the video amplifier will be a-c coupled, and the voltage level corresponding to *black* will be a function of average signal level which is in turn dependent on the average illumination of the televised scene.   To prevent this shift of voltage level corresponding to blanking, the output of the video amplifier is coupled to the kinescope grid through a d-c restorer, the diode of which conducts on the peaks of the synchronizing pulses.

Before the composite video signal is used for synchronization purposes, the picture portion of the signal should be removed. This separation of the sync signal from the picture signal is easily accomplished by a clipping circuit. An arrangement for handling the composite television signal is shown in Fig. 17-11. The relative simplicity of the circuitry of Fig. 17-11

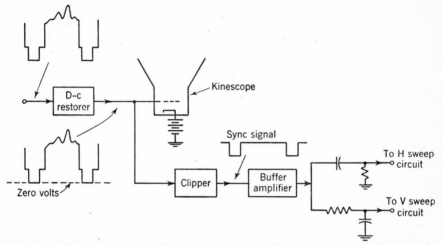

FIG. 17-11. Separation of picture, horizontal sync, and vertical sync signals from composite television signal.

is worth noting. It is possible to construct a usable sync signal which is simpler than the one described in Sec. 17-4, but the sync signal described above has the merit of requiring relatively simple circuitry at the receiver. Since receivers outnumber transmitters by many millions, economy in the receiver is very important.

17-6. The Synchronizing Signal Generator.[1] We inquire now into the generation at the transmitter of the synchronizing signal, as shown in Fig. 17-9. This inquiry will be of interest not alone in connection with television circuitry but also as an example of how many of the basic pulse and digital circuits are combined into a system. A very large number of different systems may be used to generate the sync signal and the system to be consid-

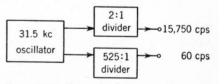

FIG. 17-12. A method for securing synchronous signals at field rate, line rate, and twice the line rate.

ered in what follows is the system used in one of a number of commercially available synchronizing signal generators.

The line repetition rate is 15,750 lines per second, while the field rate is 60 cps. In Fig. 17-12 is shown a very commonly used scheme for generating synchronous signals of these two frequencies. A master oscillator of frequency 31.5 kc is divided by 2 to yield 15.75 kc and divided also by 525 to provide signal with a 60-cycle repetition rate. The division by 525 may be done in easy steps since $525 = 7 \times 5 \times 5 \times 3$, the factors being small. One may see in this easy factorability the reason for selecting exactly 525 lines per frame rather than say some neighboring odd number. The 31.5-kc frequency will further be found of advantage during the equalizing and vertical pulse interval where the pulses occur at twice the line rate.

The principle used, in the system presently under discussion, for the generation of the synchronizing waveform will be made clear from an

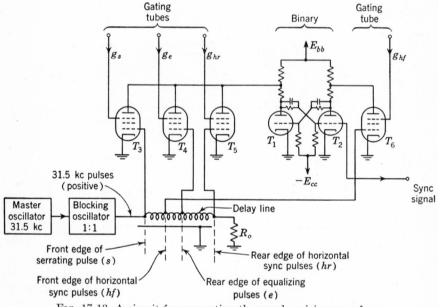

FIG. 17-13. A circuit for generating the synchronizing waveform.

examination of the circuit of Fig. 17-13 and the waveform diagram of Fig. 17-14. The synchronizing waveform consists of a sequence of transitions between two voltage levels. We may hope therefore to cause the sync waveform to appear directly at one of the electrodes of a binary if we can cause the binary to make transitions between its states at the correct time. We will now show that the required waveform will be developed at the grid of T_2 in Fig. 17-13.

Let us designate by 0 the binary state in which the grid voltage of T_2 is low (below cutoff) and by 1 the state in which the grid voltage is high (at clamp). It is required then that the binary make a transition from 0 to 1 at the leading edge of each pulse in the sync waveform and a transition from 1 to 0 at each trailing edge. The triggering pulses are injected into the binary in such a fashion as to be able to cause a transition in only one direction. Two pulse inputs will therefore be required, one to cause transitions from state 0 to 1 and a second to cause transitions in the reverse direction. Tubes T_3 to T_6 are multigrid gating tubes used, as described in Sec. 14-5, as an *AND* circuit. The pulse signal for transmission to the binary is applied to the first grid, while the gating signal is applied to the third grid. Thus, say, when tube T_6 is conducting, a positive pulse on the first grid of T_6 will cause the binary to go from 0 to 1. If, however, the binary is already in the state 1, the pulse will have no effect. Pulses applied to the first grids of tubes T_3, T_4, or T_5 will produce the reverse transitions when the corresponding tube is caused to conduct by the gating waveforms g_s, g_e, or g_{hr}.

Four continuous pulse trains at a 31.5-kc rate are available from the delay line in Fig. 17-13. These pulse trains are displaced in time from

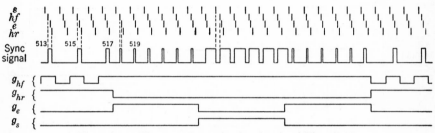

Fig. 17-14. The waveforms in the circuit of Fig. 17-13.

one another and are indicated as the pulse trains *s*, *hf*, *e*, and *hr* in Fig. 17-14. The pulse *hf* being applied through T_6 will produce all positive-going transitions in the sync waveform. These transitions are mostly the *front* edge of the *horizontal* sync pulses but include also the front edges of the equalizing pulses and the rear edges of the serrating pulses. The three remaining pulse trains are used to establish the timing of the other transitions in the sync waveform. The delay times between taps on the delay line are selected to be equal to the required pulse durations in the waveform. For example, the delay time between the tap *hf* and the tap *hr* is equal to the time between the *front* and *rear* edges of the *horizontal* sync pulses. Finally, we see in Fig. 17-14 the four gating waveforms required. In each of the gating waveforms the higher level corresponds to the gate being open for transmission. By carefully observing the temporal relations in Fig. 17-14 we can now verify that with the pulse trains and gates as given, the transitions induced in the binary will be those required to produce the sync signal.

We consider next the matter of the generation of the gating waveforms which appear in Fig. 17-14. These gates all recur at field rate, 60 cps. Hence, as was anticipated earlier, we shall have to divide the 31.5-kc master signal by 525. The mechanism to be used for division consists of a system of binary dividers involving feedback. The reason for selecting such a relatively complicated division scheme is that there will be made available in the process an extensive variety of waveforms which will be of use in generating the gates. The details of the divider chain are indicated in Fig. 17-15, where each box represents a binary. The grids of the two tubes in the binary are labeled, A, A', respectively, for the first binary up to KK' for the last. The first three binaries together would normally count to 8 except for the feedback from C to B. The feedback is of the type described in Sec. 11-3 in connection with Figs. 11-3 and 11-4. This feedback advances the count by two so that the first three binaries reset on the sixth pulse. The second set of three binaries (D, E, and F) similarly count to 6 so that these two sets together would constitute a $6 \times 6 = 36$ counter except for the over-all feedback

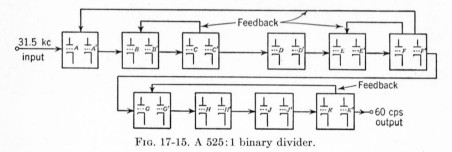

FIG. 17-15. A 525:1 binary divider.

from F to A, which reduces the count by 1. Altogether binaries A through F constitute a 35-scale counter. Binaries G to K count to 15 rather than 16 because of the feedback from K to G. The over-all result gives a division by $\{[(8 - 2)(8 - 2)] - 1\}(16 - 1) = 525$.

The waveforms at the unprimed grids of the binaries are displayed in Fig. 17-16 in waveforms A to K. Note that in waveforms G to K the time scale has been compressed so that only the transition which occurs directly under pulse 35 corresponds in time to the transition which is caused by pulse 35 in waveforms A through F. But the waveforms indicated are not the only ones available. In the first place, each signal is available with reversed polarity at the primed grids. More importantly, the various waveforms may be combined in many ways to yield an almost endless variety of new waveforms. Three methods for combining waveforms are indicated in Fig. 17-17a, b, and c. The circuit in Fig. 17-17a is that of an AND circuit (see Sec. 13-3). If both signals X and Y are in state 0, the output E_o is in state 1. Otherwise E_o is in state 0. The circuit in Fig. 17-17b is a gate (see Sec. 14-5), or else we may consider it in the present application to be another form of AND circuit. The output will be in state 1 unless both X and Y are in state 1.

In this latter case the output will be in state 0. Finally, in Fig. 17-17c we have a binary with provision for unsymmetrical triggering from two signals. The negative-going edges of the two input waveforms will cause transitions in the binary, provided in each case that the binary is in a state in which it may respond. We shall refer to the output of

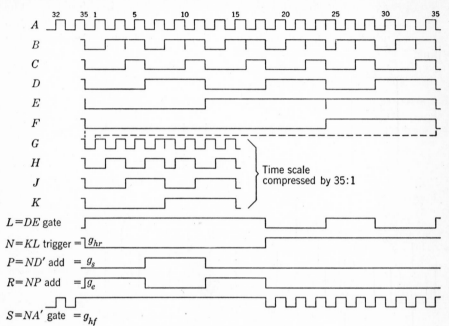

FIG. 17-16. Waveforms A to K are obtained from Fig. 17-15. Waveforms L to S are obtained through the use of the circuits of Fig. 17-17.

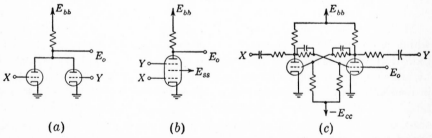

FIG. 17-17. Three methods for combining the waveforms in Fig. 17-16. (a) A double-triode AND circuit. b) A coincidence gate. (c) A binary.

Fig. 17-17a as an XY add, the output of b will be called an XY gate, while the output in c will be described as an XY trigger. Referring back now to Fig. 17-16, we may now verify that the waveforms L through S are correctly drawn and it appears that the last four of these waveforms are precisely the gates required.

We have now completed the description of the generation of the sync waveform, but before leaving the matter it is important to note that the scheme given above is by no means the only method for generating a sync signal. On the contrary, there are innumerable methods possible, many of which are considerably simpler than the method given above. The present system has the advantage of being digital in character. The operation does not depend critically on the characteristics of vacuum tubes, and all timing is done by a passive circuit element, that is, a delay line.

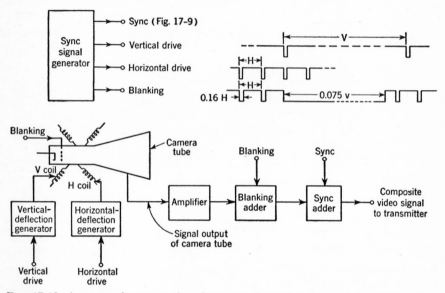

FIG. 17-18. A system for generating the composite video signal at the transmitter.

17-7. Synthesis of Composite Television Signal. The method by which a composite television signal is generated at the transmitter is indicated in Fig. 17-18. The basic signal sources required are furnished by the sync generator and by the camera tube. The camera tube has, in common with a kinescope, an electron gun and, similarly, requires a set of deflecting coils. A horizontal- and a vertical-deflection generator are required to sweep the electron beam over the photosensitive surface in the camera tube. Sync pulses are, of course, required for these deflection generators to keep the operation of the camera synchronous with the rest of the system. It is, of course, possible to derive these signals from the sync signal of Fig. 17-9. More commonly, however, the sync generator at the transmitter is designed to provide additional signals, known as *drive* signals, specifically for the deflection circuits. The *horizontal drive* signal consists of a train of pulses which occur at line rate.

The *vertical drive* signal pulses occur at field rate, that is, separated by the interval $V = \frac{1}{60}$ sec. The drive-signal pulse durations are not critical, since these pulses are used simply as triggers for the deflection generators.

During the horizontal and vertical retrace times it is necessary to cut off the electron beam in the camera tube. For this purpose the sync generator also makes available a *blanking* signal which may be applied to the grid of the electron gun in the camera tube. The blanking pulse which occurs at line rate has a width $0.16H$ and is timed relative to the sync pulses in the manner indicated in Fig. 17-10. At the end of each field there occurs a longer blanking pulse $(0.075V)$ which keeps the electron beam cut off during the longer vertical retrace period.

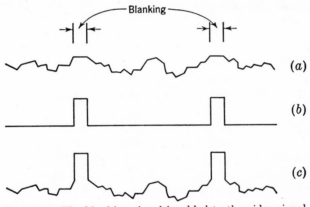

FIG. 17-19. The blanking signal is added to the video signal.

The signal from the camera tube is amplified in a video amplifier and is then combined with the blanking signal. The reason for adding the blanking signal at this point may be seen from Fig. 17-19. In Fig. 17-19*a* we have the camera-tube signal. The intervals marked *blanking* are the intervals when the camera tube beam is cut off and the output signal is zero. In Fig. 17-19*b* the blanking signal itself is shown, and in Fig. 17-19*c* the result of adding the two signals is given. The advantage of the waveform in Fig. 17-19*c* is that the tops of the blanking pulses may be set conveniently at any desired d-c level through the use of a d-c restorer circuit. This feature is of great importance because the d-c level of the signal conveys the average brightness of the scene being televised. Finally, as in Fig. 17-18, the sync signal itself is added, the blanking pulses serving as the pedestals on which the sync pulses are superimposed, as in Fig. 17-10.

17-8. Bandwidth Requirements of a Television Channel. We may make a very crude estimate of the bandwidth requirements for a television channel by estimating the bandwidth required for the transmission of a pattern such as is shown in Fig. 17-20. The pattern is selected as being the one which will make the maximum demands on the response of the system since the amount of detail in the pattern is maximum. We consider that the number of transitions from black to white,

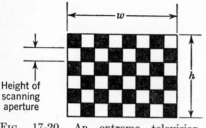

Fig. 17-20. An extreme television pattern.

in the vertical direction, is as large as possible, that is, equal to the number of lines in the frame. We consider further that the scanning aperture is of negligible width. If, then, the resolution (detail) in the horizontal direction is to equal the resolution in the vertical direction, then during the course of scanning a single line the number of transitions in brightness must equal $(w/h)n$. Here $w/h \equiv A$ is the aspect ratio and n is the number of lines in the frame. If we neglect retrace times, then to transmit a pattern as in Fig. 17-20 requires a video signal which is a square wave of frequency

$$f = \tfrac{1}{2}An^2f_p \tag{17-1}$$

in which f_p is the frame frequency, that is, the number of complete pictures scanned per second. Since, however, the eye has a limited ability to distinguish an abrupt transition in intensity from a more gradual transition, we may estimate roughly that the system response may well be adequate if it is possible to transmit a sine wave rather than a square wave of the frequency given in Eq. (17-1).

Equation (17-1) above neglects entirely the possibility of a misalignment between the pattern and the scanning aperture. Suppose, say, that the scanning aperture were displaced upward or downward by one half line with respect to the pattern in Fig. 17-20. In this case the picture transmitted would be a uniform gray independently of the bandwidth of the system, and a wide bandwidth would be of no advantage. It has been found on an empirical basis that the effect generally of misalignment may be taken into account by modifying Eq. (17-1) to the extent of a factor K ($= 0.64$), which is called the *utilization coefficient*.

For the commercial system used in this country in which $n = 525$ and $f_p = 30$ frames per second, we find

$$f = \frac{0.64}{2} \times \frac{4}{3} \times (525)^2 \times 30 = 3.5 \text{ Mc}$$

In this system the bandwidth actually allotted to the picture transmission is slightly less than 4.5 Mc.

We shall turn our attention in the following sections to a brief discussion of some features of another type of pulse system, i.e., radar.

17-9. Basic Elements of a Radar System.[2] The word *radar* is coined from *ra*dio, *d*irection, *a*nd *r*ange. The purpose of a *radar* system is to determine the orientation and distance of a target with respect to the location of the radar installation. The operating principle of a radar set is as follows. A short burst of high-frequency radiation is transmitted outward from an antenna. Some of the radiation, reflected from the target, is received by the radar set a short time later. The distance of the target is determined by the time elapsed between outgoing and incoming reflected signals. Since the velocity of the radiation is constant and equal to 3×10^8 m/sec, then a round trip will take 10.8 μsec per statute mile, or 12.4 μsec per nautical mile. The orientation of the target is determined by the orientation of the antenna when the target reflection is received.

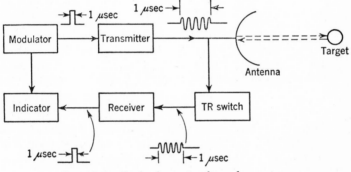

Fig. 17-21. Basic elements of a radar system.

The basic elements of a radar system are given in Fig. 17-21. Typically, for a high-power ground-based search radar system, the transmitter frequency might be of the order of 3000 Mc, the peak power of the order of 1 megawatt, the pulse duration about 1 μsec, and the pulse repetition rate about 400 sec^{-1}. The transmitter is a high-frequency *magnetron* vacuum-tube oscillator which is quiescent until turned on by a pulse from the modulator. The signal from the transmitter is fed to a wave guide which terminates in an antenna. If the outward-going radiation strikes a target, say an airplane, a small amount of energy will be reflected back to the antenna. The transmit-receive (TR) switch permits the use of a single antenna both for transmission and reception. This TR switch is a special gas tube which is shunted across the wave guide at the input to the receiver. The tube acts as a short circuit under high power and hence keeps the transmitted pulse from reaching and hence paralyzing the receiver. At low power the TR tube acts as an open circuit and hence the reflected energy is fed to the receiver.

In the receiver the incoming signal is heterodyned with a local oscillator and the carrier frequency is reduced to a lower frequency (say, 30 Mc). This intermediate-frequency signal is amplified about 1 million times and is then applied to a detector which yields as an output the pulse envelope. The receiver output is a pulse, nominally of the form of the modulator pulse except delayed in time by an amount depending on the location of the target. This pulse is applied to the indicator. The indicator is a device used to furnish a visual display from which the location of the target may be determined. The modulator pulse is also applied to the indicator in order to establish a reference time.

We shall consider, in the next several sections, various types of radar indicators.

17-10. Type A and R Indicators. One type of radar indicator, called an A *scope*, is an ordinary cathode-ray oscilloscope. The vertical deflection is the received video signal, that

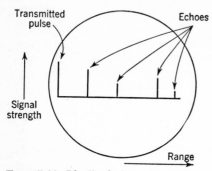

is, the modulation envelope of the radio-frequency pulse. The horizontal deflection is a sweep voltage which starts at the instant the modulator emits its pulse. In other words, the indicator is synchronized to the modulator. An idealized A-scope presentation is indicated in Fig. 17-22. By measuring the length of the sweep from the origin to the point where a received *echo* is seen, the distance to the target can be determined. This method is fairly rough. The wave-

FIG. 17-22. Idealized A-scope presentation (neglecting *noise*) on the screen of a CRO.

forms required for an A-scope presentation (for the system specified in Sec. 17-9) are shown in Fig. 17-23. Note that the maximum range corresponds to a time which is less than the interval between modulator pulses since some time must be allowed for the sweep circuit to recover.

If we should wish to see more detail at some particular range, then a delayed A scope (called an R *scope*) can be used. A linear delay device (cathode-coupled monostable multi, phantastron, or sweep-comparator circuit) is used to obtain a delayed trigger. This trigger is used to start a fast sweep, say, 0.25 to 1 nautical mile long (3 to 12 μsec). Thus, say, a target at 100 miles (1240 μsec) is to be observed in a system whose pulse repetition rate is 400 sec^{-1}. The R-sweep waveforms are indicated in Fig. 17-24.

A knob on the delay unit (usually a potentiometer controlling a d-c bias) can be calibrated in range and it is possible to obtain accuracies of

0.1 per cent of maximum range in this way. Precision time-delay circuits are discussed in Chap. 16.

17-11. Plan-position Indicator, PPI.[3] In a search system in which it is desired to see all the targets in the sky, the antenna would be designed to give a vertical beam of radiation and the antenna would rotate continuously in azimuth, say, at 10 rpm. The indicator is called a PPI (*plan-position indicator*) or RTB (*radial time base*). To achieve such a

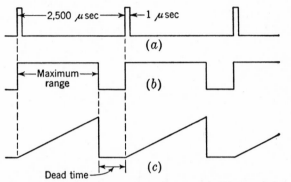

FIG. 17-23. Waveforms for A-scope presentations. (*a*) The modulator pulses, the leading edges of which are used to trigger the sweep. (*b*) The gate for sweep formulation and blanking. (*c*) The sweep for beam deflection.

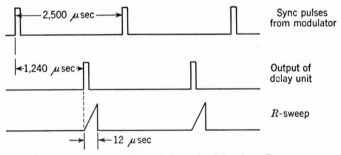

FIG. 17-24. Illustration of the principle of an R sweep.

display, a coil is mounted on the neck of a cathode-ray tube and is rotated in synchronism with the antenna mount. The current through this coil is made to increase linearly with time, starting with each modulator pulse. Thus a radial sweep is obtained and the distance from the center of the tube is proportional to the distance to each target. The echos are not presented as vertical lines as on the A scope, but instead the video signal is used to intensity-modulate the CRO beam, exactly as in a television set. Thus a target appears as a bright spot (more accurately, an arc whose length is determined by the beam width and range) on the scope face. Figure 17-25a shows a PPI display.

The PPI is also called a *polar coordinate display* or a *resolved time-base* (RTB) *indicator*. It gives the position of a target in polar coordinates, as shown in Fig. 17-25b. The range is R and the angle from north is θ. For a 400-cps pulse repetition frequency and an antenna rotary speed of 10 rpm (or 1 revolution in 6 sec) the antenna travels 0.15° during a sweep. Thus each sweep is not truly radial, but is bent 0.15°.

17-12. Resolved Sweeps.[3] The PPI display which uses a rotating deflection coil has a serious limitation. At any given time it is possible to move the CRO beam only along a nominally straight line. Actually, it is often desirable, during the sweep *dead time*, to be able to move the beam to an arbitrary position. This freedom of beam motion may be

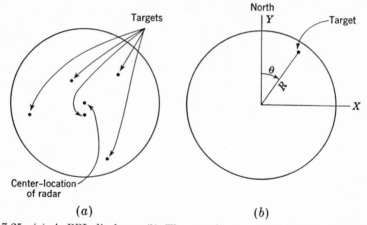

FIG. 17-25. (a) A PPI display. (b) The coordinates R and θ of a PPI display.

achieved if two fixed deflecting coils (or sets of deflecting plates) are substituted for the single rotating coil. In order to achieve a PPI display, it will now be necessary to provide X and Y deflecting signals in accordance with the relationships

$$x = R \sin \theta = kt \sin \theta$$
$$y = R \cos \theta = kt \cos \theta \qquad (17\text{-}2)$$

The sweep voltage is $R = kt$, k being the sweep speed. The angle θ is the angle of rotation of the antenna, and hence θ is also a function of time. The two required deflecting signals are linear sweeps modulated, respectively, by $\sin \theta(t)$ and $\cos \theta(t)$. Since very many radial sweeps are formed during one antenna rotation, $\theta(t)$ will vary much more slowly than kt.

In Eq. (17-2) the radial sweep has been *resolved* into its X and Y components. These sweeps are therefore referred to as *resolved* sweeps, and a device used to generate such sweeps is known as a *resolver*.

There are two general methods of obtaining the desired X and Y voltages. Depending upon whether the resolution is done prior to or after the sweep voltage is formed, the method is called *preresolution* or *postresolution*. These two methods are indicated schematically in Fig. 17-26a and b. In the preresolution system the X and Y sweeps are generated by separate circuits and hence care must be taken that these circuits are properly calibrated so that the sweep speed is the same in both (k_x must equal k_y). In the postresolution system the sweep kt must pass through the resolver undistorted and this imposes wideband requirements on the resolver (Prob. 17-2).

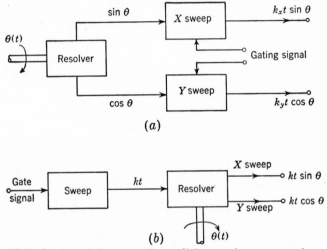

(a)

(b)

FIG. 17-26. Methods of resolving a rotating radial sweep into rectangular components. (a) A pre-time-base resolution system; (b) a post-time-base resolution system.

A preresolution scheme using a sine-cosine potentiometer (Sec. 16-5) is given in Fig. 17-27. (The bootstrap sweep is discussed in Sec. 7-8; the clamp is of the four- or six-diode type described in Secs. 14-11 and 14-12.) A similar channel (fed from $E \cos \theta$, instead of $E \sin \theta$) is needed for the Y sweep. One of the difficulties that may be encountered is in the choice of proper time constants. Thus, during any single sweep the coupling capacitor from the cathode follower to the charging resistor R must maintain its voltage so that C_D acts like a battery. However, as the antenna rotates and the output of the sine-cosine potentiometer changes, C_D must take on a new value of voltage. It may be difficult to satisfy these two conflicting requirements simultaneously, if high precision (say, 0.1 per cent) is desired. Note that R_D cannot be replaced by a diode, since C is to charge positively during half a revolution of the antenna and negatively during the other half.

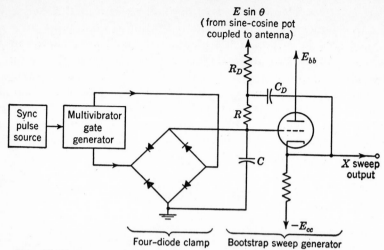

FIG. 17-27. A preresolution scheme using a sine-cosine potentiometer.

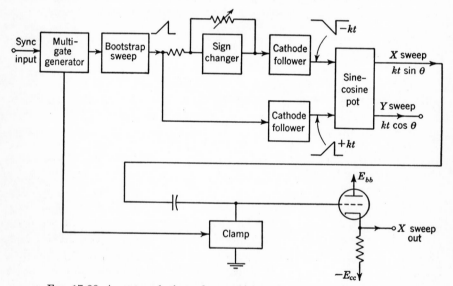

FIG. 17-28. A postresolution scheme using a sine-cosine potentiometer.

A postresolution circuit that has been found capable of an accuracy of a few tenths of 1 per cent is given in Fig. 17-28.   The bootstrap sweep is conventional and is excited from a large d-c voltage.   The sign changer is an operational amplifier with an adjustment so that exactly unity gain may be obtained.   This converts the positively generated sweep into a negative-going sweep so that the sine-cosine potentiometer can be fed in a push-pull manner, as indicated in the figure.   The clamp is of the type shown in Fig. 17-27.   The Y-sweep signal also has associated with it a clamp and cathode follower (not shown in the figure).

An *induction resolver* (Sec. 16-5) may also be used to obtain resolved sweeps.   In the postresolution scheme the sweep voltage is first generated and this signal is applied to the rotor of the resolver.   The resolver is mechanically coupled to the antenna and sweep outputs modulated by the sine and cosine of the antenna angle are available from the two stator windings.   Circuits for driving resolvers are basically the same as the circuits (Chap. 8) which are suitable for current sweeps.   The resolver is basically a transformer and as a result has a relatively limited frequency response.   It is therefore fairly difficult to transmit through it an accurately linear sweep voltage.   Accuracies of about ± 2 per cent in range can be obtained.

A resolver used in a preresolution scheme is shown in Fig. 17-29.   A carrier-frequency signal $\sin \omega t$ is applied to the resolver stator.   The

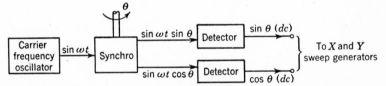

Fig. 17-29. An induction resolver used in a preresolution scheme.

output from the two stator windings is this carrier, amplitude-modulated by the sine and cosine, respectively, of the angle of rotation θ.   Two detectors are employed to yield two d-c voltages (for fixed θ) proportional to $\sin \theta$ and $\cos \theta$.   These output voltages may then be used to modulate, say, a bootstrap sweep as in Fig. 17-27.

In spite of the relative complexity in the use of resolvers as against sine-cosine potentiometers, resolvers nevertheless find extensive application.   The resolver has the advantage of longer life because there are no rubbing parts as in the sine potentiometer.   The output from a resolver is smooth since there is no problem associated with a brush jumping from one wire to the next.   Finally, it is sometimes possible to use the output of the resolver to drive a deflection coil directly.

17-13. Other Types of Displays.   We discuss in this section a number of other types of displays.

Off-centered PPI.[4]   The center of the sweep in a PPI is sometimes moved as much as several tube-face radii from the center of the CRO as shown in Fig. 17-30.   This procedure allows targets in a particular direction to be observed with more care.   The off centering may be done by several means: (1) permanent magnets, (2) a separate coil which can be rotated to give the proper direction of off centering, the amount of the displacement being determined by the d-c coil current, (3) two fixed coils at 90° in space through which d-c current may be passed, and (4) for a resolved sweep, the centering may be done by adjusting the voltage levels to which the sweep is clamped during the *dead time*.

Delayed PPI. In this type of PPI scan the start of the radial sweep is delayed in time so that the center of the display corresponds to, say, 50 miles rather than zero.

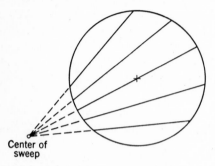

FIG. 17-30. Off-center PPI display.

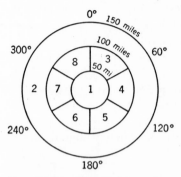

FIG. 17-31. The division of an area into sectors for examination by separate radar readers.

B Scan.[5] A *B* scan is a rectangular display in which range is plotted horizontally and angle is plotted vertically. Thus a polar section of a PPI is mapped into a cartesian plane. The *B* scan is very useful when, because of the presence of many targets, it is desired to divide into several sections the area under surveillance by the radar. The region around the radar might be divided, for example, into eight sections as in Fig. 17-31, and each section would be examined by a separate reader.

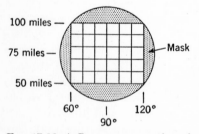

FIG. 17-32. A *B*-scan presentation of sector 4 of Fig. 17-31.

The annular ring 1 is the territory observed by one reader who would have a PPI with a 50-mile sweep. If the traffic beyond 100 miles is light, then this region 2 could be assigned to a second reader who would have a delayed PPI, with the center of his scope corresponding to 100 miles. The region between 50 and 100 miles might contain many aircraft and hence is broken up into sectors and each sector is put onto a *B* scope and given to a separate reader. One radar set thus might have many different scopes. Sector 4 would have a *B*-scope display shown in Fig. 17-32.

In a *B*-scope presentation, the delayed range sweep for *Y* deflection is obtained exactly as for the delayed PPI. The *X* sweep is obtained from a linear potentiometer which is rotated in synchronism with the antenna. The start of the X sweep may be controlled by rotating the frame of the potentiometer. It is also possible to use an induction resolver. If this device is used, the X axis deflection is proportional to sin θ and not θ. If the angular sector is not too great, then sin $\theta \cong \theta$, and the distortion is not too great. Of course, an a-c carrier scheme and detector must be used. The carrier is commonly 1,500 cps.

The B scope gives a very distorted map. Hence, lines of constant angle and lines of constant range must be "written" electronically on the scope face. These electronic angle marks and range marks, which are also very useful for PPI's particularly of the delayed or off-center type, are discussed in Sec. 17-14.

17-14. Electronic Marking on a Display. *Angle Marks.* A simple and accurate technique for generating angle marks electronically is the photoelectric scheme shown in Fig. 17-33. If the rotating disk is geared

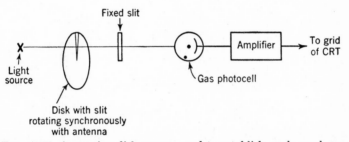

Fig. 17-33. A rotating-disk system used to establish angle markers.

to the antenna through a 36:1 gear ratio, then an angle marker will appear at every 10°. The slit system must be wide enough so that the time the photocell is energized is equal at least to the duration of one sweep.

If two narrow slots and one wider one are on the disk, separated 120° apart, and if the gear ratio is 12:1, then 10° marks, with every third widened, will appear on the CRO.

The alignment so that one line comes at north is done by stopping the antenna at north and turning the disk on its shaft until the photocell receives light through the wide slot.

Range Marks. Range marks are pulses separated in time by a precisely known interval and corresponding to some convenient range interval. These pulses are applied to the cathode-ray tube with such a polarity as to increase the beam brightness. The generation of precise time intervals is discussed in Chap. 16.

Video Mapping.[6] It is often important to mark the location of distinctive features of the terrain (such as airports, railroads, towns, rivers, etc.) on a PPI. These can, of course, be put on the outside face of the indicator with a grease pencil, but there will be errors due to parallax.

Also, a separate map will have to be drawn for each scope, and it will have to be redrawn whenever a change of scale is made or if off centering is used.   A technique for writing the map electronically through the video channel is indicated in Fig. 17-34.

A PPI tube (with no video modulation applied) is used as a scanner. The map could be on a photographic negative.   Plate glass covered with colloidal graphite on which fine lines are scratched to identify the important landmarks has also been used.   The light from the sweep is picked up by the photocell after modulation by the map transparency and is carried to all indicators.

A device similar to the video mapper but using a rectangular sweep instead of a radial one, called a *flying spot scanner*, is available commercially for obtaining television pictures from film.

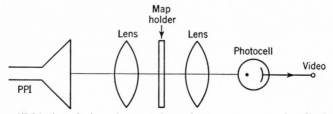

FIG. 17-34. A technique for superimposing a map on a radar display.

Electronic Tags.   In the processing of radar data it is sometimes desirable to place, with precision, an electronic *mark* or *tag* at some point on a radar display.   This tag may take the form of a dot, a tiny circle, a small line inclined at a specified angle, etc.   A circuit for writing any number of dots (for example, three) at precisely chosen X and Y coordinates on a resolved-sweep PPI is given in block diagram form in Fig. 17-35.*   This diagram represents that part of the circuit which determines the X positions of the tags.   A similar channel is needed for the Y coordinates.   The basic philosophy used in designing this circuit is that one tag is to be written during the first sweep dead time, the next tag during the second sweep dead time, and the third tag during the third dead time.   This process is then repeated with the first tag again written in the fourth recovery interval, etc.   The operation of the circuit may be understood by referring to the waveforms indicated in Fig. 17-36.

The modulator pulses trigger a ring counter (Fig. 11-21) which has a scale of 3 and has outputs C_1, C_2, and C_3.   The outputs are positive for a time duration equal to the time T between pulses and are negative for twice this interval.   The positive portions of the three outputs do not overlap, but appear in time sequence, separated from one another by the

* This system was developed at the Electronic Research Laboratories, Department of Electrical Engineering, Columbia University.

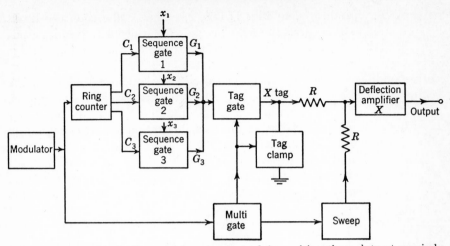

FIG. 17-35. The block diagram of a circuit used for writing three dots at precisely chosen X and Y coordinates on a PPI display. (The Y channel is not indicated.)

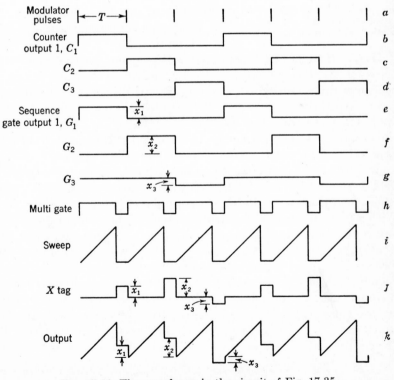

FIG. 17-36. The waveforms in the circuit of Fig. 17-35.

interval T, as indicated in Fig. 17-36b, c, and d. The counter output $C_n(n = 1, 2, $ or $3)$ controls the sequence gate G_n, which delivers an output only if C_n is positive. The sequence gates are of the six-diode bridge type of Fig. 14-21.* The signal input to the bridge is a d-c voltage x_n corresponding to the x_n position of the nth tag. The output G_n of the sequencing gates is x_n when C_n is positive and zero when C_n is negative. These waveforms are given in Fig. 17-36e, f, and g. The value of x may be either positive or negative, and in this illustration x_1 and x_2 have been chosen positive, while x_3 is negative.

The sweep and dead times are established by a monostable multi triggered by the modulator. The multi gate output is given in Fig. 17-36h, and the sweep output is shown in Fig. 17-36i. The multi output

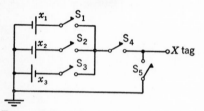

FIG. 17-37. The series-parallel arrangement of gates in Fig. 17-35 simulated with switches.

also controls two six-diode gates called the *tag gate* and the *tag clamp*. These gates are needed in order to select the X voltages only during the dead times rather than over the total time T between pulses as they appear at the output of the sequence gates. The entire arrangement is equivalent to a series-parallel arrangement of switches, as indicated by the configuration of Fig. 17-37. Switches S_1, S_2, and S_3 close in sequence, each for an interval T. Switch S_4 (the tag gate) closes for each dead time and is open for each sweep time. Switch S_5 (the tag clamp) brings the output to zero for each sweep time and is open for each dead time. Hence, the X tag output is as pictured in Fig. 17-36j.

Finally, the sweep and tag outputs are added at the input to the deflection amplifier whose output waveform is given in Fig. 17-36k. This is the waveform needed in order to allow the sweep to proceed undistured in each cycle and to position the cathode-ray beam to position x_1 during the first dead time, to x_2 during the second recovery interval, etc.

With a very simple modification the above circuit will produce a circle whose center is at the desired position x_n, y_n. A sinusoidal oscillator of frequency, say, 5 kc, is phase-shifted so that two components in quadrature are obtained. The sine component is added, by means of a transformer to each of the d-c voltages x_n. The cosine component is added in a similar manner to each of the d-c voltages y_n in the Y channel. If these two components are equal, the resulting Lissajous figure is a circle centered at x_n, y_n. The radius of the circle is controlled by the amplitude of the oscillator.

* This type of gate requires push-pull control voltages and these are obtained from the two plates of a binary. However, this detail has not been included in Fig. 17-35.

If the amplitudes of the two oscillator components are not equal, or if the phase shift is not 90°, an ellipse is obtained. By reducing the phase shift to zero, a straight line results whose orientation depends upon the relative magnitudes of the two oscillator components and whose center is always at x_n, y_n. If the modulating voltage is nonsinusoidal, other forms of the tag waveforms result.

If the voltages x_n and y_n are not constant but rather are programmed in time, then the tag, instead of remaining at a fixed position, will move across the face of the scope along the path determined by the program.

REFERENCES

1. Instruction Manual, Type 2200 Synchronizing Signal Generator, Tel-Instrument Co., Inc., Carlstadt, N.J.
   Applegarth, A. R.: Synchronizing Generators for Electronic Television, *Proc. IRE*, vol. 34, pp. 128W–139W, March, 1946.
   Baracket, A. J.: Television Synchronizing Signal Generator, *Electronics*, vol. 21, pp. 110–115, October, 1948.
   Welsh, W.: Television Synchronizing Signal Generator, *Proc. IRE*, vol. 43, pp. 991–995, August, 1955.
   Fink, D. G.: "Television Engineering," 2d ed., pp. 553–567, McGraw-Hill Book Company, Inc., New York, 1952.
2. Soller, J. T., M. A. Starr, and G. E. Valley, Jr.: "Cathode Ray Tube Displays," Massachusetts Institute of Technology Radiation Laboratory Series, vol. 22, chap. 1, McGraw-Hill Book Company, Inc., New York, 1948.
3. Ref. 2, chap. 13.
4. Ref. 2, chap. 12.
5. Ref. 2, chap. 11.
6. Ref. 2, sec. 16-12.

CHAPTER 18

TRANSISTORS IN PULSE AND DIGITAL CIRCUITS

Transistors are semiconductor devices which are used to perform many of the functions of vacuum tubes. Transistors have the relative advantages that they are smaller in size, they require no filament power, they operate at lower supply voltages, they have correspondingly lower power dissipation, and they have appreciably longer life than tubes. Transistors have properties which make them particularly suitable for use as switches in pulse and digital circuits. This chapter is devoted to a study of the physical behavior of a transistor, its characterization as a circuit element, and its operation in switching applications.

18-1. Semiconductors.[1] The relatively high electric conductivity of metals results from the fact that, in the solid crystalline state, the valence electrons are easily detached from the atom. These electrons, which are not bound to an individual atom, constitute the carriers of electricity. They move under the influence of an electric field and their drift motion constitutes the flow of an electric current. The number of free carriers per unit volume in a solid serves as a measure of its electric conductivity. In copper the number of conduction electrons available is about 10^{22} electrons per cubic centimeter and the resistivity is about 1.7×10^{-6} ohm-cm. A good insulator, on the other hand, has a resistivity of the order of 10^{15} ohm-cm.

The operation of transistors depends on the characteristics of a type of solid called a *semiconductor*, which has an electrical conductivity which lies between the very high conductivity of the metals and the very low conductivity of insulators. The semiconductors most commonly employed in transistors are germanium and silicon. The resistivity of pure (called *intrinsic*) germanium is 60 ohm-cm at 25°C, while that of silicon is 60×10^3 ohm-cm. In a semiconductor the outermost (valence) electrons are neither so tightly bound to the atom as in an insulator nor so loosely held as in the conductor. The density of electrical carriers in a semiconductor lies in the range 10^5 to 10^{11} per cubic centimeter.

In a crystal the atoms are arranged in a regular ordered array which is referred to as a lattice structure. Each atom is situated at one corner of a regular tetrahedron. This structure is illustrated symbolically in two dimensions in Fig. 18-1a. Germanium has a total of 32 electrons in its atomic structure, and, of these, 4 are valence electrons so that the atom is tetravalent. The inert ionic core of the germanium atom carries a positive charge of +4 measured in units of the electronic charge. The binding forces between neighboring atoms result from the fact that each of the valence electrons of a germanium atom is shared by one of its four nearest neighbors. This *electron-pair bond*, or *covalent bond*, is represented in Fig. 18-1a by the two dotted lines which join each atom to each of its neighbors. The fact that the valence electrons serve to bind one atom to the next also results in the valence electron being

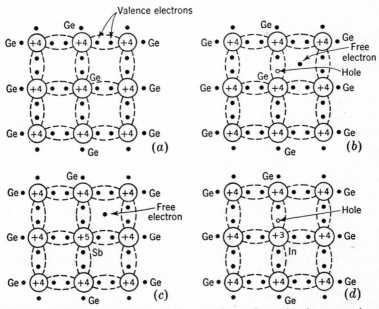

FIG. 18-1. Symbolic representation of the atomic configuration in germanium. (a) All covalent bonds are complete. (b) A covalent bond is broken to form a free electron and a hole. (c) A pentavalent impurity is added to furnish a conduction electron. (d) A trivalent impurity is added to furnish a conduction hole.

more tightly bound to the nucleus. Hence, in spite of the availability of four valence electrons the crystalline structure has a low conductivity.

As a result of the thermal agitation within the germanium crystal a certain fraction of the covalent bonds will be broken and thereby carriers of electricity will be available. This situation is illustrated in Fig. 18-1b. Here an electron, which for the far greater period of time forms part of a covalent bond, is pictured as being dislodged and therefore free to wander in a random fashion throughout the crystal. The energy required to break such a covalent bond is about 0.75 ev for Ge and 1.12 ev for Si. The absence of the electron in the covalent bond is represented by the small circle in Fig. 18-1b, and such an incomplete covalent bond is called a *hole*.   The importance of the hole is that it may serve as a carrier of electricity which is comparable in effectiveness to the free electron.   The mechanism by which a hole may serve as a conductor of electricity is qualitatively as follows.   When a bond is incomplete so that a hole exists, it is relatively easy for an electron in a neighboring atom to leave its covalent bond to fill this hole.   An electron moving from a bond to fill a hole leaves a hole in its initial position.   Hence, the hole effectively moves in the direction opposite to that of the electron.   This hole, in its new position, may now be filled by an electron from another covalent bond and the hole will correspondingly move one more step in the direction opposite to the motion of the electron.   Here we have a mechanism for the conduction of electricity which does not involve the free electron.

The motion of the hole in one direction actually means the transport of a negative charge an equal distance in the other direction.   So far as the flow of electric current is concerned, the result will be unaltered if we compute the current flow by assigning to the hole a positive charge equal in magnitude to the electronic charge.   We are then considering that the holes are physical entities whose displacement constitutes the flow of current.   It has been determined experimentally for Ge that the rate of drift of holes under the influence of an electric field is about half the rate of drift of electrons.

In a pure semiconductor the number of holes and free electrons are equal.   Thermal agitation continues to produce new hole-electron pairs, while other hole-electron pairs disappear as a result of recombination.   In pure germanium at room temperature there is about one hole-electron pair for each 5×10^{10} germanium atoms.   With increasing temperature, the density of hole-electron pairs increases and correspondingly the conductivity increases.

18-2. Donor and Acceptor Impurities.   If, to pure germanium, a small amount of impurity is added in the form of a substance with *five* valence electrons, the situation results which is pictured in Fig. 18-1c.   The impurity atoms will displace some of the germanium atoms in the crystal attice.   Four of the five valence electrons will occupy covalent bonds, while the fifth will be nominally unbound and will be available as a carrier of current.   The energy required to detach this fifth electron from the atom is only of the order of 0.01 ev.   Suitable pentavalent impurities are antimony, phosphorus, or arsenic.   Such impurities donate excess negative electron carriers and are therefore referred to as *donor*, or *n-type*, impurities.

If a trivalent impurity is added (boron, gallium, or indium), then only three of the covalent bonds can be filled and the vacancy that exists in the fourth bond constitutes a hole.   This situation is illustrated in Fig. 18-1d.   Such impurities make available positive carriers because they create holes

which can accept electrons.   These impurities are consequently known
as *acceptor*, or *p-type*, impurities.   The amount of impurity required to be
added to have an appreciable effect on the conductivity is very small.
For example, if a donor-type impurity is added to the extent of one part
in 10^8, the resistivity of germanium at 27°C will drop from 47 to 4
ohm-cm.

In intrinsic (pure) germanium both electrons and holes are available as
carriers.   The number of electrons and holes is equal, and their number
is determined by the statistical equilibrium which is established between
the process of generation of new hole-electron pairs and the process of
recombination.   If intrinsic germanium is "doped" with *n*-type impurities, not only does the number of electron carriers increase, but the
number of hole carriers decreases below that which is available in the
intrinsic semiconductor.   The reason for the decrease in the number of
holes is that the larger number of electrons present increases the rate of
recombination of holes with electrons.   Similarly, the number of electron
carriers in a semiconductor can be reduced by doping with *p*-type impurities.   The quantitative rule which applies is that

$$np \cong n_i{}^2 = p_i{}^2 \tag{18-1}$$

where n_i and p_i are, respectively, the electron- and hole-carrier concentration in the intrinsic semiconductor, while n and p are, respectively,
the electron and hole concentrations in the doped semiconductor.

We have the important result that the doping of an intrinsic semiconductor not only increases the conductivity but serves also to produce
a conductor in which the electric carriers are either predominantly holes
or predominantly electrons.

18-3. Drift and Diffusion.   In a metallic conductor, current results
from the existence of an electric field within the conductor.   As a result
of this field, a *drift* motion of electric charges in the direction of the
force resulting from the electric field is superimposed on the random
erratic motion of the electrons.   This conduction current is proportional to the electron concentration and the drift velocity.   This same
drift type of conduction may occur in a doped semiconductor, but additionally the transport of charges in a semiconductor may be accounted
for by a mechanism, called *diffusion*, not ordinarily encountered in
metals.   The essential features of diffusion will appear in the following
considerations.

Suppose that in a semiconductor there is no electric field but that there
exists a gradient in the density of carriers.   If these carriers are, say,
holes, then the existence of a gradient implies that, if an imaginary surface
be drawn in the semiconductor, the density of holes immediately on one
side of the surface is larger than the density on the other side.   The holes

are in a random motion as a result of their thermal energy. Accordingly holes will continue to move back and forth across this surface. We may then expect that in a given time interval more holes will cross the surface from the more dense to the less dense side than in the reverse direction. This net transport of charge across the surface constitutes a flow of current. It should be noted that this net transport of charge is not the result of mutual repulsion among charges of like sign but is simply the result of a statistical phenomenon. This diffusion is exactly analogous to that which occurs in a neutral gas if there exists a pressure gradient in the gaseous container. The diffusion current is proportional to the concentration gradient (the rate of change of concentration with distance).

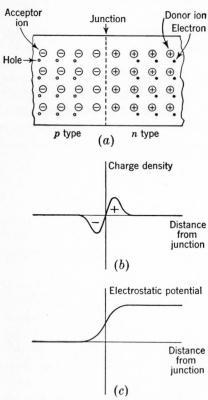

18-4. The p-n Junction.[2] We consider now the electrical characteristics of a junction between a sample of n-type and p-type germanium. This junction, illustrated in Fig. 18-2a, is formed by introducing donor impurities into one side and acceptor impurities into the other side of a single crystal of germanium.

Initially there are nominally only p-type carriers to the left of the junction and only n-type carriers to the right. As a result of the density gradient across the junction, holes will diffuse to the right across the junction and electrons to the left. An electric field will appear across the junction, and when the field becomes large enough, the process of diffusion will be restrained and equilibrium will be established. The equilibrium charge distribution is illustrated in Fig. 18-2b. The electric charges are confined to the neighborhood of the junction and consist of immobile ions whose neutralizing mobile charges have combined with

Fig. 18-2. An abrupt symmetrical junction between p-type and n-type germanium. (a) The lattice structure and distribution of carriers; (b) the charge density near the junction; (c) the potential variation across the junction.

charges of opposite sign which have diffused across the junction. That is, the positive holes which neutralized the acceptor ions near the junction in the p-type germanium have disappeared as the result of combination with electrons which have diffused across the junction. Similarly the neutralizing electrons in the n-type germanium have combined with holes. These unneutralized ions in the neighborhood of the junction are referred to as *uncovered* charges. The electrostatic potential variation in the region of the junction is shown in Fig. 18-2c. This potential variation constitutes a *potential energy barrier* against the further diffusion of holes across the barrier. The form of the potential energy barrier against the flow of electrons across the junction is similar to that shown in Fig. 18-2c except that it is inverted, since the electronic charge is negative.

The essential electrical characteristic of a p-n junction is that it constitutes a diode which permits the easy flow of current in one direction but restrains the flow in the opposite direction. We now consider qualitatively how this diode action comes about. In Fig. 18-3, a battery is shown connected across the terminals of a p-n junction. The negative terminal of the battery is connected to the p side of the junction, the positive terminal to the n side. The polarity of connection is such as to cause both the holes in the p-type and the electrons in the n-type to move *away* from the junction. As a consequence no carriers are available to cross the junction and the current which flows is nominally zero. Actually a small current flows because a small number of hole-electron pairs are generated throughout the crystal as a result of

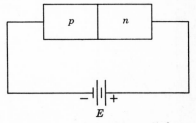

Fig. 18-3. A voltage E is applied to a p-n junction diode.

thermal energy. The holes so formed in the n-type germanium will wander over to the junction, fall down the potential energy hill, and thus cross the junction. A similar remark applies to the electrons thermally generated in the p-type germanium. This small current is the diode *reverse* current. This reverse current will increase with increasing temperature, and hence the back resistance of a crystal diode decreases rapidly with increasing temperature.

The mechanism of conduction in the reverse direction may be described alternatively in the following way. When no voltage is applied to the p-n diode, the potential barrier across the junction is as shown in Fig. 18-2c. When a voltage E is applied to the diode in the direction shown in Fig. 18-3, the height of the potential energy barrier is increased by the amount E. This increase in the barrier height serves to reduce the flow of *majority carriers* (that is, holes in p-type and electrons in n-type). However, the *minority carriers* (that is, electrons in p-type and holes in

n-type), since they fall down the potential energy hill, are uninfluenced by the increased height of the barrier.

If the external voltage E is applied with the polarity opposite to that indicated in Fig. 18-3, a relatively large current will flow. In this case the height of the potential energy barrier at the junction will be lowered by the amount E. The equilibrium which was initially established between the forces tending to produce diffusion of majority carriers and the restraining influence of the potential energy barrier at the junction will be disturbed. We shall make no large error if we assume that for small currents, the ohmic drop across the body of the crystal is negligible. In this case the voltage E applied to the crystal terminals appears essentially across the junction. A theoretical analysis of the p-n junction

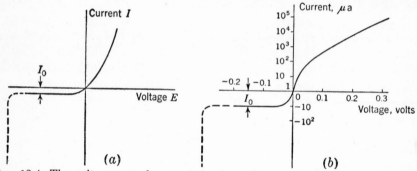

Fig. 18-4. The volt-ampere characteristic of an ideal p-n junction: (a) plotted on linear scale to show form; (b) semilog plot to show typical current and voltage values.

diode yields for the diode current I as a function of applied voltage E the formula

$$I = I_0(\epsilon^{E/E_T} - 1) \tag{18-2}$$

Here I_0 is the magnitude of the diode reverse current,

$$E_T = \frac{T}{11,600} = \frac{kT}{q}$$

q is the magnitude of the electronic charge, k is the Boltzmann constant, $k = 1.381 \times 10^{-23}$ joule/°K, and T is the temperature in degrees Kelvin. This formula applies quite well in practice. Linear and logarithmic plots of current vs. voltage for a typical junction diode are shown in Fig. 18-4. The quantity E_T has the value 0.026 volt at room temperature (25°C). Therefore when E in Eq. (18-2) is negative and large in magnitude in comparison with 0.026 volt, the reverse current which flows is I_0. However, as the magnitude of the reverse-biasing voltage is increased, a critical voltage is finally reached where the diode volt-ampere characteristic exhibits an abrupt and marked departure from Eq. (18-2), as is indicated in Fig. 18-4 by the dotted portion of the curves. At this critical voltage large reverse currents flow and the diode is said to be in the *break-*

down region.   We discuss next the physical basis for the occurrence of breakdown.

As the reverse voltage across the diode junction increases, the height of the barrier increases and the maximum electric field encountered in the junction region also increases.   When the field becomes sufficiently large, the electrons which constitute the current carriers may acquire a sufficient velocity to produce new carriers by removing valence electrons from their covalent bonds.   These new carriers may in turn produce additional carriers again through the process of ionization by collision, etc.   This cumulative process, which is referred to as *avalanche multiplication*, results in the flow of large reverse currents and the diode is said to be in the region of *avalanche breakdown*.   Even if the initially available carriers do not acquire sufficient energy to produce ionization by collision it is possible to initiate breakdown through a direct rupture of the covalent bonds because of the existence of the strong electric field.   Under these circumstances the breakdown is referred to as a *Zener breakdown* and the reverse voltage at which the breakdown occurs is called the *Zener voltage*. However, in either case, at breakdown, the reverse current becomes very large and the current is largely independent of the voltage.   The situation within the diode before breakdown as well as the volt-ampere characteristic after breakdown are very closely analogous to what occurs in a glow tube.[3]

A point of interest in connection with breakdown in junction diodes is that the diode will recover when the magnitude of the reverse voltage is reduced below the breakdown voltage, provided the diode has not been damaged by excessive heat dissipation in the breakdown region.   As a

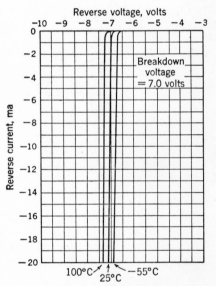

FIG. 18-5. Volt-ampere characteristic of a voltage-reference breakdown diode. (Texas Instrument type 653C4 silicon diode.)

result it has been possible to manufacture junction diodes which are suitable as voltage reference sources for use in much the same fashion as glow-tube regulators.   The volt-ampere characteristic in the reverse direction for a typical low-voltage silicon voltage-reference diode is shown in Fig. 18-5.   Breakdown diodes are available with reference voltages in the range from several volts to several hundred volts.

The principal use of the junction diode is as a power rectifier. The crystal diodes, whose parameters are described in Sec. 4-1, and which are used as diode clamps and as switching elements, are usually of the point-contact variety. A point-contact diode consists of a pointed tungsten wire in the form of a spring which presses against the surface of a germanium or silicon wafer to which impurities have been added. In the manufacturing process a surge of current is passed through the diode and a *p-n* junction of extremely small area is formed at the point contact.

18-5. The Junction Transistor.[4] A junction transistor consists of a germanium (or silicon) crystal in which a layer of *n*-type germanium is sandwiched between two layers of *p*-type germanium. Alternatively a transistor may consist of a layer of *p*-type between two layers of *n*-type

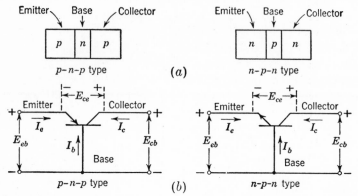

FIG. 18-6. (*a*) A *p-n-p* and an *n-p-n* transistor; (*b*) circuit representation for the two transistor types.

material. In the former case the transistor is referred to as a *p-n-p* transistor and in the latter case as an *n-p-n* transistor. The two types of transistors are represented in Fig. 18-6*a*. The representations employed when the transistors are used as circuit elements are shown in Fig. 18-6*b*. The three portions of the transistors are known, respectively, as *emitter*, *base*, and *collector*. The arrow on the emitter lead specifies the direction of current flow when the emitter-base junction is biased in the *forward* direction. In both cases, however, the emitter, base, and collector currents, I_e, I_b, and I_c, respectively, are assumed positive when the currents flow *into* the transistor. The symbols E_{eb}, E_{cb}, and E_{ce} are the emitter-base, collector-base, and collector-emitter voltages, respectively.

We may now begin to appreciate the essential features of a transistor as an active circuit element by considering the situation depicted in Fig. 18-7*a*. Here a *p-n-p* transistor is shown with voltage sources which serve to bias the emitter-base junction in the forward direction and the base-collector junction in the reverse direction. The variation of electric potential through the unbiased transistor is shown in Fig. 18-7b.   The potential distribution of the biased transistor is indicated in Fig. 18-7c. The dashed curve applies in the case before the application of external biasing voltages and the solid curve to the case where the biasing voltages are applied.   In the absence of applied voltages the potential barriers at the junctions adjust themselves to the height (a few tenths of a volt)

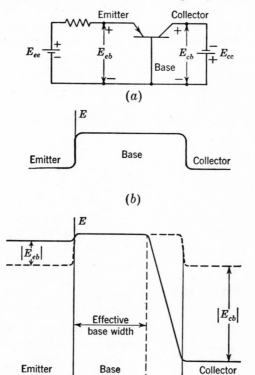

(a)

(b)

(c)

FIG. 18-7. (a) A p-n-p transistor with biasing voltages; (b) the potential energy barriers at the junctions of the unbiased transistor; (c) the potential variation through the transistor in the presence of the biasing voltages (solid line).   (The factors that determine the effective base width are discussed in Sec. 18-10.)

required so that no net current flows across them.   As noted earlier, externally applied voltages appear essentially across the junctions. Hence, the forward biasing of the emitter-base junction lowers the emitter-base potential barrier by $|E_{eb}|$ volts, while the reverse biasing of the base-collector junction increases the base-collector potential barrier by $|E_{cb}|$ volts.   The lowering of the emitter-base barrier permits the diffusion of holes from the emitter to the base, i.e., the emitter *emits* or *injects* holes into the base.   In the base region the potential is uniform (there is no electric field), and hence the emitted holes must diffuse across the base to the base-collector junction. At this junction the holes fall down the potential barrier and are therefore *collected* by the collector. An important feature worthy of note is that through the use of a transistor a current furnished by a low-voltage source E_{ee} can be used to control the current furnished by a high-voltage source E_{cc}.

It is desirable that the ratio of the collector current to the emitter current be as close as possible to unity. Several features of construction are normally incorporated into a transistor in order to achieve this end. First, the doping of the emitter is made much larger than the doping of

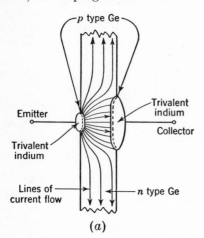

the base. This features ensures (in a p-n-p transistor) that the transport of current across the emitter junction consists almost entirely of the flow of holes. Such a situation is required since the current which results from electrons crossing the emitter junction from base to emitter does not contribute holes which may be collected by the collector. Second, the width of the base region is made small so that the holes diffuse across the base in a short time and hence little opportunity is afforded for a loss of holes due to recombination with electrons.

One type of transistor construction[5] is indicated in Fig. 18-8a. This type of transistor is known as a *diffused-junction* or *alloy* type of transistor. The center section is a thin wafer of n-type germanium. Two small dots of indium are attached to opposite sides of the wafer and the whole structure is raised for a short time to a high temperature. At the junction between the indium and the wafer enough indium dissolves into the

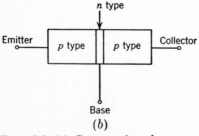

FIG. 18-8. (*a*) Cross section of a p-n-p diffused-junction transistor; (*b*) cross section of a grown-junction transistor.

germanium to change the germanium from n-type to p-type. The collector is made larger than the emitter so that the collector subtends a large angle as viewed from the emitter. Because of this geometrical arrangement very little emitter current follows a diffusion path which carries it to the base rather than the collector.

A second type of construction[6] gives rise to a type of transistor which

is called a *grown-junction* transistor.   This type of construction is illustrated in Fig. 18-8*b*.   It is made by drawing a single crystal from a melt
of germanium whose type is changed during the crystal drawing operation by adding *n*- or *p*-type impurities as required.

Transistors are normally not symmetrical, i.e., emitter and collector
may not be interchanged without changing the electrical properties of
the transistor.   In the diffused-junction transistor this lack of symmetry
results from the larger mechanical dimensions of the collector.   In the
grown-junction transistor lack of symmetry results from the fact that the
conductivity of the collector is usually much less than the conductivity
of the emitter.

Another type of transistor (which is a natural extension of the point-
contact diode) consists of two sharply pointed tungsten wires pressed
against a semiconductor wafer.   These point-contact transistors are
capable of operating at a higher speed than junction transistors.   Also, in
some applications a single point-contact transistor will replace two junction transistors.   However, at the present state of the art,* the repro-
ducibility and reliability of point-contact transistors is very poor.

**18-6. Characteristics of Transistors—The Grounded-base Configura-
tion.**   Transistors, when employed in pulse circuits, are most commonly
used as switches which are turned
on or *off*.   In a typical application a
transistor might be employed in the
manner indicated in Fig. 18-9.
Here an *n-p-n* transistor is shown
in a *grounded-base* configuration.
This configuration is also referred to
by the designation *common base*,

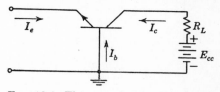

FIG. 18-9. The grounded-base transistor
configuration.

since the base is common to the input and output circuits.   Assume initially that the emitter current is zero or even that the emitter junction is
slightly reverse-biased.   The collector current will then be very small.
The collector and base terminals then constitute the terminals of a switch
which is open-circuited.   Suppose now that a forward-biasing emitter
current is caused to flow in the emitter circuit.   Then a current will flow
in the collector circuit which will be not much smaller than the emitter

* At the time of this writing (1956) a survey of transistor manufacturers reveals
that nearly all have discontinued production of point-contact transistors in favor of
junction transistors.   Additionally, almost all the development work in transistor
circuitry presently being done is again in connection with junction transistors.   Moreover, the theory of junction-transistor operation has now advanced to such a point
that it is possible to design junction transistors to meet previously established specifications.   The understanding of the operation of point-contact transistors is not at a
comparable level.   For these reasons the discussion of the present chapter is confined
entirely to the junction transistor.

current and the collector base switch will effectively be closed. A voltage drop will develop across the load resistor R_L and the collector-to-base voltage will decrease. To be able to describe quantitatively the operation of this switch circuit, we require a set of transistor characteristics which relate the collector-to-base voltage to the collector current for various values of emitter current. Such a set of characteristics is shown in Fig. 18-10 for a Sylvania type 2N35 *n-p-n* transistor. This transistor is a low-power transistor (comparable to a receiving-type tube) intended for medium-speed switching applications. The charactersitics

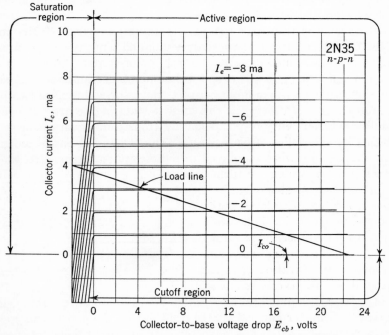

FIG. 18-10. Common-base characteristics of the Sylvania type 2N35 transistor.

of Fig. 18-10 may be divided into three regions which are particularly worthy of note.

Active Region. Consider, first, collector voltages which bias the collector junction in the reverse direction and which are larger than several tenths of a volt. In this region the collector current is essentially independent of collector voltage and depends only on the emitter current. The region of operation in which the collector is reversed-biased and the emitter is forward-biased is called the *active* region. In this region the collector current is nominally the same (actually slightly smaller) than the emitter current. This result is to have been anticipated on the basis of the preceding theoretical discussion. The ratio of the change in magnitude of the collector current to the change in magnitude of the emitter current at *constant collector-to-base voltage* is designated by the symbol α.

$$\alpha \equiv \frac{|\Delta I_c|}{|\Delta I_e|} \qquad (18\text{-}3)$$

An average value of α may be obtained by noting that when the collector-to-base voltage drop E_{cb} is, say, about 5 volts, then an emitter-current increment of -4 ma yields a collector-current increment of 3.9 ma. Hence $\alpha = 3.9/4.0 = 0.98$. Typically, values of α lie in the range 0.95 to 0.99, with $\alpha = 0.98$ being a reasonable average value.

Cutoff Region. The characteristic for $I_e = 0$ passes through the origin but is otherwise similar to the other characteristics. This characteristic is not coincident with the voltage axis, though the separation is difficult to show on the scale to which the characteristics are drawn. The nominally constant collector current corresponding to $I_e = 0$ is the *reverse saturation collector current I_{co}*, and, for the 2N35 transistor it is of the order of 2 μa. The region below and to the right of the $I_e = 0$ characteristic, for which the emitter and collector junctions are both reverse-biased, is referred to as the *cutoff* region.

Saturation Region. The region to the left of the ordinate $E_{cb} = 0$ and above the $I_e = 0$ characteristics in which both emitter and collector junctions are forward-biased is called the *saturation* region. *Bottoming* occurs in this region and, for a given value of E_{cc} and R_L, the collector current is approximately independent of the emitter current. The forward biasing of the collector in this region accounts for the large change in collector current with small changes in collector voltage. The magnitude of emitter current required to bias the transistor in Fig. 18-9 to the point of saturation ($E_{cb} = 0$) may be estimated in the following way. From the form of the curves of Fig. 18-10 and from the definition of α, we may write

$$I_c = I_{co} - \alpha I_e \qquad (18\text{-}4)$$

The minus sign results from the arbitrary convention that the symbols I_c and I_e represent current flow *into* the transistor. Since I_{co} is small compared with the value of I_e necessary to drive the transistor into saturation, then $|I_c| \cong \alpha |I_e|$. Also, since the collector-to-base voltage is zero, then $|I_c| = |E_{cc}/R_L|$. Hence an emitter current equal to or larger than

$$|I_e|_{sat} = \left| \frac{E_{cc}}{\alpha R_L} \right| \qquad (18\text{-}5)$$

will bias the transistor into the saturation region.

In connection with the characteristic of Fig. 18-10 we may take note of the fact that with increased temperature the current I_{co} increases while the relative spacing of the individual curves remains essentially the same. Hence, with increased temperatures the curves shift in the upward direction. Experimentally, for a germanium transistor, it is found that I_{co} doubles for each increase of 10°C. Correspondingly an increase of 30°C will multiply the current I_{co} by the factor 2^3. For silicon transistors, a 10°C temperature change increases I_{co} by the factor 3. On the other hand, the value of I_{co} for silicon is so much smaller than for germanium that actually the operation of a silicon transistor is appreciably less sensitive to temperature changes.

Analytic expressions for the transistor characteristics which are valid in all three regions are given in Sec. 18-20.

To see how effective the circuit of Fig. 18-9 is when used as a switch, let us consider an example in which $R_L = 6.1$ K and $E_{cc} = 22.5$ volts. The load line for these values of R_L and E_{cc} has been superimposed on the transistor curves in Fig. 18-10. If the emitter current is zero or if the emitter junction is slightly reverse-biased, the collector voltage E_{cb} will be very close to E_{cc} so that the switch is *off*. At the other extreme, if the emitter current is about 4.0 ma, the voltage drop at the collector will be zero and the full voltage E_{cc} will appear across the load so that the switch is *on*. Larger emitter currents will actually reverse the voltage at the collector so that a voltage slightly larger than E_{cc} may appear across the load.

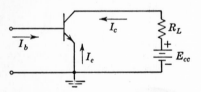

18-7. The Grounded-emitter Configuration. A transistor switch which

uses a transistor in a grounded-emitter configuration is shown in Fig. 18-11. The characteristics of operation in this configuration may be appreciated qualitatively on the basis of our earlier discussion of the grounded-base configuration. The base current is

$$I_b = -(I_c + I_e) \qquad (18\text{-}6)$$

Combining this equation with Eq. (18-4), we find

$$I_b = -I_{co} + \alpha I_e - I_e = -I_{co} - (1 - \alpha)I_e \qquad (18\text{-}7)$$

Therefore when the base current is zero, the emitter and collector currents will be

$$I_e = -\frac{I_{co}}{1 - \alpha} \qquad I_c = \frac{I_{co}}{1 - \alpha} \qquad (18\text{-}8)$$

Since α is close to unity, these currents will be relatively large. For example, if $\alpha = 0.98$ and $I_{co} = 2$ μa, the collector current at zero base current will be 2 $\mu a/(1 - 0.98) = 0.10$ ma. Hence, if the switch is initially to be open, we shall prefer to have some current in the base lead. As a matter of fact, we may select $I_b = -I_{co}$ since in this case $I_e = 0$ and $I_c = I_{co}$.

Common-emitter characteristics are shown in Fig. 18-12. Here the abscissa is the collector-to-emitter voltage E_{ce}, the ordinate is the collector current, and the curves are given for various values of base current. For fixed base current, the collector current is not a very sensitive function of collector-to-emitter voltage. However, the slopes of the curves

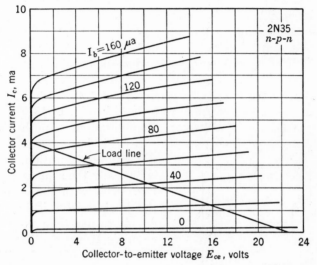

Fig. 18-12. Common-emitter characteristics for the type 2N35 transistor.

in Fig. 18-12 are larger than in the common-base characteristics of Fig. 18-10. Observe that in general in Fig. 18-12 the base current is much smaller than the collector current, as is to be expected.

By eliminating I_e from Eqs. (18-4) and (18-6), we find

$$I_b = -\frac{I_{co}}{\alpha} + \frac{1-\alpha}{\alpha}I_c \qquad (18\text{-}9)$$

This equation is based upon the assumption that the collector-to-base voltage is held constant. However, if E_{cb} is larger than several volts, the voltage across the collector junction will be much larger than that across the emitter junction. If this condition is satisfied, we may consider that $E_{ce} = E_{cb}$. Hence, in Fig. 18-11, at fixed E_{ce} the change ΔI_b in base current divided by the change ΔI_c in collector current is

$$\frac{\Delta I_b}{\Delta I_c} = \frac{1-\alpha}{\alpha} \qquad (18\text{-}10)$$

Hence, while the spacing in the vertical direction of the curves in Fig. 18-10 is determined by α, the corresponding spacing in Fig. 18-12 is determined by $(1 - \alpha)/\alpha$. It should be noted that since the parameter I_b is the small difference between two nearly equal large currents I_e and I_c, the common-emitter characteristics are normally subject to a wide variation.

A load line has been superimposed on Fig. 18-12 corresponding, in this case, to a load resistor $R_L = 5.6$ K and a supply voltage of 22.5 volts. The transistor is in the cutoff condition when the base current is about -2 μa and the collector-to-emitter voltage is very close to the supply voltage. The saturation region may be defined as the one in which *bottoming* occurs and hence as the region where the collector current is approximately independent of base current, for given values of E_{ce} and R_L. Hence, we may consider that the onset of saturation occurs at the knee of the transistor curves in Fig. 18-12. Saturation occurs for the given load line at a base current of 100 μa, and at this point the collector voltage is too small to be read in Fig. 18-12.

18-8. The Grounded-collector Configuration. Another transistor circuit configuration, shown in Fig. 18-13, is known as the grounded-collector configuration. The circuit is basically the same as the circuit of Fig. 18-11 with the exception that the load resistor is in the emitter circuit rather than in the collector circuit. If we continue to specify the operation of the circuit in terms of the currents which flow, the operation for the grounded collector is much the same as for the grounded emitter. When the base current is $I_{co} = 2$ μa, the emitter current will be zero and no current will flow in the load. As the transistor is brought out of this back-biased condition by increasing the base current, the transistor will pass through the active region and eventually reach the region of saturation. This saturation region will again occur at a base current of about 100 μa and in this condition all the supply voltage except for a very small drop across the transistor will appear across the load.

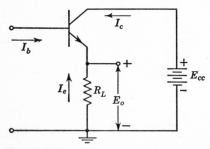

Fig. 18-13. The grounded-collector transistor configuration.

18-9. A Vacuum-tube–Transistor Analogy.[7] It is possible to draw a very rough analogy between a transistor and a vacuum tube In this analogy the base, emitter, and collector of a transistor are identified, respectively, with the grid, cathode, and plate of a vacuum tube. Correspondingly the grounded-base, grounded-emitter, and grounded-collector configurations are identified, respectively, with the grounded-grid, grounded-cathode, and grounded-plate (cathode-follower) vacuum-tube circuits, as in Fig. 18-14.

Consider, for example, the circuits of Fig. 18-14a. For the tube circuit, we find that in the normal amplifier region $|I_k| = |I_b|$. In the transistor circuit, in the active region, we find that $|I_e| \cong |I_c|$, the difference between I_e and I_c being of the order of 2 per cent. In both the transistor and tube circuits of Fig. 18-14a, we find that the input impedance is low because of the large current at low voltage which must be furnished by the driving generator. In Sec. 18-12 we shall find that the grounded-base transistor circuit is capable of providing a voltage gain. When used as a voltage amplifier, the grounded-base circuit does

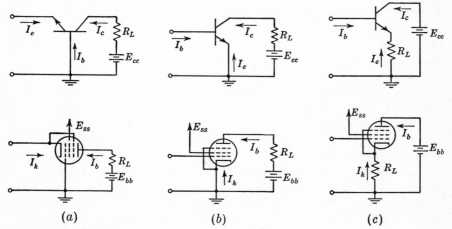

FIG. 18-14. Transistor configurations and their analogous vacuum-tube circuits: (a) grounded base, (b) grounded emitter, (c) grounded collector.

not invert the polarity of the input signal. In these respects also the transistor and tube circuits of Fig. 18-14a are analogous. The cutoff region of the transistor corresponds to the region in the vacuum tube where the tube grid bias is larger than the cutoff bias. The active region of the transistor corresponds to the region in which the tube operates as a linear amplifier. This region covers not only the region within the grid base but also the region of positive grid voltages where the tube operates linearly. The saturation region of the transistor corresponds to the tube region where the grid is so far positive with respect to the cathode that the plate current of the tube is almost independent of grid voltage. In the transistor, however, the base takes current at all points in its active region, while in the tube the grid draws appreciable current only when it is positive. The analogy may be improved by assuming that cutoff occurs in the tube at zero grid bias, i.e., the grid base is zero.   Even if we make this assumption, we should find a difference between tube and transistor in that some small currents flow in the transistor at cutoff while no currents flow in the tube.   In addition, at a later point we shall find in transistors certain effects which have no counterpart in tubes.

The grounded-emitter transistor configuration of Fig. 18-14b may be expected to have a higher input impedance than the grounded-base since in the former case the input current is the relatively small difference current between the collector and emitter currents.   We shall find again, in this case, that when the configuration is used as a voltage amplifier a large gain is possible.   We may verify, even at this point, that such a grounded-emitter amplifier will produce a polarity inversion.   In all these respects the grounded-emitter configuration is analogous to the grounded-cathode vacuum-tube amplifier stage.

In Fig. 18-14c, the grounded-collector configuration is compared to the grounded-plate (cathode-follower) circuit.   As a matter of fact, the grounded-collector configuration is often referred to as the *emitter-follower* circuit.   We noted above that when the operation of the grounded-collector circuit was described in terms of the input current, its operation was much the same as the operation of the grounded-emitter circuit. If, however, we describe the operation in terms of the input voltage, the similarity of this circuit to the cathode follower becomes apparent.

In the emitter-follower circuit the input current is again relatively small and the voltage difference between base and emitter is essentially the small voltage drop across the forward-biased emitter junction when operating in the active region.   Hence, we may expect the input voltage and output voltage, as in a cathode follower, to be nominally the same. The emitter follower, as the cathode follower, may be expected to provide a gain of the order of unity without polarity inversion when used as a voltage amplifier.   The emitter follower may also be expected to handle an input signal comparable in size to the collector supply voltage.   The input current swing from cutoff to saturation is the same for grounded-emitter and grounded-collector operation, but in grounded-collector operation the input voltage swing is larger.   Hence, as in the cathode follower, the input impedance for the grounded-collector circuit may be expected to be the largest for the three configurations.

We shall have occasion later (Sec. 18-12) to discuss in more detail the input and output impedances, the voltages and current gains, etc., for the various configurations.   We shall find additional points of correspondence between the pairs of circuits shown in Fig. 18-14.   But it need hardly be emphasized that the correspondence is far from exact.   The analogies are principally useful as mnemonic devices and for the purpose of providing an approximate appreciation of the operation of a transitor circuit to one who is more familiar with vacuum-tube circuits. For example, we may note that the most generally useful tube circuit is the grounded-cathode circuit, independently of whether the circuit is used as an amplifier or as a switch. We may then expect from our analogy that the grounded-emitter configuration will occupy the same preferred position in transistor configurations. This anticipated result is borne out in practice.

18-10. Voltage and Current Limits in Transistor Switching Circuits.[8] A number of precautions must be observed in connection with the maximum voltages applied to transistors and the maximum current which is permitted to flow.

Independently of which transistor configuration is used in a switching application, it is important to note that the power dissipated in the transistor is small in both the *on* condition and in the *off* condition. In the former condition the current is high but the transistor voltages are small. In the latter condition the voltages are high but the currents are low. Herein lies a disadvantage of the grounded-collector circuit for switching application. For unless the input voltage is large enough to swing the transistor all the way from cutoff to saturation, the transistor will operate in the active region. In this region both the currents and voltages are high and if the transistor is left in this active region for a relatively long time the allowable transistor dissipation may well be exceeded.

The dissipation will normally be largest at the collector junction, since emitter and collector currents are usually comparable and the voltage at the collector junction is usually larger than at the emitter junction. However, even if the dissipation is not exceeded, there is an upper limit to the maximum allowable collector-junction voltage since at high voltages there is the possibility of voltage breakdown in the transistor. This breakdown will normally occur at the collector junction where the voltage is highest. Two types of breakdown which are possible are the avalanche breakdown and Zener breakdown which were discussed earlier in Sec. 18-4. Even if the reverse voltage is not large enough to produce breakdown, a large reverse voltage may still cause difficulty. For suppose that there is some ionization by collision. Then the carriers may increase in number sufficiently to produce a value of α in excess of unity. In this case, in certain circuit configurations, the emitter input circuit of the transistor may exhibit a negative resistance characteristic over some range of operation. In such a situation regeneration is possible and the transistor circuit may behave like a binary device which has two stable states and this circumstance will interfere with the normal operation of the circuit. (Point-contact transistors normally have an α larger than unity and have been used extensively in the past to build single transistor binary circuits.   Unfortunately, as noted in Sec. 18-5, satisfactory transistors of this type have not been manufactured.)

A third type of voltage breakdown may occur in transistors and is known as *punch-through* breakdown.   At the junction between n-type and p-type semiconductors there exists an electric field.   This field results from the uncovered charges which exist in the neighborhood of the junction.   These uncovered charges are the ions of the impurity atoms. There are equal numbers of charges on the two sides of the junction, since there are no fields within the body of the semiconductor and all electric lines originating on positive charges on one side of the junction must terminate on negative charges on the other side of the junction. At the junction between two semiconductors, one of which is doped more heavily than the other, the field extends further into the less heavily doped semiconductor.   This is so, because the less heavily doped (higher resistivity) semiconductor has fewer impurity atoms per unit volume. In a p-n-p diffused-junction transistor, for example, the resistivity of the p-type collector and emitter may be as low as 0.001 ohm-cm while the n-type base has a resistivity of 1.5 ohm-cm.   In such a case the collector-junction field will extend almost entirely into the base as in Fig. 18-7.   With increasing collector voltage the field extends further and further into the base until finally it reaches the emitter junction. Beyond this point the collector-emitter impedance is low and normal transistor action is not possible.   Commercial transistors usually carry a maximum collector-voltage rating in the range 15 to 30 volts.   This maximum collector voltage is determined by Zener, avalanche, or punch-through breakdown, whichever occurs first.

18-11. A Linear Equivalent Circuit for a Transistor.   So far, we have been concerned only with the static characteristics of a transistor.   In the active region the transistor operates with reasonable linearity, and we shall now inquire into a small-signal equivalent circuit which represents the operation of the transistor in this active region.   Such an equivalent circuit is useful not only generally in studying transistors used as amplifiers, etc., but will also be of value in determining the transient response of the transistor as it moves through the active region.

Let us start by considering the simple equivalent transistor circuit of Fig. 18-15a.   We set up this circuit on more or less intuitive grounds so that it represents the more obvious transistor characteristics.   Small (lower-case) letters are used to represent variations of currents or voltages from their quiescent values.   Here r'_e represents the dynamic resistance obtained from the volt-ampere characteristic of the emitter junction, and the generator provides an output current αi_e as required.   This equivalent circuit gives the result that the impedance seen looking back into the output terminals is infinite in the case where the emitter-to-base input terminals are open-circuited. Actually, under these conditions we would see the back-biased resistance of the collector junction and hence as in Fig. 18-15b we should shunt the current generator αi_e with a resistance r_c' which represents this back-biased dynamic resistance obtained from the collector-junction volt-ampere characteristic. The circuit of Fig. 18-15a also indicates a lack of dependence of emitter current on collector voltage. Actually, there is some small dependence and a physical reason for this dependence is not hard to find. As was noted earlier, an increase in collector voltage effectively narrows the

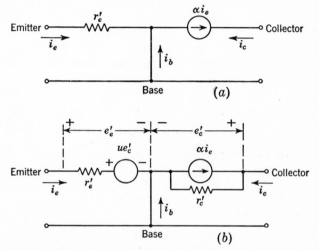

FIG. 18-15. (a) A rudimentary equivalent circuit for the transistor in the active region. (b) An improved equivalent circuit that takes into account the finite back resistance of the collector junction and the influence of collector voltage on the emitter junction.

base width. The diffusion of minority carriers across the base is consequently more rapid, fewer carriers pile up near the emitter junction, and the emitter current increases even for a fixed emitter-junction voltage. This effect of collector voltage on emitter current may be taken into account as in Fig. 18-15b by including a voltage source ue_c' in series with r_e', e_c' being the voltage across the collector junction.

There are some additional effects which need to be taken into account in connection with the equivalent circuit. However, before we do this, we shall make a transformation of the circuit of Fig. 18-15b into another circuit in which the generator ue_c' does not appear explicitly. This new circuit is shown in Fig. 18-16 and should be considered in conjunction with Table 18-1. This table gives the transformation equations and in addition specifies typical values of the parameters in each of the circuits. The derivation of the equations of transformation is an entirely straight-

TABLE 18-1. TYPICAL PARAMETER VALUES AND THE EQUATION OF
TRANSFORMATION BETWEEN THE CIRCUITS OF FIGS. 18-15a
AND 18-16

Parameter in Fig. 18-15b	Transformation equations	Parameter in Fig. 18-16
$r'_e = 40$ ohms	$r_e = r'_e - (1 - \alpha)ur'_c$	$r_e = 20$ ohms
$u = 5 \times 10^{-4}$	$r'_b = ur'_c$	$r'_b = 1000$ ohms
$r'_c = 2 \times 10^6$ ohms	$r_c = (1 - u)r'_c$	$r_c = 2 \times 10^6$ ohms
$\alpha = 0.98$	$a = \dfrac{\alpha - u}{1 - u}$	$a = 0.98$

forward matter and is left as an exercise for the student. The transformed circuit, we observe, accounts for the effect of the collector circuit
on the emitter circuit essentially through the resistor r'_b rather than
through the generator ue'_c. We observe also that $r_c \cong r'_c$, $a \cong \alpha$, and
that while r_e is appreciably different from r'_e, r_e is nevertheless still small.

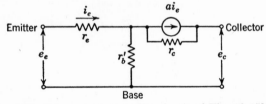

FIG. 18-16. A circuit that is equivalent to the circuit of Fig. 18-15b. The generator
ue'_c has been eliminated in the transformation.

A theoretical result[9] which has been verified experimentally is that the
emitter resistance r'_e is related to the emitter current by the formula

$$r'_e = \frac{E_T}{|I_e|} \tag{18-11}$$

where I_e is the d-c component of emitter current and $E_T = T/11{,}600$.
At room temperature (25°C) and with I_e expressed in milliamperes,
Eq. (18-11) reduces to

$$r'_e = \frac{26}{|I_e|} \qquad \text{ohms}$$

We return now to the completion of the equivalent circuit. There is,
among many minor effects, one more important effect which must be
included. This effect is a result of the finite resistivity of the base region.
As a result of this finite resistivity there will be an ohmic voltage drop
in the base region which is proportional to the base current i_b. This
effect may be taken into account therefore by including a resistor r''_b
in series with the base lead. If this resistor is included in the circuits of

Fig. 18-15b and Fig. 18-16, the two equivalent circuits which result are shown in Fig. 18-17. The circuit of Fig. 18-17a has the relative disadvantage that it involves one more element than the circuit in Fig. 18-17b; on the other hand, the former circuit has the advantage that it puts explicitly in evidence the two sides of the emitter and collector junctions, a feature not shared by the latter circuit. We shall find the availability of the junctions an important asset, when, at a later point, we seek to modify the equivalent circuit to take into account

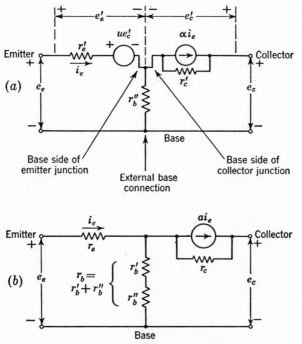

FIG. 18-17. (a) The equivalent circuit of Fig. 18-15b with the *base spreading resistance* r_b'' added. (b) The base spreading resistance is added to the circuit of Fig. 18-16.

high-frequency effects. In the low-frequency range of operation, however, the circuit of Fig. 18-17b is simpler to use. Note that in this circuit the resistance of the base is taken into account entirely through r_b'', and not through r_b' which replaces essentially the generator ue_c'. The resistor r_b'' is called the *base spreading resistance* and is usually of the order of several hundred ohms. The resistor $r_b = r_b' + r_b''$ is called the *base resistance*. No special designation is attached to r_b'.

We may now reasonably ask how it happens that account need be taken of the base resistivity while no mention has been made of the resistivities of the emitter and collector. The reason for this discrimination rests on the geometry of the transistor. The typical geometry of a diffused-junction p-n-p transistor is shown in Fig. 18-8a. Recalling particularly that the base region is very thin (often of the order of 1 mil), we see that the base current must flow through a very long, narrow path. The cross-sectional area for current flow in emitter and collector is very much larger. Hence, usually the ohmic drop in the base alone is of importance.

One other effect in a transistor, which we may note for the sake of completeness, is the modification[10] of the base spreading resistance with current. As the collector voltage varies, the effective base width changes and hence the base spreading resistance is actually not constant. This effect may be taken into account by including still another generator in series with r_b''. Ordinarily, however, this effect is small, and we shall not deal with it further. There are also further effects in a transistor which result from leakage over the surface of the transistor. These effects are presently not very well understood, are second-order effects, and shall be neglected here.

In low-frequency applications we shall use the equivalent circuit of Fig. 18-17b. In connection with this circuit the point must be made that the circuit is the most general linear, lumped, active, resistive, four-terminal network. Hence, if the parameters are determined by *measurements* made on the transistor, the equivalent circuit will be a correct representation. That such is actually the case may be seen in the following way. In Fig. 18-18 the box represents an arbitrary four-terminal network, active or not. If linearity applies, then the characteristics of the box may be specified in an entirely general way by specifying the parameters r_{11}, r_{12}, r_{21}, and r_{22} in the equations

Fig. 18-18. An arbitrary transmission circuit.

$$e_e = r_{11}i_e + r_{12}i_c$$
$$e_c = r_{21}i_e + r_{22}i_c \tag{18-12}$$

If the circuit is passive, $r_{12} = r_{21}$; otherwise not. We may verify that the circuit of Fig. 18-18 together with Eqs. (18-12) correctly represents the transistor in the grounded-base configuration if we select the resistance parameters in accordance with the formulas

$$r_{11} = r_e + r_b \qquad r_{12} = r_b$$
$$r_{21} = r_b + ar_c \qquad r_{22} = r_c + r_b \tag{18-13}$$

Lastly, it must be pointed out that the form shown in Fig. 18-17b is not the only form which is capable of representing a general four-terminal

active network.   In principle, an infinite variety of forms are possible
and indeed other forms are often used.   (See Prob. 18-5.)

18-12. Transistors as Small-signal Amplifiers.[11]   In Chap. 1 we dealt
with the small-signal equivalent circuit of vacuum-tube amplifier stages.
In that chapter we noted that an amplifier stage could be completely
specified by stating a Thévenin-theorem equivalent circuit with respect to
the amplifier-stage output terminals.   We shall follow the same procedure now for the transistor circuit.

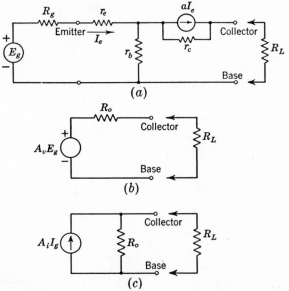

FIG. 18-19. (a) A generator E_g of impedance R_g drives a transistor in the grounded-
base configuration.   (b) The Thévenin-theorem equivalent circuit with respect to
the output terminals.   (c) The Norton-theorem equivalent circuit. I_e, I_g, and E_g
represent sinor (phasor) quantities.

Consider the circuit of Fig. 18-19a.   Here a generator E_g of internal
impedance R_g is shown connected to the input of a grounded-base transistor amplifier stage.   We desire the equivalent circuit looking back
into the collector-base output terminals of the amplifier.   The load
resistor R_L is to be considered external to and therefore not part of the
amplifier.   The equivalent circuit is shown in Fig. 18-19b.   The open-
circuit voltage gain A_v and output impedance R_o are computed to be

$$A_v = \frac{ar_c + r_b}{R_g + r_b + r_e} \tag{18-14}$$

$$R_o = r_c - r_b \frac{ar_c - R_g - r_e}{R_g + r_b + r_e}$$

$$= \frac{r_c r_b(1 - a) + (r_e + R_g)(r_c + r_b)}{R_g + r_b + r_e} \tag{18-15}$$

These expressions may be simplified if we take account of the relative order of magnitude of the values of the parameters normally encountered in a transistor. We note from Table 18-1 that $r_c \gg r_b \gg r_e$ and that $a \cong 1$. Hence

$$A_v \cong \frac{r_c}{R_g + r_b} \tag{18-16}$$

$$R_o \cong \frac{r_c[r_b(1 - a) + r_e + R_g]}{R_g + r_b} \tag{18-17}$$

We observe that A_v and R_o depend on R_g. This feature results, of course, from the fact that the input impedance of the transistor is not infinite. In this respect the transistor is a somewhat more complicated device than the vacuum tube, at least when the tube is used in the grounded-cathode and grounded-plate (cathode-follower) configurations. On the other hand a vacuum tube in the grounded-grid configuration would give rise to the same complication that A_v and R_o depend on the driving-source impedance.

The open-circuit gain is a maximum $(A_v)_{\max}$ when $R_g = 0$. In this case Eqs. (18-16) and (18-17) reduce to

$$(A_v)_{\max} = \frac{r_c}{r_b} \quad \text{and} \quad (R_o)_{R_g=0} = r_c\left[(1 - a) + \frac{r_e}{r_b}\right] \tag{18-18}$$

The gain in the presence of a load is, of course, directly determinable from A_v and R_o with the result

$$A = A_v \frac{R_L}{R_L + R_o} \tag{18-19}$$

If R_g is small enough, then $(A_v)_{\max}$ and $(R_o)_{R_g=0}$ may be substituted in Eq. (18-19) in place of A_v and R_o.

The dual of Thévenin's theorem is Norton's theorem which states that a voltage source E in series with a resistor R is equivalent to a current source E/R in parallel with a resistor R. Hence the Norton-theorem equivalent circuit for the transistor consists of a current generator $A_v E_g/R_o$ shunted by a resistor R_o.

We have

$$\frac{A_v E_g}{R_o} = \frac{R_g A_v}{R_o} \frac{E_g}{R_g} = A_i I_g \tag{18-20}$$

where
$$A_i \equiv \frac{R_g A_v}{R_o} \quad \text{and} \quad I_g \equiv \frac{E_g}{R_g} \tag{18-21}$$

Hence, the Norton equivalent circuit with respect to the output terminals of the transistor is as shown in Fig. 18-19c. The physical meaning of the symbols A_i and I_g will appear in the following considerations.

We note that the Thévenin-theorem circuit becomes particularly simple [Eq. (18-18)] in the case where R_g is very small. We shall now see that the Norton-theorem circuit becomes particularly simple when R_g is very large.

If the input source which is represented in Fig. 18-19a by E_g and R_g were itself replaced by a Norton equivalent, then E_g/R_g would be the current furnished by the equivalent current generator source. This current may be considered the input current to the transistor, I_g, in the same way that E_g is the input voltage to the transistor. If $R_L \ll R_o$ then $A_i I_g$ is the load current and hence A_i represents the current gain. The current gain A_i goes to a maximum as R_g becomes infinite and is given by

$$(A_i)_{\max} = \frac{ar_c + r_b}{r_c + r_b} \cong a \qquad (18\text{-}22)$$

while for R_o we have

$$(R_o)_{R_g = \infty} = r_c + r_b \cong r_c \qquad (18\text{-}23)$$

When R_g is small in comparison with the transistor input impedance, the equivalent circuit of Fig. 18-19b will be more convenient to use. If R_g is large in comparison with the input resistance, the equivalent circuit of Fig. 18-19c will be more convenient. If neither condition applies, then, of course, the exact expressions must be used.

The input resistance R_i to the transistor depends on the value of R_L and is given by

$$R_i = r_e + r_b \frac{r_c(1 - a) + R_L}{r_b + r_c + R_L} \qquad (18\text{-}24)$$

The range of R_i may be seen by computing R_i for $R_L = 0$ and $R_L = \infty$. Assuming again that $r_c \gg r_b \gg r_e$, we have approximately

$$R_i = r_e + r_b(1 - a) \qquad \text{for } R_L = 0 \qquad (18\text{-}25)$$
$$R_i = r_b \qquad\qquad\quad \text{for } R_L = \infty \qquad (18\text{-}26)$$

18-13. Comparison of Transistor Amplifier Configurations. The grounded-emitter and grounded-collector configurations may be discussed in exactly the manner in which the grounded-base configuration was handled in the previous section. We shall not repeat the analysis for these cases, but shall instead summarize the results in tabular form. Table 18-2 gives exact expressions for A_v, A_i, R_o, and R_i for the various configurations. The maximum voltage gain $(A_v)_{\max}$ may be obtained from the table simply by letting $R_g = 0$ in the expressions for A_v. Similarly the expressions for $(A_i)_{\max}$ may be obtained from A_i by letting $R_g \to \infty$. Note that the quantities A_v, A_i, and R_o in Table 18-2 are the parameters in the equivalent circuits of Fig. 18-19b and c. To compute the voltage or current gain in a particular case, it is still necessary to take account of the loading effect of R_L. The formulas of Table 18-2

TABLE 18-2. EXACT FORMULAS FOR THE VARIOUS TRANSISTOR CONFIGURATIONS

Equivalent-circuit parameters	Grounded base	Grounded emitter	Grounded collector
Open-circuit voltage gain A_v	$\dfrac{ar_c + r_b}{R_g + r_b + r_e}$	$-\dfrac{ar_c - r_e}{R_g + r_b + r_e}$	$\dfrac{r_e}{R_g + r_b + r_e}$
Short-circuit current gain A_i	$\dfrac{R_g(ar_c + r_b)}{r_c(R_g + r_b + r_e) - r_b(ar_c - R_g - r_e)}$	$\dfrac{-R_g(ar_c - r_e)}{r_c(1-a)(R_g + r_b + r_e) + r_e(R_g + r_b + ar_c)}$	$\dfrac{R_g r_c}{r_c(R_g + r_b + r_e) + r_e(1-a)(R_g + r_b)}$
Output resistance R_o	$r_c - r_b\dfrac{ar_c - R_g - r_e}{R_g + r_b + r_e}$	$r_c(1-a) + r_e\dfrac{R_g + r_b + r_e}{R_g + r_b + ar_e}$	$r_e + r_c(1-a)\dfrac{R_g + r_b}{R_g + r_b + r_e}$
Input resistance R_i	$r_e + r_b\dfrac{r_e - ar_c + R_L}{r_b + r_c + R_L}$	$r_b + r_e\dfrac{r_e + R_L}{r_c(1-a) + r_e + R_L}$	$r_b + r_c\dfrac{r_e + R_L}{r_c(1-a) + r_e + R_L}$

TABLE 18-3. APPROXIMATE FORMULAS ($r_c \gg r_b \gg r_e$) FOR THE VARIOUS TRANSISTOR CONFIGURATIONS

Numerical values calculated for $r_c = 2$ Meg, $r_b = 1$ K, $r_e = 20$ ohms, $a\ (\cong \alpha) = 0.98$

Parameters	Conditions	Grounded base	Grounded emitter	Grounded collector
$(A_v)_{max}$	$R_g = 0$	$\dfrac{r_c}{r_b} = 2,000$	$-\dfrac{r_c}{r_b} = -2,000$	1
$(A_i)_{max}$	$R_g = \infty$	$a = 0.98$	$-\dfrac{a}{1-a} = -49$	$\dfrac{1}{1-a} = 50$
R_o	$R_g = 0$	$r_c\left(1 - a + \dfrac{r_e}{r_b}\right) = 80$ K	$r_c\left(1 - a + \dfrac{ar_e}{r_b}\right) \cong 80$ K	$r_e + r_b(1-a) = 40$ ohms
R_o	$R_g = \infty$	$r_c = 2$ Meg	$r_c(1-a) = 40$ K	$r_c(1-a) = 40$ K
R_i	$R_L = 0$	$r_e + r_b(1-a) = 40$ ohms	$r_b + \dfrac{r_e}{1-a} = 2$ K	$r_b + \dfrac{r_e}{1-a} = 2$ K
R_i	$R_L = \infty$	$r_b = 1$ K	$r_b = 1$ K	$r_c = 2$ Meg

are useful for general reference purposes but are too complicated to yield any easy insight into transistor performance.

An easier comparison may be made from Table 18-3.   Here we have computed for the various configurations the voltage gain $(A_v)_{max}$ when the input is a zero-impedance voltage source, the current gain $(A_i)_{max}$ when the input is a perfect current source, and the output impedance for both cases.   In addition the total range over which the input impedance may vary has also been tabulated.   In this table we have taken account of the approximations which may be allowed due to the fact that $r_c \gg r_b \gg r_e$.   In computing numerical values parameters, we have used $r_c = 2$ Meg, $r_b = 1$ K, $r_e = 20$ ohms, and $a\ (\cong \alpha) = 0.98$.

The table brings out the relative versatility of the grounded-emitter configuration.   This configuration is capable of both a voltage gain and a current gain, features not shared by the other configurations.   To realize a gain nominally equal to $(A_v)_{max}$ would require not only that a zero-impedance voltage source be used but also that R_L be many times larger than the output impedance.   Normally, however, so large a value of R_L is not feasible.   Suppose, for example, that a manufacturer specifies a maximum collector voltage of, say, 30 volts.   Then we should not be inclined to use a collector supply voltage in excess of this maximum voltage since, in such a case, the collector voltage would be exceeded if the transistor were driven to cutoff.   Suppose further that the transistor is designed to carry a collector current of, say, 5 ma when biased in the middle of its active region.   Then the load resistor should be selected to have a resistance of about 15 volts/5 ma = 3 K.   Using the values in Table 18-3, we compute for the grounded emitter a voltage gain

$$A_v = -2{,}000 \times \tfrac{3}{83} = -72 \qquad\qquad (18\text{-}27)$$

Of course the load resistor may be smaller than 3 K, as when, for example, a transistor is used to drive another transistor.   Or in some applications a much higher load resistor may be acceptable.   When used as a voltage amplifier, the grounded-base configuration is capable roughly of the same gain as the grounded emitter.   The grounded base has, however, the relative disadvantage of a lower input resistance if the load resistance is small.

The grounded-collector circuit, like the cathode follower, has a maximum voltage gain $(A_v)_{max}$ which is, at most, unity.   To achieve this gain, the load resistor must be very large in comparison with the output impedance.   Since R_o is only about 40 ohms, a load resistor of the order of 400 or 500 ohms is adequate.   The grounded emitter also exhibits the greatest variation of input impedance with load resistance.

The grounded emitter and grounded collector are both capable of providing current gain which is nominally the same in both cases.   It is to be noted, however, that in both cases the current gain is not a very stable characteristic. We can compute, for the grounded-emitter case that

$$\frac{d(A_i)_{\max}}{(A_i)_{\max}} = \frac{1}{1 - a} \frac{da}{a} \qquad (18\text{-}28)$$

If $a = 0.98$, then $1/(1 - a) = 50$ and Eq. (18-28) indicates that a 1 per cent change in a will result in a 50 per cent change in $(A_i)_{\max}$. An approximately similar relationship applies in the grounded-collector case. For this reason, too, we may expect that transistor characteristic curves of collector current vs. collector voltage for various values of base current (Fig. 18-12) will be subject to a great deal of variation.

The results given in Table 18-3 also serve to give added support to the analogies made in Fig. 18-14 between the various transistor and tube configurations.

18-14. Equivalent Circuit of a Transistor at High Frequencies.[12] So far we have assumed that the transistor responds instantly to changes of input voltage or current. Actually, of course, such is not the case. To begin with, the mechanism of the transport of current carriers from emitter to collector junction is essentially one of diffusion. Hence, to find out how the transistor behaves at high frequencies, it is necessary to examine this diffusion mechanism in more detail. For this purpose we must return to the equivalent circuit of Fig. 18-17a which, unlike the circuit of Fig. 18-17b, has the advantage that the various nodes in the circuit can actually be identified with physical junctions in the transistor.

The analysis of the diffusion mechanism at high frequencies is unfortunately too complicated for our purposes to warrant a detailed discussion. It is sufficient to note here simply that the diffusion mechanism can be taken into account by modifying the circuit of Fig. 18-17a so that α and u become frequency-dependent, while the resistance r'_e and r'_c must be replaced by frequency-dependent impedances. The equations which specify this frequency dependence are suggestive of the equations which are encountered in connection with a lossy transmission line. Some such result is to have been anticipated in view of the fact that some time delay must be involved in the transport of carriers across the base region by the process of diffusion. Even having these transmission-line equations available does not put us in a much improved position because the equations are quite complicated. Hence, if we used them, we would have an equivalent circuit which is quite accurate but, unfortunately, not manageable. It is therefore necessary to make approximations in using the equations. Of course, as the approximations become more rough, the equivalent circuit becomes simpler. It is therefore a matter of engineering judgment to decide at what point we have a reasonable compromise between accuracy and manageability of equivalent circuit.

Experience shows that as a first reasonable approximation the diffusion phenomenon can be taken into account by assuming a relatively simple frequency dependence for α and by shunting the transistor junctions by diffusion capacitances C_{de} and C_{dc}, as shown in Fig. 18-20 and as discussed below.

The Frequency Dependence of α.   The frequency dependence of α is given approximately by

$$\alpha = \frac{\alpha_o}{1 + j\omega/\omega_\alpha} \tag{18-29}$$

In this equation, α_o is the low-frequency value of α. The form of the equation indicates a frequency response which is identical with that of a simple resistance-capacitance network. The angular frequency ω_α ($= 2\pi f_\alpha$) is the angular frequency at which the magnitude of α is $0.707\alpha_o$.

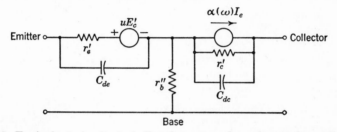

FIG. 18-20. Equivalent circuit, including frequency dependence of α and diffusion capacitances across the junctions. I_e and E_c' are sinor quantities and are functions of frequency.

The frequency f_α is termed the transistor *cutoff frequency*.   At frequencies which are appreciably less than f_α Eq. (18-29) is reasonably accurate. The approximation is progressively poorer as f approaches and exceeds f_α.   The parameter u in Fig. 18-17a has much the same frequency dependence as α.   General-purpose transistors have frequencies f_α in the range of hundreds of kilocycles.   Special-purpose high-frequency transistors may have f_α's in the range of tens of megacycles.

The Diffusion Capacitances.   The diffusion capacitances which are required to be shunted across the junctions are of the order of magnitude of

$$C_{de} = \frac{1}{1.5\omega_\alpha r_e'} \quad \text{and} \quad C_{dc} = \frac{1}{1.5\omega_\alpha r_c'} \tag{18-30}$$

We may note in passing that

$$\omega_\alpha = \frac{2D}{W_o{}^2} \tag{18-31}$$

where W_o is the zero-signal thickness of the base region and D is the diffusion constant in the base region which measures the ratio of the diffusion current to the gradient of carriers which produces the diffusion. Equations (18-30) and (18-31) indicate the importance of making W_o as small as possible to improve the response at high frequency.

If we compute the diffusion capacitances for the case $r'_e = 40$ ohms, $r'_c = 2$ Meg, and $f_\alpha = 10$ Mc, we find $C_{de} = 400$ $\mu\mu$f and $C_{dc} = 0.05$ $\mu\mu$f. Observe that, in spite of the fact that $C_{dc} \ll C_{de}$, the time constants associated with emitter and collector circuits are identical and are given by Eq. (18-30) to be $1/1.5\omega_\alpha$.

The Barrier Capacitances. In addition to the diffusion capacitances there are also barrier capacitances which must be included in the equivalent circuit. It will be recalled (see Fig. 18-7) that the transistor is largely free of electric field except in the neighborhood of the junctions. These regions of electric field are regions in which energy is stored electrostatically and this energy storage may be taken into account by including capacitors across the junctions which store equivalent amounts of energy. These barrier capacitances are not constant, but vary inversely with the cube root or with the square root of the junction voltage, depending on whether the junction is gradual (as in grown-junction transistors) or abrupt (as in fused-junction transistors). This capacitance variation results from the fact, noted earlier, that the width of the junction region increases with junction voltage. Hence, with increase in collector voltage, the effective separation of the capacitor "plates" increases with a consequent reduction in capacitance. Since the emitter-junction voltage is normally smaller than the collector-junction voltage, the emitter-junction barrier capacitance C_e should be larger than the collector-junction barrier capacitance C_c. On the other hand, the collector cross-sectional area may be larger than the emitter cross-sectional area (Fig. 18-8) so that the two capacitances may well be comparable. In typical transistors these capacitances will lie in the range 5 to 25 $\mu\mu$f. When these barrier capacitances are added to the equivalent circuit of Fig. 18-20, it is clear that the barrier capacitance may be neglected across the emitter junction and the diffusion capacitance may be neglected across the collector junction.

We shall make two further simplifying assumptions in our high-frequency equivalent circuit. First, we shall neglect the generator uE'_c in Fig. 18-20. We may do this principally because at high frequencies the generator uE'_c, which is small to start with, is shunted through the small r'_e by the large capacitor C_{de}. Second, we shall assume that $C_{de} = 1/\omega_\alpha r'_e$; that is, we shall neglect the factor 1.5 which appears in the denominator of Eq. (18-30). This last assumption will effect an appreciable simplification in the mathematical analysis since (as we shall see later) it makes the time constant of the emitter circuit the same as the time constant associated with α. We may justify this modification of Eq. (18-30) on the basis that the response of a transistor turns out to be much more sensitively dependent on the frequency response of α than on the time constant of the emitter circuit. Finally, then, the high-frequency equivalent circuit in the active region is as shown in Fig. 18-21. Note that in this figure C_d represents the diffusion capacitance, whereas C_c represents the barrier capacitance. For simplicity, we have dropped the primes on r'_e, r''_b, and r'_c. We must remember, then, that the emitter and base resistances used in the high-frequency equivalent circuit are not the same as those used in the low-frequency equivalent circuit. On the other hand, r'_c and r_c are so nearly equal that no error is involved in using the low-frequency value for the collector resistance.

18-15. Transient Response of Transistors.[13] When transistors are used as switches, the times required to turn the transistor from the *off* condition to the *on* condition, and vice versa, are of great interest. In

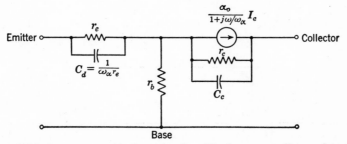

FIG. 18-21. High-frequency equivalent circuit. The base spreading resistance is r_b.

this section we shall accordingly inquire into the response of a transistor to a step of current or to a pulse of current applied at the input.

We shall assume initially for simplicity that the load resistance R_L is small enough so that the transistor is operating with its output terminals essentially short-circuited. Under these circumstances the elements r_c and C_c appear in shunt with r_b. Since $r_b \ll r_c$, we may neglect r_c. Let us assume further that over the frequency range of interest, which is of the order of ω_α, the reactance of C_c is large in comparison with r_b so that we may neglect C_c as well. Our equivalent circuit, in the grounded-base configuration, then becomes as shown in Fig. 18-22. In writing the expression for the emitter impedance, we have made use of the fact that $C_d = 1/\omega_\alpha r_e$.

Let us compute now the output current i_o in response to a current step I_1 at the input. Some small complication is involved here since we are seeking the time response of the circuit and α is given in terms of its frequency response. We might therefore compute initially the frequency response of the circuit and then evaluate the time response from this frequency response. This method involves Fourier transformations. A much simpler approach is to follow the procedure indicated in the equivalent circuit of Fig. 18-23. Here we have included a subsidiary circuit (R and C) in Fig. 18-23a which takes into account the frequency dependence of α. It is easily verified that

$$\alpha_o I_R = \frac{\alpha_o I_e}{1 + j\omega/\omega_\alpha} \tag{18-32}$$

provided that we set $RC = 1/\omega_\alpha$. (I_R and I_e are the sinor currents corresponding to the time function i_R and i_e, respectively.) Of course, in this latter equivalent circuit we shall find that the result depends only on the ω_α and not on R or C individually.

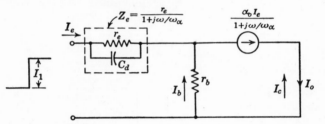

FIG. 18-22. Approximate equivalent circuit under short-circuited output conditions.

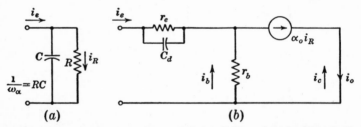

FIG. 18-23. Equivalent circuit in which an RC circuit is used to simulate the frequency dependence of α. The current i_R in (b) is calculated from the circuit in (a).

For the grounded-base configuration of Fig. 18-23, the output current i_o ($= -i_c$) is given by

$$i_o = \alpha_o I_1 (1 - \epsilon^{-\omega_\alpha t}) \tag{18-33}$$

This result is almost evident from Fig. 18-23a because at $t = 0$, $i_R = 0$; at $t = \infty$, $i_R = i_e = I_1$; the time constant is $1/\omega_\alpha$ and $i_o = \alpha_o i_R$. The rise time is $2.2/\omega_\alpha$ and is the time required for the output current to rise from 0.1 to 0.9 of its final value if the transistor operation remains in the active region.

Suppose the transistor has a load resistor R_L. The saturation current I_s will then be very nearly equal to E_{cc}/R_L. The input current step required to drive the transistor just to the point of saturation is, from Eq. (18-5), $(I_1)_{sat} = I_s/\alpha_o$. Suppose, however, that the input current

Table 18-4. Response of the Various Configurations to an Input Current Waveform

	Grounded base	Grounded emitter	Grounded collector
Response to an input current step I_1	$i_o = \alpha_o I_1(1 - \epsilon^{-\omega_\alpha t})$	$i_o = \dfrac{-\alpha_o}{1 - \alpha_o} I_1(1 - \epsilon^{-(1-\alpha_o)\omega_\alpha t})$	$i_o = I_1 + I_1 \dfrac{\alpha_o}{1 - \alpha_o}(1 - \epsilon^{-(1-\alpha_o)\omega_\alpha t})$
Rise time	$\dfrac{2.2}{\omega_\alpha}$	$\dfrac{2.2}{(1 - \alpha_o)\omega_\alpha}$	$\dfrac{2.2}{(1 - \alpha_o)\omega_\alpha}$
Time T_o to reach saturation	$\dfrac{1}{\omega_\alpha} \ln \dfrac{\alpha_o I_1}{\alpha_o I_1 - I_s}$	$\dfrac{1}{(1 - \alpha_o)\omega_\alpha} \ln \dfrac{\alpha_o I_1}{\alpha_o I_1 - (1 - \alpha_o) I_s}$	$\dfrac{1}{(1 - \alpha_o)\omega_\alpha} \ln \dfrac{\alpha_o I_1}{I_1 - (1 - \alpha_o) I_s}$
Time T_1 to fall from saturation to zero current	$\dfrac{1}{\omega_\alpha} \ln \dfrac{\alpha_o I_2 + I_s}{\alpha_o I_2}$	$\dfrac{1}{(1 - \alpha_o)\omega_\alpha} \ln \dfrac{\alpha_o I_2 + (1 - \alpha_o) I_s}{\alpha_o I_2}$	$\dfrac{1}{(1 - \alpha_o)\omega_\alpha} \ln \dfrac{I_2 + (1 - \alpha_o) I_s}{I_2}$
Approximations assumed	$(1 + \omega_\alpha r_c C_c) \dfrac{r_b + R_L}{r_c} \ll 1$	$\dfrac{R_L}{r_c} \ll 1 - \alpha_o$ $\omega_\alpha C_c R_L \ll 1$	$\dfrac{R_L}{r_c} \ll 1 - \alpha_o$ $\omega_\alpha C_c R_L \ll 1$

step I_1 is larger than $(I_1)_{sat}$. Then the collector current will go from zero to I_s in a finite time T_o. If we assume that the load resistance is small enough so that it has no appreciable effect on the response of the transistor then the time T_o may be computed from Eq. (18-33) to be

$$T_o = \frac{1}{\omega_\alpha} \ln \frac{\alpha_0 I_1}{\alpha_o I_1 - I_s} \tag{18-34}$$

Equation (18-34) applies whenever I_1 is large enough to drive the transistor to saturation.

Table 18-4 summarizes the situation for the three transistor configurations. The row giving times T_1 has to do with the return of the output current to zero and will be discussed later. Observe that in each case the response is a simple exponential except that in the grounded-collector case the exponential is preceded by a step. To make the tabulation more useful, the last column has been included which specifies the exact approximations which are required to apply in order for the results to hold. The tabulation indicates that the rise time of the grounded-base configuration is $1 - \alpha_o$ times the rise time in the other configurations. On the other hand (Table 18-3), this factor is very nearly the factor by which the common-collector and common-emitter current gains are multiplied to obtain the gain of the common base.

18-16. Effect of Collector Capacitance.[14] We shall now consider the effect on transient response of the collector capacitance C_c which has heretofore been neglected. The collector capacitance becomes important when the load resistor is no longer small enough to satisfy the conditions specified in Table 18-4.

Let us consider the grounded-base configuration of Fig. 18-24a. We may recognize that the emitter impedance can have no effect on the transient response since we have assumed a current-source driver so that the emitter impedance is in series with an infinite impedance. Hence, the circuit response may be determined from the circuit of Fig. 18-24b. There are two time constants associated with this circuit. One of these is the time constant $1/\omega_\alpha$ associated with α as given in Fig. 18-24c. The other is the time constant $R'C_c$, where R' is the resistance shunting C_c. As we have already noted, $r_c \gg r_b$ and in most cases of practical interest $r_c \gg R_L \gg r_b$. Hence, $R'C_c \cong R_L C_c$. If $1/\omega_\alpha \gg R_L C_c$, then the time constant associated with the transient response will be $1/\omega_\alpha$. Alternatively if $R_L C_c \gg 1/\omega_\alpha$, the response will be determined by $R_L C_c$. The response for the case $1/\omega_\alpha = R_L C_c$ may be written down without great difficulty, but the result is not particularly illuminating and lends itself to no generally useful result.

For the grounded-emitter and grounded-collector circuits the results also hold that the effect of the time constant $R_L C_c$ or the effect of the frequency dependence of α predominates, depending on whether $R_L C_c$ is much larger or much smaller than $1/\omega_\alpha$. For these configurations, however, there is a useful rule which applies when $R_L C_c \cong 1/\omega_\alpha$. The rule, which we state without proof, is that, provided the conditions

$$\frac{R_L}{r_c} \ll 1 \qquad \text{and} \qquad \omega_\alpha r_c C_c \gg 1 \qquad (18\text{-}35)$$

are satisfied, the effect of collector capacitance is to increase the time constant in the responses given in Table 18-4 by the factor $\omega_\alpha R_L C_c + 1$.

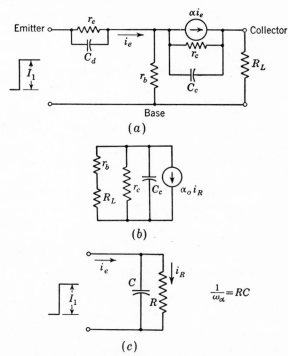

Fig. 18-24. (a) Equivalent circuit taking into account collector capacitance. (b) Simplified circuit which results owing to fact that the input drive is provided by a current source. (c) The equivalent circuit from which to calculate i_R.

Hence, the rise times and turn-on times T_o are increased by the same factor.

18-17. Delay Time in a Transistor.[15] The approximations made in connection with the diffusion equations which lead to the equivalent circuit of Fig. 18-20 have caused us to lose one important effect. This effect is the existence of a *delay* in the transistor. Such a delay is to be anticipated from the fact that a finite time is required for the carriers to diffuse across the base region. Hence if a current step is applied to the emitter, a response at the collector will appear only after some delay time.

One way in which this delay may be represented in an equivalent circuit is indicated in Fig. 18-25. Here a resistance-capacitance delay line is used. The line attenuation increases with frequency, and this accounts for the falling off with frequency of the effective value of α. It appears then that we have not completely lost sight of this delay, since we have used a resistance-capacitance delay line, except that we have reduced the line to a single section as in Fig. 18-23a. The important practical difference between the equivalent circuits of Figs. 18-23 and 18-25 is that the former indicates a slow rise in output current in response to an abrupt input current, while the latter circuit indicates a time interval before there is any response at the output.

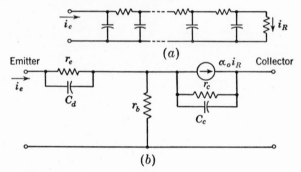

Fig. 18-25. A modification of the equivalent circuit to take into account the delay through the transistor. The current i_R in (b) is obtained from (a).

18-18. Storage Time in a Transistor.[13] When an input current step has turned a transistor switch to the *on* condition, an input step of reverse polarity may, of course, be used to turn the transistor *off*. If, in the *on* condition, the transistor is in the active region, then the turnoff transient may be computed from the active region equivalent circuit of Fig. 18-22. In particular, the time constant associated with the turn-off transient is the same as that for the turn-on transient. If, however, the transistor in the *on* condition is in the saturation region, an additional complication arises which results in an abnormally large delay before the transistor can respond to the turn-off signal.

The origin of this delay which is referred to as *storage-time delay* may be seen in Fig. 18-26 which shows the minority carrier density in the base region for various situations. In the cutoff condition where both emitter and collector junctions are back-biased the minority carrier density is zero at the junctions and quite small throughout the base region. What few minority carriers are present are the result of thermal generation of electron-hole pairs. In the active region of operation the minority carrier density is high at the emitter and nominally zero at the collector where the carriers are being rapidly swept across the collector junction. The gradient in density across the base region is precisely what gives rise to the diffusion process which accounts for current flow across the base. Of course, when an input signal is applied to drive the emitter junction to the back-biased condition, this process will not be complete until the minority carriers in the base region have been removed. The equivalent circuit of Fig. 18-25, or more simply of Fig. 18-23, is adequate to compute the time involved.

In the saturation region (to which our equivalent circuits do not apply) both the emitter and the collector are emitting carriers into the base region. Also, since both junctions are forward-biased, the voltages across the junctions will be small and the process of collection at the junctions will be relatively slow. As a result the density of minority carriers in the base region builds up to an abnormally large level. Since the turn-off process cannot really begin until this abnormal carrier density has been removed, a relatively long delay may elapse before the transistor responds to a turn-off signal at the input. In an extreme case this storage-time delay may be two or three times the rise or fall time

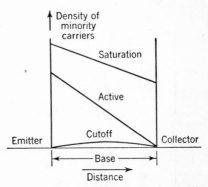

Fig. 18-26. Minority-carrier density in base in the cutoff, active, and saturation regions of operation.

through the active region. In any event, it is clear that when transistor switches are to be used in an application where speed is at a premium, it is advantageous to restrain the transistor from entering the saturation region.

18-19. Over-all Transistor Response. The complete response of a transistor which is driven from cutoff to saturation and back again to cutoff is shown in Fig. 18-27. A grounded-emitter switch is shown, since this configuration is the most useful. The general results, however, apply also to the other configurations. In the response shown in Fig. 18-27d, the *delay time* is T_d, and T_o is the *rise time* (defined as the time required for the output current to reach the saturation level I_s). The *storage time* is T_s (also called the *hold time*), and T_1 is the *decay time* (also called the *fall time*). As a matter of practice it often turns out that the delay time T_d is relatively small enough to be neglected.

We consider that the driving current is furnished as a result of a voltage pulse, of the form shown in Fig. 18-27b, applied through a large resistor R_g. At the moment the transistor is driven out of the cutoff region, the impedance seen looking into the transistor input terminals is small. Hence, if R_g is adequately large, the transistor input current at this time is $I_1 = E_1/R_g$, as indicated in Fig. 18-27c.

The rise time T_o is a function of the driving current I_1. The dependence of T_o on I_1 is given in Table 18-4. The storage time is a function both of I_1 and of the input-pulse duration. As the input-pulse duration becomes larger, the number of minority carriers stored in the base region becomes larger and the storage time increases. As the input pulse increases further in duration, an equilibrium distribution of stored carriers is finally attained and thereafter T_s no longer increases. The storage time also increases with increasing I_1.

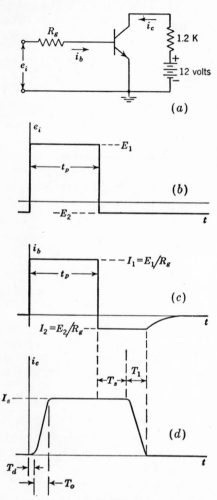

(a)

(b)

(c)

(d)

FIG. 18-27. (a) Grounded-emitter switch circuit; (b) driving-voltage waveform; (c) input current waveform; (d) output current response for small R_L.

It is found that even when the emitter current of a transistor is in the reverse direction, the parameter α remains nearly constant and equal approximately to the normal transistor α. This means that if the input current to the transistor in Fig. 18-27 were reversed rather than simply reduced to zero, the output current would start to fall toward a negative value rather than toward zero. Accordingly the fall time of the transistor may be reduced appreciably by causing the input current signal to *reverse* at the end of the pulse. It is for this reason that an input waveform has been indicated in Fig. 18-27b which attains at its termination a *negative* voltage level $-E_2$. Because of the storage of minority carriers in the base region, the impedance presented at the transistor input terminals in response to the voltage $-E_2$ does not immediately attain the large value corresponding to cutoff. Instead, the input impedance persists at a low value, and if R_g is large enough, a reverse current flows which is given by $|I_2| = E_2/R_g$. The input impedance continues to be small, and the reverse current continues at the value I_2 until the minority carriers in the immediate neighborhood of the transistor junctions have been swept away. At this point the impedances of the junctions begin to increase sharply, and the input current starts to fall, eventually becoming zero after the minority carriers throughout the base region have had time to drift over to the junctions.

The over-all result of driving the transistor well back into the cutoff region at the termination of the pulse is that the fall time is appreciably reduced. The collector current does not approach the zero current axis asymptotically but rather falls to zero in a finite time T_1. The fall time is given in Table 18-4.

It is found frequently, as indicated in Fig. 18-27c and d, that the reverse current remains constant at the value I_2 until just about the time i_c becomes zero. In some circumstances, however, depending on the geometry of construction of the transistor and on the value of R_g, the reverse current may start to fall to zero before the collector current has become zero. In such cases the formulas given for the fall time T_1 are somewhat in error.

The times typically encountered in switching a representative switching transistor may be seen in Fig. 18-28. Here an 8-μsec switching pulse is applied to a Sylvania 2N35 n-p-n transistor. The collector supply voltage is 12 volts and $R_L = 1.2$ K, so that $I_s = 12/1.2 = 10$ ma. The driving-pulse duration is long enough to ensure no further increase of T_s with pulse duration.

18-20. Analytic Expressions for Transistor Characteristics.[16] So far our attention has been focused on the active region and we have investigated the speed with which a transistor switch may be moved through the active region from the *off* condition to the *on* condition, and vice versa. We must now consider the d-c conditions with respect to currents and voltages which apply at these *on* and *off* end points of the switching operation. Certain information concerning d-c conditions is available from the transistor characteristic curves as in Figs. 18-10 and 18-12. But the information is not complete. For example, consider the grounded-emitter switch of Fig. 18-29 in which R_g is the resistance of the driving generator. If we know the base current I_b which is being used to drive the transistor to saturation, then we may determine from the common-emitter characteristics of Fig. 18-12 the collector current and the collector-to-emitter voltage. But suppose we desire to know under these conditions the base-to-emitter voltage, E_{be}. We are required to know E_{be} in order to permit a determination of I_b. To find E_{be}, we require a set of transistor characteristics which give E_{be} vs. I_b for, say, various values of I_c. Furthermore, we note that the collector-to-emitter voltage

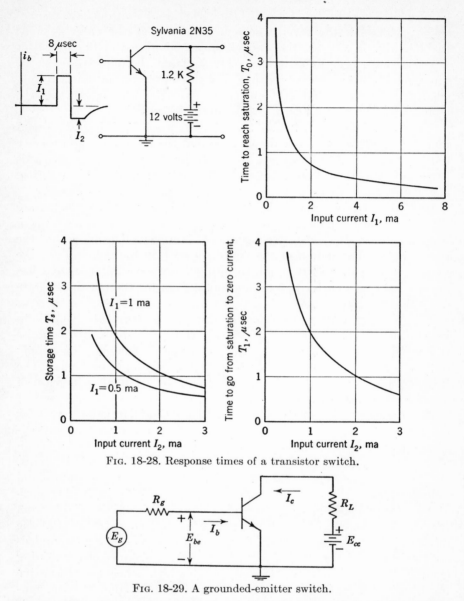

Fig. 18-28. Response times of a transistor switch.

Fig. 18-29. A grounded-emitter switch.

in the saturation region cannot be read with precision from the curves of Fig. 18-12. This situation often turns out to be highly inconvenient since there are circuits (involving two or more transistors) in which the operation may be affected by a change of several tenths of a volt in collector-to-emitter voltage. Hence more detailed transistor characteristics may be required. Similar remarks may be made in connection

with the other transistor configurations.   The over-all intention of the
above remarks is to point out that a complete specification of transistor
characteristics would require a large number of quite detailed families of
curves.

Fortunately, there is an alternative solution to the problem which
results from the fact that it is possible to write analytic expressions which
relate the collector and emitter currents to the voltages across the collector
and emitter junctions.   These expressions, which we state without proof,
are the following:

$$I_e = \frac{\alpha_I I_{co}}{1 - \alpha_N \alpha_I} \left(\epsilon^{E_c'/E_T} - 1 \right) - \frac{I_{eo}}{1 - \alpha_N \alpha_I} \left(\epsilon^{E_c'/E_T} - 1 \right) \qquad (18\text{-}36)$$

$$I_c = \frac{\alpha_N I_{eo}}{1 - \alpha_N \alpha_I} \left(\epsilon^{E_c'/E_T} - 1 \right) - \frac{I_{co}}{1 - \alpha_N \alpha_I} \left(\epsilon^{E_c'/E_T} - 1 \right) \qquad (18\text{-}37)$$

The quantities which appear in these equations have the following meaning: I_{co} is the collector reverse saturation current, $E_T = T/11,600$, while

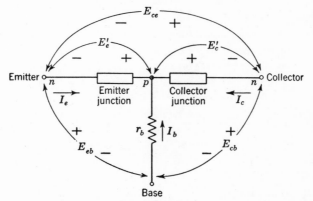

FIG. 18-30. Definition of the quantities E_e' and E_c' which appear in Eqs. (18-36) and
(18-37).   The polarities assigned to the voltages E_e' and E_c' apply to an n-p-n transistor.

α_N is the "normal" alpha of the transistor.   These three parameters
were introduced earlier except that α_N was previously designated simply
by the symbol α.   The symbols I_{eo} and α_I refer to the reverse saturation current and the transistor alpha when the transistor functions in
"inverted" fashion.   That is to say, I_{eo} is the emitter reverse saturation
current.   This is the current which flows across the emitter junction
when the emitter junction is reverse-biased and the collector current is
zero.   Similarly α_I is the transistor α under the condition that the
collector junction is forward-biased and therefore acting as the emitter
while the emitter is reverse-biased and acting as the collector.   The
symbol E_e' stands for the voltage drop from the p-type material to the
n-type material across the emitter *junction* as indicated in Fig. 18-30.
The symbol E_c' stands for the drop across the collector junction with the

same polarity convention. Observe that a junction is forward-biased when E' is positive and back-biased when E' is negative. Provided that this polarity convention is observed, Eqs. (18-36) and (18-37) apply equally to either a p-n-p or an n-p-n transistor. The convention with respect to the currents is the same as given previously; that is, the positive direction of current is into the transistor. Our interest is in the cutoff and saturation regions, but it should be noted that these equations apply to all three regions.

We may note, in passing, that the form of Eqs. (18-36) and (18-37) is not unreasonable in view of Eq. (18-2), which applies to a simple junction diode. In the present case the currents are given by the sum of two terms, because in a transistor the current across a junction depends not only on that junction voltage but also to a smaller extent on the voltage across the other junction.

The parameters α_N, α_I, I_{co}, and I_{eo} are not independent but are related by the equation

$$\alpha_N I_{eo} = \alpha_I I_{co} \tag{18-38}$$

Hence if α_N and I_{co} are known, both α_I and I_{eo} may be determined from a measurement of the emitter reverse saturation current. For many commercial transistors I_{eo} lies in the range from $0.5I_{co}$ to I_{co}. For the 2N35 transistor $I_{eo} \cong 0.8I_{co} \cong 1.6$ μa, and hence $\alpha_I \cong 0.8\alpha_N \cong 0.78$.

Equations (18-36) and (18-37) may be applied to determine d-c voltages and currents in connection with the circuit of Fig. 18-30. We have neglected, as before, the resistivity of the emitter and collector material and have included the base spreading resistance r_b. The polarities assigned to the junction voltages E_e' and E_c' are correct for an n-p-n transistor.

If Eq. (18-36) is multiplied by α_N and is added to Eq. (18-37), the result is

$$I_c = I_{co}(1 - \epsilon^{E_c'/E_T}) - \alpha_N I_e \tag{18-39}$$

Similarly, if Eq. (18-37) is multiplied by α_I and is added to Eq. (18-36), the result is

$$I_e = I_{eo}(1 - \epsilon^{E_e'/E_T}) - \alpha_I I_c \tag{18-40}$$

Equation (18-39) is the analytic expression for the collector-current curves of Fig. 18-10. In the active region, for E_c' more negative than about 0.1 volt, the exponential term is negligible compared with unity and Eq. (18-39) reduces to Eq. (18-4).

Equations (18-39) and (18-40) may be solved for the junction voltages with the result

$$E_e' = E_T \ln\left(1 - \frac{I_e + \alpha_I I_c}{I_{eo}}\right) \tag{18-41}$$

and

$$E_c' = E_T \ln\left(1 - \frac{I_c + \alpha_N I_e}{I_{co}}\right) \tag{18-42}$$

We now see that given any two currents, say I_e and I_c, then the third current may be found from

$$I_b + I_c + I_e = 0 \qquad (18\text{-}43)$$

and the junction voltages may be obtained from Eqs. (18-41) and (18-42). Or conversely, if E_c' and E_e' are given, the currents may be found from Eqs. (18-36), (18-37), and (18-43).

18-21. D-C Conditions in Cutoff and Saturation Regions. Let us now apply the results of Sec. 18-20 to find the d-c currents and voltages in the grounded-emitter switch of Fig. 18-29.

The Cutoff Region. We noted earlier that in order to drive the transistor to cutoff it was not sufficient to reduce the base current to zero, since under these circumstances the collector current will flow across the emitter junction and the emitter junction will not be back-biased. We found instead that if the base current is set to be equal to the collector reverse saturation current I_{co}, the emitter current will be zero. Let us now compute the back-biasing voltage which must be applied between base and ground (emitter) in order to achieve this cutoff condition. We assume an *n-p-n* transistor as in Fig. 18-29.

At cutoff $I_e = 0$ and $I_c = I_{co}$ and Eq. (18-41) becomes

$$E_e' = E_T \ln \left(1 - \frac{\alpha_I I_{co}}{I_{eo}} \right)$$
$$= E_T \ln \left(1 - \alpha_N \right) \qquad (18\text{-}44)$$

At room temperature ($T = 300°$ K), $E_T = 0.026$ and for $\alpha_N = 0.98$, $E_e' = -0.1$ volt. However, in the neighborhood of cutoff we may expect that the value of α may be smaller than the nominal value $\alpha = 0.98$. If, for example, we take $\alpha = 0.9$, we then find that $E_e' = -0.06$ volt. For a *n-p-n* transistor, E_e' is the voltage drop from the base side to the emitter side of the emitter junction. To find the voltage drop from the base to emitter terminal, we must add the voltage drop across the base spreading resistance. This drop is $I_{co}r_b$. For $I_{co} = 2$ μa and $r_b = 250$ ohms, this drop is only 0.5 mv and may be neglected. In Fig. 18-29 the drop across R_g will also ordinarily be negligible. We conclude that the transistor is cut off by a back-biasing emitter-to-base voltage of less than 100 mv.

When the transistor is in cutoff, the collector and base currents are very small and hence, unless R_g and R_L are very large, we may consider that the base-to-emitter voltage and the collector-to-emitter voltage are the same as the applied voltages E_g and E_{cc}. Under these circumstances we shall be interested principally in the small residual currents which flow. We may find these currents by recognizing that, if the back bias on each junction is of the order of 0.1 volt (or larger), then the exponential terms in Eqs. (18-36) and (18-37) may be neglected.   Under these circumstances the currents are given by

$$I_e = \frac{I_{eo}(1 - \alpha_N)}{1 - \alpha_N\alpha_I} \qquad (18\text{-}45)$$

$$I_c = \frac{I_{co}(1 - \alpha_I)}{1 - \alpha_N\alpha_I} \qquad (18\text{-}46)$$

Observe that these currents are constant and not functions of the junction voltages.   As an example, assume $I_{co} = 2.0 \,\mu a$, $I_{eo} = 1.6 \,\mu a$, $\alpha_N = 0.98$, and $\alpha_I = 0.78$.   Then $I_e = 0.14 \,\mu a$, $I_c = 1.9 \,\mu a$, and $I_b = -2.0 \,\mu a$.

The Saturation Region.   In this region both junctions are forward-biased and the currents which flow will be largely determined by the circuit external to the transistor.   Therefore the points of principal interest are the voltages which exist across the transistor terminals.   The junction voltages may be computed as a function of the currents from Eqs. (18-41) and (18-42).   Consider a common-emitter switch using a supply voltage $E_{cc} = 22.5$ volts and 5.6-K load resistor.   The load line for this case is shown in Fig. 18-12.   Here we find that at saturation $I_c = 4.0$ ma and $I_b = 0.1$ ma so that $I_e = -4.1$ ma.   In addition, for the 2N35 transistor $I_{co} \cong 2.0 \,\mu a$, $\alpha_N \cong 0.98$, $\alpha_I \cong 0.78$, and $I_{eo} \cong 1.6 \,\mu a$.   Substituting in Eqs. (18-41) and (18-42), we find $E'_e = 0.17$ volt and $E'_c = 0.06$ volt.   Hence we find that to drive the transistor into saturation requires a base-to-emitter voltage E'_e of only about 0.17 volt.   The voltage drop between the base terminal and the emitter terminal will be a little larger than this value.   This feature results from the ohmic drop across the base spreading resistance and the ohmic drop across the small but finite resistance of the emitter material.   It is therefore most frequently found in practice that when the transistor is driven well into saturation, the base-to-emitter terminal voltage is more nearly 0.2 or 0.25 volt.   Observe further that the collector-to-emitter voltage is $E'_{ce} = E'_e - E'_c = 0.17 - 0.06 = 0.11$ volt.   Note that the collector-to-emitter voltage is smaller than the base-to-emitter voltage.   Suppose that to drive the transistor further into saturation we use a base current of, say, 200 μa rather than 100 μa.   Then, as may be seen in Eqs. (18-41) and (18-42), E'_e will not change appreciably but E'_c will become 0.11 volt

TABLE 18-5. CUTOFF AND SATURATION CONDITIONS IN AN $n\text{-}p\text{-}n$ (2N35)
GROUNDED-EMITTER TRANSISTOR

	I_c	I_b, μa	E_{be}, volts	E_{ce}, volts
Cutoff.........	2 μa	-2	-0.1	E_{cc}
Saturation.....	4 ma	100	0.2	0.11
	4 ma	200	0.2	0.06

so that the collector-to-emitter voltage will drop to 0.06 volt. Observe that the nominal cancellation of junction voltages leads to a collector-to-emitter voltage in the *on* condition which is measured in millivolts. Cutoff and saturation conditions in the grounded-emitter configuration for the 2N35 *n-p-n* transistor are summarized in Table 18-5.

In the next several sections we shall discuss some illustrations of transistors in switching applications.

18-22. A Transistor Binary Circuit. A transistor binary circuit is shown in Fig. 18-31. We recall the rough identification noted earlier between the base, collector, and emitter with the grid, plate, and cathode, respectively, of a vacuum tube. With this identification in mind, the

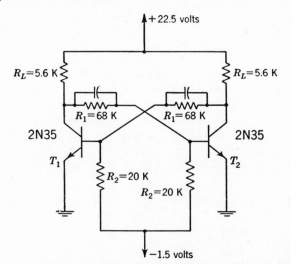

FIG. 18-31. A binary circuit. Commutating capacitors $\cong$ 150 $\mu\mu$f.

analogy between the present transistor binary and the vacuum-tube binary of Fig. 5-5 is too obvious to require elaboration.

Let us compute the stable states of the binary of Fig. 18-31. In order that a stable state be established, it is enough that either a transistor be cut off or that a transistor be in saturation so that the loop gain be less than unity. But for the sake of stability (see Sec. 5-1), it is common practice to arrange that, in a stable state, one transistor be in cutoff and the other transistor in saturation. Assume then that transistor T_2 is in saturation and T_1 in cutoff. Since the resistances of the coupling network (R_1 and R_2) are large in comparison with the load resistor R_L, we may determine the collector voltage of T_2 by drawing a load line corresponding to 5.6 K on the common-emitter characteristics of Fig. 18-12. We note from this load line that the collector current is 4 ma and that the transistor will be in saturation if the base current is larger than 100 μa. The corresponding collector-to-ground voltage E_{ce2} for transistor T_2 has already been computed in Table 18-5 to be 0.11 volt for $I_b = 100$ μa and only 0.06 volt for $I_b = 200$ μa. This voltage is of interest at the present time only in so far as it affects the base voltage of transistor T_1. We shall make little error if we assume $E_{ce2} = 0$. This is, as a matter of fact, the value we would be inclined to estimate if we tried to read the voltage from the curves of Fig. 18-12.

Since we have assumed T_1 cut off we may neglect the very small base current (2 μa) of T_1. We therefore have for the base-to-emitter voltage of T_1

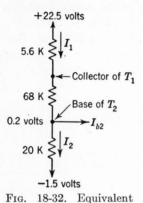

+22.5 volts

5.6 K $\quad I_1$

←— Collector of T_1

68 K

Base of T_2

0.2 volts $\quad I_{b2}$

20 K $\quad I_2$

−1.5 volts

FIG. 18-32. Equivalent circuit from which to calculate I_{b2} of Fig. 18-31.

$$E_{be1} = -1.5 \frac{68}{68 + 20} = -1.16 \text{ volts} \quad (18\text{-}47)$$

Since, from Table 18-5, a voltage of the order of −0.1 volt is adequate to keep the transistor cut off, we see from Eq. (18-47) that transistor T_1 is certainly cut off.

We must now verify that the transistor T_2 is in saturation. In Table 18-5 we find that in the saturation region $E_{be} \cong 0.2$ volt. Hence, the equivalent circuit from which to calculate the base current of T_2 is given in Fig. 18-32. In drawing this circuit, we have neglected the small cutoff collector current of T_1 which flows in the 5.6-K resistor. From Fig. 18-32 we have

$$I_1 = \frac{22.5 - 0.2}{68 + 5.6} \text{ ma} = 302 \text{ } \mu a \qquad I_2 = \frac{0.2 + 1.5}{20} \text{ ma} = 85 \text{ } \mu a$$

and

$$I_{b2} = I_1 - I_2 = 302 - 85 = 217 \text{ } \mu a$$

It has therefore been verified that T_2 is indeed in saturation since only 100 μa of base current is required to drive T_2 into saturation. And the corresponding collector-to-emitter voltage will be less than the 60 mv which results when $I_b = 200$ μa. The collector-to-emitter voltage of T_1 is evidently, from Fig. 18-31, $E_{ce1} = 22.5 - 5.6 \times 0.302 = 20.8$ volts.

In summary, a stable state of the binary is characterized by the following voltages and currents:

$$I_{c1} \cong 0 \qquad I_{c2} = 4 \text{ ma} \qquad I_{b1} \cong 0 \qquad I_{b2} = 217 \text{ } \mu a$$
$$E_{be1} = -1.16 \qquad E_{be2} \cong 0.2 \qquad E_{ce1} = 20.8 \qquad E_{ce2} = 0.06 \text{ volt}$$

The second stable state is one in which T_2 is cut off and T_1 is in saturation and the currents and voltages above are interchanged between T_1 and T_2.

By and large, all the considerations of Chap. 5 with respect to triggering of the binary apply equally well to the transistor binary. In the transistor binary, however, unlike the vacuum-tube binary, the resolution time is increased because of the minority-carrier-storage effect. Therefore, where resolution time is at a premium, steps must be taken to prevent the transistor from entering the saturation region in the stable state. One way to achieve this goal is to use junction diodes which restrain the collector junction from developing a forward bias. For example, suppose in Fig. 18-31 that the collectors of the transistor were connected through diodes to a reference voltage of say $+1$ volt. Then the transistor which is *on* in the stable state would have a collector voltage of $+1$ volt and the transistor would not be in saturation. Of course, as discussed in Sec. 4-1, junction diodes suffer from storage effects also, but the storage times in diodes are quite appreciably smaller than in transistors.

One difficulty with the scheme outlined above is that low-impedance voltage-reference sources must be supplied. Hence, the breakdown diodes described in Sec. 18-4 are particularly appropriate for use in the present application since they provide their own reference voltage. An ingenious scheme[17] for using breakdown diodes to avoid saturation in a binary is shown in the self-biased binary circuit of Fig. 18-33. Diodes D_1 and D_2 are nominally identical as are diodes D_3 and D_4. The operation of the circuit depends on the fact that the breakdown voltage E' of diodes D_3 and D_4 is larger than the breakdown voltage E of diodes D_1 and D_2. Both diodes D_3 and D_4 are always in the breakdown region. Depending, however, on which stable state the binary happens to find itself, diode D_1 will be either in the breakdown region or in the forward-biased condition. If D_1 is in the breakdown region, diode D_2 will be forward-biased, and vice versa. In either of the stable states the

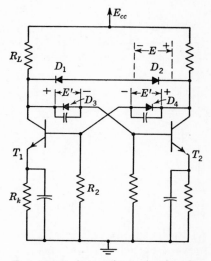

Fig. 18-33. A transistor circuit using breakdown diodes to prevent the transistors from entering the saturation region.

voltage difference between the collectors will be equal to the reference voltage of diode D_1 or D_2.

Assume the binary is in a state in which transistor T_1 is conducting and T_2 is nonconducting. Then the collector voltage of T_2 is higher than the collector voltage of T_1. Therefore diode D_1 is forward-biased and the voltage across D_1 is nominally zero. Diode D_2 is in the breakdown region and maintains across itself a voltage E with the polarity indicated. The voltage drop from collector to base of T_2 is $E + E'$ and the corresponding voltage drop for T_1 is $E' - E$. Since $E' > E$, the conducting transistor as well as the nonconducting transistor has a positive voltage drop from collector to base. For the n-p-n transistors indicated, this result means that the collector junctions are back-biased, as is required to avoid saturation.

A simpler method[18] of avoiding saturation is to design the binary circuit so that in a stable state one transistor is at cutoff while the other is within its normal range of operation (the active region). It will be recalled (see Sec. 5-1) that under these circumstances the d-c stability of the binary will suffer. A common-emitter resistor may be used to advantage to restore some measure of stability.

18-23. A Direct-connected Binary Circuit.[19] The binary circuit of Fig. 18-34 is especially interesting because of its extreme simplicity. If, in a vacuum-tube binary, similar direct connection were made from plate to grid, the binary would have only one stable state in which both tubes would be conducting heavily. To see, however, that the transistor binary has two distinct stable states, let us consider an example for which $E_{cc} = 1.5$ volts and $R_L = 2$ K.

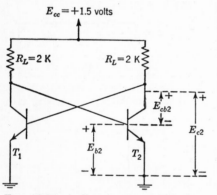

$E_{cc} = +1.5$ volts

$R_L = 2$ K $R_L = 2$ K

E_{cb2}

E_{c2}

T_1 E_{b2} T_2

FIG. 18-34. A direct-connected binary.

Initially, let us neglect entirely the presence of transistor T_1. Then the circuit of Fig. 18-34 consists simply of transistor T_2 whose emitter is grounded and whose collector and base are connected through resistors R_L to the supply voltage. The base-to-emitter junction is then certainly forward-biased. A first guess at the base current is that the base current is $E_{cc}/R_L = 1.5/2$ ma $= 750$ μa. From Fig. 18-12 we see that this current is certainly large enough to drive the transistor into saturation. Hence, we may expect that actually the base-to-emitter voltage E_{b2} of T_2 will be of the order of several tenths of a volt and the collector voltage E_{c2} will be quite low. The calculation which follows will justify these tentative assumptions.

As a first approximation let us assume $I_c = 750$ μa and $I_b = 750$ μa so that $I_e = -1,500$ μa. Then, from Eq. (18-41) using $\alpha_I = 0.78$ and $I_{eo} = 1.6$ μa, we compute $E'_e = 0.165$ volt. To find the voltage drop between the base and emitter terminals, we must add the drop $I_b r_b$ due to the flow of base current through the base spreading resistance. Note that r_b here is the base spreading resistance and not the base resistance used in the equivalent circuit of Fig. 18-17b. The reason for this feature is that the base resistance in Fig. 18-17b takes into account the generator ue_c' which appears in Fig. 18-17a and which does not occur explicitly in Fig. 18-17b. However, the effect of the generator ue_c' is already included in Eqs. (18-36) and (18-37).

For a base spreading resistance $r_b = 250$ ohms, the corresponding $I_b r_b$ drop is 0.188 volt so that $E_{be} = 0.165 + 0.188 = 0.35$ volt. As a second approximation, we take $I_b = (1.5 - 0.35)/2$ ma $= 575$ μa. We consider still that $I_c = 750$ μa so that $I_e = -750 - 575 = -1,325$ μa. Recalculating E_e' from Eq. (18-41), we find that $E_e' = 0.160$ volt. Since E_e' has changed only very slightly, no additional corrections of the approximation are required. We now calculate

$$E_{be} = E_{b2} = 0.160 + I_b r_b = 0.160 + 0.144 = 0.3 \text{ volt}$$

Next, using $I_c = 750$ μa, $I_e = -1,325$ μa, $\alpha_N = 0.98$, and $I_{co} = 2.0$ μa, we compute from Eq. (18-42) that $E_c' = 0.146$ so that

$$\begin{aligned} E_{ce} = E_{c2} &= -E_c' + E_e' \\ &= -0.146 + 0.160 = 0.01 \text{ volt} \end{aligned}$$

Now let us restore the transistor T_1 to the circuit. We may easily verify that the currents which flow in transistor T_1 are small enough to have no appreciable effect on the above computations. From the circuit of Fig. 18-34 we have that

$$E_{e1}' = E_{be1} = E_{c2} = 0.01 \text{ volt}$$
and
$$E_{c1}' = E_{bc1} = E_{cb2} = E_{c2} - E_{b2} = -0.3 \text{ volt}$$

For these numerical values of E_{e1}' and E_{c1}' and for $I_{co} = 2.0$ μa, $\alpha_N = 0.98$, and $\alpha_I = 0.78$, we find, from Eqs. (18-36) and (18-37), that $I_{c1} = 13$ μa and $I_{e1} = -11$ μa. The exact values of these currents are not so important as is the result that the currents in T_1 are small enough so that the currents and voltages computed for transistor T_2 remain unaltered.

The binary of Fig. 18-34 has therefore two stable states in which one transistor is in saturation and the second transistor is very nearly at cutoff. The voltage swing at a collector is only of the order of 0.3 volt but this voltage is sufficient for turning transistor switches *on* and *off*.

18-24. Monostable and Astable Transistor Multivibrators. Consider the monostable transistor multi of Fig. 18-35. The analogy between this circuit and the monostable vacuum-tube multi of Fig. 6-1 is too obvious to require elaboration. We shall now explain the waveforms indicated in Fig. 18-36. Our discussion will be brief because the monostable multi has already been considered in detail in Chap. 6.   In the stable state T_2 is *on* and T_1 is *off*.   The base current of T_2 is 22.5/120 ma = 188 μa approximately.   From a 10-K load line in Fig. 18-12 we find that saturation occurs for a base current of 60 μa and that I_c = 2.25 ma.   Hence, T_2 is indeed in saturation.   From Eqs. (18-41) and (18-42) the base voltage

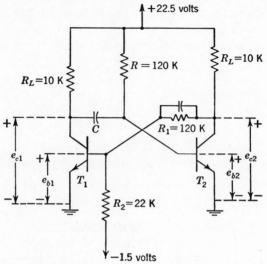

FIG. 18-35. A monostable multivibrator.

$e_{b2} \cong 0.2$ volt and the collector voltage $e_{c2} \cong 0.1$ volt.   Neglecting the small value of e_{c2}, we find

$$e_{b1} = -(1.5)\,\frac{120}{120 + 22} = -1.25 \text{ volts}$$

which is certainly enough to cut off T_1.   Therefore, the collector of T_1 is at the supply voltage, e_{c1} = 22.5 volts.

If a negative trigger is applied at the collector of T_1 or a positive trigger at the base, the multi will make a transistion to its quasi-stable state.   The transistor T_1 will go *on* and T_2 will go *off*.   At saturation, $e_{b1} \cong 0.2$ volt and the equivalent circuit from which to calculate the base current i_{b1} is given in Fig. 18-37.   We have

$$I_1 = \frac{22.5 - 0.2}{10 + 120} \text{ ma} = 170 \text{ } \mu\text{a} \qquad I_2 = \frac{0.2 + 1.5}{22} \text{ ma} = 77 \text{ } \mu\text{a}$$

and
$$i_{b1} = I_1 - I_2 = 170 - 77 = 93 \text{ } \mu\text{a}$$

Hence, we have confirmed that T_1 is in saturation.   From Eqs. (18-41) and (18-42), $e_{b1} \cong 0.2$ volt and $e_{c1} \cong 0.1$ volt.   The voltage e_{c2} = 22.5 $- 10I_1$ = 20.8 volts.   Since, at the transition, e_{c1} drops practically by an amount equal to the full supply voltage, e_{b2} will drop by the same amount, 22.4 volts. Since initially e_{b2} was at 0.2 volt, the voltage e_{b2} will drop to

$$-22.4 + 0.2 = -22.2 \text{ volts}$$

These values are indicated on the waveforms of Fig. 18-36.

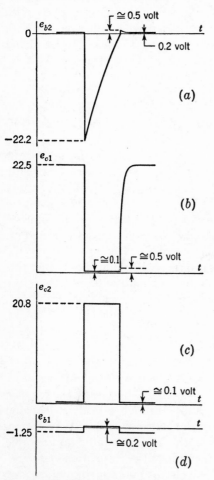

The multi remains in the stable state so long as transistor T_2 remains cut off and e_{c1}, e_{c2}, and e_{b1} maintain the values computed above. The voltage e_{b2}, however, rises exponentially toward 22.5 volts as C charges through R. The transistor T_2 comes out of cutoff when e_{b2} is of the order of -0.1 volt. At this point T_2 goes *on* and T_1 goes *off*. The collector voltage e_{c2} drops abruptly to nearly zero. An overshoot develops in e_{b2}, which decays as the capacitor C recharges through the flow of base current. The abrupt but small voltage rise in e_{b2} appears also at e_{c1} since collector and base are connected through C. The base current of T_2 which recharges C flows also through

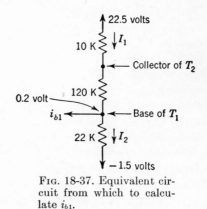

Fig. 18-36. Waveforms of the monostable multivibrator.

Fig. 18-37. Equivalent circuit from which to calculate i_{b1}.

the load resistor of T_1. The time constant associated with the decay of the overshoot in e_{b2} and with the exponential rise of e_{c1} is $R_L C$.

We propose to calculate the overshoot in e_{b2} in the same manner that was used in Chap. 5 in connection with the vacuum-tube multi. For this purpose we require to know the value of a resistance to be considered connected from the base to emitter of T_2 to account for the base current which flows when e_{b2} goes positive. This resistor r will correspond to the grid resistor r_c in Fig. 6-6. When the input to the base is an abrupt positive step which brings the transistor into the active region, we may neglect the voltage drop that appears across the emitter junction because of the effect of the large diffusion capacitance across this junction. We may therefore estimate that the resistor r is of the order of the base spreading resistor which we have taken to be 250 ohms. Recognizing that immediately before the reverse transition the voltage across C is nominally zero, we estimate that the overshoot in e_{b2} is

$$e_{b2} \text{ (overshoot)} = 22.5 \frac{r}{r + R_L} = \frac{22.5 \times 0.25}{10.25} = 0.55 \text{ volt}$$

It is interesting to make a comparison of the waveforms of Fig. 18-36 with the waveforms of Fig. 6-5. Observe the extent to which a transistor is more nearly an ideal switch than is a vacuum tube. In a transistor multi the collector voltage swings are very nearly equal to the supply voltage. Note, in comparing the waveform e_{b2} with the grid waveform at G_2, the absence of a *grid base region*, i.e., in the transistor there is no region of linear operation where the control terminal draws no current. Note also in the transistor waveforms the absence of any perceptible undershoot. Of course, there must be some small undershoot, but this undershoot can be only of the order of tens of millivolts and therefore not perceptible.

The circuit diagram of a transistor astable multi is shown in Fig. 18-38a. The waveforms at a collector and a base of one of the transistors is shown in Fig. 18-38b. The waveforms for the other transistor are, of course, identical except that when one transistor is *on* the other is *off*. These waveforms should be compared with the waveforms of Fig. 6-17 for the vacuum-tube astable multi. Note again in the case of the transistor multi waveforms the absence of a jump through a grid base region and the absence of undershoots in either the collector or base waveforms.

Breakdown diodes may be used[17] in both the monostable and astable multi to prevent the transistors from going into the saturation region.

18-25. The Blocking Oscillator.[20] The circuit diagram of a transistor blocking oscillator is shown in Fig. 18-39a and the collector waveform is shown in Fig. 18-39b. Qualitatively, the operation of the transistor oscillator is so nearly identical to the operation of the vacuum-tube blocking oscillator (Sec. 9-9) that the description need not be repeated. Since the transistor is almost a perfect switch, then the pulse amplitude in the transistor oscillator is very nearly equal to the collector supply voltage.

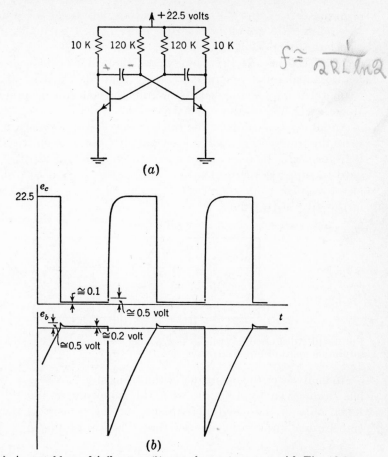

$$f \cong \frac{1}{2RL\ln 2}$$

(a)

(b)

FIG. 18-38. (a) An astable multivibrator; (b) waveforms (compare with Fig. 18-36).

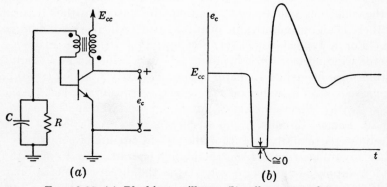

(a)   (b)

FIG. 18-39. (a) Blocking oscillator; (b) collector waveform.

As we saw in Sec. 9-13, the backswing may be of the order of two or three times the amplitude of the pulse. In a vacuum-tube oscillator this large backswing need not be a matter of any particular concern. In a transistor, however, the maximum allowable reverse collector voltage before breakdown occurs is severely limited. Hence, in a transistor oscillator it may be important to shunt the collector winding of the pulse transformer with a diode to suppress the backswing.

An alternative form of the blocking oscillator is shown in Fig. 18-40. Here the transistor is used in the common-base configuration. The pulse transformer is therefore required to be noninverting. The diode D_2 is used to suppress the backswing, while diode D_1 is used to keep the collector voltage from going negative and hence keeps the transistor out of the saturation region.

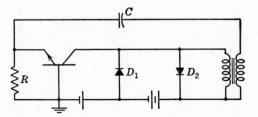

FIG. 18-40. An alternative form of the blocking oscillator. Diodes are used to prevent saturation and to suppress backswing.

An analysis of the operation of the transistor blocking-oscillator circuit has been given by Linvill[16] with the following results. If account is taken only of the α cutoff frequency of the transistor, then, for unity transformer turns ratio, the rise time t_r is given by

$$t_r = \frac{2.20}{\omega_\alpha} \tag{18-48}$$

For $\omega_\alpha = 10^7$ sec^{-1}, $t_r = 0.22$ μsec. If the base spreading resistance r_b and the collector capacitance C_c are taken into account, then it turns out that there is an optimum value of turns ratio n which gives minimum rise time. For a typical transistor, the optimum *step-down* ratio n from collector winding to emitter winding is found to be 5.5 and results in a rise-time improvement by a factor of approximately 2, so that $t_r = 0.1$ μsec. This value is optimistic because the effect of transformer leakage inductance and stray capacitance have not been taken into consideration.

18-26. Logical Circuits. The excellent switch properties of transistors make them particularly useful for the logical circuits of computers.[19] A further advantage results from the ability of transistors to operate from very low supply voltages (1.5 volts) as in the direct-connected binary of Fig. 18-34. A three-input *OR* circuit is shown in Fig. 18-41. Initially the base voltages are held at a value which places the transistors in the cutoff region. A positive signal of the order of 0.1 volt at the base of any of the transistors will cause a drop in the output voltage. The output voltage change will be, ideally, only 1.5 volts but the important point is that such an output signal is, in turn, more than enough to operate another transistor switch. Furthermore, the d-c levels of the output signal are such that this output signal may again be direct-connected to a succeeding grounded-emitter transistor switch. The number of transistors which can be used in the circuit of Fig. 18-41 is limited principally by the leakage current through the transistors in the *off* condition. If the total leakage current is too large, the difference between the two output levels will not be large enough to operate a succeeding switch.

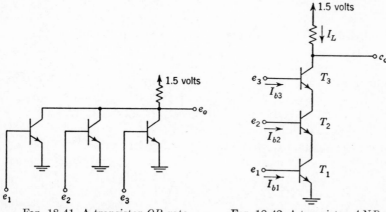

FIG. 18-41. A transistor *OR* gate. FIG. 18-42. A transistor *AND* gate.

The circuit of Fig. 18-41 may also be used as an *AND* circuit. To have the circuit operate as an *AND* gate, it is only necessary that in the initial state all the transistors be in the *on* condition. The transistor *AND* circuit is then analogous to the vacuum-tube *AND* circuit of Fig. 13-11 with the exception again that the transistor circuit operates from a much smaller supply voltage and the output of the transistor circuit may be direct-connected to other transistor gates. The transistor lends itself, however, to another type of *AND* configuration to which vacuum tubes are not adaptable. Such a transistor *AND* circuit is shown in Fig. 18-42. In the *AND* circuit of Fig. 13-11 or Fig. 18-41 the current drawn from the supply when none of the inputs is excited is the sum of the currents drawn by all the tubes or all the transistors. This current may be uncomfortably large for a many-input circuit. The *AND* circuit of Fig. 18-42, on the other hand, draws no quiescent current. At a complete coincidence of all input signals, the current taken from the supply voltage is equal to the current drawn by a single transistor. A most important feature of the circuit of Fig. 18-42 is that, in spite of the fact that the transistors are stacked one upon another, signals which make excursions between common levels may be used for all inputs. For example, the signal voltages to all the input terminals of the gate may be derived by direct connection to binaries of the type shown in Fig. 18-34.

Let us, as a matter of fact, assume that the three inputs of the AND circuit are connected to the collectors (or bases) of three binaries of the type in Fig. 18-34. Suppose also that the voltages consequently being applied to the input are in each case at the higher of the two voltage levels of which the binary is capable. Then we may easily show that in spite of the stacking of transistors in Fig. 18-42 the tentative assumption that all transistors are *on* is consistent with the transistor characteristics. For if we assume that all the transistors are *on*, we may consider that the drop from collector to emitter is in each case only of the order of tens of millivolts. Then if all the base electrodes are maintained positive by several tenths of a volt with respect to ground, the drop from base to emitter for the top transistor T_3 will be only slightly less than the corresponding drop for the bottom transistor. For example, assume that the common base-to-ground voltage is, say, 0.3 volt and that the drop across the transistors is 35 mv, then the drop from base to emitter of T_3 is 0.23 volt, which is still enough to keep T_3 *on*. It is found, as a matter of practice, that as many as five transistors may be stacked to constitute a five-input gate. We may note that the current through the bottom transistor is somewhat larger than through the top transistor. The collector current of T_3 is I_L, while the collector current of T_1 is $I_L + I_{b2} + I_{b3}$. On the other hand, the base-to-emitter voltage of T_1 will be larger than the corresponding voltage of T_3, which is in the right direction to permit T_1 to carry the larger current.

REFERENCES

1. Shockley, W.: "Electrons and Holes in Semiconductors," D. Van Nostrand Company, Inc., New York, 1950.
   Shockley, W.: Transistor Electronics: Imperfections, Unipolar and Analog Transistors, *Proc. IRE*, vol. 40, pp. 1289–1313, November, 1952.
   Terman, F.: "Electronic and Radio Engineering," chap. 21, "Transistors and Related Semiconductor Devices," McGraw-Hill Book Company, Inc., New York, 1955.
   Moll, J. L.: Junction Transistor Electronics, *Proc. IRE*, vol. 43, pp. 1807–1819, December, 1955.
2. Shockley, W.: The Theory of *P-N* Junctions in Semiconductors and *P-N* Junction Transistors, *Bell System Tech. J.*, vol. 28, pp. 435–489, 1949.
   Conwell, E. M.: Properties of Silicon and Germanium, *Proc. IRE*, vol. 40, pp. 1327–1337, November, 1952.
3. Millman, J., and S. Seely: "Electronics," 2d ed., chap. 10, McGraw-Hill Book Company, Inc., New York, 1951.

4. Bardeen, J., and Brattain, W. H.: Physical Principles Involved in Transistor Action, *Phys. Rev.*, vol. 75, pp. 203–231, July, 1949.

5. Law, R. R., C. W. Mueller, J. I. Pankove, and L. D. Armstrong: A Developmental Germanium *P-N-P* Junction Transistor, *Proc. IRE*, vol. 40, pp. 1352–1357, November, 1952.

6. Saby, J. S.: Fused Impurity *P-N-P* Junction Transistor, *Proc. IRE*, vol. 40, pp. 1358–1360, November, 1952.

7. Gialcoletto, L. J.: Junction Transistor Equivalent Circuits and Vacuum-tube Analogy, *Proc. IRE*, vol. 40, pp. 1490–1493, November, 1952.

8. McKay, K. G., and K. B. McAfee: Electron Multiplication in Silicon and Germanium, *Phys. Rev.*, vol. 91, pp. 1079–1084, September, 1953.
   McKay, K. G.: Avalanche Breakdown in Silicon, *Phys. Rev.*, vol. 94, pp. 877–884, May, 1954.
   Sheehan, W. E.: "Some Practical Considerations Concerning the Limiting Operating Voltages of Junction Transistors," Raytheon Mfg. Co., Newton, Mass.

9. Shockley, W., M. Sparks, and G. K. Teal: *p-n* Transistors, *Phys. Rev.*, vol. 83, pp. 151–162, 1951.

10. Early, J. M.: Effects of Space-charge Layer Widening in Junction Transistors, *Proc. IRE*, vol. 40, pp. 1401–1406, November, 1952.

11. Lo, A. W., R. O. Endres, I. Zawels, F. D. Waldhauer, and C. C. Cheng: "Transistor Electronics," chaps. 2 and 3, Prentice-Hall Inc., New York, 1955.
    Shea, R. F.: "Transistor Circuits," chaps. 2, 3, and 4, John Wiley & Sons, Inc., New York, 1953.

12. Early, J. M.: Design Theory of Junction Transistors, *Bell System Tech. J.*, vol. 32, pp. 1271–1312, November, 1953.
    Pritchard, R. L.: Frequency Variation of Current-amplification Factor for Junction Transistors, *Proc. IRE*, pp. 1476–1481, November, 1952.

13. Moll, J. L.: Large Signal Transient Response of Junction Transistors, *Proc. IRE*, vol. 42, pp. 1773–1778, December, 1954.

14. Easley, J. W.: The Effect of Collector Capacity on the Transient Response of Junction Transistors, Bell Telephone Laboratories Memorandum MM-55-6414-32, September, 1955.

15. Moll, J. L.: Frequency Response of Transistors in Common Emitter Connection, Bell Telephone Laboratories Memorandum MM-55-2521-10, August, 1955.

16. Ebers, J. J., and J. L. Moll: Large-signal Behavior of Junction Transistors, *Proc. IRE*, vol. 42, pp. 1761–1772, December, 1954.
    Ebers, J. J., and S. L. Miller: Design of Alloyed Junction Germanium Transistors for High-speed Switching, *Bell System Tech. J.*, vol. 34, pp. 761–781, July, 1955.
    Bright, R. L.: Junction Transistors Used as Switches, *Trans. AIEE, Communication and Electronics*, no. 17, pp. 111–121, March, 1955.

17. Linvill, J. G.: Nonsaturating Pulse Circuits Using Two Junction Transistors, *Proc. IRE*, vol. 43, pp. 826–834, July, 1955.

18. McMahon, R. E.: Designing Transistor Flip-Flops, *Electronic Design*, vol. 3, pp. 24–27, October, 1955.

19. Beter, R. H., W. E. Bradley, R. B. Brown, and M. Rubinoff: Surface Barrier Transistor Switching Circuits, Philco Corporation Publication, Philadelphia, Pa.

20. Linvill, J. G.: Junction Transistor Blocking Oscillator, *Proc. IRE*, vol. 43, pp. 1632–1639, November, 1955.

PROBLEMS

CHAPTER 1

1-1. Given an amplifier with a midband gain of 1,000 (real and negative). It is made into a feedback amplifier with $\beta = \frac{1}{10}$ (real and positive).

a. As the frequency is varied, to what value can the gain of the amplifier without feedback fall before the gain of the amplifier with feedback falls 3 db?

b. What is the ratio of the half power frequencies with feedback to those without feedback?

c. If $f_1 = 20$ cps and $f_2 = 50,000$ cps for the amplifier without feedback, what are the corresponding values after feedback has been added?

1-2. An amplifier without feedback gives an output of 36 volts with 7 per cent second-harmonic distortion when the input is 0.028 volts.

a. If 1.2 per cent of the output is fed back into the input in a degenerative circuit, what is the output voltage?

b. For an output of 36 volts, if only 1 per cent second-harmonic distortion is tolerable, what is the input voltage?

1-3. Assume that the parameters of each tube are $r_p = 10$ K, $R_g = 1$ Meg, $R_L = 50$ K, and $\mu = 60$. Neglect the reactances of all capacitors. Find the gain and output impedance of the circuit at the terminals (*a*) AN, (*b*) BN.

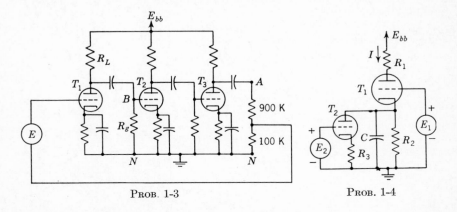

PROB. 1-3   PROB. 1-4

1-4. E_1 and E_2 are sinor input voltages. Draw the equivalent circuit from which to calculate the signal current I.

1-5. A feedback amplifier has two sets of input terminals. The external signal is applied to input 1 and the gain for this signal is A_1. The feedback signal is applied to input 2 and the gain for this signal is A_2.

a. Show that for voltage feedback

$$A_f = \frac{A_1}{1 - \beta A_2} \quad \text{and} \quad Z_f = \frac{Z}{1 - \beta A_2}$$

b. Show that for current feedback

$$A_f = A_1 \quad \text{and} \quad Z_f = Z + (1 - A_2)Z_s$$

1-6. *a.* If the positive supply voltage changes by ΔE_{bb}, how much does the plate voltage change?

b. How much does the cathode voltage change, under the conditions in part (*a*)?

c. Repeat parts (*a*) and (*b*) if E_{bb} is constant but E_{cc} changes by ΔE_{cc}.

d. If $R_L = 0$ so that the circuit is a cathode follower, show that if $(\mu + 1)R_k \gg r_p$, the cathode voltage changes by $\dfrac{\Delta E_{bb}}{\mu + 1}$ or $-\Delta E_{cc}\dfrac{r_p/R_k}{\mu + 1}$. What is the physical significance of these results?

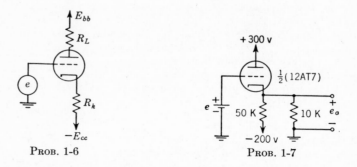

PROB. 1-6　　　　　　　　　　PROB. 1-7

1-7. What is (*a*) *e* when the output is zero, (*b*) e_o if $e = -100$ volts, and (*c*) the grid-to-cathode voltage when $e_o = +50$ volts?

1-8. (*a*) If $e = 0$, find e_o. (*b*) If $e = 100$, find e_o. (*c*) If the grid-to-cathode voltage is zero, find e_o. (*d*) If $e_o = 0$, find e.

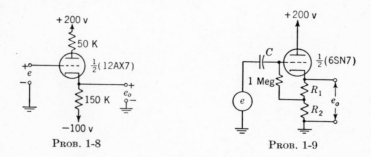

PROB. 1-8　　　　　　　　　　PROB. 1-9

1-9. The reactance of C and the impedance of the generator are both negligible. $R_1 + R_2 = 10$ K. The input signal e is symmetrical with respect to ground. Find R_1 and R_2 if the tube is to handle, without distortion and without drawing grid current, the largest possible amplitude of signal. What is the maximum signal the tube will handle in this case?

1-10. (*a*) Find the quiescent current.   Find the effective impedance seen between terminals (*b*) *A* and *N* and (*c*) *B* and *N*.

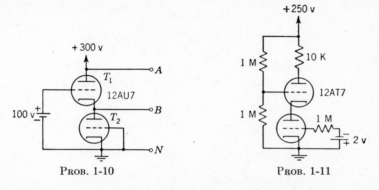

PROB. 1-10   PROB. 1-11

1-11. Find the quiescent tube currents in the cascode circuit shown.

1-12. Each triode section is operated at a quiescent grid-to-cathode voltage of -2 volts and a quiescent plate-to-cathode voltage of 250 volts.   Find the value of (*a*) the resistance *R*, (*b*) the grid-to-ground voltage of each section, and (*c*) the effective cathode impedance R_{k1} of T_1.   (*d*) If T_2 were replaced by a resistor of value R_{k1} [found in (*c*)], calculate the negative supply voltage required to maintain the same quiescent current as above.

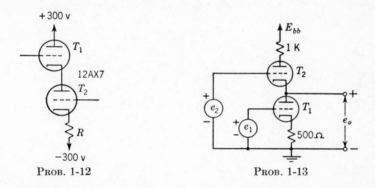

PROB. 1-12   PROB. 1-13

1-13. Each tube shown has a plate resistance $r_p = 10$ K and an amplification factor $\mu = 20$.   Find the gain (*a*) e_o/e_1 and (*b*) e_o/e_2.

1-14. *a.* Prove that in a paraphase amplifier (Fig. 1-15) the signal current i_1 is always larger than i_2 in magnitude.

b. Prove that if i_1 is to exceed i_2 by less than 10 per cent that

$$R_k > 10 \frac{r_p + R_L}{\mu + 1}$$

1-15. *a.* In the paraphase amplifier circuit of Fig. 1-15 show that the voltage across R_k is

$$\frac{1}{2} \frac{\mu e}{\mu + 1} \frac{1}{1 + (r_p + R_L)/2(\mu + 1)R_k} \cong \frac{e}{2}$$

b. Assume that the amplification factors of the two sections are identical and constant but that the plate resistances r_{p1} and r_{p2} are functions of plate current. Show that the single-ended gain at the plate of T_1, assuming that R_k is large compared with $(R_{L2} + r_{p2})/(\mu + 1)$, is

$$A \cong \frac{\mu R_{L1}}{R_{L1} + r_{p1} + r_{p2} + R_{L2}}$$

Explain why this circuit tends to keep amplitude distortion low.

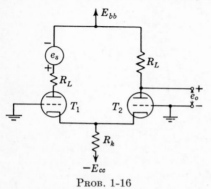

1-16. *a.* A signal voltage e_s is applied in series with the plate of T_1. Assuming that R_k is very large, prove that the output voltage e_o is given by

$$e_o = \frac{R_L e_s}{2(R_L + r_p)}$$

b. Prove that the output impedance Z_o at the plate of T_2 is given by

$$Z_o = \frac{R_L(R_L + 2r_p)}{2(R_L + r_p)}$$

PROB. 1-16

1-17. Prove (*a*) Eq. (1-21) and (*b*) Eq. (1-22).

1-18. *a.* Given a cathode follower with the grid resistor R_g connected from grid to cathode. Prove that the input impedance Z_i is greater than R_g and is given by

$$Z_i = \frac{R_g}{1 - A}$$

b. For a 12AU7 with $R_k = 20$ K and $R_g = 1$ Meg, find the value of Z_i.

1-19. Design an operational amplifier whose output (for a sinusoidal signal) is equal in magnitude to its input and leads the input by $45°$.

1-20. Consider a single-stage operational amplifier with a gain of 100. If $Z_1 = R$ and $Z' = -jX_c$ with $R = X_c$, calculate the gain as a complex number.

1-21. Given an operational amplifier consisting of R and L in series for Z_1 and C for Z'. If the input is a constant E, find the output e_o as a function of time. Assume an infinite open-loop gain.

1-22. Sketch an operational amplifier circuit having an input e and an output which is approximately $-5e - 3de/dt$.

1-23. For the circuit shown, prove that the output voltage is given by

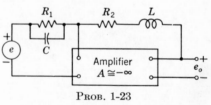

PROB. 1-23

$$-e_o = \frac{R_2}{R_1}e + \left(R_2C + \frac{L}{R_1}\right)\frac{de}{dt} + LC\frac{d^2e}{dt^2}$$

1-24. Given an operational amplifier with Z_1 consisting of a resistor R in parallel with a capacitor C and Z' consisting of a resistor R'. The input is a sweep voltage $e = \alpha t$. Prove that the output is a sweep voltage that starts with an initial step. Thus, show that

$$e_o = -\alpha R'C - \alpha\frac{R'}{R}t$$

Assume an infinite open-loop gain.

1-25. An operational amplifier has a base amplifier whose *unloaded* open-loop gain and impedance are A_u and Z_u, respectively. These are the values of gain and output impedance with the impedance Z' omitted.

a. Draw the equivalent circuit of the operational amplifier. Include an external impedance Z_L across the output terminals.

b. Find the expression for the ratio E_o/E_i which gives the gain without feedback but with the amplifier loaded with Z'.

c. From part (*b*) deduce that the open-loop loaded gain A and output impedance Z (with the base amplifier loaded by Z') are given by

$$A = A_u \frac{Z' + Z_u/A_u}{Z_u + Z'} \quad \text{and} \quad Z = \frac{Z_u Z'}{Z_u + Z'}$$

HINT: Write

$$\frac{E_o}{E_i} = \frac{AZ_L}{Z_L + Z}$$

d. Find the expression for E_o/E_e which gives the gain with feedback. Write

$$\frac{E_o}{E_e} = \frac{A_f Z_L}{Z_L + Z_f}$$

and prove that A_f is given by Eq. (1-24) and that the output impedance with feedback Z_f is given by

$$Z_f = \frac{Z}{1 - AZ_1/(Z_1 + Z')} = \frac{Z}{1 - A\beta}$$

CHAPTER 2

2-1. Prove by direct integration that the area under the curve of Fig. 2-3*d* is zero.

2-2. A symmetrical square wave of peak-to-peak amplitude E and frequency f is applied to a high-pass RC circuit. Show that the percentage tilt is given by

$$P = \frac{1 - \epsilon^{-1/2fRC}}{1 + \epsilon^{-1/2fRC}} \times 200 \quad \%$$

If the tilt is small, show that this reduces to Eq. (2-6).

2-3. A 10-cps symmetrical square wave whose peak-to-peak amplitude is 2 volts is impressed upon a high-pass circuit whose lower 3-db frequency is 5 cps. Calculate and sketch the output waveform. In particular, what is the peak-to-peak output amplitude?

2-4. A 10-cps square wave is fed to an amplifier. Calculate and plot the output waveform under the following conditions. The lower 3-db frequency is (*a*) 0.3 cps, (*b*) 3.0 cps, (*c*) 30 cps.

2-5. *a.* A square wave whose peak-to-peak value is 1 volt extends ± 0.5 volt with respect to ground. The duration of the positive section is 0.1 sec and of the negative section is 0.2 sec. If this waveform is impressed upon an RC differentiating circuit whose time constant is 0.2 sec, what are the steady-state maximum and minimum values of the output waveform?

b. Prove that the area under the positive section equals that under the negative section of the output waveform. What is the physical significance of this result?

2-6. A square wave whose peak-to-peak value is 1 volt extends ± 0.5 volt with respect to ground. The half period is 0.1 sec. This voltage is impressed upon an RC differentiating circuit whose time constant is 0.2 sec. What are the steady-state maximum and minimum values of the output voltage?

2-7. The pulse from a high-voltage generator (a magnetron) rises linearly for 0.05 μsec and then remains constant for 1 μsec. The rate of rise of the pulse is measured with an RC differentiating circuit whose time constant is 250 $\mu\mu$sec. If the positive output voltage from the differentiator has a maximum value of 50 volts, what is the peak voltage of the generator?

√ **2-8.** Prove that for the same input, the output from the two differentiating circuits will be the same if $RC = L/R'$. Assume that the initial conditions are those of rest (no voltage on C and no current in L).

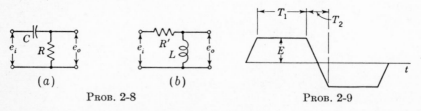

(a)   (b)
PROB. 2-8   PROB. 2-9

2-9. The input to a high-pass RC circuit is periodic and trapezoidal as indicated. Assume that the time constant RC is large compared with either T_1 or T_2. Find and sketch the steady-state output if, say, $RC = 10T_1 = 10T_2$.

2-10. *a.* Derive Eqs. (2-14) and (2-15).

b. Prove that the peak of the output pulse occurs at

$$x = 2.30\frac{n}{n-1}\log n$$

2-11. A symmetrical square wave whose peak-to-peak amplitude is 2 volts and whose average value is zero is applied to an RC integrating circuit. The time constant equals the half period of the square wave. Find the peak-to-peak value of the output amplitude.

2-12. The periodic waveform shown is applied to an RC integrating network whose time constant is 10 μsec. Sketch the output. Calculate the maximum and minimum values of output voltage with respect to ground.

2-13. A symmetrical square wave whose average value is zero has a peak-to-peak

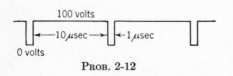

100 volts
←10μsec→ ←1μsec
0 volts
PROB. 2-12

amplitude of 20 volts and a period of 2 μsec. This waveform is applied to a low-pass circuit whose upper 3-db frequency is $1/2\pi$ Mc. Calculate and sketch the steady-state output waveform. In particular what is the peak-to-peak output amplitude?

√ **2-14.** An ideal 1-μsec pulse is fed to an amplifier. Calculate and plot the output waveform under the following conditions. The upper 3-db frequency is (*a*) 10 Mc, (*b*) 1.0 Mc, (*c*) 0.1 Mc.

2-15. A square wave whose peak-to-peak amplitude is 2 volts extends ± 1 volt with respect to ground. The duration of the positive section is 0.1 sec and that of the negative section 0.2 sec. If this waveform is impressed upon an RC integrating circuit whose time constant is 0.2 sec, what are the steady-state maximum and minimum values of the output waveform?

2-16. The square wave shown is fed to an RC coupling network. What is the voltage waveform across R and also across C if (a) RC is very large, say, $RC = 10T$, and (b) RC is very small, say, $RC = T/10$.

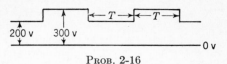

PROB. 2-16

2-17. a. Prove that an RC circuit behaves as a reasonably good integrator if $RC \gg 15T$, where T is the period of an input sinusoid $E_m \sin \omega t$.

b. Show that the output is approximately $-(E_m/\omega RC) \cos \omega t$.

2-18. a. Three low-pass RC circuits are in cascade and isolated from one another by ideal buffer amplifiers. Find the expression for the output voltage as a function of time if the input is a step voltage.

b. Find the rise time of the output in terms of the product RC.

c. What is the ratio of the rise time of the three sections in cascade to the rise time of a single section?

2-19. a. The periodic ramp voltage shown is applied to a low-pass RC circuit. Find the equations from which to determine the steady-state output waveform.

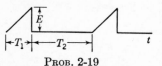

PROB. 2-19

b. If $T_1 = T_2 = RC$, find the maximum and minimum values of the output voltage and plot this waveform. NOTE: The minimum value does *not* occur at the beginning of interval T_1.

2-20. Derive (a) Eq. (2-37), (b) Eq. (2-39), and (c) Eq. (2-41).

2-21. Derive (a) Eq. (2-47), (b) Eq. (2-48), and (c) Eq. (2-49).

2-22. Find and plot the response to a step voltage of a single-stage amplifier with a 10-mh choke in the plate circuit. The plate resistance is 10 K and the total capacitance from plate to ground is 50 $\mu\mu f$.

2-23. a. A transformer has its primary winding in the plate circuit of a pentode stage. The primary inductance is L, and the voltage step-up ratio is n. The load on the secondary winding may be considered to be purely capacitive. This capacitance C is much larger than the interwinding or interturn capacitances of the transformer. If the tube furnishes a current step I_0, prove that the amplitude of the output at the secondary is $I_0 \sqrt{L/C}$. Note that the *output is independent of the step-up ratio n.* Explain this result physically.

b. Prove that the period of the output oscillation is $2n\pi \sqrt{LC}$.

2-24. a. For a ringing circuit show that the percentage P decrease in amplitude in n cycles is given by

$$\ln \left(1 - \frac{P}{100} \right) = - \frac{n\pi}{Q}$$

b. For small P show that

$$P \cong \frac{100n\pi}{Q}$$

2-25. For a critically damped ringing circuit Eq. (2-47), prove that the maximum occurs at

$$x_m = \frac{1}{\pi} \frac{1 + \Delta}{1 + 2\Delta}$$

and that the maximum value is

$$\left(\frac{e_o}{E_o} \right)_{\max} = - (2\Delta + 1)\epsilon^{-2(1+\Delta)/(1+2\Delta)}$$

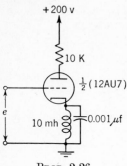

PROB. 2-26

2-26. The steady state is reached with $e = 0$. A negative step is now applied to the grid. What is the minimum size of this step needed in order that the tube remain cut off while the resonant circuit oscillates?

2-27. A 10-mh choke whose resonant frequency is 100 kc is in the plate circuit of a 12AU7 tube whose plate supply voltage is 100 volts. A steady state is reached with zero grid voltage. A negative step is applied so as to cut the tube off.

a. What is the minimum size of this step needed in order that the tube remain cut off while the circuit oscillates?

b. Plot the plate voltage (with respect to ground), and plot the coil current vs. time.

CHAPTER 3

3-1. The input to an amplifier consists of a voltage made up of a fundamental signal and a second-harmonic signal of half the magnitude and in phase with the fundamental. Plot the resultant.

The output consists of the same magnitude of each component but with the second harmonic shifted 90° (on the fundamental scale). This corresponds to perfect frequency response but bad phase-shift response. Plot the output and compare it with the input waveshape.

3-2. An ideal 1-μsec pulse is fed into an amplifier. Plot the output, if the band pass is (*a*) 10 Mc, (*b*) 1.0 Mc, and (*c*) 0.1 Mc.

3-3. A pentode amplifier stage has an unbypassed cathode resistor R_k and a load resistor R_L which is shunted by a capacitance C. If the input is a negative unit step, prove that the output voltage as a function of time is

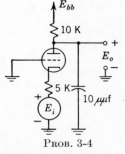

PROB. 3-4

$$e_o = \frac{g_m R_L}{1 + g_m R_k} (1 - \epsilon^{-t/R_L C})$$

3-4. For the circuit shown, calculate the nominal gain E_o/E_i, and calculate the frequency at which the output E_o will fall to the 3-db point. $\mu = 20$ and $r_p = 10$ K.

3-5. *a.* Prove that the parameter m introduced in Sec. 3-6 in connection with shunt compensation equals Q_2, the Q of the circuit at the upper 3-db uncompensated frequency.

b. Prove that $Q_2 = Q_o{}^2$, where Q_o is the Q at the resonant frequency.

3-6. Show that in a shunt compensated amplifier adjusted for critical damping the rise time is improved by the factor 1.43 over the uncompensated case.

3-7. Consider the frequency response of the shunt-compensated stage, Eq. (3-16). Prove that, at $f/f_2 = 0$,

a.
$$\frac{d}{df}\left(\frac{A_2}{A_o}\right) = 0 \qquad \text{for all values of } K$$

b.
$$\frac{d^2}{df^2}\left(\frac{A_2}{A_o}\right) = 0 \qquad \text{for } K = 1.54$$

3-8. Prove Eq. (3-18).

3-9. *a.* Show that the response of a two-stage (identical) amplifier to a unit input step is

$$\frac{e_o}{(g_m R_L)^2} = 1 - (1 + x)\epsilon^{-x}$$

where $x = t/RC$.

b. For small times show the output varies quadratically with time.

c. If the upper 3-db frequency of a single stage is f_2 and the rise time of the two-stage amplifier is $t_r^{(2)}$, show that $f_2 t_r^{(2)} = 0.55$.

d. Show that the rise time of a two-stage amplifier is 1.55 times that of a single stage.

3-10. If two cascaded stages have very unequal bandpasses, show that the combined bandwidth is essentially that of the smaller.

✓ **3-11.** An amplifier consists of two identical uncompensated stages. The total effective shunt capacitance across each stage is the same and is equal to 20 $\mu\mu$f. The 3-db bandwidth of the complete amplifier is 10 Mc. If the tubes used have g_m's of 10 millimhos, find the gain of the complete amplifier.

✓ **3-12.** The Du Mont type 2607 test probe is indicated. Assume that the cable capacitance is 100 $\mu\mu$f. The input impedance to the scope is 2 Meg in parallel with 10 $\mu\mu$f. What is (*a*) the attenuation of the probe, (*b*) C for best response, and (*c*) the input impedance of the compensated probe?

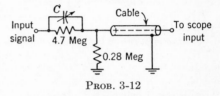

PROB. 3-12

3-13. Consider a waveform consisting of a sine wave and a d-c voltage equal to the peak E_m of the sine wave so that the resultant waveform extends from zero to $2E_m$.

a. This waveform is applied to a 3:1 compensated attenuator. Plot the output waveform and indicate the zero-voltage level.

b. If the attenuator is improperly compensated ($R_1 = 2R_2$, but $2C_1 \neq C_2$), plot the output waveform and indicate the zero level. Consider the two cases, $2C_1 > C_2$ and $2C_1 < C_2$.

3-14. Compute and draw to scale the output waveform for $C = 50$ $\mu\mu$f, $C = 75$ $\mu\mu$f, and $C = 25$ $\mu\mu$f. The input is a 20-volt step.

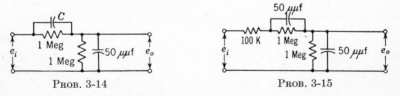

PROB. 3-14   PROB. 3-15

3-15. The input e_i is a 20-volt step. Calculate and plot to scale the output voltage.

3-16. Show that the minimum bandpass of a potentiometer is obtained when the slider is at the center. Plot the bandpass as a function of the distance of the slider from one end. If the slider is on the first or last 10 per cent of the potentiometer, how many times the minimum value will the bandpass be?

3-17. Design a cathode-compensated video amplifier stage using a 6AU6 pentode. $E_{bb} = 300$ volts, $E_{ss} = 150$ volts, the quiescent plate current is to be taken as 4 ma and the corresponding screen current as 1.5 ma. It is desired to have a gain of 5.5. A negative power supply is not available. Find (*a*) R_k, (*b*) R_L, and (*c*) C_k to give a good transient response if the plate shunting capacitance is 30 $\mu\mu$f total. (*d*) What is the bandpass under condition (*c*)? The rise time? (*e*) Find the gain-bandwidth product. (f) If the cathode resistor were bypassed with a very large capacitor, what would the gain-bandwidth product be?

3-18. A tube in an amplifier is to be operated at a quiescent plate current of 20 ma, a quiescent screen current of 5 ma, and a quiescent plate voltage of 200 volts. An output swing (peak-to-peak) of 200 volts is required when the plate current varies from 5 to 35 ma. The output capacitance is 20 $\mu\mu$f and an upper 3-db frequency of 3 Mc is required. The g_m of the tube is 10 millimhos. The grid-to-cathode voltage required for the quiescent operating point above is -10 volts. Draw a complete circuit diagram of the stage, and label each component and supply voltage (screen voltage need not be specified). What is the gain of the stage?

3-19. a. Given an amplifier stage with a load R_L, a plate shunting capacitor C, a cathode resistor R_k shunted by a capacitor C_k and operating at a transconductance g_m. Let $\alpha \equiv 1 + g_m R_k$, $\tau \equiv R_L C$, and $\rho \equiv R_k C_k / R_L C$. Assume that the plate resistance is much larger than the load resistance. Prove that the output voltage response to a negative step input E is

$$e_o = \frac{g_m R_L E}{\alpha} \left[1 - \frac{1 - \alpha}{1 - \alpha/\rho} \epsilon^{-\alpha t/\rho\tau} - \frac{\alpha(1 - 1/\rho)}{1 - \alpha/\rho} \epsilon^{-t/\tau} \right]$$

provided that $\alpha \neq \rho$.

b. If $\alpha = \rho$, prove that the response is

$$e_o = \frac{g_m R_L E}{\alpha} \left\{ 1 - \left[1 + \frac{t}{\tau}(1 - \rho) \right] \epsilon^{-t/\tau} \right\}$$

c. If $\rho = 1$, what is e_o? Interpret.

d. Plot $e_o \alpha / g_m R_L E$ as a function of t/τ for $\alpha = 2$ and for $\rho = 0$. Repeat for $\rho = 1$ and $\rho = 2$.

e. Calculate the rise-time improvement for $\rho = 2$ over that for $\rho = 1$. Also calculate the percentage overshoot.

3-20. Given an amplifier stage with a load resistor R_L and no cathode resistor. The effective capacitance across R_L is C and the transconductance is g_m. The load is changed to R_L' and a cathode resistor R_k is added and bypassed so that $R_k C_k = R_L' C$. The transconductance at the new operating current is g_m'. Prove that:

a. If R_k is chosen so that the gain remains unchanged, the rise time is multiplied by g_m/g_m'.

b. If R_k is chosen so that the rise time remains constant, the gain is multiplied by g_m'/g_m.

3-21. Derive Eq. (3-33).

3-22. A cathode follower uses a tube operating at a quiescent current of 1.1 ma. The tube parameters are: $\mu = 70$, $r_p = 50$ K, $R_k = 50$ K, $g_m = 1.4$ millimhos, $C_{gp} = 2.0$ $\mu\mu$f, $C_{gk} = 2.4$ $\mu\mu$f, and $C_{pk} = 3.6$ $\mu\mu$f. Assume an external loading capacitance of 10 $\mu\mu$f.

a. Find the gain at zero frequency and at 5 Mc. Use the exact formula.

b. Find the peak input voltage at the above frequencies which will just reduce the total plate current to zero. HINT: Draw the equivalent circuit, and calculate the current in r_p, making use of the results in (a).

3-23. a. Given a cathode follower using a self-biasing resistor R_k bypassed with C_k. The output is taken across a load R as indicated on page 619. If $\mu \gg 1$, show that the response to a unit step is

$$e_o = \frac{g_m R}{1 + g_m(R + R_k)} \left(1 + \frac{g_m R_k}{1 + g_m R} \epsilon^{-t/\tau} \right)$$

where

$$\tau = C_k R_k \frac{1 + g_m R}{1 + g_m(R + R_k)}$$

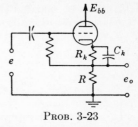

b. For small values of t/τ, show that

$$e_o \cong \frac{g_m R}{1 + g_m R} \left[1 - \frac{g_m t}{(1 + g_m R) C_k} \right]$$

c. Consider a 6L6 triode connected and operating at a point where $g_m = 2$ millimhos. $R_k = 2$ K and $R = 70$ ohms. If $C_k = 50$ μf, what is the percentage tilt in 1.5 msec.

PROB. 3-23

3-24. A video amplifier for which $R_L = 2$ K is coupled to a succeeding stage through 0.1 μf and ½ Meg. The quiescent tube current is 20 ma. The maximum supply voltage available is 300 volts. The quiescent plate voltage required is 200 volts. The amplifier is to be compensated for minimum tilt on a square wave with initial slope equal to zero. Draw the complete circuit diagram, specify components, and calculate the percentage tilt after compensation for a 200-cps square wave.

3-25. In the circuit of Fig. 3-24a prove that perfect low-frequency compensation may be obtained if C_c is shunted with a resistor R_c, provided that

$$R_c C_c = R_d C_d \qquad \text{and} \qquad \frac{R_d}{R_L} = \frac{R_c}{R_g}$$

Note that if it is necessary to isolate the grid of the succeeding stage from the d-c plate voltage of the previous stage, a large blocking capacitor may be added in series with R_c. HINT: Use steady-state analysis and show that the transfer function is independent of frequency.

3-26. Prove Eqs. (3-47) and (3-48).

3-27. An amplifier stage has the following parameters: $g_m = 5$ millimhos, $R_L = 2$ K, $R_k = 100$ ohms, $C_k = 500$ μf, $C_c = 0.25$ μf, and $R_g = 0.5$ Meg. If a 200-cps square wave is applied to the input, find the percentage tilt in the output waveform.

3-28. Derive Eqs. (3-54) and (3-55).

3-29. An amplifier stage has a load resistor R_L and cathode resistor R_k bypassed by a capacitor C_k. The output is taken at the plate. A negative input step of amplitude E is applied.

a. Prove that, if $\mu \gg 1$ and $r_p \gg R_L$, then

$$e_o = \frac{g_m R_L E}{1 + g_m R_k} (1 + g_m R_k \epsilon^{-t/\tau})$$

where

$$\tau = \frac{R_k C_k}{1 + g_m R_k}$$

b. If $t/\tau \ll 1$, show that the above equation reduces to Eq. (3-51).

3-30. A negative unit step is applied to a pentode having a cathode resistor R_k bypassed with a capacitor C_k. The total shunt capacitance at the plate is C. For each of the following cases draw the output waveform on a time scale which displays both the high- and low-frequency transient characteristics of the amplifier:

a. $R_k = C_k = 0$.

b. $C_k = 0$; $g_m R_k = 1$.

c. $g_m R_k = 1$; $R_k C_k = R_L C$.

d. $g_m R_k = 1$; C_k very large.

Draw the waveforms so that relative to one another they are to scale. Indicate time constants and percentage tilts.

3-31. Verify (*a*) Eq. (3-57) and (*b*) Eq. (3-58).

3-32. *a.* An alternative form of the totem-pole amplifier is shown. Prove that for this circuit the value of r required to make the signal currents in the two tubes the same continues to be given by Eq. (3-57).

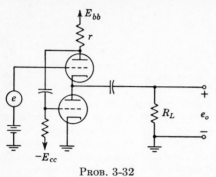

b. If the value of r is selected as in Eq. (3-57), prove that the gain A, with the load connected, is given by

$$A = \frac{2\mu^2 R_L}{2R_L(\mu^2 + \mu + 1) + r_p(\mu + 1)}$$

c. This alternative amplifier employing a 6BX7 tube is to be used to drive a 75-ohm cable which is to be matched at both ends. Compute the value of r and the value of the resistor which must be included in series with the amplifier output

PROB. 3-32

in order to increase the effective output impedance to 75 ohms. What is the gain of the amplifier in the presence of the cable load?

CHAPTER 4

4-1. For a 12AU7 tube evaluate r_c as a function of E_c with E_b as a parameter. Choose values of $E_b = 150$, 100, and 50 volts.

4-2. *a.* If a 2.5-K resistor is connected from the grid of a 5965 tube to ground, how much bias voltage is developed across this resistor?

b. What plate current flows under the conditions in (*a*) if the supply voltage is 200 volts and the load resistance is 10 K?

4-3. *a.* Consider a triode with the grid in clamp as a result of the grid being tied to the plate-supply voltage through a resistor R_g, as shown in Fig. 4-6. If the input is a negative-going ramp voltage, $e = -\alpha t$ for $t > 0$, prove that the grid voltage e_c will be negative if $C\alpha > E_{bb}/R_g$. What is the physical interpretation of this inequality?

b. Prove that

$$e_c = -(\alpha R_g C - E_{bb})(1 - \epsilon^{-t/R_g C})$$

provided that e_c is negative.

c. What is the voltage e_c if the inequality in (*a*) is not valid?

4-4. For the diode clipping circuit of Fig. 4-7*a*, assume that

$$E_R = 10 \text{ volts} \qquad e_i = 20 \sin \omega t$$

and that the diode forward resistance is 500 ohms. Neglect all capacitances. Draw to scale the input and output waveforms and label the maximum and minimum values, if *a)* $R = 1$ K, (*b*) $R = 10$ K, and (*c*) $R = 100$ K.

4-5. In the diode clipping circuit of Fig. 4-7*a* and *d*, $e_i = 20 \sin \omega t$, $R = 10$ K, and $E_R = 10$ volts. The reference voltage is obtained from a tap on a 100-K bleeder connected to a 100-volt source. Neglect all capacitances. The diode forward resistance is 500 ohms. In both cases draw the input and output waveforms to scale. Which circuit is the better clipper? HINT: Apply Thévenin's theorem to the reference-voltage bleeder network.

4-6. The input voltage e_i to the clipper shown is a 10-μsec pulse whose voltage varies between zero and 100 volts. The diode forward resistance is 1 K. Sketch the output waveform e_o and indicate the time constants of the exponential portions.

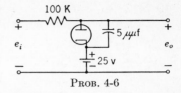

PROB. 4-6

4-7. The diode forward resistance is 500 ohms and the capacitance across the diode is 5 $\mu\mu$f. For the periodic waveform shown, sketch the steady-state output voltage, indicating all important voltages values and time constants.

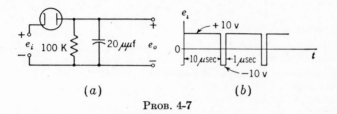

(a) (b)

PROB. 4-7

4-8. A symmetrical 5-kc square wave whose output varies between +100 and −100 volts is impressed upon the clipping circuit shown. The diode forward resistance

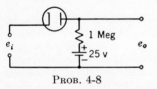

PROB. 4-8

may be taken as zero and the backward resistance as infinite. Sketch the steady-state output waveform, indicating numerical values of the maximum, minimum, and constant portions and the time constants of the exponential portions, if (a) all capacitances are neglected, (b) the diode capacitance of 10 $\mu\mu$f is taken into account, but the load capacitance is neglected (an unrealistic situation), and (c) both the diode and load capacitances (each equal to 10 $\mu\mu$f) are taken into consideration.

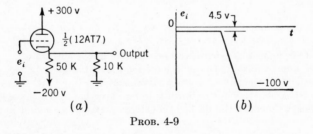

(a) (b)

PROB. 4-9

4-9. a. What is the magnitude of e_i when the output is zero?

b. Draw the output waveform if the input is as shown. Plot the output directly below the input and to the same time scale.

c. What is the grid-to-cathode voltage when the output is +50 volts?

4-10. The input e_i to the circuit shown is a sinusoidal voltage whose peak value is 80 volts. Sketch the output voltage e_o to the same time scale as the input, and calculate the maximum and minimum values of the output.

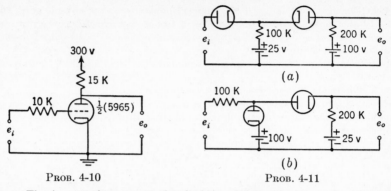

PROB. 4-10   PROB. 4-11

4-11. *a.* The input voltage e_i to the double-ended limiter shown in (a) varies linearly from zero to 150 volts. Sketch the output voltage e_o to the same time scale as the input voltage. Assume ideal diodes.

b. Repeat (a) for the circuit shown in (b).

4-12. The circuit of Fig. 4-10 is used to "square" a 10-kc input sine wave whose peak value is 50 volts. It is desired that the output voltage waveform be flat for 90 per cent of the time. Crystal diodes are used having a forward resistance of 100 ohms and a backward resistance of 100 K.

a. Find the values of E_1 and E_2.

b. What is a reasonable value to use for R?

4-13. *a.* For the circuit of Fig. 4-12, $E_{cc1} = E_{cc2} = -5$ volts, $R_k = 3$ K, $R_L = 10$ K, and $E_{bb} = 200$ volts. The tube is a 12AU7. Make a plot of the variation of e_o with e_i. Show where the clipping levels occur.

b. Calculate the ratio e_o/e_i for the region between clipping levels by using the linear equivalent circuit. Compare with the average gain calculated from the plot obtained in (a).

4-14. For the circuit of Fig. 4-12, $R_k = 100$ K, $R_L = 20$ K, $E_{bb} = 300$ volts, and the tube is a 12AX7. The input is sinusoidal. It is desired that the peak-to-peak output be limited to 20 volts and that the output be symmetrical with respect to its quiescent value.

a. Find E_{cc1} and E_{cc2}.

b. At what input signal amplitude will the output start being clipped?

c. For what peak input signal will the input tube start drawing grid current?

d. What is the gain of the circuit in the region of linear operation?

e. Draw an input sinusoid of peak value 50 volts, and directly below it and to the same time scale draw the output voltage waveform.

4-15. The triangular waveform shown is to be converted into a sine wave by using clipping diodes. Consider the dashed waveform sketched as a first approximation

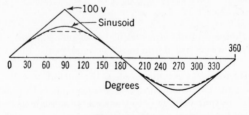

PROB. 4-15

to the sinusoid. This dashed waveform is coincident with the sinusoid at 0°, 30°, 60°, etc. Devise a circuit whose output is this broken-line waveform when the input is the triangular waveform. Assume ideal diodes and calculate the values of all supply voltages and resistances used.

4-16. In the diode restorer circuit of Fig. 4-16a and b, $E = 20$ volts, $T_1 = 1$ msec, $T_2 = 10$ msec, $R = 10$ K, $C = 0.01$ μf, and $R_f = 500$ ohms.

a. Compute exactly the output waveform e_o.

b. Repeat (a) if the diode terminals are reversed.

c. Repeat (a) and (b) if $C = 0.1$ μf and $R = 1$ Meg.

4-17. A symmetrical 10-kc square wave whose peak excursions are ± 10 volts with respect to ground is impressed upon the diode clamping circuit of Fig. 4-16b. If $R = 10$ K, $C = 1$ μf, the diode is assumed perfect, and the source impedance is zero,

a. Sketch the output waveform.

b. If the diode forward resistance is 1 K, sketch the output waveform. Calculate the maximum and minimum voltages with respect to ground.

c. Repeat (b) if the source impedance is 1 K.

4-18. An attempt is to be made to restore the maximum value of the periodic waveform indicated to a value of $+10$ volts. The diode used has a volt-ampere characteristic which passes through the origin, with a forward resistance of 1 K and infinite

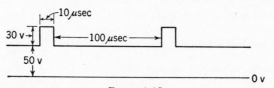

PROB. 4-18

backward resistance. Assume zero source impedance. The coupling capacitor has a value of 0.001 μf. Because of the load the effective resistance across the diode when it is not conducting is 1 Meg.

a. Indicate the circuit to be used.

b. Make a careful sketch of the output waveform. Label all d-c voltages and all time constants.

c. Indicate two important areas on your sketch and state the ratio of these two areas.

4-19. An attempt is made to restore the minimum value of the waveform of Prob. 4-18 to ground. The same diode, coupling capacitance, and load resistance are used as in Prob. 4-18. Make a careful sketch of the output waveform, and label all important voltages with respect to ground. Also indicate the time constants of all exponential portions of the waveform.

4-20. The signal shown is to have its negative excursion restored to ground voltage. Use $R = 100$ K, $C = 0.001$ μf, and a diode with $R_f = 1$ K.

a. Sketch the circuit.

b. Draw the output waveform and label all important voltage values.

c. How could you improve the operation of the circuit?

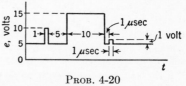

PROB. 4-20

4-21. A sinusoidal voltage of peak value 10 volts is impressed upon the clamping circuit of Fig. 4-16b. The capacitance C is extremely large and $R = 100$ K.

a. If $R_f = 0$, what is the voltage across C?

b. If $R_f = 1$ K, what is the voltage across C and what are the peak positive and negative values of the output voltage?

c. Repeat (*a*) and (*b*) for the circuit of Fig. 4-16c.

4-22. The waveform of Fig. 4-23a is applied to the circuit of Fig. 4-16b. The linear voltage swing is 100 volts in 1 msec. The duration of the flat portion is 1 msec. The capacitance C is arbitrarily large, $R = 10$ K, and $R_f = 500$ ohms. Compute the output waveform, if the generator impedance is (*a*) zero and (*b*) 500 ohms. (*c*) Repeat (*a*) and (*b*) if the diode is reversed.

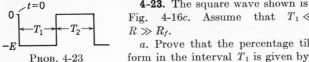

PROB. 4-23

4-23. The square wave shown is applied to the circuit of Fig. 4-16c. Assume that $T_1 \ll RC$, $T_2 \gg R_fC$, and $R \gg R_f$.

a. Prove that the percentage tilt P of the output wave form in the interval T_1 is given by

$$P \cong \left(1 + \frac{E_{bb}}{E}\right)\frac{T_1}{RC} \times 100 \quad \%$$

b. Assume that $T_1 = T_2 = 0.1$ msec, $RC = 1$ msec, and $E = 10$ volts. Sketch the output waveform for values of $E_{bb} = 0, 40, 90,$ and 190 volts. Prove that the positive peak value of the output is E if $T \geq \dfrac{E}{E + E_{bb}} RC$.

4-24. Modify the circuit of Fig. 4-24a, so that the resistor R is connected to ground instead of to the cathode. Will the modified circuit function properly as a clamping circuit? Consider signal amplitudes which are (*a*) small and then (*b*) large compared with E_R.

4-25. The input to the circuits of Fig. 4-25 is a 20-volt rms sine wave of frequency 1 kc. The tube is a 12AU7 with $E_{bb} = 200$ volts, $R_L = 10$ K, $R_g = 1$ Meg, and $C = 0.1$ μf. Sketch, to the same time scale, the input voltage, the grid voltage, and the plate voltage. Find the maximum and minimum values of these voltages.

4-26. *a.* Explain the operation of the synchronized clamping circuit shown. What determines the amplitude of the control voltage e_c?

b. If the tube is a 12AU7 operated at a supply voltage of 250 volts, to what voltage will the output be clamped?

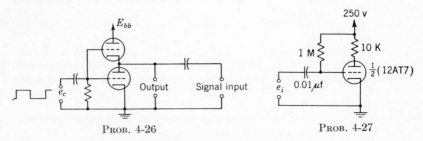

PROB. 4-26   PROB. 4-27

4-27. *a.* A pulse generator whose output impedance is 10 K, delivers 100-volt 2-msec negative pulses to the amplifier shown. Sketch the grid voltage and the plate voltage. Calculate the maximum and minimum values of these voltages. Neglect shunt capacitances.

b. Repeat (*a*) for a 10-volt pulse.

4-28. A symmetrical square wave of period $T = 1,000$ μsec whose voltage varies between $+100$ and -100 volts is applied through a very large resistor to the grid of a 12AU7 tube. The tube plate-supply voltage is 200 volts and the plate load resistor is

10 K. Neglect the input capacitance of the tube. The signal at the plate of the tube is transmitted through a high-pass RC circuit. Draw the output waveform across R, and label all voltages with respect to ground if (a) $RC \gg T$ and $R \gg 10$ K, (b) $RC \gg T$ and $R = 10$ K, and (c) $C = 0.1$ μf and $R = 10$ K. Assume that when the tube conducts it is equivalent to a 7-K resistor.

4-29. In the peaking circuit of Fig. 4-32, the tube is a 12AT7, $E_{bb} = 100$ volts, $R = 10$ K, $R_g = 1$ Meg, $C = 0.1$ μf, and $L = 10$ mh. The input square wave has a peak-to-peak value of 10 volts and a frequency of 10 kc.

a. If the capacitance shunting L is neglected, sketch the output waveform. Calculate the maximum and minimum voltage values and the time constants of the exponential portions of the output waveform.

b. If the capacitance shunting L is 25 μμf, calculate and sketch the output waveshape.

c. If the capacitance shunting L is 400 μμf, calculate and sketch the output waveshape.

4-30. Consider a parallel RLC combination ringing in the plate circuit of a pentode. At $t = 0$, the inductor current is I and the capacitor voltage is E_o. At this instant the grid is clamped to the cathode. If the zero-grid volt-ampere characteristic of the pentode is represented by a constant current I_o, prove that Eqs. (2-47) to (2-49) are valid for this circuit, provided that Δ is interpreted to be $\Delta = (I - I_0)R/E_o$.

4-31. Consider a parallel combination of L, C, and R' in the plate circuit of a triode. At $t = 0$, the inductor current is I and the capacitor voltage is E_o. At this instant the grid is clamped to the cathode. Approximate the zero-grid volt-ampere characteristic by a straight line corresponding to a resistance r_p with the zero-current intercept at E'. Prove that Eqs. (2-47) to (2-49) are valid for this circuit, provided that R and Δ are interpreted to be

$$ R = \frac{R'r_p}{R' + r_p} \quad \text{and} \quad \Delta = \frac{IR}{E_o} - \frac{E_{lb} - E'}{E_o}\frac{R'}{R' + r_p} $$

4-32. In the circuit of Fig. 4-35 the tube is a 5965, $E_{bb} = 200$ volts, $R_L = 20$ K, $C = 50$ μμf, $R_g = 1$ Meg, and $C_g = 0.001$ μf. The input is a 100-kc square wave whose peak-to-peak amplitude is 10 volts. Calculate and sketch the output voltage.

4-33. In the circuit of Fig. 4-39 the tube is a 12AT7, $E_{bb} = 300$ volts, $R_{L1} = R_{L2} = 15$ K, $R_{g1} = R_{g2} = 1$ Meg, $C_1 = 0.1$ μf, and $C_2 = 250$ μμf. The input is a 20-volt peak-to-peak 10-kc square wave. Neglect all shunt capacitances. Calculate and plot the waveforms at G_1, P_1, G_2, and P_2.

4-34. In the discussion in connection with the two-stage overdriven amplifier of Fig. 4-39, it is assumed that $R_{g1}C_1 \gg T_2$ so that the second tube remains cut off during the interval $T_1 < t < T_1 + T_2$. If this restriction is removed, redraw all the waveforms in Fig. 4-40. Assume that $\tau_2 \gg T_1 + T_2$ but that $R_{g1}C_1 \ll T_2$.

4-35. In the discussion in connection with the two-stage overdriven amplifier of Fig. 4-39, it is assumed that $\tau_2 \gg T_1$ so that the first tube remains cut off during the interval $0 < t < T_1$. If this restriction is removed, redraw all the waveforms in Fig. 4-40.

4-36. a. For the cathode-follower circuit of Fig. 4-43 find the maximum and minimum values of the input voltage (between cutoff and zero grid-cathode voltage). Neglect C.

b. Plot the output waveform if the input is a 100-kc square wave whose peak-to-peak value is 100 volts. First neglect C and then repeat for $C = 100$ μμf. Assume $g_m = 4$ millimhos.

c. Repeat (*b*) if the peak-to-peak input voltage is 10 volts.

4-37. *a.* Draw a block diagram of a system which can be used to obtain a single pulse (of positive polarity) per cycle of an input sine wave.

b. Draw the circuit of each block in (*a*), and indicate the input and output waveshapes of each block.

CHAPTER 5

5-1. A fixed-bias binary using a 12AU7 tube has the following parameters: $R_L = 20$ K, $R_1 = 1$ Meg, $R_2 = 0.25$ Meg, $E_{bb} = 200$ volts, and $E_{cc} = 50$ volts. Find the two tube currents, plate voltages, and grid voltages.

5-2. A fixed-bias binary using a 6SN7 tube has the following parameters: $R_L = 20$ K, $R_1 = R_2 \gg R_L$, $E_{bb} = 250$ volts, and E_{cc} is adjustable. Calculate the range of voltages over which E_{cc} may be varied so that (*a*) both tubes are in clamp, (*b*) one tube is in clamp and the other is part on (operating within its grid base), (*c*) one tube is in clamp and the other is cut off, (*d*) one tube is part on and the other is cut off, and (*e*) both tubes are cut off.

5-3. A fixed-bias binary is to be designed using a 12AT7 tube operating from a 300-volt power supply so as to give an output plate swing of 200 volts. Choose $R_1 = 2R_2 \gg R_L$. (*a*) Find R_L. (*b*) Over what range of values of E_{cc} will one tube operate in clamp and the second tube be beyond cutoff?

5-4. A fixed-bias binary using a 6SN7 tube has the following parameters: $R_L = 25$ K, $R_1 = R_2 = 1$ Meg, $E_{bb} = 300$ volts, and $E_{cc} = 100$ volts. Calculate the two tube currents. Is this a well-designed multi?

5-5. A self-biased binary using a 12AU7 tube has the following parameters:

$$R_L = R_k = 20 \text{ K} \qquad R_1 = R_2 \gg R_L \qquad E_{bb} = 250 \text{ volts}$$

Calculate the plate, grid, and cathode voltages with respect to ground.

5-6. *a.* Verify the voltage values on Fig. 5-8*a*. The 5963 tube characteristics are the same as those of the 12AU7.

b. Verify the voltage values in Fig. 5-8*b*.

5-7. Given a 6SN7 operating as a self-biased binary with one tube on and drawing 2 ma and the other tube cut off with its grid-to-cathode voltage 3 volts below cutoff. The circuit parameters are as follows: $E_{bb} = 300$ volts, $R_1 = 1$ Meg, and $R_2 = 0.5$ Meg. Find R_k and R_L. HINT: Use a method of successive approximations and start by neglecting the grid base of the tube.

5-8. A 6SN7 tube operates as a self-biased binary with $R_L = 20$ K, and with $R_1 = R_2 \gg R_L$.

a. If $R_k = 30$ K, over what range of E_{bb} will the circuit operate with one tube in clamp and the other below cutoff?

b. If $E_{bb} = 250$ volts, over what range of R_k will the circuit operate with one tube in clamp and the other below cutoff?

5-9. Find the tube currents and the voltages at each plate, grid, and cathode.

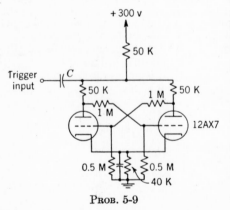

PROB. 5-9

5-10. Find the tube currents and the voltages at each plate and grid for the symmetrical binary indicated.

5-11. A cathode-coupled binary using a 6SN7 has the following parameters: $R_L = 20$ K, $a = \frac{1}{3}$, $R_k = 30$ K, and $E_{bb} = 240$ volts.

    a. Find E^+ first approximately and then more exactly.

    b. Find E^-.

    c. For an input sine wave $e = 100 \sin \omega t$, plot e, e_{bn1}, e_{kn}, and e_{bn2} as a function of $\alpha = \omega t$. Put numerical values of voltage and angle on your graph.

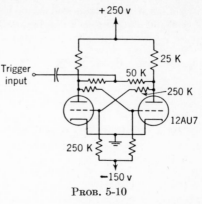

PROB. 5-10

5-12. The input to a cathode-coupled binary is the set of pulses shown. Plot e_{bn2} vs. time. Assume that $E^+ = 80$ volts, $E^- = 60$ volts, $E_{bb} = 200$ volts, the plate swing is 150 volts, and T_2 is *on* at $t = 0$.

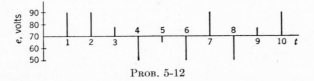

PROB. 5-12

5-13. Verify Eqs. (5-9) and (5-10).

5-14. *a.* The cathode binary of Fig. 5-17 is modified by adding a resistor R_{k2} in series with the cathode of T_2, as indicated in Fig. 5-21. Calculate the approximate value of R_{k2} which must be used in order to eliminate hysteresis.

    b. A resistor R_{k1} in series with the cathode of T_1 is used in place of R_{k2}. Calculate the approximate value of R_{k1} which must be used in order to eliminate hysteresis.

CHAPTER 6

6-1. A plate-coupled monostable multi using a 5965 tube has the following parameters: $E_{bb} = 250$ volts, $R_L = 25$ K, $R = 1$ Meg, $R_1 = 0.5$ Meg, and $R_2 = 1$ Meg. The input trigger source frequency is 100 cps. Find (*a*) E_{cc} so that the voltage at G_1 is -15 volts in the stable state, (*b*) C so that the width of the output waveform is 2 msec, and (*c*) the overshoot at G_2. (*d*) Plot the waveforms at G_2, P_1, P_2, and G_1 to scale.

6-2. A plate-coupled monostable multi using a 6SN7 tube is operated from a 1,000-cps trigger source and a 300-volt supply voltage. It is desired to have a gate width of 800 μsec and a gate amplitude of 200 volts. The overshoot in I_2 is to be kept small, say, 5 per cent. Choose the voltage at G_1 in the stable state to be about 25 per cent beyond cutoff. (*a*) Find R_L, C, R, a, and E_{cc}. (*b*) Plot the waveforms at each plate and grid to scale.

6-3. A plate-coupled monostable multi using a 12AT7 tube is operated from a 500-cps trigger source and a 250-volt supply voltage. It is desired to have a gate width of 1,500 μsec and a swing at each plate of 150 volts. Choose the voltage at G_1 in the stable state to be about 50 per cent beyond cutoff. Find (*a*) R_L, C, R, a, and E_{cc} and (*b*) the overshoot at G_2. (*c*) Plot the waveforms at each grid and plate to scale.

6-4. *a.* A plate-coupled monostable multi has been adjusted so as to have a small overshoot. Prove that the gate width is given approximately by

$$\frac{T}{RC} \cong \frac{I_1 R_{L1} + E_{co}}{E_{bb} - E_{co}}$$

HINT: $\ln (1 + x) \cong x$ for $|x| \ll 1$.

b. Let the plate load resistor R_{L2} of T_2 be held constant while the plate load resistor R_{L1} of T_1 is varied. Under these circumstances the output swing at P_2 is constant, the grid current I_c is decreased as the plate swing $I_1 R_{L1}$ at P_1 is decreased, but the recovery time constant τ is increased. Prove that for small overshoots

$$\tau I_c = (E_{bb} - E_{co}) \frac{T}{R}$$

What is the physical significance of this result?

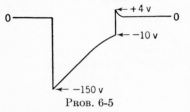

+4 v
0
0
−10 v
−150 v
PROB. 6-5

6-5. A plate-coupled monostable multi has the waveform shown at grid G_2. The supply voltage is 250 volts and $r_c = 1$ K. (*a*) Draw the waveform at P_1 and (*b*) evaluate R_L.

6-6. A plate-coupled monostable multi using a 12AU7 tube has the following parameters: $E_{bb} = 300$ volts, $R_L = 15$ K, $R = 1$ Meg, $C = 0.001$ μf, $R_1 = 900$ K, and $R_2 = 100$ K. For the minimum gate width, calculate (*a*) E_{cc}, (*b*) T, (*c*) I_c, and (*d*) the swing at P_2. (*e*) Repeat the above calculations for the maximum gate width.

6-7. *a.* If a positive pulse is applied through a capacitor to the first grid G_1 of a plate-coupled monostable multi, prove that the minimum value E_T^+ of this pulse is $E_T^+ = E_{co} - E_F$.

b. If a negative pulse is applied through a capacitor to the second grid G_2 of a plate-coupled monostable multi, prove that the minimum value E_T^- of this pulse is $E_T^- = (E_{co} - E_F)/aA$, where A is the gain of T_2 and $a = R_2/(R_1 + R_2)$.

6-8. A monostable cathode-coupled multi uses a 6SN7 tube with $R_L = R_k = 10$ K and $E_{bb} = 250$ volts.

a. Find the maximum E_{max} and minimum E_{min} voltage which may be applied to the first grid.

b. Find the voltage swings at each plate, both for maximum and minimum gate widths.

c. To a first approximation $T/RC = \alpha(E - E_{min})$. Find α.

d. Calculate I_c for the maximum gate width.

e. Plot the plate, grid, and cathode waveforms for the maximum gate width.

6-9. A monostable cathode-coupled multi using a 5965 tube with $R_L = R_k$ and $E_{bb} = 250$ volts is triggered at the rate of 500 pulses per second. It is desired that the voltage swing at P_2 be 75 volts. The waveforms are to have very little overshoot and are to be symmetrical (the *off* time to equal the *on* time). Find (*a*) R_L, (*b*) E, (*c*) C, and (*d*) R.

6-10. In a cathode-coupled monostable multi, $E_{bb} = 250$ volts, $R_L = R_k = 10$ K, $r_c = 1$ K, $I_c = 1$ ma, $I_2 = 10$ ma, E is adjusted so that $I_1 = 7$ ma and $E_{co} = -10$ volts. Draw the waveforms at P_1, G_2, and P_2. Indicate all voltage values with respect to ground, including all overshoots.

6-11. *a.* It is possible to eliminate the undershoot in the voltage at P_2 of a cathode-coupled monostable multi by choosing $R_k = \mu r_c$. Explain this result physically. Plot (*b*) the waveform at P_1 if $R_k = \mu r_c$ and (*c*) the waveform at P_2 if $R_k > \mu r_c$.

6-12. *a.* If $I_2' = I_2 + \Delta I_2$ is the peak plate current in T_2 of a cathode-coupled monostable multi when its grid current is I_{c2}, prove that

$$I_2' R_k = -I_{c2}(R_L + R_k + r_c) + I_1(R_L + R_k) + E_{co2}$$

HINT: Equate the voltage across C at $t = T-$ to that at $t = T+$.

b. The above equation gives one relationship between I_2' and $E_{c2} = I_{c2}r_c$. A second relationship between I_2' and E_{c2} is given by a load line. Devise a graphic method, using positive-grid tube characteristics for finding I_2' and E_{c2}.

6-13. *a.* In a cathode-coupled monostable multi prove that it is possible for the value of $E_{\min}$ to be negative.

b. If a 6SN7 tube is used with $E_{bb} = 300$ volts, $R_L = 30$ K, find R_k so that $E_{\min} = 0$.

6-14. With respect to the linearity of the delay of the cathode-coupled monostable multi consider the following problem.

a. The relationship between an independent variable x and a dependent variable y is quadratic and of the form $y = A_1 x + A_2 x^2$ with x variable from 0 to x_m. A straight line is drawn between the end points of this curve. The fractional error ϵ is defined as the difference between the curve and the straight line divided by the maximum value of the dependent variable. Show that the maximum error occurs at $x = x_m/2$ and is given by $\epsilon = -A_2 x_m/4A_1$, provided that the error is small enough so that

$$y_m \cong A_1 x_m$$

b. Apply the result of (*a*) to Eq. (6-20) and show that the error in linearity of T with respect to $I_{10} = I_1 - I_0$ is $\epsilon = I_{10}(R_L - R_k)/8E'$.

c. In terms of the slope $dy/dx \equiv S$, show that $\epsilon = (S_o - S_m)/8S_o$, where S_m is the slope at $x = x_m$ and S_o is the slope at $x = 0$.

6-15. *a.* The definition of the error between a curve and a straight line is given in Prob. 6-14. If the curve is defined by $y = A_1 x + A_3 x^3$, prove that the maximum error occurs at $x = \dfrac{x_m}{\sqrt{3}}$ and that $\epsilon = -\dfrac{2}{3\sqrt{3}}\dfrac{A_3}{A_1}x_m^2$.

b. Consider a cathode-coupled monostable multi with $R_L = R_k$. Applying the result of (*a*), show that

$$\epsilon = -\frac{2}{9\sqrt{3}}\left(\frac{I_{10}R_L}{E'}\right)^2$$

6-16. *a.* Using the linear equivalent circuit for the vacuum tubes of the cathode-coupled monostable multi show that

$$I_{10} = \frac{\mu(E - E_{\min})}{r_p + (\mu + 1)R_k + R_L}$$

b. Apply the results of Prob. 6-14c to find the error in linearity of I_{10} with respect to E. What is the interpretation of S_m and S_o?

c. What is the total error in linearity of T with respect to E?

6-17. Consider a cathode-coupled monostable multi with $R_{L1} \neq R_{L2}$. Prove that the expressions in the text for $E_{\max}$, $E_{\min}$, T, and I_c remain valid, provided that R_L is taken to be R_{L1}. Also, prove that Eq. (6-14) for γ remains valid, provided that R_L is replaced by R_{L2}.

6-18. A cathode-coupled monostable multi using a 12AU7 has the following parameters: $E_{bb} = 200$ volts, $R_{L1} = 150$ K, $R_{L2} = 25$ K, $R_k = 5$ K, $R = 2$ Meg, and $C = 0.001$ μf. (*a*) Find $E_{\min}$. For $E = 0$, find (*b*) the output voltage swing at P_2 and (*c*) the gate width.

6-19. Consider the effect of B supply variations on the delay time T of the monostable cathode-coupled multi. First, find ΔI_1 and ΔI_2 for a given change ΔE_{bb}. Assume that the second tube has its grid clamped to its cathode. Finally, find ΔT as a function of ΔE_{bb}.

6-20. If the resistor in the cathode-coupled monostable multi is connected to an auxiliary voltage U instead of to E_{bb}, but if T_2 is in clamp, show that (a) the gate width is given by Eq. (6-16) with E_{bb} replaced by U, (b) the maximum and minimum values of E are unaltered, and (c) the trigger size required is the same as with $U = E_{bb}$.

6-21. For the multi of Prob. 6-20, show that the delay varies linearly with changes in U, provided that U is large and the changes in U are small.

6-22. a. The resistor R in a cathode-coupled monostable multi is coupled to an auxiliary voltage U instead of to E_{bb}. The voltage U is small enough so that T_2 is not in clamp but T_1 is beyond cutoff. Prove that the delay is given by

$$\frac{T}{RC} = \ln \frac{I_1 R_L}{U - E_{co2} - I_1 R_k}$$

b. For what values of the d-c voltage E (with respect to ground) on the grid of T will this circuit become astable?

6-23. Consider a cathode-coupled monostable multi with the resistor R connected between G_2 and cathode. Assume that R is much greater than R_L or R_k. Find expressions for (a) T, (b) $E_{\min}$, (c) $E_{\max}$, (d) the swing at each plate, (e) I_c, and (f) E_T.

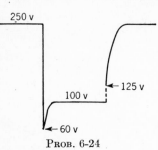

PROB. 6-24

6-24. A 12AU7 astable multivibrator has the waveform shown at one of its plates. The voltages given are the voltages with respect to ground. Find the value of the plate circuit resistors of the tubes. Draw the waveform at the grid, and mark the voltage with respect to ground at every important point on the waveform, for example, flat portions, sudden jumps, etc.

6-25. A symmetrical astable plate-coupled multi using a 6SN7 has the following parameters: $E_{bb} = 150$ volts, $R_L = 10$ K, $R = 1$ Meg, and $C = 0.001$ μf. Calculate the period and the overshoots, and plot the plate and grid waveforms.

6-26. Calculate the frequency of the multi of Prob. 6-25 as E_{bb} is adjusted from 50 to 250 volts in 50-volt steps.

6-27. An astable plate-coupled multi using a 12AT7 has the following parameters: $E_{bb} = 240$ volts, $R_{L1} = R_{L2} = 12$ K, $R_1 = 1$ Meg, $R_2 = 2$ Meg, $C_1 = C_2 = 0.001$ μf. Calculate the gate widths T_1 and T_2 and the overshoots. Plot the plate and grid waveforms.

6-28. Consider a symmetrical astable plate-coupled multi with each resistor R connected between grid and cathode (instead of between grid and the B supply).

a. Find an expression for the overshoot in voltage at the grid and for the period T.

b. Plot the plate and grid waveforms, and indicate all important voltage values.

6-29. Consider the plate-coupled astable multi of Fig. 6-16 to which has been added a common cathode resistor R_k. Prove that

$$I_c = \frac{I R_L + E_{co}}{R_L + r_c + R_k(1 + \gamma)}$$

where γ is defined by Eq. (6-14).

CHAPTER 7

7-1. In Fig. 7-3 draw a line $O'A'$ parallel to OA and displaced from it by a distance equal to $\frac{1}{2}(e_s - e_s')_{max}$. If the displacement error ϵ_d' is defined as the distance from the sweep voltage e_s to the line $O'A'$ divided by E_s, show that $\epsilon_d' = \frac{1}{2}\epsilon_d$. Note that, whereas ϵ_d is always positive, ϵ_d' may be positive or negative.

7-2. *a.* An exponential sweep is obtained when a capacitor C is charged from a supply voltage E through a resistor R. If the peak sweep voltage is E_s, prove that the slope error ϵ_s is given exactly by $\epsilon_s = E_s/E$.

b. Prove that the displacement error ϵ_d is given by

$$\epsilon_d = \frac{E}{E_s} - \frac{RC}{T} + \frac{RC}{T}\ln\frac{E_s RC}{ET}$$

where T is the sweep duration.

c. If $T/RC \ll 1$, prove that

$$\epsilon_d \cong \frac{1}{8}\frac{E_s}{E} = \frac{1}{8}\epsilon_s$$

7-3. To the circuit of Prob. 7-2 a resistor R_1 is added across C. Prove that the slope error is given by $\epsilon_s = E_s/aE$, where $a = R_1/(R_1 + R)$.

7-4. The deviation from linearity of a sweep voltage is small so that this voltage may be approximated by the sum of a linear and a quadratic term. Prove that under these circumstances Eq. (7-1) is valid.

7-5. The characteristics of an 884 thyratron tube are described in Sec. 7-2. This tube is used in the sweep circuit of Fig. 7-5 with the following parameters: $E_{bb} = 400$ volts, $E_{cc} = 10$ volts, $C = 0.0025$ μf, and $R = 1$ Meg. Calculate (*a*) the sweep frequency, (*b*) the sweep amplitude, (*c*) the slope and displacement errors, and (*d*) a suitable value for r.

7-6. The characteristics of an 884 thyratron tube are described in Sec. 7-2. Design a 60-cps sweep using this tube. The sweep amplitude is to be 25 volts and the slope error is not to exceed 5 per cent. Specify reasonable values for E_{bb}, E_{cc}, R, and C, and give reasons for your choice.

7-7. Design a thyratron-driven sweep (Fig. 7-7) whose duration is 100 μsec and whose amplitude is 50 volts. The triggering waveform is a 1,000-cps train of pulses which are 1 μsec wide and 4 volts in amplitude. The tube used has a grid-control ratio of 10 and a maintaining voltage of 20 volts. The power supply voltage is 250 volts. Specify reasonable values for E_{cc}, R_1, R_2, R, and C, and give reasons for your choice.

7-8. Consider the sweep circuit of Fig. 7-9. The thyratron grid-control ratio is 8 and the maintaining voltage is 16 volts.

a. If the circuit is adjusted for recurrent operation (S closed), find the maximum and minimum values of the output signal (at the cathode of T_5).

b. Calculate the slope and displacement errors.

c. If the circuit is adjusted so that a driven sweep is obtained (S open), calculate a reasonable value for the resistor R.

7-9. In the vacuum-tube sweep circuit of Fig. 7-10, the tube is a 12AU7, $E_{bb} = 300$ volts, $R = 100$ K, $R_g = 1$ Meg, and $C_g = 0.001$ μf. The input gate is a negative 10-μsec pulse whose amplitude is 30 volts.

a. What is the sweep duration?

b. What is the minimum output voltage, with respect to ground?

c. If a 10-volt sweep is desired, what is the value of C?

d. What is the approximate value of the recovery time constant?

e. How would you modify the circuit in order to reduce the recovery time? Suppose, for example, that the input gate is to be a symmetrical 50-kc square wave whose peak-to-peak amplitude is 30 volts.

7-10. A given waveform is observed on a CRO. It is desired to view a selected portion of this waveform in more detail by spreading it out in time by some factor, say 5. Devise a circuit which will function as such a *sweep magnifier*.

7-11. The Miller sweep circuit of Fig. 7-18 uses a 6AU6 pentode with a screen voltage of 150 volts. The parameters in the circuit have the following values: $E_{bb} = 300$ volts, $R_L = 10$ K, $R = 1$ Meg, $C = 0.003$ μf, and $E_{cc} = 2$ volts. The switch S is opened for 750 μsec. (*a*) Plot the output waveform. Neglect the small jump in voltage at $t = 0$. Calculate (*b*) the output voltage with respect to ground at the beginning and at the end of the sweep, (*c*) the displacement error, and (*d*) the recovery time constant, assuming a switch impedance of 1 K.

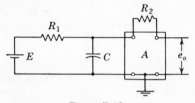

PROB. 7-12

7-12. For the circuit shown, prove that a truly linear sweep is obtained if

$$A = 1 + \frac{R_2}{R_1}$$

The gain A is that of the amplifier with R_2 removed. Discuss this circuit.

7-13. *a.* Verify that the circuit indicated is the operational amplifier equivalent of the Miller sweep circuit of Fig. 7-18. The output impedance R_o and the gain A refer to the amplifier with input terminals X, Z, with output terminals Y, Z, and with C removed.

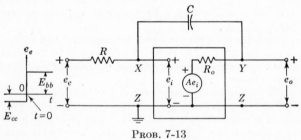

PROB. 7-13

b. Prove that the jump Δe_o in output voltage at $t = 0$ is given by

$$\Delta e_o = \frac{R_o E}{(1 - A)R + R_o}$$

where $E = E_{bb} + E_{cc}$

c. For a single-stage pentode amplifier with $A \gg 1$, show that $\Delta e_o = E/g_m R$.

d. Evaluate Δe_o if $E = 300$ volts, $R_L = 30$ K, $g_m = 3$ millimhos, and $R = 1$ Meg.

e. Assume that the circuit of Fig. 7-20 is used. The pentode parameters are as in (*d*) and the cathode follower has a transconductance of 3 millimhos. Evaluate Δe_o.

7-14. *a.* Consider a resistor r added in series with the capacitor C of the Miller sweep of Fig. 7-18. Using the equivalent circuit given in Prob. 7-13 (but with the addition of r), prove that the jump Δe_o in output voltage at $t = 0$ is given by

$$\Delta e_o = \frac{(R_o + Ar)E}{(1 - A)R + R_o + r}$$

b. Under what conditions will the jump be positive? Negative? Zero?

c. Show that the jump is eliminated if r is chosen equal to $1/g_m$ (for a single-stage pentode amplifier).

7-15. The screen-gated phantastron circuit of Fig. 7-24 uses a 6AU6 tube having the following parameters: $E_{bb} = 300$ volts, $R_L = 100$ K, $R = 1$ Meg, and $C = 0.001$ μf. The bleeder resistors are so adjusted that the suppressor is at zero volts and the screen at 150 volts during the sweep time. Calculate (*a*) E_1 and E_3 (Fig. 7-25), approximately, (*b*) the sweep amplitude, (*c*) the sweep duration T_s, (*d*) the per cent change in T_s for a 10 per cent change in supply voltage, and (*e*) the displacement error. (*f*) If a plate-catching diode is added, as in Fig. 7-26, then the relationship between E and the delay time T is $T = \alpha E$. Find α.

7-16. An astable circuit may be obtained by cross-coupling two monostable screen-coupled phantastrons. Sketch such a circuit and explain its operation.

7-17. It is desired to obtain a time delay which will be inversely proportional to a d-c voltage E. Show that a screen-coupled phantastron will give this relationship (approximately) if the charging resistor R is connected to E instead of to E_{bb}.

7-18. The bootstrap sweep circuit of Fig. 7-30 uses a 12AU7 tube with the following parameters: $E_{bb} = 250$ volts, $C = 500$ $\mu\mu$f, $C_d = 0.01$ μf, $R_d = 0.2$ Meg, $R = 1$ Meg, and $R_k = 10$ K. The switch S is opened for 100 μsec. (*a*) Plot the waveform at the output of the cathode follower. Calculate (*b*) the output voltage at the beginning and at the end of the sweep, (*c*) the displacement error, and (*d*) the recovery time constant.

7-19. Repeat Prob. 7-18 if R_D is replaced by a diode whose forward resistance is 1 K.

7-20. Repeat Prob. 7-18 if a 20-K resistor is added in series with C. Switch S is in parallel with the series combination of C and the 20-K resistor.

7-21. Show that the effective impedance shunting C in Fig. 7-31 is a series combination of a resistance $R/(1 - A)$ and a capacitance $C_D(1 - A)$. In other words, verify that the circuit shown is equivalent to Fig. 7-31 as far as the calculation of e_c is concerned. Remembering that the initial current through C is E_{bb}/R, verify Eq. (7-16).

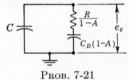

PROB. 7-21

7-22. The bootstrap circuit of Fig. 7-30 uses a 6SN7 tube with the following parameters: $E_{bb} = 300$ volts, $R = 1$ Meg, $C = 0.1$ μf, and $R_k = 15$ K. The capacitor C_D is replaced by a $\frac{1}{25}$-watt neon lamp whose voltage is 65 volts over the range 30 to 300 μa. With switch S closed, the lamp current is 200 μa. Switch S has a resistance of 1,000 ohms. It is opened for a time T_s, at the end of which time the sweep has made a 100-volt excursion. Calculate (*a*) the cathode voltage with S closed, (*b*) the value of R_D, (*c*) the lamp current at the end of the sweep, (*d*) the sweep time T_s, (*e*) the ratio T_s/τ, where τ is the restoration time constant, and (*f*) the displacement error.

7-23. The bootstrap circuit of Fig. 7-30 uses a 12AU7 tube with the following parameters: $E_{bb} = 250$ volts, $R = 2$ Meg, and $R_k = 10$ K. The capacitor C_D is replaced by a neon bulb whose voltage is 75 volts over the range 50 to 250 μa. It is desired to have as large a sweep voltage as possible and still have the neon lamp current within its normal range. Calculate (*a*) the cathode voltage with S closed, (*b*) the value of R_D, (*c*) the sweep amplitude across C, and (*d*) the value of C for a 1-sec sweep.

7-24. *a.* For the bootstrap shown prove that the amplifier gain A must be given by $A = 1 + R/R_1$ if a truly linear sweep is to be obtained.

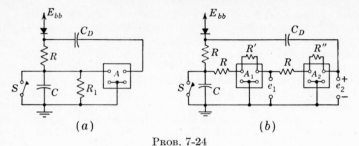

PROB. 7-24

b. A linear push-pull sweep is to be obtained from the circuit shown ($e_1 = -e_2$). Find the values of R'/R and R''/R. The forward gains of the operational amplifiers may be taken as infinite.

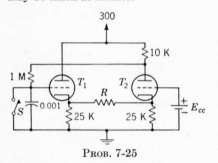

PROB. 7-25

7-25. *a.* Find the value of R which will cause the bootstrap circuit shown to give an exactly linear sweep. The tube parameters are $\mu = 13$ and $r_p = 16$ K.

b. What is the sweep speed? The quiescent current in T_2 is 5 ma.

7-26. By considering the initial conditions in the circuit of Fig. 7-33, prove that $d^2e_s/dt^2 = 0$ at $t = 0$. This physical argument explains why the t^2 term is missing in Eq. (7-20).

7-27. Verify Eqs. (7-17) to (7-19).

7-28. The circuit of Fig. 7-33 has the following parameters: $E = 250$ volts, $L = 700$ henrys, $R = 100$ K, and $C = 0.005$ μf. The switch S is opened for 500 μsec. Calculate (a) the sweep amplitude and (b) the displacement error. (c) If switch S were left open, sketch the output waveform across C. What would be the approximate value of the peak output voltage? (d) If the inductor were not in the circuit, repeat (a) and (b).

7-29. The sweep circuit of Fig. 7-34 has the following parameters: $E_{bb} = 300$ volts, $E_{gn} = 100$ volts for T_2, $r = 1$ K, and $C = 0.01$ μf. The pentode is a 6AU6 with a screen voltage of 150 volts. The screen current is 0.4 of the plate current. The cathode resistor is adjusted so that the capacitor current is approximately 0.7 ma during the sweep time. The thyratron maintaining voltage is 20 volts and its grid-control ratio is 10. Calculate (a) the maximum and minimum values of e_s, (b) the cathode resistance, (c) the sweep frequency, and (d) the displacement error (approximately).

CHAPTER 8

8-1. Prove that the critical damping resistance for the current sweep coil of Fig. 8-1 is given by the expression

$$R_D = \frac{R_c}{1 + R_L/4R_c}$$

where $R_c = \frac{1}{2} \sqrt{L/C}$.

For the coil specified by the first entry in Table 8-1, calculate what percentage error is made if R_L is neglected in the calculation of R_D.

8-2. Verify Eq. (8-3).

8-3. *a.* Prove that the maximum deviation between the actual sweep and the ideal sweep in Fig. 8-3 is $k\sqrt{LC}\,\epsilon^{-1} = 0.36k\sqrt{LC}$ and that this occurs at $t = \sqrt{LC}$.

b. Show that the actual sweep differs from the linear sweep by less than 5 per cent if t exceeds $3\sqrt{LC}$.

8-4. A deflection coil has an inductance L and is fed from a voltage source e through a resistance R (which includes the coil resistance). Neglect the capacitance. If the input is of the form $e = A + Bt$, show that the current is

$$i = \frac{A - Lk}{R}(1 - \epsilon^{-Rt/L}) + kt$$

where $k = B/R$.

In order to have a truly linear sweep, A must equal Lk. If the pedestal does not have this proper value, what happens to the sweep? Make a rough plot for $A = 1.1Lk$ and for $A = 0.9Lk$.

8-5. *a.* Consider the effect of omitting both the impulsive current and the step of current in Eq. (8-2). Assume that the damping resistance has been adjusted so that the circuit is critically damped. Under these conditions, prove that if $y \equiv i_L/k\sqrt{LC}$ and $x \equiv t/\sqrt{LC}$, then

$$y = (x + 2)\epsilon^{-x} + x - 2$$

b. Prove that at $x = 0$, $y = 0$, $dy/dx = 0$, and $d^2y/dx^2 = 0$.

c. Plot this response and that given by Eq. (8-6) to the same scale. What is the effect of omitting the step of current?

8-6. *a.* Consider the effect of omitting both the impulsive current and the linear current in Eq. (8-2). Assume that the damping is very heavy ($R = 0.1R_c$). Under these conditions prove that

$$i_L \cong \frac{kL}{R + R_L}\left(1 - \epsilon^{-\left(\frac{R + R_L}{L}\right)t}\right)$$

HINT: Note that $[(R + R_L)/L]RC \ll 1$, and expand the square root in Eq. (8-7) by the binomial expansion.

b. Show that for small values of t, $i_L \cong kt$. Plot i_L as given in (*a*) and kt on the same graph.

c. Consider the coil whose parameters are given by the first row in Table 8-1. What is the maximum sweep length over which the displacement error will be less than 1 per cent?

8-7. Prove that Eq. (8-10) is valid for Fig. 8-5*b*, provided that E is taken to be the quiescent voltage across R_2 and e_o is interpreted as the departure of the output voltage from its quiescent value.

8-8. Verify that the waveform at the cathode of T_2 in Fig. 8-6 is as indicated. At what times does this voltage pass through zero?

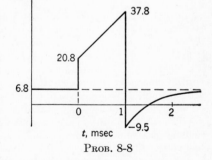

PROB. 8-8

8-9. The switching circuit of Fig. 8-6 has the following parameters: $E_{bb} = 200$ volts, $E_{cc} = 100$ volts, $R_g = 1$ Meg, $R_2 = 300$ K, $R_1 = 10$ K, and $C_1 = 0.01$ μf. The tube T_1 is a 6SN7. The input square wave is symmetrical with a half period of 1 msec and peak-to-peak amplitude E_p.

a. Assuming C_g very large, find the minimum value of E_p which will keep the tube cut off during the sweep time.

b. Repeat (*a*) if $C_g = 0.01$ μf.   Sketch the grid-to-ground voltage.

8-10. It is desired to drive the coil in the writing head of a magnetic storage drum with the coil current waveform indicated in (*a*).   The coil inductance is 0.4 mh, the coil resistance is 1.5 ohms, and the self-resonant frequency of the coil is 5 Mc.   Assume that the external stray capacitance across the coil is 25 $\mu\mu$f.

a. Calculate the damping resistance.   Is the circuit overdamped or underdamped?

b. Calculate and sketch the current waveform of the driver.

c. If the impulsive term is omitted in the driver current, how is the coil current waveform modified?

d. Calculate and sketch the voltage waveform of the coil.

e. Sketch and label the current waveform required to drive the coil if the coil current has the waveform indicated in (*b*).

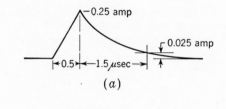

(*a*)

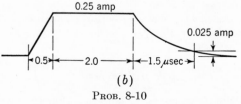

(*b*)

Prob. 8-10

8-11. *a.* Consider a coil with no shunt damping resistor.   If this coil is in the plate circuit of a driver tube, find the grid voltage e_i needed to produce a linear coil current kt.

b. For the typical coils of Table 8-1, prove that

$$e_i \cong \frac{kLC}{g_m}\, \delta(t) + \frac{kL}{\mu}\left(1 + \frac{r_p t}{L}\right)$$

Note that, if the impulsive term is neglected, the input may be approximated by a step voltage if the sweep time $T_s \ll L/r_p$ and by a sweep voltage (without a step) if $T_s \gg L/r_p$.

8-12. Modify the current sweep of Fig. 8-6, so that the coil is in the plate circuit of T_2.   The coil is described by the second entry in Table 8-1.   It is required that the current change by 100 ma in 10^{-3} sec. T_1 is a 6J5 and T_2 is a 6L6.   The plate and screen supply voltages of the 6L6 are to be 350 and 250 volts, respectively.   Take the g_m and r_p of the 6L6 to be 5 millimhos and 33 K, respectively.   To avoid large tube nonlinearities, an initial current of 25 ma is to flow in the 6L6.   The grid-to-cathode voltage of a 6L6 is -26 volts for a plate current of 25 ma and a plate voltage of 350 volts.

a. Compute the required waveform at the grid of T_2 (neglect stray capacitance and adjust matters so that the coil is critically damped).

b. Compute (or arbitrarily select) C_g, R_g, R, C_1, R_1, and E_{cc} to give the required waveform. Choose $R_2 = 1$ Meg.

c. Draw and label with voltage levels the complete waveform (including decays) at the grid and plate of T_2. In calculating the overshoot at the plate, assume that the grid drops immediately to its quiescent value at the end of the sweep.

8-13. *a.* For the circuit of Fig. 8-10, assume that $\mu \gg 1$ and $r_p \gg Z_L$, where Z_L is the coil impedance. Prove that the equivalent circuit for calculating the tube current i is as indicated.

b. If the input voltage e_i is a step of magnitude E, prove that i is given by

$$i = \frac{g_m E}{1 + g_m R_k} (1 + g_m R_k \epsilon^{-t/\tau})$$

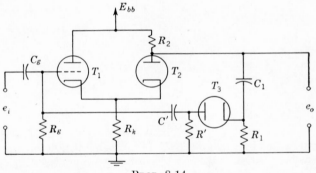

PROB. 8-13

where $\tau = R_k C_k / (1 + g_m R_k)$. Plot this current waveform and show that it contains a spike.

c. Assume that the coil is critically damped. The spike time constant is to be adjusted to $2\sqrt{LC}$ (approximating the delay in the sweep). The step current is to be properly chosen. Under these circumstances, prove that R_k and C_k are given by

$$R_k = \frac{ER}{kL} - \frac{1}{g_m} \qquad \text{and} \qquad C_k = \frac{g_m E}{kR_k}$$

8-14. If the input e_i to the circuit shown is a positive gate, then the output e_o will be a trapezoidal voltage with a spike, as indicated in Fig. 8-11. Explain the operation of the circuit.

PROB. 8-14

8-15. The coil described in the third row of Table 8-1 is used in the circuit of Fig. 8-15. The coil current is to change by 100 ma in 10^{-4} sec. The damping resistor is chosen for critical damping. Find R_1 and C_1.

8-16. A television horizontal sweep circuit has the following constants: The sweep coil has an inductance of 30 mh, the peak-to-peak sweep current is 300 ma, the primary of the autotransformer has an inductance of 30 mh, and its secondary inductance is 120 mh, the coil and transformer resonant frequencies are alike and each equals 100 kc, and $E_{bb} = 250$ volts. Find (*a*) the booster voltage and (*b*) the high-voltage supply. (*c*) Plot the voltage at the bottom of the deflection coil *with respect to ground*. What is the d-c value of this voltage?

CHAPTER 9

9-1. Verify that the circuit of Fig. 9-3 is equivalent to that in Fig. 9-2.

9-2. Verify Eq. (9-11).

9-3. In Fig. 9-8, S = mean circumference of the coils, d = distance between the inside surface of the secondary coil and outside surface of the primary coil, a_p = thickness of a primary wire, and a_s = thickness of a secondary wire.

a. Prove that the leakage inductance is given by

$$\sigma = \frac{\mu_o N_p{}^2 S}{\lambda} \left(d + \frac{a_p + a_s}{2} \right)$$

b. Assume that the current is distributed uniformly throughout the windings. Prove that now the expression for σ is the same as in (*a*) except that the numeral 2 must be replaced by 3.

Note: If the flux density H is not constant, then Eq. (9-13) becomes

$$\sigma I_p{}^2 = \mu_o \int H^2 \, dV$$

9-4. Consider a transformer with a one-layer primary and a two-layer secondary winding. Each layer of the secondary has the same number of turns. In (*a*) both

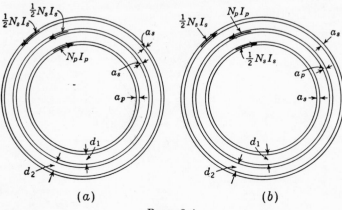

(a)   **(b)**

Prob. 9-4

secondaries are wound over the primary. In (*b*) the primary is interleaved between secondary windings. Replace the coils by current sheets located at the center of the coil wires. The mean circumference of the windings is S.

a. Indicate the magnetic field intensity as a function of the distance between windings (as in Fig. 9-8*b*).

b. Prove that for the configuration in (*a*) the leakage inductance is given by

$$\sigma = \frac{\mu_o N_p{}^2 S}{4\lambda} \left(4d_1 + d_2 + 2a_p + 3a_s \right)$$

and in (*b*) by

$$\sigma = \frac{\mu_o N_p{}^2 S}{4\lambda} \left(d_1 + d_2 + a_p + a_s \right)$$

This problem illustrates the advantage of interleaving with respect to reducing the leakage inductance.

9-5. A two-layer transformer is connected as an autotransformer. Show that this type of connection reduces the leakage inductance by the ratio $(n - 1)^2/n^2$, where n is the step-up ratio of the autotransformer.

9-6. A transformer has the following parameters: primary and secondary each one layer of 132 turns, wire No. 38 having a diameter $= 0.0102$ cm, diameter including insulation $= 0.0125$ cm, insulation between windings $= 0.031$ cm, mean circumference $S = 5.4$ cm, and dielectric constant of insulation between windings $\epsilon = 3.5$. NOTE: $\epsilon_o = 10^{-9}/36\pi$ farad/m.

PROB. 9-6

a. Consider the two windings as constituting a parallel plate capacitor. Prove that the interwinding capacitance is 89 $\mu\mu$f.

b. Consider two adjacent turns as parallel conductors, as shown in the sketch. From electrostatics, the capacitance per meter of such a configuration is given by $\pi\epsilon/\cosh^{-1}(D/a)$. Prove that the effective capacitance across the winding is only 0.06 $\mu\mu$f, even if it is assumed that all the space surrounding the wires has a dielectric constant of 3.5.

9-7. Verify Eq. (9-20).

9-8. Consider a transformer with a single-layer primary and a single-layer secondary. A grounded electrostatic shield is inserted between the primary and the secondary midway between windings. Calculate the ratio of the effective primary shunt capacitance C'' with the shield to the capacitance C' without the shield as a function of the step-up ratio n for (a) a noninverting transformer and (b) an inverting transformer.

9-9. Verify that the primary inductance L_p for the pot core of Fig. 9-10 is given by $L_p = 1.1 N_p^2$ μh.

9-10. The windings on the pot-core transformer of Fig. 9-10 are placed side by side in slots in a bobbin so that each winding takes the approximate shape of a flat disk. The distance between windings is 2 mm. The insulation of the wire has a dielectric constant of 3.5. Each winding has 100 turns and the transformer is of the inverting type. Calculate (a) the leakage inductance, (b) the primary inductance, (c) the coefficient of coupling, and (d) the effective capacitance C'.

9-11. A transformer is used for peaking. The primary winding (of inductance L) is in the plate circuit of a pentode and a damper diode is across this winding. The load on the secondary winding may be considered to be purely capacitive. This load capacitance C_L is much larger than the transformer capacitance C'. A step of voltage is applied to the grid and the amplifier delivers a current step I_0 to the plate.

a. Prove that the amplitude of the output pulse at the secondary is $I_0 \sqrt{L/C_L}$, *which is independent* of the step-up ratio n. Explain this result physically. Neglect the leakage inductance.

b. Prove that the pulse duration is $n\pi \sqrt{LC_L}$.

c. Compare the outputs obtained from two transformers; one has $n = 1$, $L = 20$ mh, and $C_L = 50$ $\mu\mu$f, and the second has $n = 10$, $L = 0.5$ mh, and $C_L = 50$ $\mu\mu$f. The current step is 5 ma.

9-12. Verify (a) Eq. (9-25), (b) Eq. (9-26), and (c) Eq. (9-28).

9-13. Verify Eq. (9-30).

9-14. A cup-core transformer having the dimensions given in Fig. 9-10 has 70 turns on each winding. A 20-volt step is applied to the primary and the output is taken from the open-circuited secondary. Because of saturation of the core a pulse is observed at the output. Find the width of this output pulse.

9-15. A transformer has the following parameters: $L = 5.0$ mh, $\sigma = 20$ μh, $C = 100$ $\mu\mu$f, $R_1 = R_2 = 500$ ohms, and $n = 1$. Find the response to a 1-μsec, 20-volt pulse, and plot.

9-16. A transformer has the following parameters: $L = 7.5$ mh, $\sigma = 60$ μh, $C = 75$ $\mu\mu$f, $R_1 = 250$ ohms, $R_2 = 1$ K, and $n = 3$. Find the response to a 10-volt, 3-μsec pulse, and plot.

9-17. A transformer has the following parameters:

$$L = 70 \text{ mh} \qquad \sigma = 200 \text{ }\mu\text{h} \qquad C_L = 500 \text{ }\mu\mu\text{f}$$
$$C' = 20 \text{ }\mu\mu\text{f} \qquad R_L = 1 \text{ K} \qquad N_p = 150 \qquad N_s = 60$$

the generator resistance = 300 ohms, and the transformer winding resistances are negligible. Find and plot the response to a 10-μsec, 1-volt pulse.

9-18. A pulse transformer with a step-up ratio of 2:1 is to pass a 1-μsec pulse with less than 10 per cent tilt and less than 10 per cent overshoot. The generator impedance is 1 K and the load impedance is 1 Meg in parallel with 25 $\mu\mu$f. For what values of primary and leakage inductances must the transformer be designed?

9-19. *a.* Verify Eq. (9-42).

b. For a turns ratio $n:1$, prove that this equation is valid, provided that μ is divided by n and A is the new loop gain.

9-20. A free-running blocking oscillator uses one-half of a 6SN7 tube with a 140-volt power supply. The grid winding of the transformer has twice as many turns as the plate winding. From the positive grid characteristics of Fig. A-4 calculate the plate voltage, plate current, grid voltage, and grid current at the peak of the pulse.

9-21. Verify Eq. (9-49).

9-22. For the blocking oscillator considered in Sec. 9-13, the resistor $R = 1.5$ K (instead of being adjusted for critical damping). Find the magnitude of the backswing at the plate.

9-23. The inductance L of a transformer is increased by adding N turns to the primary winding. For each transformer the load is adjusted for critical damping.

a. If the core does not saturate, show that the plate backswing increases approximately as $\sqrt{L}$.

b. If the core saturates, show that the plate backswing remains constant as N increases.

9-24. A monostable blocking oscillator uses one-half of a 6SN7 tube with $E_{bb} = 200$ volts and $E_{cc} = 100$ volts. The grid winding of the transformer has 30 turns and the plate winding 10 turns. The grid resistor is 100 K and the grid capacitor is 0.1 μf. Using the positive-grid characteristics of Fig. A-4, find the plate voltage and current at the peak of the pulse.

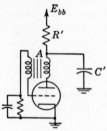

9-25. It is desired to decouple a blocking oscillator from the power supply line by means of the $R'C'$ circuit shown. The pulse width is 2 μsec, the peak plate current is 0.25 amp, and the period is 2,500 μsec.

a. Calculate the minimum value of C' so that the tilt at point A does not exceed 5 volts.

PROB. 9-25

b. Calculate a reasonable value for R'. Explain.

CHAPTER 10

10-1. A type RG-59/U coaxial cable has a capacitance of 20 $\mu\mu$f/ft and a characteristic impedance of 73 ohms. Find the length required for a 0.5-μsec delay.

10-2. Calculate L, C, Z_o, and T for a type RG-65/U cable. The parameters of this cable are listed below Eq. (10-3).

10-3. Verify Eqs. (10-4), (10-5), and (10-12).

10-4. A unit step voltage is impressed upon one section of a constant-k prototype filter which is terminated at both ends in a resistance $R_o = \sqrt{L/C}$. If $T \equiv \sqrt{LC}$, prove that the output is given by

$$e_o = 0.5 - 0.5\epsilon^{-2t/T} - 0.578\epsilon^{-t/T} \sin \sqrt{3}\, \frac{t}{T}$$

10-5. Design a delay line using constant-k prototype sections. The line is to have a nominal impedance of 500 ohms, a delay of 1.0 μsec, and a rise time of 0.2 μsec. Calculate the number of sections needed, the value of C, the value of L, and the cutoff frequence f_c. Assume that commercial capacitors are available having values of capacitance which are multiples of 50 $\mu\mu$f. What will be the impedance of the line?

10-6. Repeat Prob. 10-5 for a delay line using m-derived sections with $m = 1.27$. Find L_1, C_1, f_c, and the characteristic impedance.

10-7. Prove (a) that for the m-derived filter f_c and Z_o are given by the same expressions as for the constant-k protype section, and (b) verify Eq. (10-18).

10-8. a. Prove that the Fourier spectrum of a pulse of unit amplitude and width t_p extending from $t = 0$ to $t = t_p$ is given by $(1 - \epsilon^{-i\omega t_p})/j\omega$.

b. An ideal low-pass filter is one having zero attenuation in the passband and infinite attenuation outside this region. It also has a phase shift β which is proportional to frequency, $\beta = \omega t_d$, within the passband, $|f| < f_c$. Prove that the output of the ideal low-pass filter to a unit amplitude pulse is given by

$$e_o = \frac{1}{\pi} S_i(x) + \frac{1}{\pi} S_i(y)$$

where $x = 2\pi f_c(t - t_d)$ and $y = 2\pi f_c(t_p - t + t_d)$ and $S_i(x)$ is the sine integral,

$$S_i(x) \equiv \int_0^x \frac{\sin x\, dx}{x}$$

NOTE: The frequency spectrum of the output of a system equals the product of the spectrum of the input voltage and the transmission characteristic of the system. By evaluating the inverse Fourier transform of this product, the output of the system as a function of time is obtained.

The response to a unit step input voltage is obtained by allowing t_p to approach infinity. Since $S_i(\infty) = \pi/2$, the response to a unit step is $e_1 = 0.5 + S_i(x)$. Using numerical values of $S_i(x)$, plot e_1 vs. t.

c. Prove that t_d represents the delay; the time between the 50 per cent amplitude points on the input and output voltages.

d. Evaluate the rise time t_r (for e_o to increase from 0.1 to 0.9), and prove that $t_r = 0.445/f_c$. This result should be compared with the rise time of the output of an amplifier whose input is a step voltage and whose upper 3-db frequency is f_2, namely, $t_r = 0.35/f_2$. (See E. Jahnke and F. Emde, "Tables of Functions," 2d ed., pp. 78–86, Teubner Verlagsgesellschaft, Leipzig, 1933.)

10-9. Show that $e = f(t - x/v)$ represents a wave traveling to the right with a velocity v. Choose for f an arbitrary shape (such as a semicircle) and plot e vs. t at $x = 0$ and at some arbitrary point $x = x_1$.

10-10. Show that Eqs. (10-25) and (10-26) satisfy the transmission-line differential equations for arbitrary functions f_1 and f_2. What are the expressions for v and R_o in terms of the line parameters L and C?

10-11. Explain how to adjust experimentally the terminations at each end of a line so that the line is properly matched at both ends. Assume that a square-wave generator (or a pulse generator) and a CRO are available.

10-12. A unit step voltage is applied from a zero-impedance generator to an ideal line which is short-circuited at the receiving end. Plot the current at the input end of the line as a function of time.

10-13. A generator whose output impedance matches the characteristic impedance R_o of a line is connected to the input of this line. Plot the voltage at the beginning of the line as a function of time, if the termination is (a) R_o, (b) a short circuit, and (c) an open circuit. First consider a step input, and then repeat the problem for a ramp input, $e = \alpha t$ for $t > 0$ and $e = 0$ for $t < 0$.

10-14. A unit step voltage is applied to an open-circuited line through a zero-impedance generator. Plot the output voltage as a function of time if (a) the line is lossless and (b) the attenuation of the line is such that the signal which reaches one end of the line is 80 per cent of the signal introduced at the other end of the line.

10-15. A unit step voltage is applied to a lossless line through a zero-impedance generator. The line is terminated in a resistor R equal to $3R_o$. Plot the voltage at the receiving end of the line as a function of time. Indicate the values of the voltage jumps at each discontinuity.

10-16. A unit step voltage is applied to a lossless shorted line from a generator whose impedance is R_g. Plot the input voltage as a function of time if (a) $R_g = R_o$, (b) $R_g = 9R_o$, and (c) $R_g = R_o/9$. (d) Plot the input current as a function of time under conditions (a), (b), and (c).

10-17. A unit step voltage is applied to a lossless open-circuited line from a generator whose impedance is R_g. Plot the input voltage as a function of time if (a) $R_g = R_o$, (b) $R_g = 9R_o$, and (c) $R_g = R_o/9$. (d) Plot the input current as a function of time under conditions (a), (b), and (c).

10-18. *a.* A unit step voltage is applied to a lossless open-circuited line from a generator whose impedance R_g is twice the characteristic of the line. Plot the voltage at the end of the line as a function of time. Indicate the magnitudes of any abrupt changes in voltage.

b. Repeat (a) if the generator output is a narrow pulse instead of a step. Show that the results of (a) and (b) are compatible.

c. Repeat (a) and (b) if $R_g = R_o/2$.

10-19. A pulse whose width t_p is less than the one-way delay time t_d is applied to a line. Plot the input and output voltage waveforms as a function of time, taking attenuation into account, if (a) $R_g > R_o$ and $R < R_o$, (b) $R_g > R_o$ and $R > R_o$, and (c) $R_g < R_o$ and $R < R_o$. Choose $|\rho| = |\rho'| = 0.5$ and $\epsilon^{-a} = 0.8$.

10-20. A pulse is applied from a generator whose resistance equals the characteristic impedance of a line to a lossless shorted line. Plot the input voltage as a function of time, if (a) $t_p < 2t_d$ and (b) $t_p > 2t_d$. (c) Repeat (b) if the line is now assumed to have attenuation.

10-21. Verify the waveforms in Fig. 10-22.

10-22. Find the output voltage across R in Fig. 10-21 if R is approximately equal to R_o. Consider the two cases $R = R_o(1 + \epsilon)$ and $R = R_o(1 - \epsilon)$, where $\epsilon \ll 1$.

10-23. A pulse suffers distortion of the types indicated in Figs. (10-6), (10-11), and (10-12) when passing down a delay line. Assuming that the oscillations in the output pulse die down within a pulse width, prove that the width t_p between 50 per cent points is the same for input and output pulses. HINT: Consider a pulse as the difference of two step voltages, as indicated in Fig. 2-3.

10-24. A thyratron pulse-shaping circuit has an open-circuited delay line connected from plate to ground, as indicated. The tube is biased below cutoff. A short positive pulse is applied to the grid. The amplitude of this pulse is large enough to cause conduction. Calculate the waveforms across the 500- and 200-ohm resistors. The line has a one-way delay time of 2 μsec and a characteristic impedance of 1 K. The tube drop in the thyratron is 20 volts.

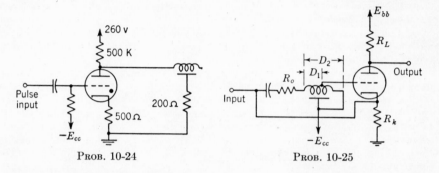

PROB. 10-24   PROB. 10-25

10-25. The circuit shown is a double-pulse decoder. Assume that the pulse width $t_p < D_1$ where D_1 is the delay time to the tap on the delay line. The input pulses are of negative polarity. Explain the operation of the circuit. Show that if the amplitude of the pulses and the biasing voltage E_{cc} are properly chosen an output will be obtained, provided that the spacing between the two input pulses is $2D_2 - D_1 \pm t_p$.

10-26. *a.* A distributed amplifier uses one stage of four 6AK5 tubes to obtain a gain of ϵ^2. What is the maximum possible cutoff frequency?

b. If this single-stage amplifier is designed for $f_c = 177$ Mc, what is the maximum possible gain?

Compare these results with the two-stage amplifier considered in Sec. 10-8.

10-27. A distributed amplifier using 6AK5 tubes is to be designed with a cutoff frequency of 50 Mc and a gain of at least 100. The grid and plate lines are each to have a characteristic impedance of 170 ohms. Calculate (*a*) the number of stages m, (*b*) the number of tubes per stage n, (*c*) the over-all gain G, (*d*) the capacitance and inductance in each section of grid and plate lines C_g, L_g, C_p, L_p, and (*e*) the gain that would be obtained if all the tubes used above were put into a single stage.

CHAPTER 11

11-1. Write the following decimal numbers in binary notation: (*a*) 23, (*b*) 41, (*c*) 152, and (*d*) 325.

11-2. Draw a scale-of-4 binary counter with feedback of the type indicated in Fig. 11-3 which will reduce the circuit to a 3:1 counter. Explain the operation of this circuit with the aid of a waveform diagram.

11-3. Draw a scale-of-8 binary counter with feedback of the type indicated in Fig. 11-3 which will reduce the circuit to a 5:1 counter. Explain the operation of this circuit with the aid of a waveform diagram.

11-4. Draw a block diagram of a binary counter chain, including feedback loops, so that the system becomes (*a*) a 59:1 counter, (*b*) an 83:1 counter, and (*c*) a 131:1 counter.

11-5. Repeat Prob. 11-2 using feedback of the type indicated in Fig. 11-6.

11-6. Repeat Prob. 11-3 using feedback of the type indicated in Fig. 11-6.

11-7. The circuit shown is used in connection with the counter of Fig. 11-6, the waveform chart for which is given in Fig. 11-7. The numbered circles represent neon bulbs. The connections of the neon tube circuit to the counter are as indicated. The voltages given correspond to the case when the counter is reset to zero. Show that in each state of the counter only one neon tube will glow, namely, the one which

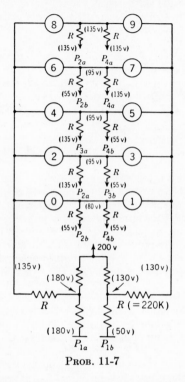

PROB. 11-7

gives the correct registration of the count. Keep in mind that the maintaining voltage of the neon tube is about 55 volts and that the breakdown voltage is about 65 volts.

11-8. The Potter Instrument Company decade counter consists of a scale-of-16 which is modified to a 10:1 counter by means of the feedback connections shown.

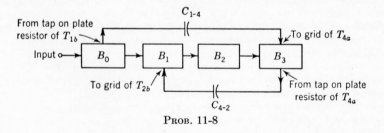

PROB. 11-8

The amplitude of the positive pulse fed back from T_4 to T_2 through C_{4-2} is large enough to cause a transition. Only negative pulses are effective in causing all other transitions. Draw a waveform chart for this circuit. Show that the count proceeds in the normal fashion (without feedback) up to and including the ninth input pulse. Show that the feedback causes the counter to be reset to zero at the tenth input pulse.

11-9. Consider a reversible binary counter which is set at the decimal number *ten*. Show that if pulses are fed to this counter, the system will read *nine* after the first pulse, *eight* after the second pulse, etc., down to *zero* after the tenth pulse. What will the counter read after the eleventh pulse?

11-10. A dekatron tube is used to count the positive pulses from a 2-kc generator. This generator triggers a monostable multi which delivers 100-μsec wide pulses. The output from one plate of the multi is connected through an RC differentiating circuit ($R = 330$ K and $C = 300$ μμf) to the *guide No.* 2 electrodes. The output from the other multi plate is similarly connected to the *guide No.* 1 electrodes (with $C = 0.1$ μf). The remainder of the circuit is as indicated in Fig. 11-12, except that no positive bias is used. Assume that the maintaining voltage is 190 volts. It is found experimentally that the quiescent guide voltage is +10 volts (due to the ionization in the neighborhood of the conducting cathode) and that the glow will transfer from a guide to the nearest cathode when the guide voltage reaches +25 volts.

a. Sketch, to the same time scale, the waveforms at the input at $1G$ and at $2G$. Assume a swing of 100 volts at each multi plate.

b. Explain carefully the operation of the circuit.

c. Sketch the output waveform. Calculate the peak value of this voltage.

d. Find the minimum allowable value of the coupling capacitor to *guide No.* 1. Sketch the voltage waveform at $1G$ when this minimum value of C is used.

11-11. *a.* Sketch, to the same time scale, the output voltages from the right-hand plate of each tube in a scale-of-3 ring counter.

b. Consider one application of such a sequence of waveforms. Draw a block diagram of your system and explain its operation.

11-12. A present feature is to be added to a binary counter. By means of push buttons the counter is to be preset so that it delivers an output pulse when the input count reaches 100. Draw a schematic diagram of the circuit, showing where the push buttons are located and explain the operation of the circuit.

11-13. *a.* Both diodes in the storage counter circuit of Fig. 11-23 are reversed. Explain the operation of the circuit if the input polarity remains negative. Sketch the output waveform.

b. Prove that Eq. (11-3) is valid for the circuit of (*a*).

11-14. Consider the bootstrap storage counter of Fig. 11-28, but with both diodes reversed. The input pulses are negative and have a width equal to approximately 25 per cent of the interval between pulses. Plot, to the same time scale, the waveforms at the input, the grid and the output if (*a*) $C_3 = 0$, (*b*) C_3 is small, and (*c*) C_3 is large. Assume that a steady-state condition is reached between pulses even for case (*c*). Show the overshoot at the end of the pulse due to the discharge of C_1. If this circuit is to be used as a staircase generator, then the output should be taken from the grid via another cathode follower. Why?

11-15. Consider the bootstrap storage counter of Fig. 11-28, but with both diodes reversed. Neglect grid current and assume that the initial grid voltage is zero and the corresponding output voltage is E_o. The gain of the cathode follower may be taken as unity. The input is a square wave whose value is E volts for one half cycle and zero volts for the other half cycle.

a. Prove that the output is constant at E_o, if $E < E_o$.

b. Prove that, if $E > E_o$, the nth step is given by $\Delta e_n = -[(E - E_o)C_1/(C_1 + C_2)]$.

c. If $E = 3.0$ volts, $E_o = 1.0$ volts, and $C_1 = C_2$, draw the waveforms at the input, at the junction of the two diodes, at the grid, and at the output.

11-16. Consider the bootstrap storage counter of Fig. 11-28. The cathode follower has a gain $A < 1$. Assume that the grid voltage starts at a value E_{oi} and that the grid base of the triode is zero.

a. Prove that the voltage after the *n*th pulse is

$$e_n = \frac{E}{1 - A} - \left(\frac{E}{1 - A} - E_{oi}\right)x^n$$

where $x = 1 - (1 - A)[C_1/(C_1 + C_2)]$.

b. Prove that if the gain A approaches unity, then the above expression for e_n reduces to $e_n = E_{oi} + nEC_1/(C_1 + C_2)$. Interpret this equation physically.

c. If $E = 100$ volts, $E_{oi} = 0$, and $C_2 = 9C_1$, find the size of the first and eleventh steps in voltage. Compare these values with those obtained if no feedback is used.

11-17. The capacitor C_2 is shunted by a resistor R in a storage counter in order to convert the circuit into a frequency or capacitance meter. The pulse amplitude is E. The pulse width is small compared with the interval $T = 1/f$ between pulses. Prove that the average output voltage under steady-state conditions is given by

$$E_{dc} = \frac{ERC_1f}{1 + \dfrac{C_1/C_2}{1 - \epsilon^{-T/RC_2}}}$$

If $C_2 \gg C_1$ and $RC_1f \ll 1$, show that the above relationship reduces to Eq. (11-15).

11-18. The circuit shown is used as a simple capacitance meter. The voltmeter resistance is R.

a. Prove that the average output voltage is $E_{dc} = RCfE(1 - \epsilon^{-T_2/RC})$, where f is the frequency of the input waveform.

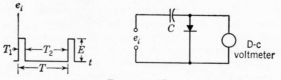

PROB. 11-18

b. If $RC \ll T_2$, prove that the voltmeter may be calibrated to read directly in capacitance values.

c. The voltmeter has a 50-μa movement and its resistance is 10 K. The pulse-generator duty cycle is $T_1/T = \frac{1}{10}$. Choose $T = 10RC$. To what value must the pulse amplitude E be adjusted?

d. Range switching is accomplished by changing the frequency of the pulse generator without changing its duty cycle or amplitude. Find the generator frequency for a full-scale meter reading of (*a*) 1,000 $\mu\mu$f, (*b*) 0.01 μf, and (*c*) 0.1 μf.

11-19. It is desired to store a voltage on a capacitor C and to "read out" through a cathode follower.

a. If $C = 0.01$ μf and the voltage across the capacitor is 50 volts, how much grid current can be tolerated if the voltage is to change by no more than 0.1 per cent in 1 sec?

b. What is the effective leakage resistance across C in (*a*)?

CHAPTER 12

12-1. *a.* By proceeding as in Fig. 12-2, verify the synchronization results depicted in Fig. 12-3.

b. Show that the dividing curve between $T_s/T_p = n$ and $T_s/T_p = n + 1$, where n is an integer, is given by $nT_p/T_o = 1 - E_p/E_s$. Obtain this result by considering the geometry of Fig. 12-2.

12-2. A free-running thyratron sweep has an amplitude of 100 volts and a period of 1,200 μsec. If 6-volt pulses at a frequency of 4,000 cps are applied to the grid of the thyratron, what are the amplitude and frequency of the synchronized waveform? Assume a thyratron grid-control ratio of 8.

12-3. *a.* A free-running thyratron sweep has an amplitude of 100 volts and a frequency of 1 kc. If 2-volt pulses are applied to the grid, over what range may the pulse frequency be varied to obtain 1:1 synchronization? Assume that the thyratron grid-control ratio is 10.

b. If 5:1 synchronization is to be obtained $(f_p/f_s = 5)$, over what range of frequency may the pulse source be varied?

12-4. Show that if pulses from a high-impedance source are applied to one grid of a symmetrical multi, such that $1.5T_o < T_p < 2T_o$, then the output will consist of adjacent cycles which are not alike.

12-5. A symmetrical astable multi has a free period of 1,000 μsec. The grid waveform drops from ground potential to -110 volts abruptly and then increases linearly to the cutoff voltage of -10 volts in one-half cycle. Positive pulses whose spacing is 150 μsec are applied from a high-impedance source to one grid. Calculate the minimum amplitude of the pulses such that the multi period after synchronization is (*a*) 900 μsec and (*b*) 600 μsec.

12-6. A symmetrical astable multi whose free-running frequency is 500 cps has a plate swing of 110 volts and a cutoff voltage of -10 volts. Positive pulses of amplitude 4 volts are applied from a high-impedance source to one grid. Assume that the exponential portion of the grid waveform is linear.

a. If 1:1 synchronization is to be obtained, over what range may the pulse frequency be varied?

b. If 3:1 synchronization is to be obtained $(f_p/f_s = 3)$, over what range may the pulse frequency be varied?

12-7. A symmetrical astable multi is synchronized with positive pulses from a high-impedance source. Draw a diagram, analogous to Fig. 12-3, showing the range of synchronization as a function of pulse amplitude and frequency.

12-8. Positive pulses from a high-impedance source are applied simultaneously to both grids of a symmetrical astable multi, with f_p/f_o large, say 8.3. Show that as the amplitude of the pulses is increased the synchronized output remains symmetrical and that f_p/f_s is always an even integer.

12-9. Frequency division of 6:1 is obtained with an astable multi. *Negative* pulses are applied simultaneously to both grids. The *off* time of T_1 is twice that of T_2. Sketch the waveshapes at G_1 and G_2 showing the superimposed pulses.

12-10. Positive pulses are applied through a small capacitor to grid 1 of a symmetrical astable multi from a low-impedance pulse generator. It is found that the time interval required for the complete multivibrator waveform is five times the interval between pulses. An examination of the grid waveforms shows that the termination of the *off* period of tube 1 does *not* take place at the occurrence of a pulse. Sketch the waveforms at both grids and show the pulses superimposed on these waveforms. Explain the action of the circuit.

12-11. A symmetrical multi is synchronized with positive pulses applied to one grid through a high-impedance source. The free-running period $T_o = 6.8T_p$, where T_p is the period of the pulse source. Make a rough plot of the ratio T_s/T_p as a function of the pulse amplitude, where T_s is the period of the synchronized multi.

12-12. *a.* A monostable multi has a width of 1,200 μsec. Negative pulses from a 4-kc source are applied to one grid. Sketch the resulting grid and plate waveforms.

b. Positive pulses from a low-impedance 4-kc source are applied to one grid. The synchronized multi is now found to have a period of 750 μsec. Sketch the resulting grid and plate waveforms.

12-13. *a.* With respect to Fig. 12-10, assume that E_c and E_f remain constant but that E_i is variable. Prove that the per cent change in period T_o is y times the per cent change in $E_c - E_i$, where

$$y = \frac{E_c - E_i}{E_f - E_i} \frac{1}{\ln \dfrac{E_f - E_i}{E_f - E_c}}$$

b. The initial level E_i may be taken as zero, with no loss in generality. Why? If $E_i = 0$ and if $E_c/E_f \ll 1$, prove that $y \cong 2E_f/(2E_f + E_c)$. Note that $y \to 1$ as $E_f \to \infty$ and that y decreases as E_f decreases. What is the physical interpretation of this result?

c. If $E_c = 100$ volts, calculate y first for $E_f = 300$ volts and then for $E_f = 150$ volts.

12-14. The sweep circuit of Fig. 12-1 is used as a 3:1 divider for pulses which occur at a 2,500-cps rate. The thyratron maintaining voltage is 15 volts, $E_{bb} = 250$ volts, $E_{cc} = 9$ volts, and the grid-control ratio is 8. Find reasonable values for the time constant RC and the pulse amplitude E_p.

12-15. In the resonant stabilization circuit of Fig. 12-11, the waveforms are drawn for $T_s = 1.5T_k$. Plot the corresponding waveforms for $T_s = 1.25T_k$, $T_s = 1.50T_k$, $T_s = 1.75T_k$, and $T_s = 1.0T_k$. Keep T_s constant and vary T_k. Discuss these plots. Which condition would you use to stabilize a free-running blocking oscillator (no sync pulses)?

12-16. *a.* Will the circuit of Fig. 12-11 be satisfactory if the counting ratio is changed from 6? For example, consider counting ratios of 3, 4, 12, and 24.

b. In (*a*) $T_s = 1.5T_k$. Consider now $T_s = 2.5T_k$, and discuss the circuit as a divider. Choose counting ratios of 3, 4, 6, 12, and 24. Compare with (*a*).

c. Extend the discussion in (*b*) to the case $T_s = (n + \frac{1}{2})T_k$, where n is any integer.

12-17. Consider the resonant stabilization circuit of Fig. 12-11. The blocking-oscillator pulse width is 1 μsec and the peak tube current is 0.5 amp. The grid waveform drops to -100 volts and decreases toward zero with a time constant of 100 μsec. The cutoff voltage is -10 volts. The pulse frequency is 100 kc and the counting ratio is 10:1.

Find (*a*) C_k if $E_o = 20$ volts, (*b*) L_k if $T_s = 1.5T_k$, (*c*) the minimum pulse amplitude, and (*d*) the maximum pulse amplitude.

12-18. Repeat Prob. 12-3 for synchronization with a sine wave of 2-volt peak-to-peak amplitude.

12-19. Repeat Prob. 12-6 for synchronization with a sine wave of 8-volt peak-to-peak amplitude.

12-20. Verify Eq. (12-5).

CHAPTER 13

13-1. The *OR* circuit of Fig. 13-6*a* uses 5965 tubes with $E_{bb} = 250$ volts, $E_{cc} = 10$ volts, and $R = 50$ K. The pulse amplitude is 10 volts. Find the output amplitude if (*a*) one input is excited and (*b*) two inputs are excited. (*c*) Repeat (*a*) and (*b*) for the circuit of Fig. 13-6*b* and a pulse amplitude of 100 volts.

13-2. *a.* In the diode *AND* circuit with $E_{bb} > E$, prove that the time T for the output pulse to rise to its full value E is

$$T = RC_o \ln \frac{E_{bb}}{E_{bb} - E}$$

where C_o is the output capacitance. See Fig. 13-9b.

b. If the capacitance C_d of each diode is taken into consideration, prove that the output waveform has an abrupt jump E' in voltage given by

$$E' = \frac{nC_dE}{C_o + (n + 1)C_d}$$

13-3. The two-input AND circuit shown uses diodes whose forward resistance is 500 ohms. The quiescent current in T_o is 6 ma, while the currents in T_1 and T_2 are each 4 ma.

a. Calculate the quiescent output voltage e_o and the values of R_o and R.

b. Calculate the quiescent output voltage when one input diode is cut off. Calculate this result approximately by assuming that the currents through R_o and the remaining input diode do not change. Also calculate the result exactly.

c. Assume that diode T_o is omitted, that the currents in T_1 and T_2 remain 4 ma each, and that the output e_o is the same as that found in (a). Find R_o and R.

d. If the conditions are as indicated in (c) but one of the diodes is cut off, find the output voltage e_o. Compare with the result (b) when T_o acts as a clamp.

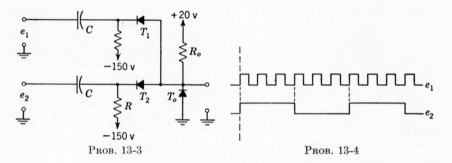

PROB. 13-3   PROB. 13-4

13-4. a. The input signals shown are applied to the circuit of Prob. 13-3. Each signal has a peak-to-peak value of 30 volts. Neglect capacitances and assume zero diode forward resistance. Draw the output waveform and label each voltage level.

b. Repeat (a) for the case where e_1 is 10 volts peak to peak and e_2 remains at 30 volts peak to peak.

13-5. Consider two signals: a 1-kc sine wave and a 10-kc square wave. The peak sine wave voltage exceeds the peak-to-peak square-wave voltage. Sketch the output if the inputs are applied to an (a) OR circuit and (b) AND circuit.

13-6. Solve Prob. 13-5, if the peak sine-wave voltage is less than the peak pulse voltage.

13-7. Consider the diode AND circuit of Fig. 13-10, and assume ideal diodes. During the pulse duration the input capacitor will charge and this will result in a tilt in the pulse waveform at the input to the diode.

a. Prove that the effective resistance through which C is charged is $ER_k/(E + E_{cc})$, where E is the pulse amplitude. Note that if $R_k = 16$ K, $E = 10$ volts, and $E_{cc} = 150$ volts, this effective resistance is only 1 K.

b. If no more than a 10 per cent tilt is to result, what is the minimum allowable value of C for a 20-μsec wide pulse?

13-8. Find E_o and E_1 if (a) there are no pulses at either A or B, (b) there is a 30-volt positive pulse at A or B, and (c) there are positive pulses at both A and B. (d) What is the minimum pulse amplitude which must be applied in order that the circuit operate properly? Assume zero diode forward resistance.

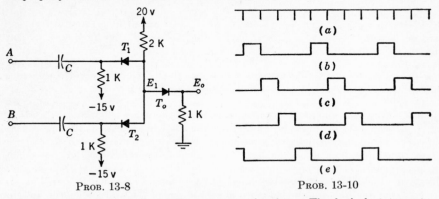

PROB. 13-8   PROB. 13-10

13-9. A, B, and C represent the presence of pulses. The logical statement— A or B and C—can have two interpretations. What are these?

In block diagram form draw the circuit to perform each of the two logical operations.

13-10. A regular sequence of triggering pulses is available as in (a). It is required that these pulses be used to generate the gating waveforms of (b), (c), (d), and (e). Each of these four gating waveforms is to be separate, that is, available from a separate set of terminals. The time duration of the gate waveform is to be the same as the interval between pulses. The gates are to occur in sequence as shown.

One possible circuit for generating these waveforms may be arrived at as follows: Let the pulses drive a scale-of-4 circuit consisting of two binaries. Draw the waveforms at the four plates of the multis, and show that these waveforms may be combined in four coincidence circuits to give the required result.

13-11. Given three inputs to a circuit. A pulse is to be obtained from the output if any two of the three inputs are excited with a pulse. No output is to be obtained for any other combination of inputs. Draw a block diagram of the circuit to perform this logical operation.

13-12. In block diagram form draw a circuit to perform the following logical operation: If pulses A_1, A_2, and A_3 occur simultaneously or if pulses B_1 and B_2 occur simultaneously, an output pulse should be delivered, provided that pulse C does not occur at the same time. No output is to be obtained if A_1, A_2, A_3, B_1, and B_2 occur simultaneously.

13-13. A single-pole double-throw switch is to be simulated with AND, OR, and

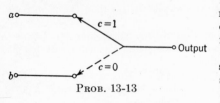

PROB. 13-13

$INHIBITOR$ circuits. Call the two signal inputs a and b. A third input c receives the switching instructions in the form of a code: 1 (a pulse is present) or 0 (no pulse exists). It is desired that $c = 1$ sets the switch to a and $c = 0$ sets the switch to b, as indicated schematically. In block diagram form show the circuit for this switch.

13-14. In block diagram form draw a circuit which satisfies simultaneously the conditions (a), (b), and (c) as follows:

a. An output pulse is delivered if any pair of input pulses A_1, A_2, and A_3 is present, provided that pulse B is also present.

b. An output pulse is delivered if B is absent, provided that any one of the pulses A_1, A_2, or A_3 are present.

c. No output pulse is delivered if A_1, A_2, and A_3 are all present.

13-15. In block diagram form sketch a 2:1 divider circuit for a train of regularly spaced pulses. As basic building blocks use *AND, OR, INHIBITOR* circuits and/or delay lines.

13-16. In the SEAC package of Fig. 13-17, there is a complete coincidence at one of the *AND* circuits. Calculate the voltage to which the grid of the 6AN5 tube would be driven if the grid were not clamped to $+2$ volts.

13-17. A continuous train of regularly spaced pulses is applied to the input of the dynamic binary counter of Fig. 13-29. Draw the pulse trains at the output (B) of each stage of the counter. Compare these waveforms with the corresponding waveforms of the static binary counter of Fig. 11-2. Consider 16 input pulses.

13-18. Construct a dynamic binary counter, using the circulating storage circuit of Fig. 13-28b as a basic building block.

13-19. For the one-bit storage circuit of Fig. 13-32 draw the waveforms at (a) the input, (b) the erase terminal, (c) the junction of the OR and μ unit, and (d) the junction of the OR and $INHIBITOR$ block.

13-20. Two stages of a NORC binary counter are indicated. Explain the operation of the circuit. Assume a continuous train of 1 Mc pulses, and sketch the output waveforms of each stage.

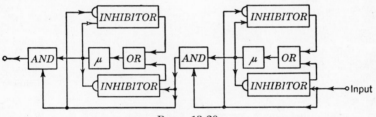

PROB. 13-20

13-21. *a.* The NORC *AND* circuit is indicated. Assuming zero diode forward resistance R_f, explain the operation of the circuit.

b. Assume $R_f = 1$ K for the remainder of this problem. Find the grid voltage and the output voltage if all inputs are low (-25 volts).

c. Repeat (b) if all inputs are high ($+10$ volts).

d. Find the grid voltage if e_1 is high, but e_2 and e_3 are low.

e. Find the grid voltage if e_1 and e_2 are high but e_3 is low.

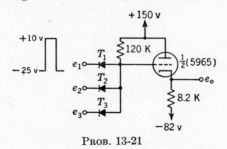

PROB. 13-21

13-22. *a.* The NORC *OR* circuit is indicated. Assuming zero diode forward resistance R_f, explain the operation of the circuit.

b. Assume $R_f = 1$ K for the remainder of this problem. Find the grid and output voltages if all inputs are low (-25 volts).

c. Repeat (*b*) if one input e_1 is high ($+10$ volts) and the others are low.

d. Find the grid voltage if e_1 and e_2 are high but e_3 is low.

e. Find the grid voltage if all three inputs are high.

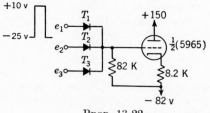

PROB. 13-22

13-23. Construct in block diagram form a *half adder-subtractor* based upon the *EXCLUSIVELY-OR* circuit of Fig. 13-25a.

13-24. In the *adder* circuit of Fig. 13-36 consider *A* and *B* as pulse trains representing (in binary notation) the decimal numbers 7 and 3, respectively. Trace the pulses through the circuit, and observe where each carry pulse originates. Demonstrate that the output is the sum $A + B$.

13-25. Construct a *full subtractor* from two *half subtractors*. Consider two input pulse trains *A* and *B* representing (in binary notation) the decimal numbers 8 and 3, respectively. Trace the pulses through the circuit, and observe where each borrow pulse originates. Demonstrate that the output is $A - B$.

13-26. The circuit shown is a *complete adder* which is *not* composed of *half adders*. The delay line *D* has a delay equal to the time between pulses. Prove that *C* is the carry line and that $S = A + B$.

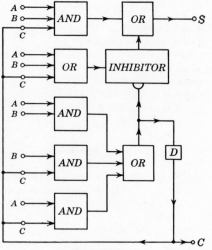

PROB. 13-26

13-27. The circuit shown is the SEAC *adder* and is *not* composed of *half adders.* The delay D is equal to the time between pulses. Prove that C is the carry line and that $S = A + B$.

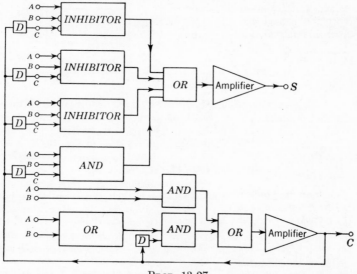

PROB. 13-27

13-28. The *equality comparator* of the SEAC computer is indicated. The pulse trains A and B represent the numbers to be compared. The delay D is equal to the time between pulses. A priming pulse T occurs before the first pulses of A and B. Verify that after the last pulses of A and B have appeared, a pulse is emitted at C if and only if A and B are identical.

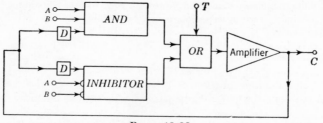

PROB. 13-28

13-29. *a.* The *two-stage cyclic counter* of the SEAC computer is indicated. The input pulse train is applied at the points marked A. The delay D is equal to the time between pulses. Verify that the circuit functions as follows: With dynamic binaries B_1 and B_2 in state 0, the next pulse at A puts B_1 into state 1. With B_1 in state 1 and B_2 in state 0, the next pulse at A puts B_2 into state 1. With both B_1 and B_2 in state 1, the next pulse at A puts B_1 in state 0. With B_1 in state 0 and B_2 in state 1, the next pulse at A puts B_2 in state 0, etc.

b. If the pulse train at A is 110101001, what are the pulse trains at P_1 and at the output of B_2? (See Fig. 13-2.)

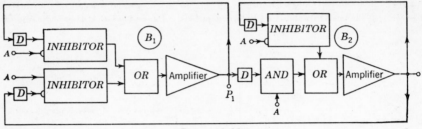

PROB. 13-29

13-30. Prove that an N-position code-operated switch requires $N \log_2 N$ diodes.

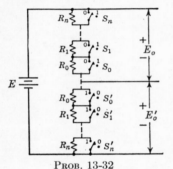

PROB. 13-32

13-31. Draw a schematic diagram of an eight-position code-operated switch. Use single-pole double-throw switches as in Fig. 13-38.

13-32. A digital-to-analogue converter is indicated. The resistance values R_n are proportional to the binary numbers 2^n. Switches S_n' and S_n are controlled from the relay representing the number 2^n and are in position 1 if this relay is excited. The input E is a d-c voltage.

a. Prove that E_o is a voltage proportional to the binary number to which the relays are excited.

b. What does E_o' represent?

CHAPTER 14

14-1. Explain how to modify the gate of Fig. 14-2 if the input pulses are negative.

14-2. The gates in Fig. 14-5 are of the type indicated in Fig. 14-2. The input pulses are extremely narrow, are 20 volts in amplitude, and occur at a 2-Mc rate. The control voltage makes a transition from -35 volts to zero volts in negligible time, and the output impedance of this control input is 500 ohms. The total capacitance shunting the output of the gate is 10 $\mu\mu$f and $R_L = 10$ K.

a. If no more than 2 volts of the signal input is to be fed back into the control circuit, what is R_1?

b. What is a reasonable value for C_1?

c. What is the amplitude of the output pulse?

d. Should the time constant R_1C_1 be the same for each of the gates G_o, G_1, G_2 of Fig. 14-5?

14-3. Consider a gate having the same specifications as in Prob. 14-2, and calculate the amplitude of the output pulses, if R_1 and C_1 have the following values, respectively: (a) 2.5 K, 50 $\mu\mu$f; (b) 2.5 K, 100 $\mu\mu$f; (c) 10 K, 10 $\mu\mu$f; (d) 10 K, 100 $\mu\mu$f.

14-4. *a.* A threshhold gate which is enabled by any one of a number of control inputs is indicated. The control signal levels are zero and -50 volts. Explain the operation of this gate.

b. Each control-source impedance is 1 K and the load impedance is 10 K. The maximum allowable current which may be

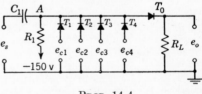

PROB. 14-4

drawn from a control source is 1 ma. The gate is to be closed within 1 μsec after a control voltage changes from zero to -50 volts. The signal input is a 10-volt pulse. The capacitance across the output is 15 $\mu\mu$f. Find R_1.

c. Find the maximum value of C_1.

d. How soon after a control voltage changes from -50 volts to zero will the gate be open, if $C_1 = 25 \ \mu\mu$f?

e. Only one control input is enabled. Find the peak output voltage, if $C_1 = 25 \ \mu\mu$f.

f. Repeat (e) if all four control inputs are at zero volts.

14-5. The circuit shown represents the essential elements of a reversible counter (see Sec. 11-6). The binaries B_0, B_1, etc., constitute the counter and B_c is a control binary which determines whether the counter adds or subtracts. The combination

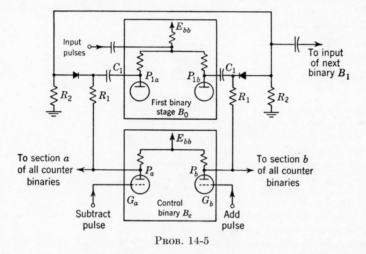

PROB. 14-5

R_1, C_1, R_2 and the diode constitute a threshold gate which is repeated in each binary circuit. The two output levels of each binary are zero and $+70$ volts, respectively. The combination C_1R_1 differentiates the square-wave output from the counter binaries.

a. Explain the operation of this reversible counter.

b. If the pulses to be counted occur at a 2-Mc rate, what is the order of magnitude of the time constant R_1C_1?

c. The output impedance of the control binary is 500 ohms. If no more than 10 per cent of the voltage step at a counter binary is to be fed back to the control binary, what is R_1?

d. If C_2 is the shunt capacitance across R_2, explain why R_2C_2 should be of the order of magnitude of 0.5 μsec.

14-6. In Fig. 14-8, $C = 200 \ \mu\mu$f, $R_L = 100$ K, $E_{bb} = 30$ volts, and the control voltages come from binaries whose two stable levels are $+30$ and -20 volts, respectively. The signal input is a 20-volt pulse and the output is to be an 18-volt pulse. The gate is to be energized within 60 μsec after all binaries reach the 30-volt state. Neglect all stray capacitances. The resistor R_L is connected to a bias voltage E' instead of to ground. Find (a) E', (b) R, and (c) the maximum allowable value of R'. (d) Calculate the voltage at A if 0, 1, 2, or 3 of the binaries are in the 30-volt state.

14-7. In the transmission gate shown the signal e_s is a 1-Mc pulse train whose pulses are 0.1 μsec wide. The control voltage e_c is a pulse train occurring at a slower rate whose pulses are 0.2 μsec wide and are timed as indicated. The diode T_2 is necessary to reduce the fall time at point A when a pulse is present in e_c. Diode T_3 and 50-volt supply are used for clamping so as to provide the proper d-c levels. The capacitance of C_2 is much larger than that of C_1.

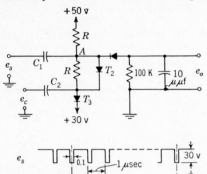

PROB. 14-7

a. Sketch the waveform at A if a pulse is present in e_s but not in e_c. Indicate voltage levels and explain.

b. Sketch the waveform at A if a pulse is present in e_c but not in e_s. Explain.

c. Sketch the waveform at A if there is a coincidence of pulses at e_s and e_c. Sketch the output waveform.

d. If there is to be no more than a 20 per cent capacitive attenuation through the gate, what is the minimum value of C_1?

e. After a control pulse occurs the voltage at A must return to its quiescent value before the next pulse of e_s. Find the maximum value of R for which the above condition is satisfied.

f. If the voltage across C_2 is not to change by more than 1 volt, find C_2.

g. Find the tilt in the output pulse.

h. If the amplitude of the pulses of e_c varies between 40 and 60 volts, indicate how to modify the circuit so that it will continue to operate properly.

14-8. In Fig. 14-10b, $E_{cc} = 0$, $E_{bb} = 300$, $R_L = 5$ K, $R_k = 15$ K, and the tube is a 6SN7. The signal e_s is a sinusoid whose peak value is 10 volts.

a. For proper operation of the circuit, what are the minimum values of E_2 and E_1?

b. What is the pedestal voltage?

c. What are the maximum and minimum output voltages?

d. Plot the output waveform, assuming that the width of the control voltage pulse equals 2 cycles of the signal voltage.

14-9. Consider the two-diode gate of Fig. 14-14. A diode back resistance R_b is very much larger than any other resistance in the circuit. The *leakage L* is defined as the change in output voltage per unit change in signal input during the interval when the bridge is nonconducting. If capacitances are neglected, prove that

$$L \cong \frac{2R_L}{R_b} \frac{R_c}{R_c + R_2}$$

14-10. Consider the two-diode bridge of Fig. 14-14 in which there is an unbalance in control voltages so that $e_{c1} \neq e_{c2}$.

a. If the average control voltage is $e_a \equiv (e_{c1} + e_{c2})/2$ and the unbalanced control voltage is $e_u \equiv e_{c1} - e_{c2}$, prove that $e_{c1} = e_a + e_u/2$ and $e_{c2} = e_a - e_u/2$.

b. The *unbalance U* is defined as the change in output voltage per unit change in unbalance voltage. If R_s and R_f are neglected, prove that

$$U = \left(2 + \frac{R_c}{R_L} + \frac{2R_c}{R_2}\right)^{-1}$$

HINT: Note that in Fig. 14-17 points A and B are at the same potential as far as the unbalanced voltage is concerned.

c. What percentage of the unbalanced voltage appears across the output of the bridge whose parameters are given in Sec. 14-10.

14-11. Verify Eq. (14-10) as follows: Assume that T_1 and T_2 are back-biased and that T_3 and T_4 are conducting. Then calculate the currents in T_3 and T_4 due to E, E_s, and E_n separately. The minimum value of E_n is then found from the condition that the resultant current must flow in the forward direction in T_3 and T_4.

14-12. Prove Eq. (14-12). Hint: If R and R_f are much less than R_L and R_c, then points P_1, P_2, P_3, and P_4 in Fig. 14-22a are all approximately at ground potential.

14-13. *a.* Prove that the exact expression for the gain A of a six-diode gate is

$$A = \left[1 + \frac{R_f + R_s + R/4}{R_L} + \frac{2R_s + R_f + R/2}{R_c} \left(1 + \frac{R_f}{2R_L} \right) \right]^{-1}$$

Hint: To Fig. 14-22b add R_f, R, and R_s, and note that points P_1 and P_2 are at the same potential.

b. Find the numerical value of A if $R_L = R_c = 100$ K, $R = R_s = 1$ K, and $R_f = 0.25$ K.

14-14. There will be some leakage through the diode gates of Figs. 14-14, 14-20, and 14-21 because of the shunt capacitances. Assume $C_d = C_s = 5$ μμf and $C_o = 10$ μμf. The other circuit parameters are given in the text. Find, approximately, for $f = 1$ Mc the percentage of the signal voltage which leaks through the capacitances to the output for (a) the six-diode gate, (b) the four-diode gate, and (c) the two-diode gate.

14-15. *a.* Prove that the signal source input impedance to the four-diode gate of Fig. 14-20 is approximately $R_2/2 + R_cR_L/(R_c + 2R_L)$ if the bridge conducts and is $R_s + R_2/2 + R_f/2$ if the bridge is nonconducting. The resistance R_s is that of the signal source.

b. Prove that the signal source input impedance to the six-diode gate of Fig. 14-21 is approximately $R_cR_L/(R_c + 2R_L)$ if the bridge conducts and is $R_b/2$ if the bridge is nonconducting.

Note that the nonconducting impedance may be quite small for the four-diode gate, but is very large for the six-diode gate.

14-16. *a.* Prove that the control source input impedance to the four-diode gate of Fig. 14-20 is approximately R_b and $R_f + R_2$, respectively, for the conducting and nonconducting states of the bridge.

b. Prove that for the six-diode gate of Fig. 14-21 the impedances in (a) are R_b and R_c, respectively.

14-17. Verify Eq. (14-21).

14-18. Verify Eq. (14-22).

14-19. In Fig. 14-33, $E_{bb} = 250$ volts and the tube is a 12AU7. Find the voltage to which the output is clamped during the positive excursion of the control voltage.

CHAPTER 15

15-1. Verify Eqs. (15-2) and (15-3).

15-2. The input to the comparator of Fig. 15-2 is a 400-cps sinusoid whose peak value is 40 volts. The reference level $E_R = 0$. The amplifier gain is 10 and

$$\tau_1 = \tau_2 = 100 \ \mu\text{sec}$$

What is (a) the initial slope of the output pulse and (b) the peak value of the output? (*i*) If $\tau_1 = 100$ μsec and $\tau_2 = 10$ μsec, what is the peak value of the output?

15-3. *a.* If, in Fig. 15-2, the time constant $\tau_2 = R_2C_2$ is much smaller than

$$\tau_1 = R_1C_1,$$

prove that the maximum value of the output e_{max} is approximately given by $A\alpha\tau_2$

b. If the second differentiation is obtained from a peaking coil L in the plate circuit (instead of using R_2C_2), prove that $e_{max} \cong g_m L \alpha$.

c. The circuit uses a 12AU7 tube and has the following parameters: $R_1 = 100$ K, $C_1 = 500$ $\mu\mu$f, $\alpha = 10^5$ volts/sec, and $L = 10$ mh. Verify that $\tau_2 \ll \tau_1$. Evaluate e_{max}.

d. In order to increase the output pulse a second stage of amplification is added and L is replaced by a transformer. Sketch the circuit. Indicate the transformer winding polarities.

15-4. The negative sweep voltage from a phantastron is used as the input to a comparator consisting of a pick-off diode followed by an amplifier. It is desired that the output be a step (rather than a pulse). Sketch (*a*) the circuit and (*b*) the input and output waveforms. (*c*) What is the initial slope of the output step? (*d*) What determines the total time duration of the front edge of the step?

15-5. A single triode used as a comparator is operated at cutoff. The heater voltage changes so that there is equivalently a voltage change ΔE_H in series with the cathode. Show that the output voltage will change by an amount which is equivalent to a change Δe_i in the signal input to the grid, where

$$\Delta e_i = \frac{\mu + 1}{\mu} \Delta E_H$$

This result shows that filament voltage changes may be troublesome.

15-6. In the difference amplifier of Fig. 15-9 the heater voltage changes so that there is equivalently a voltage change ΔE_H in series with each cathode. Show that the output voltage will change by an amount which is equivalent to a change Δe_i in the signal input to the grid, where

$$\Delta e_i \cong \frac{\Delta E_H}{g_m R_k}$$

provided that $(\mu + 1)R_k \gg r_p$.

15-7. How are the waveforms of Fig. 15-11 modified if the critically damped transformer has a decay time which is large compared with $CRR_g/(R + R_g)$?

15-8. *a.* If instead of R_c, a damper diode is used in the multiar circuit of Fig. 15-10 across the transformer winding in the cathode of the amplifier, should the plate or cathode of the diode be placed at the cathode of the amplifier?

b. Explain the operation of the circuit with the damper diode.

c. What is the advantage of using a damper diode over a damping resistor?

15-9. In the multiar circuit of Fig. 15-10, $E_{bb} = 400$ volts, $R_g = 2$ Meg, and $C_g = 50$ $\mu\mu$f. The amplifier grid base is 10 volts. The transformer turns ratio is 2:1. The output pulse at the cathode has a peak value of 40 volts. The input is a negative-going sweep whose amplitude is 100 volts and whose slope is 1 volt/μsec. What is (*a*) the minimum value of C, (*b*) the minimum value of R, and (*c*) the highest repetition rate at which the circuit will operate properly?

15-10. In the multiar circuit of Fig. 15-10 the input is zero and $E_R = 0$.

a. Show that continuous oscillations result. Sketch the waveforms at the grid, plate, and cathode of the amplifier. Assume that the diode is ideal with its break at a voltage of -0.5 volts.

b. Repeat (*a*) with a sinusoidal input voltage which has an amplitude which is much greater than the grid base of the amplifier.

c. Repeat (*b*) with an input sinusoidal voltage whose amplitude is less than the grid base.

15-11. If the transformer in the multiar circuit of Fig. 15-10 is allowed to ring, show that multiple pulses of the type indicated in Fig. 15-13 *may* be obtained. Explain.

15-12. An attempt is made to use the multiar circuit for positive-going input waveforms. The polarity of the diode T_1 and of E_R is reversed. The resistor R_g is connected to a negative voltage within the grid base of the amplifier instead of to the voltage E_{bb}. Explain the operation of the circuit and show that multiple pulses of the type indicated in Fig. 15-13 will take place. Assume C so large that the voltage across it may be considered constant.

15-13. Show that a multiar circuit may be compensated for changes in filament temperature by shunting R in Fig. 15-10 by a diode.

15-14. *a.* For the a-c coupled multivibrator comparator of Fig. 15-15, show that a change in heater voltage is equivalent to a change in input signal Δe_i given by

$$\Delta e_i = -\frac{1}{\mu}\frac{R_L + r_p}{R_L + R_k}\Delta E_H$$

where ΔE_H is the effective change in voltage in series with the cathode due to the change in filament temperature.

b. Assume a 10 per cent change in filament voltage, $R_L = R_k = 100\ K$, and that the tube is a 12AX7. Find Δe_i.

15-15. *a.* For the a-c coupled multivibrator comparator of Fig. 15-15, show that a slowly varying change ΔE_{cc} in the negative supply is equivalent to a change in input signal Δe_i given by

$$\Delta e_i = \frac{1}{\mu}\frac{R_L + r_p}{R_L + R_k}\Delta E_{cc}$$

b. For a slowly varying change ΔE_{bb} in the positive supply, show that

$$\Delta e_i = -\frac{1}{\mu^2}\frac{R_L + r_p + R_k}{R_L + R_k}\Delta E_{bb}$$

c. Evaluate Δe_i in (*a*) and (*b*) if the tube is a 12AX7 with $R_L = R_k = 100$ K for a 0.1-volt change in either supply voltage.

15-16. Find the expressions for Δe_i in (*a*) and (*b*) of Prob. 15-15 if the frequency of the power supply variations is high enough so that these changes pass through the capacitor C.

15-17. *a.* In the storage counter circuit of Fig. 15-17 the grid-control ratio = 8, $E_{bb} = 250$ volts, tube drop = 15 volts, input pulse height = 50 volts, $C_2 = 10C_1$, $R = 1$ Meg, and $C = 1,000\ \mu\mu$f. If the circuit is to function as a 5:1 counter, what is the value of E?

b. What is the peak value of the output pulse?

15-18. Explain how d-c restoration is suppressed by the circuits shown. In (*a*) the resistance R is much larger than the diode forward resistance or the grid-to-cathode conducting resistance. In (*b*), $R \ll R_g$.

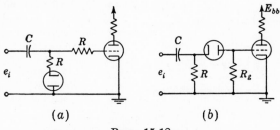

(*a*)   (*b*)

PROB. 15-18

15-19. The cathode-coupled clipper of Fig. 15-20 uses a 12AX7 with $E_{bb} = 300$ volts, $R_L = 50$ K, $R_{k1} = 100$ K, and $E_{cc2} = 56$ volts.

a. Find the value of E_{cc1} which will cause the circuit to clip symmetrically.

b. At what input signal amplitude will the output start being clipped?

c. What is the peak-to-peak value of the output?

d. What is the gain in the region of linear operation?

e. For what input signal amplitude will T_1 start drawing grid current?

15-20. Verify Eq. (15-10).

15-21. In the circuit of Fig. 15-22 the 12AX7 and the associated elements in the cathode of T_1 are replaced by a 2-Meg resistor.

a. By what factor is the common-mode rejection ratio divided over that of the original circuit?

b. The dynamic cathode impedance of T_1 in Fig. 15-22 is 47 Meg. Is it possible to use a 47-Meg resistor in place of the 12AX7 tube in the cathode of T_1?

15-22. In Fig. 15-22 the filament voltage of the 12AX7 changes by 10 per cent. This is equivalent to a 0.1-volt battery in series with the cathode of the 12AX7.

a. Calculate the change in output voltage due to this change in filament voltage.

b. This filament voltage change is equivalent to an input signal change of Δe_i. Calculate Δe_i.

c. If the 5651 maintaining voltage drifts by 0.1 volt, calculate the equivalent change Δe_i in input signal.

d. The filament voltage of the 5755 changes by 10 per cent. Calculate the equivalent change Δe_i in input signal.

CHAPTER 16

16-1. Verify Eq. (16-2).

16-2. Verify (*a*) Eq. (16-3) and (*b*) Eq. (16-4).

16-3. Verify Eq. (16-8) for (*a*) $p = 3$ and (*b*) $p = 4$.

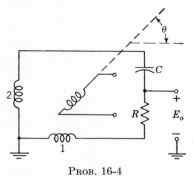

PROB. 16-4

16-4. In the induction resolver circuit indicated, the rotor current is $i = I_0 \sin \omega t$, $\omega RC = 1$, and the impedance of R and C in series is large enough not to load down the stator windings appreciably. If the mutual inductances between rotors and stator windings are $M \cos \theta$ and $M \sin \theta$, respectively, prove that the output is given by

$$E_o = \frac{\omega M I_o}{\sqrt{2}} \sin \left(\omega t + \theta + \frac{\pi}{4} \right)$$

16-5. *a.* The load on a sine potentiometer is R_L. If R is half the total potentiometer resistance (the resistance to ground), prove that output voltage will differ from $E \sin \theta$ by P per cent where

$$P = \frac{100x}{1 + x} \quad \text{and} \quad x = \frac{R}{R_L} (\sin \theta)(1 - \sin \theta)$$

b. Prove that the maximum error $P_{\max}$ occurs at $\theta = 30°$ and is given by

$$P_{\max} = \frac{25R/R_L}{1 + R/4R_L}$$

c. If an error of no more than 1 per cent is to be obtained, prove that R_L must be at least 12.4 times the total potentiometer resistance.

16-6. Prove that the phase-shifting circuit of Fig. 16-14 will give four-phase voltages, provided that $\omega C_1 R_1 = \omega C_2 R_2 = 1$.

16-7. Prove that E_1, E_2, and E_4 of Fig. 16-14 are three-phase voltages, provided that $\omega C_1 R_1 = 1/\sqrt{3}$ and $\omega C_2 R_2 = \sqrt{3}$.

16-8. Prove that E_1 and E_2 are two-phase voltages, provided that $\omega L = R_k$ and $\omega R C = 1$.

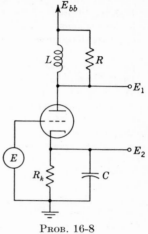

PROB. 16-8

CHAPTER 17

17-1. A sine-cosine potentiometer is excited unsymmetrically by grounding one input and applying a d-c voltage E to the other input terminal.

a. Show that two of the outputs are $\frac{1}{2}E(1 + \sin\theta)$ and $\frac{1}{2}E(1 - \sin\theta)$. Note that these voltages are always positive.

b. Show how a push-pull sweep, $kt \sin\theta$, can be obtained from the above outputs by using a difference amplifier.

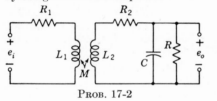

PROB. 17-2

17-2. The equivalent circuit of an induction resolver is indicated. The symbols have the usual meaning in connection with a transformer. If the output of the resolver is to be a linear sweep voltage, $e_o = Mkt$, show that the input voltage e_i must have the form

$$\frac{e_i}{L_1 k} = A_1 t^2 + A_2 t + A_3 + LC\,\delta(t)$$

where

$$A_1 = \frac{R_1}{2L_1}\left(\frac{R_2}{R} + 1\right)$$

$$A_2 = \frac{R_1}{L_1}\left(R_2 C + \frac{L_2}{R}\right) + \frac{R_2}{R} + 1$$

$$A_3 = R_2 C + \frac{L}{R} + \frac{R_1 L_2 C}{L_1}$$

where $L = L_2 - (M^2/L_1)$ and $\delta(t)$ is the unit impulse defined in Sec. 8-1.

17-3. In the preresolution sweep circuit of Fig. 17-27 the resistor R_D may be replaced by a diode if two bootstrap generators are used. One of these generators gives a positive X sweep and the other a negative X sweep. Draw the complete circuit for the X channel, indicating how the positive and negative sweeps are added together, and show any synchronized clamps or d-c restorers needed.

17-4. Given a PPI indicator with a resolved voltage sweep. It is desired to simulate a radar echo at a fixed position x_A and y_A. This means that as the sweep passes through the point x_A, y_A, a pulse is generated and it is used to brighten the trace. The coordinates x_A and y_A are available as d-c voltages. Design a system (in block-diagram form only) for this radar simulator.

CHAPTER 18

18-1. *a.* Prove that the dynamic forward resistance of a semiconductor junction diode varies inversely with the current.

b. Evaluate the dynamic resistance at a current of 1 ma and at room temperature (25°C).

18-2. Verify the transformation equations in Table 18-1.

18-3. *a.* Show that Eq. (18-12) correctly represent a transistor in the grounded-base configuration, provided that the resistance parameters r_{11}, etc., are given by Eq. (18-13). (Since these resistance parameters refer to the grounded-base configuration they are often written r_{11b}, etc.)

b. Compute the resistance parameters, r_{11e}, etc., for the common-emitter configuration and the parameters r_{11c}, etc., for the common-collector configuration.

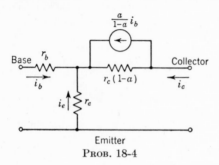

Emitter

PROB. 18-4

18-4. When a transistor is used in the grounded-emitter configuration, the equivalent circuit of Fig. 18-17 is sometimes inconvenient, since the current generator in the equivalent circuit is not proportional to the input current which, in this case, is the base current. Show then that an alternative equivalent circuit may be drawn in the form shown.

18-5. A set of parameters which is frequently used to characterize a transistor in its linear range of operation are the so-called *hybrid* parameters h_{11}, etc., which are defined in connection with the circuit of Fig. 18-18 by the formulas

$$e_e = h_{11}i_e + h_{12}e_c$$
$$i_c = h_{21}i_e + h_{22}e_c$$

a. Compute the values of the hybrid parameters h_{11}, etc., in terms of r_e, r_b, r_c, and a for the grounded-base configuration. (Since the parameters so computed refer to the common-base configuration they are often written h_{11b}, h_{12b}, etc.)

b. In terms of r_e, r_b, r_c, and a compute the hybrid parameters h_{11e}, etc., for the common-emitter configuration and h_{11c}, etc., for the common-collector configuration.

18-6. Verify Eqs. (18-14) and (18-15) for A_v and R_o. Verify Eq. (18-24) for R_i.

18-7. For the grounded-emitter configuration, compute A_v, R_o, and R_i. Compare your results with the entries in the second column of Table 18-2.

18-8. For the grounded-collector configuration, compute A_v, R_o, and R_i. Compare your results with the entries in the third column of Table 18-2.

18-9. For each of the three transistor configurations compute the voltage gain A_v in terms of the transistor parameters and the generator impedance R_g. Compare your results with the entries in the first row of Table 18-2.

18-10. Consider a transistor in the common-base configuration. Show that, if the load resistor $R_L \ll r_c$ (collector resistance), an approximate equivalent circuit may be drawn in the form shown. Remember that $r_b \ll r_c$.

18-11. A transistor has parameters $r_e = 25$ ohms, $r_b = 800$ ohms, $r_c = 2$ Meg.

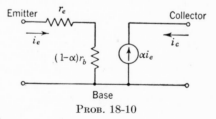

Base

PROB. 18-10

and $\alpha = 0.98$. It is driven from a generator whose output resistance is $R_g = 1,000$ ohms and has a load $R_L = 2$ K. Compute for the common-emitter and for the common-base configurations (a) the voltage gain, (b) the current gain, (c) the power gain, i.e., the ratio of the power delivered to the load to the power delivered to the input terminals of the transistor.

18-12. Referring to Fig. 18-23, show that the frequency dependence of α can be taken into account by considering that i_R and i_e are related by the equation

$$i_e = i_R + \frac{1}{\omega_\alpha} \frac{di_R}{dt}$$

(The use of this equation avoids the necessity for making explicit reference to the auxiliary RC circuit.)

18-13. A current step of amplitude I_1 is applied to the base terminal of a transistor in the common-emitter connection. Assume that the load resistor is small enough to have no effect on the transistor transient response. Compute (a) the output current as a function of the time, (b) the rise time of the output current, and (c) the time required for the transistor to reach saturation if I_1 is large enough to drive the transistor beyond the active region. Compare the results with the entries in Table 18-4.

18-14. For the grounded-collector configuration, verify the entries in the third column of Table 18-4.

18-15. Find the response to an input current step I_1 under the condition that $R_L C_c \gg 1/\omega_\alpha$ for (a) the common-emitter configuration, (b) the common-collector configuration, and (c) the common-base configuration.

18-16. The a-c resistance between collector and emitter for a grounded-emitter transistor switch in the *on* condition may be computed as

$$R_{ac} = \left| \frac{dE_{ce}}{dI_c} \right| = \left| \frac{d(E'_e - E'_c)}{dI_c} \right|$$

where E'_c and E'_e are, respectively, the voltage drops across the collector and emitter junctions. Using Eqs. (18-41) and (18-42), show that

$$R_{ac} = E_T \left[\frac{1 - \alpha_N}{\alpha_N I_b - I_c(1 - \alpha_N) - I_{co}} + \frac{1 - \alpha_I}{I_b + I_c(1 - \alpha_I) + I_{eo}} \right]$$

Compute R_{ac} for $\alpha_N = 0.98$, $\alpha_I = 0.78$, $I_b = 200$ μa, $I_{co} = 2.0$ μa, and $I_c = 4$ ma.

18-17. Show that I_c is given approximately by

$$I_c = \frac{I_{co}}{1 - \alpha_N \alpha_I} \left[1 + \frac{\alpha_N(1 - \alpha_I)}{1 - \alpha_N + E_T \frac{1 - \alpha_N \alpha_I}{I_{eo}(R + r_b)}} \right]$$

HINT: Assume that the collector junction is reverse-biased and that the emitter junction is *slightly* forward-biased. Take advantage of the approximations which are allowed because the forward bias is small.

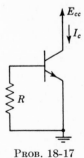

PROB. 18-17

18-18. Find the voltages and currents in the direct-connected binary of Fig. 18-34 if $E_{cc} = 20$ volts and $R_L = 50$ K.

18-19. Show that the time duration of the quasi-stable state of a transistor monostable multi is $T \cong RC \ln 2$.

18-20. Show that the frequency of a transistor astable multivibrator is

$$f \cong \frac{1}{2RC \ln 2}$$

APPENDIX: TUBE CHARACTERISTICS

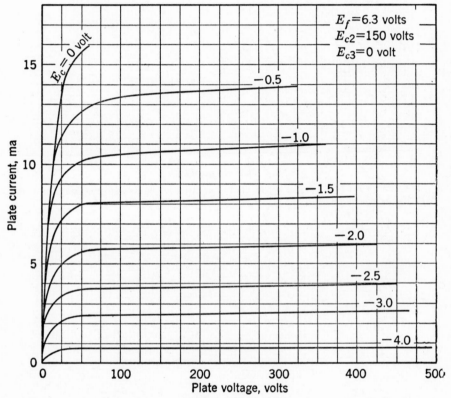

FIG. A-1. 6AU6 pentode characteristics. (*Courtesy of the General Electric Company.*)

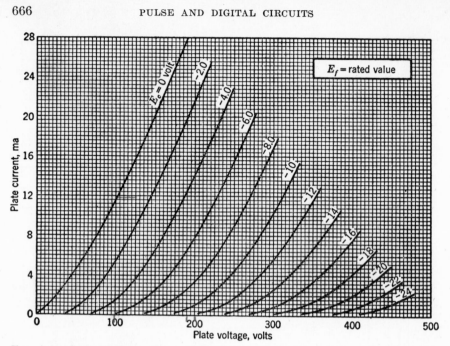

FIG. A-2. 6SN7 (6J5) negative-grid characteristics (each section). (*Courtesy of the General Electric Company.*)

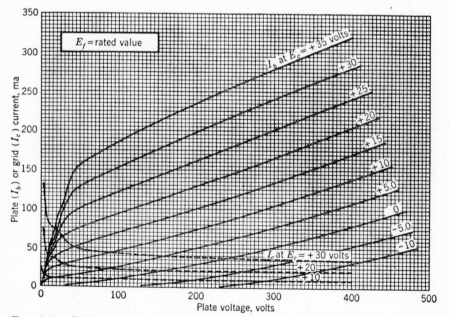

FIG. A-3. 6SN7 (6J5) positive-grid characteristics ($E_c \leq 35$ volts) (each section). (*Courtesy of the General Electric Company.*)

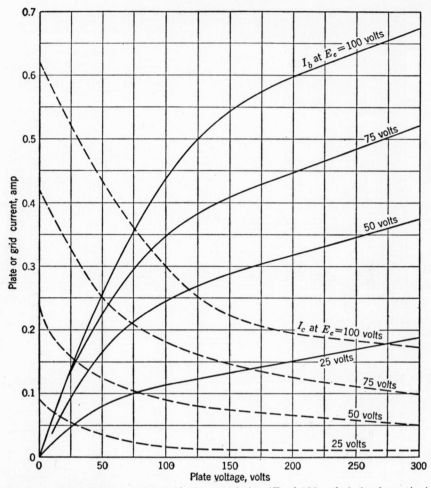

FIG. A-4. 6SN7 (6J5) positive-grid characteristics ($E_c \leq 100$ volts) (each section). (*From "Waveforms," Massachusetts Institute of Technology Radiation Laboratory Series, vol. 19, p. 213, McGraw-Hill Book Company, Inc., New York, 1949.*)

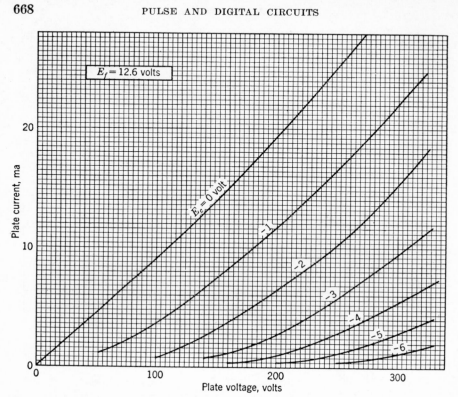

FIG. A-5. 12AT7 negative-grid characteristics (each section). (*Courtesy of the General Electric Company.*)

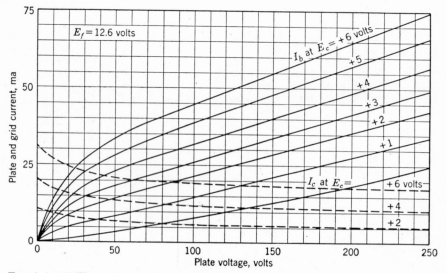

FIG. A-6. 12AT7 positive-grid characteristics (each section). (*Courtesy of the General Electric Company.*)

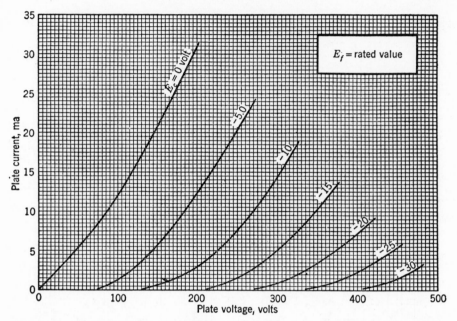

FIG. A-7. 12AU7 (5814 and 5963) negative-grid characteristics (each section). (*Courtesy of the General Electric Company.*)

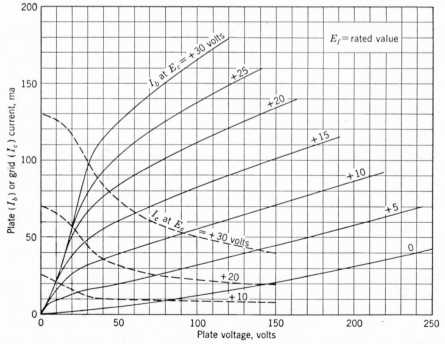

FIG. A-8. 12AU7 (5814 and 5963) positive-grid characteristics (each section). (*Courtesy of the General Electric Company.*)

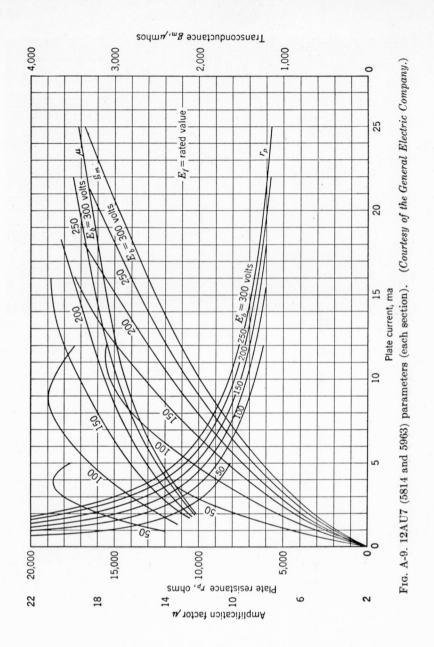

FIG. A-9. 12AU7 (5814 and 5963) parameters (each section). (*Courtesy of the General Electric Company.*)

670

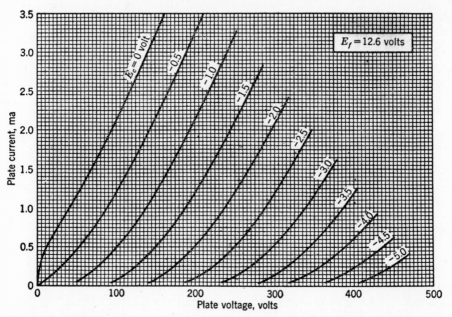

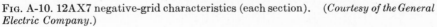

FIG. A-10. 12AX7 negative-grid characteristics (each section). (*Courtesy of the General Electric Company.*)

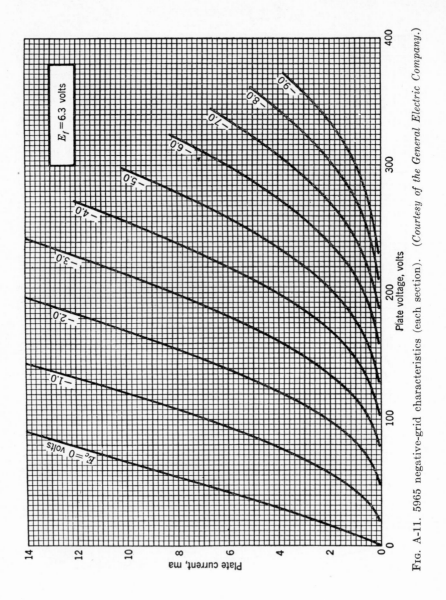

FIG. A-11. 5965 negative-grid characteristics (each section). (*Courtesy of the General Electric Company.*)

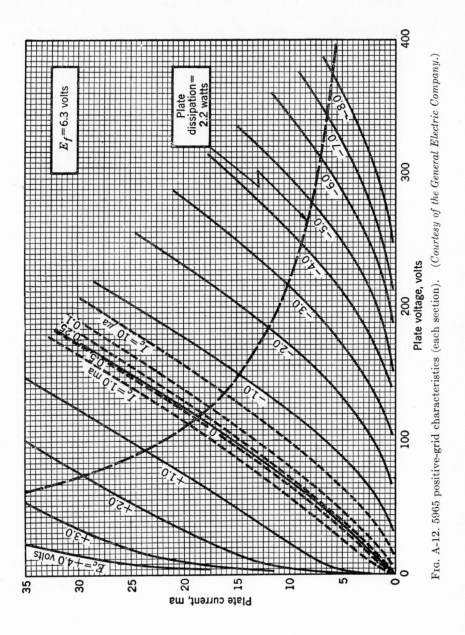

FIG. A-12. 5965 positive-grid characteristics (each section). (*Courtesy of the General Electric Company.*)

NAME INDEX

SUBJECT INDEX

Acceptor, 550–551
Acoustical delay line, 414–415, 501–502
Active element, 410
Adder-subtractor, 419–422
Alpha of transistor, 561, 579, 591–592
Amplifiers, bandwidth of, 66, 73, 316
  biasing arrangements, 84–126
  cascaded, 74–77, 96–99
  cathode follower (*see* Cathode follower)
  compensation of, high-frequency,
     67–74, 81–85
    low-frequency, 89–96
  Dietzold compensated, 72–74
  difference, 20–21, 467, 481–483
  distributed, 315–321, 502–503
  equivalent circuit of, 1, 60–61
  feedback, 4–26
    characteristics of, 8–11
    current, 5–8, 21–22, 245–246
    voltage, 4–8
  figure of merit of, 12, 65–66
  flat-top response of, 62–63, 89–99
  input capacitance of, 86
  linearity of, 9–10, 245–246
  multistage, 74–77, 96–99
  operational (*see* Operational amplifier)
  overdriven, 116, 129–139
  overshoot in response of, 67–74, 76–77,
    98
  paraphase, 18–20
  pulse (*see* RC coupled, *below*)
  push-pull, 99–101
  rate-of-rise, 39–40
  RC coupled, 58–77, 81–85, 89–99
    delay in, 59–62
    response of, amplitude, 59–63
      frequency, 59–63, 65
      rise-time, 63–77, 81–85
      step voltage, 63–77, 81–85, 89–93,
        96–99
      transient, 65–77, 81–85, 89–93, 96–
        99
    tilt in, 63
  resistance-coupled (*see* RC coupled,
    above)

Amplifiers, ringing in, 73
  screen bypass for, 95–96
  series-peaked, 72–74
  series-shunt-peaked, 72–74
  shunt-peaked, 67–74
  smear in, 73
  square-wave testing of, 64–65
  transistor, 573–578
  video (*see* RC coupled, *above*)
  wideband (*see* RC coupled, *above*)
Amplitude comparators (*see* Com-
  parators)
Amplitude-distribution analyzer, 459
Amplitude response in amplifiers, 59–63
Analogue-to-digital converter, 491–494
AND circuit, 397–400, 404–409
AND-NOT circuit, 411
Angle marks, 543
Aspect ratio, 515, 534
Astable multivibrator (*see* Multivibrator)
Attenuators, 77–81
Avalanche breakdown, 555

Backlash, 166–172
Bandwidth, 66, 73, 316, 533–534
Beam switching tube, 339–343
Berkeley counter, 153–154, 334
Biasing arrangements, amplifier, 84–126
  cathode follower, 16
  oscillator, 126
Binary, 140–173, 425–427, 595–599
  capacitor for (*see* Capacitor)
  cathode-coupled, 164–172
  cathode interface resistance in, 172–173
  commutating capacitors for, 146–147,
    151–156, 163–164
  dynamic, 415–416
  fixed-bias, 140–144
  magnetic, 425–427
  recovery time of, 152
  regeneration in, 147–149
  resolving time of, 150–156
  self-bias, 144–146
  settling time of, 152
  stable states of, 140–146

679